The Chemistry and Biology of

YEASTS

The Chemistry and Biology

of

YEASTS

Edited by

A. H. COOK

The Brewing Industry Research Foundation
Redhill, England

1958

ACADEMIC PRESS INC • PUBLISHERS • NEW YORK

Contributors

G. C. AINSWORTH, *Commonwealth Mycological Institute, Kew, England*

A. A. EDDY, *Brewing Industry Research Foundation, Nutfield, England*

G. HARRIS, *Brewing Industry Research Foundation, Nutfield, England*

M. INGRAM, *Low Temperature Station for Research in Biochemistry and Biophysics, Department of Scientific and Industrial Research, University of Cambridge, England*

H. E. JANSEN, *Heineken's Brouwerij, Rotterdam, Holland*

N. J. W. KREGER-VAN RIJ, *Centraalbureau voor Schimmelcultures, Delft, Holland*

J. LODDER, *Koninklijke Nederlandsche Gist- en Spiritusfabriek, Delft, Holland*

A. LUND, *Tuborg Breweries Ltd., Copenhagen, Denmark*

E. O. MORRIS, *Department of Microbiology, The Royal Technical College, Glasgow, Scotland*

F. F. NORD, *Fordham University, New York, New York*

MAGNUS PYKE, *Distillers Company, Ltd., Menstrie, Scotland*

C. ROBERTS, *Carlsberg Laboratorium, Copenhagen, Denmark*

W. CH. SLOOFF, *Centraalbureau voor Schimmelcultures, Delft, Holland*

W. E. TREVELYAN, *Distillers Company Ltd., Epsom, England*

SIDNEY WEISS, *Cancer Research Institute, Philadelphia, Pennsylvania*

Ö. WINGE, *Carlsberg Laboratorium, Copenhagen, Denmark*

v

685

Preface

Until recently relatively little fundamental chemical and biological research had been devoted to yeast organisms despite their long and widespread use in brewing, wine fermentation, and breadmaking.

However, yeasts have within the past few years become objects of study on a much wider scale than before and substantial progress has been made in many diverse directions. This volume was organized in response to a need for a single, adequately integrated, up-to-date source of information on the increasingly significant findings pertaining to the various phases of research on yeasts.

A wealth of technological knowledge in this field has been acquired over a long period, especially with regard to the detailed characteristics and behavior of the numerous strains of *Saccharomyces cerevisiae* and *Saccharomyces carlsbergensis* which make up brewers' and bakers' yeasts. In this connection, several works have been of great value as sources of information otherwise difficult to obtain in convenient form.

The opening chapters of the present book are devoted particularly to the biology of yeasts including the main outlines of the classification of yeasts, their distribution in nature, life histories, and genetic compositions. Succeeding chapters deal with chemical aspects, including first the chemical compounds which yeasts contain and then the metabolic changes which these constituents undergo, together with the underlying enzymic mechanisms by which the various changes are brought about. Finally certain more general subjects are reviewed, including yeast technology, pathogenic forms, and yeasts in relation to food spoilage.

For the majority of the chapters this is probably the first time that the general assessment of these broad fields has been attempted in a comprehensive fashion. Considerable attention has been directed toward making each chapter authoritative, reasonably complete, and self-contained without sacrificing the cohesion of the work as a whole. A few topics have been dealt with in more than one chapter, largely as a result of the overlapping of fields which becomes more evident with the progress of modern research. The botanist, for example, becomes enmeshed in problems of chemical composition while the chemist or the enzymologist finds himself following the arguments of the geneticist.

Classification of yeasts involves further overlapping since it depends almost equally on biochemical and morphological studies.

In preparing this book every effort has been made to include references to all significant contributions to the literature, especially the more recent studies.

So much progress has been made comparatively recently over widely scattered areas of the whole frontier of research on yeasts that the subject matter can scarcely be dealt with by a single author. This volume combines the advantages of having the material presented by a number of authors, each concerned with research in a special area of the field, and of encompassing within one volume such an ample store of information.

A. H. COOK

October, 1957

Contents

CHAPTER I

The Classification of Yeasts

J. LODDER, W. CH. SLOOFF, AND N. J. W. KREGER-VAN RIJ

1. Introduction

In a chapter on classification of yeasts one may expect to find a definition of the term "yeast." This term does not pretend to be the name of a botanical taxon;[1] it merely designates a group of fungi which have certain outstanding characteristics in common, but which may nevertheless belong to different classes.

As regards the literary meaning of the terms used for these organisms in different languages it is frequently clear that they bear particularly on the property of fermentation. For example, "yeast" (in Dutch "gist") signifies foam. Its equivalent is found in the word "Gischt" still in use in modern German. Again, the French expression "levure" is connected with the evolution of carbon dioxide which pushes upwards solid substances during fermentation. "Levure" is associated with "lever" (= to rise) just as the German word "Hefe" is connected with "heben."

---

[1] The term taxon for a taxonomic group, proposed by Lam, was accepted at the Seventh International Botanical Congress at Stockholm. See this Congress's Proceedings, 1953, Art. 8, p. 463, and J. Lanjouw, Synopsis of Proposals, 1950, Art. 8, p. 5.

One of the prominent genera in the yeasts is *Saccharomyces* which includes many well-known organisms used in the fermentation industries. Species belonging to this genus are characterized by their production of ethanol and carbon dioxide; another feature is that cells in cultures do

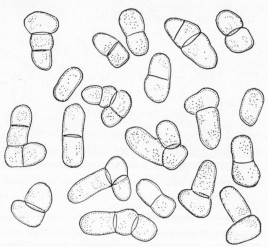

Fig. 1. *Saccharomyces carlsbergensis*. Malt extract culture and spores (×1000). (From Lodder and Kreger-van Rij, 1952.)

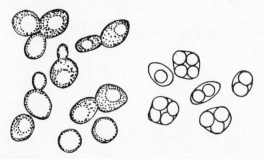

Fig. 2. *Schizosaccharomyces octosporus*. Malt extract culture (×1000). (From Lodder and Kreger-van Rij, 1952.)

not adhere to each other and, after budding out, the young cell generally comes off from the mother cell (Fig. 1).

A second genus is *Schizosaccharomyces,* which embraces many distillery yeasts. Here also alcoholic fermentation is marked but there are no budding cells. This genus reproduces by lengthwise growth, development of a partition wall and subsequent fission of this wall (Fig. 2).

Both the foregoing genera form asci and ascospores and are considered to belong to the lower Ascomycetes (Gäumann, 1949; Wolf and Wolf, 1948).

Other fungi which show unicellular growth may lack fermentative capacity as well as ascospore formation. They may reproduce not only by budding but also by fission. Reproduction by an intermediate process also occurs as in *Pityrosporum* (Fig. 3), while in *Trichosporon* (Fig. 4) both processes are found to exist simultaneously. In the latter genus, in part of the culture the fission, after forming of partition walls, is retarded as well as the separation of cells after budding, this behavior giving rise to the development of either true or pseudohyphae. Pseudohyphae are

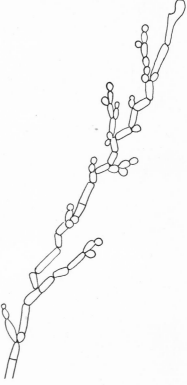

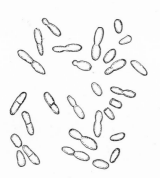

Fig. 3. *Pityrosporum ovale.* Malt extract with oleic acid culture (×1000). (From Lodder and Kreger-van Rij, 1952.)

Fig. 4. *Trichosporon cutaneum.* Slide culture, potato agar (×435). (From Lodder and Kreger-van Rij, 1952.)

typical for *Candida* (Fig. 5) but true hyphae have also been demonstrated in this genus.

From the above observations it may be concluded that neither fermentative capacity nor reproduction by budding or ascospore formation are necessarily the crucial features which mark a fungus as a "yeast," but that stress is laid on the predominantly unicellular state of the organism. Skinner (1947a) formulates the following definition: "Yeasts are true fungi whose usual and dominant growth form is unicellular."[1a] The author remarked that his definition did not exclude certain of the lower Phycomycetes that exist in the unicellular state, nor could it include the filamentous forms which are normally regarded as yeasts. These lower Phycomycetes (Chytridiales), however, produce oosporangia and flagellate zoospores, features not known in yeasts while the filamentous forms may be looked upon as border cases so common in Nature. It is unlikely therefore that these admitted weaknesses will in fact lead to real difficulty.

Some uncertainty may arise with the question as to what is meant by "usual and dominant growth," especially where parasitic fungi are concerned. For instance, Ciferri and Redaelli (1953) proposed including *Histoplasma capsulatum* in the nonsporogenous yeasts because of the usual and dominant presence of budding cells in the tissues of the host as well as under special conditions in cultures. Mrak and Phaff (1948) suggested that *Taphrina* should be discussed and treated as belonging to the yeasts. These suggestions should be carefully considered for one should realize that several fungi may develop a yeast phase, e.g., *Mucor* and *Aspergillus*, when cultured under anaerobic conditions; this, however, does not provide a reason for considering them as yeasts. It is, of course, quite a different matter whether such fungi and others could not usefully be studied in relation to yeasts.

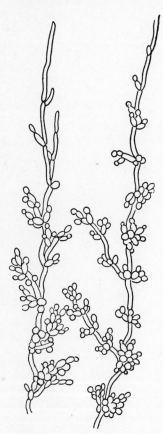

FIG. 5. *Candida tropicalis.* Slide culture, potato agar (×435). (From Lodder and Kreger-van Rij, 1952.)

Pullularia pullulans, belonging to the "black yeasts," another fungus often proposed to be studied with the yeasts, will not be dealt with in this chapter and, in this way, the tradition will be continued that only hyaline organisms and those producing red or yellow pigments are accepted among the yeasts.

[1a] Quoted with special permission of John Wiley & Sons, Inc., from A. T. Henrici's "Molds, Yeasts, and Actinomycetes," 2nd ed., 1947.

TABLE I
CLASSIFICATION OF THE ASCOSPOROGENOUS YEASTS: FAMILY SACCHAROMYCETACEAE

Saccharomycetaceae

Mycelium, arthrospores, budding cells, and pseudomycelium side by side or alone. Conjugation isogamous or heterogamous; often a diploid generation. Dissimilation oxidative and often fermentative.

Subfamily: Eremascoideae	Subfamily: Endomycetoideae	Subfamily: Saccharomycetoideae	Subfamily: Nematosporoideae	Subfamily: Lipomycetoideae
Mycelium only No fermentation	Mycelium and (or) arthrospores Spores round, oval, reniform, or hat-shaped Dissimilation oxidative and fermentative	See Table II	Mycelium and (or) budding cells Spores fusiform or needle-shaped, with or without a whip Dissimilation besides oxidative, fermentative	Budding cells Ascus sac-like, formed as protuberance of vegetative cell Spores oval, light reddish, up to 16 per ascus No fermentation
Genus *Eremascus*	Genera *Endomyces* Gametangia present *Schizosaccharomyces* Gametangia absent Arthrospores predominate Isogamous conjugation Spores round, oval, or reniform, 4–8 per ascus Fermentation		Genera *Monosporella* Budding cells, no mycelium Needle-shaped spores without whip, 1 per ascus *Nematospora* Mycelium and budding cells Spores fusiform with whip, 8 per ascus *Coccidiascus* Budding cells, no mycelium Spores fusiform without whip, 8 per ascus	Genus *Lipomyces*

TABLE II

CLASSIFICATION OF THE SUBFAMILY SACCHAROMYCETOIDEAE

Saccharomycetoideae
Budding cells, occasionally pseudomycelium and mycelium. Spores: 1–4 per ascus. Dissimilation from merely oxidative to predominantly fermentative.

Tribe: Endomycopseae	Tribe: Saccharomyceteae		Tribe: Nadsonieae
Mycelium and budding cells Multilateral budding No fermentation or weak fermentation	Budding cells, occasionally pseudomycelium, no mycelium Multilateral budding Fermentation or no fermentation		Budding cells, occasionally pseudomycelium, no mycelium Bipolar budding on broad base Fermentation
Genus *Endomycopsis*	Genera		Genera
	Saccharomyces Budding cells, occasionally pseudomycelium Spores usually round or oval, also reniform, bean-, or sickle-shaped, 1–4 per ascus Fermentation Nitrate not assimilated	*Hansenula* Budding cells, usually pseudomycelium Spores hat-shaped, or Saturn-shaped, 1–4 per ascus Often pellicle formation Dissimilation oxidative, also fermentative Nitrate assimilated	*Saccharomycodes* Lemon-shaped cells Spores round, 4 per ascus, they may conjugate in pairs *Hanseniaspora* Lemon-shaped cells Spores hat-, Saturn-shaped or round, 1–4 per ascus *Nadsonia* Lemon-shaped cells Heterogamous conjugation Spores round, warty, light brown, 1–2 per ascus
	Pichia Budding cells, usually pseudomycelium Spores hemispherical, hat-shaped, angular, or round, 1–4 per ascus Often pellicle formation Dissimilation oxidative, occasionally fermentative Nitrate not assimilated	*Schwanniomyces* Budding oval cells Spores round, warty, with a ledge, 1–2 per ascus Fermentation Nitrate not assimilated *Debaryomyces* Budding round to oval cells Heterogamous conjugation Spores round, more or less warty, 1–2 per ascus	No fermentation or weak fermentation Nitrate not assimilated *Saccharomycopsis* Budding long-oval to cylindrical cells Spores oval, 1–3 per ascus

From all these considerations it will be clear that the delimitation of the yeasts is subject to arbitrary decisions and that as a group they are far from homogeneous.

2. General Classification

The yeasts can be divided into three groups as follows:

(1) *The ascosporogenous yeasts,* i.e., those which form ascospores in a cell named the ascus. These organisms belong to the family of the Saccharomycetaceae, classified among the fungi in the Ascomycetes. For the subdivision of this family, see Tables I and II.

(2) *The ballistosporogenous yeasts,* i.e., those forming so-called ballistospores which arise on a sterigma and are ejaculated by a drop-excretion mechanism. These yeasts belong to the family of the Sporobolomycetaceae. As is pointed out in the historical survey, however, there are strong arguments in favor of the view that these spores are basidiospores (Sainclivier, 1952) in which case this family would belong to the Basidiomycetes. If the ballistospores be not considered as sexual spores these yeasts should be placed in the Fungi Imperfecti. For the subdivision of this family, see Table III.

TABLE III

CLASSIFICATION OF THE FAMILY SPOROBOLOMYCETACEAE

Sporobolomycetaceae

Mycelium, budding cells and pseudomycelium. Formation of ballistospores. Dissimilation strictly oxidative.

Genera

Sporobolomyces
Budding cells, pseudomycelium, and mycelium
Ballistospores kidney- or sickle-shaped

Bullera
Budding cells, no pseudomycelium or mycelium
Ballistospores symmetrical, round, or oval

Tilletiopsis
Mycelium, no budding cells
Ballistospores sickle-shaped

Itersonilia
Mycelium, no budding cells
Ballistospores asymmetrical, slightly dented at one side

(3) *Yeasts forming neither ascospores nor ballistospores.* These yeasts are classified in the family of the Cryptococcaceae and have their place

TABLE IV

CLASSIFICATION OF THE ASPOROGENOUS YEASTS: FAMILY CRYPTOCOCCACEAE

Cryptococcaceae

Budding cells, moreover pseudomycelium, mycelium and arthrospores may be formed. Cells hyaline, never dark or brown, carotenoid pigments may be present. Dissimilation strictly oxidative or also fermentative.

Subfamily: Cryptococcoideae		Subfamily: Trichosporoideae	Subfamily: Rhodotoruloideae
Budding cells, occasionally pseudomycelium and mycelium, no arthrospores No distinct yellow to red color due to carotenoid pigments Fermentation to no fermentation		Budding cells, pseudomycelium, mycelium, and arthrospores No distinct yellow to red color due to carotenoid pigments Occasionally fermentation	Budding cells, occasionally pseudomycelium Distinct yellow to red color due to carotenoid pigments No fermentation
Genera		Genus *Trichosporon*	Genus *Rhodotorula*
Cryptococcus Multilateral budding, no pseudomycelium or mycelium Capsulated cells, formation of starch-like compounds No fermentation	*Brettanomyces* Multilateral budding, primitive pseudomycelium Round, oval, or "ogive-shaped" cells Slow growth Strong acid formation Fermentation		
Torulopsis Multilateral budding, no pseudomycelium or mycelium No formation of starch-like compounds Generally fermentation	*Candida* Multilateral budding, pseudomycelium, occasionally mycelium Fermentation or no fermentation		
	Kloeckera Bipolar budding Lemon-shaped cells Fermentation		
Pityrosporum Polar budding Oval or bottle-shaped cells No fermentation	*Trigonopsis* Multilateral or triangular budding Oval or triangular cells No fermentation		

in the Fungi Imperfecti. The subdivision of this family is summarized in Table IV.

3. A Short History of Yeast Classification

The history of yeast taxonomy begins with the description of *Saccharomyces*, the sugar mold, by J. Meyen (1838) who confirmed Schwann's observations on fermenting liquids and introduced the generic name. Whereas the problem of the causal agent of fermentation was the subject of numerous publications, the botanical identity of the organisms concerned was only vaguely understood and it was not until Reess (1870) completed his studies on the alcohol-producing molds that the genus was more precisely defined by him as follows. Simple Ascomycetes without a true mycelium. Vegetative organs consisting of cells, reproduced by budding and subsequent detachment of the full grown cells. The cells are capable of changing into sporogenous asci. One to four unicellular spores in the ascus. Ascospores germinating by budding (Fig. 1).

Thus Reess recognized the sporulating yeasts as Ascomycetes and considered them to be related to *Exoascus* and *Endomyces* as well as to *Taphrina*, three fungi which lack differentiation in sexual organs and which develop naked asci.

In the classification of any group of organisms, interest centers in sexual reproduction. It is generally understood that those showing similar trends in the development of sexual reproductive organs and in fructification are closely related and their arrangement in a natural system of classification follows accordingly.

It is obvious that such principles could not be employed to deal with the large mass of organisms devoid of sexual reproduction and most of the yeasts for which neither a sexual act nor asci have been demonstrated have been classified as Fungi Imperfecti. The classification system of this group cannot claim the adjective "natural," as it is based on morphology of vegetative structures and on physiological characters only.

After Turpin (1838) erroneously named a yeast *Torula*, this name was used widely for anascogenous yeasts; this misuse was unintentionally spread by Hansen (1888) who provisionally applied the name to non-sporulating fermenting yeasts, no matter whether they developed filaments or lacked this capacity.

Technical microbiologists, botanists, phytopathologists, and medical mycologists have contributed to the development of classification during the past half century. The more fungi were described in which the unicellular state appeared to prevail, the more the heterogeneity of the yeasts as a group became emphasized. Classification in this period seemed practicable only by considering the two groups of ascogenous and anascogenous yeasts separately. An attempt to detect affinity between anascogenous genera and those capable of ascus formation was made by Ciferri (1930a), but the effort was, according to the author's own statement, a task far beyond the actual knowledge of that time.

A. *Ascosporogenous* (= *Ascogenous*) *Yeasts*

In classification, from the beginning stress has been laid on morphology and cytology, both of the reproductive organs (asci and ascospores) and the vegetative structures. At present ascogenous yeasts are characterized: (1) by the naked asci that result directly or indirectly from conjugation of 2 vegetative cells (Fig. 6); and (2) by the lack of the dikaryon state, a vegetative state in which each cell contains 2 nuclei, dividing synchronically during cell divisions (Fig. 7).

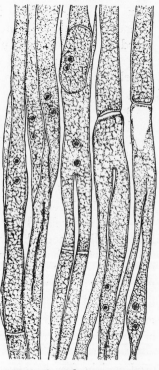

Gäumann (1949) classifies them by these characters into the order of the Endomycetales and, together with fungi belonging to the order of the Taphrinales (or

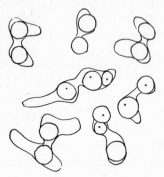

FIG. 6. *Saccharomyces acidifaciens.* Ascus formation (×1000). (From Lodder and Kreger-van Rij, 1952.)

FIG. 7. Dikaryon state in *Taphrina deformans* (×2100). (From E. M. Martin, *Am. J. Bot.* **27**, 743, 1940.)

Exoascales, dikaryon state!), into the Protascales, a subclass of the Ascomycetes.

Hansen (1904) was the first to provide a classification of the ascogenous

yeasts by recognizing 8 genera, divided in 2 groups which roughly coincide with the groups (II + III) and IV of Guilliermond. All genera were collected into one family: the Saccharomycetaceae.

In later years opinions have frequently differed as regards the number of families to be distinguished in the ascogenous yeasts. The reason is that, taking the genera *Eremascus, Endomyces, Endomycopsis,* and *Saccharomyces* in the sequence given, a gradual transition of characters is observable (Fig. 8). The characters in question are: development from the polycellular to the unicellular state, from true mycelium showing partition walls to budding cells, and reduction to the point of complete absence of gametangia. In the latter connection, the

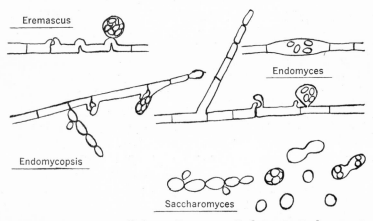

Fig. 8. Transitions in morphology: *Eremascus, Endomyces, Endomycopsis, Saccharomyces.*

proliferations on the body of the cell immediately engaged in the act of conjugation disappear, resulting in direct (somatic) conjugation of the 2 cells. Clear cut differences providing means for separation into families are therefore not demonstrable (Stelling-Dekker, 1931, p. 522).

Guilliermond who followed Schröter (1889) distinguished 2 families in the order of the Protoascines, the Endomycetes and the Saccharomycetes. In his conception (Guilliermond, 1912; Guilliermond and Tanner, 1920) the fission yeasts represent "group I" in the family of the Saccharomycetes. Guilliermond's "groups" of the Saccharomycetes are briefly characterized as follows:

I. Yeasts, multiplying by partition, asci often derived from copulation (= conjugation); one genus: *Schizosaccharomyces* Lindner.

II. Budding yeasts; sexual phenomena or traces thereof observable prior to the formation of the ascus; 5 genera: *Zygosaccharomyces* Barker; *Debaryomyces* Klöcker; *Nadsonia* (Nadson et Konokotina) Sydow; *Schwanniomyces* Klöcker; *Torulaspora* Lindner.

III. Budding yeasts; no conjugation prior to ascus formation observed; in liquid media at first a deposit, later on a more or less slimy pellicle; alcohol produced; 4 genera; *Saccharomycodes* Hansen; *Saccharomycopsis* Schiönning; *Saccharomyces* Meyen *emendavit* Reess; *Hansenia* Lindner.

IV. Budding yeasts which immediately form a dry pellicle on liquid sugar media; ascospores in characteristic shapes (lemon-shaped, hat-shaped, or angular); "Generally do not produce alcohol but ether" (= esters); 2 genera: *Pichia* Hansen and *Willia* Hansen.

V. Yeasts in which the relationships are not well known; 2 genera *Monospora* Metschnikoff; *Nematospora* Peglion.

Obviously both Hansen and Guilliermond considered physiological characters appropriate to differentiate between groups of genera, e.g., to characterize group IV, pellicle formation as well as ester production are mentioned. In this connection it should be remarked that apparently Hansen's observation on *Willia* and *Pichia* (group IV): "Die meisten Arten zeichen sich durch ihre Esterbildung aus, einige rufen keine Gärung hervor" was misunderstood by Guilliermond and shortened to: "Generally do not produce alcohol but ether." In Guilliermond's system the phenomenon of conjugation previous to ascus formation is emphasized as a character for separation of genera and accordingly *Saccharomyces* and *Zygosaccharomyces* are classified in separate "groups." In later years Guilliermond related *Saccharomyces* (diploid yeast) to *Taphrina* and sought to connect *Zygosaccharomyces* (haploid) with *Endomyces* phylogenetically (Guilliermond, 1937). Klöcker (1924), however, considered *Zygosaccharomyces* not a separate genus, but a subgenus of *Saccharomyces,* his views being based on observations of asci in *Zygosaccharomyces* which had developed without previous cell conjugation. This view was also adopted by Stelling-Dekker (1931). The conception of the genus *Saccharomyces* as an entity, furthered by the studies of Winge (1935), Winge and Laustsen (1937), and Lindegren and Lindegren (1943) has recently moulded the modern conception of the genus to such an extent that the subgenus *Zygosaccharomyces* is no longer considered valid (Wickerham, 1951; Lodder and Kreger-van Rij, 1952).

Klöcker's classification recognizes 2 families:

I. Saccharomycetaceae, divided into Saccharomycetes and Schizosaccharomycetes; and

II. Endomycetaceae.

Here the fission yeasts were placed in a subfamily of their own, the Schizosaccharomycetes, separated from the Saccharomycetes by differences in mechanics of vegetative reproduction. Klöcker's 2 families are not identical with the 2 subfamilies Saccharomycoideae and Endomycoideae adopted by Stelling-Dekker (1931). Failing to find differences striking enough to warrant the creation of separate families, she gathered them all into one family, for which she chose the name Endomycetaceae, and established the following subfamilies, mainly on the basis of vegetative reproduction:

Subfamily I. Eremascoideae
Subfamily II. Endomycoideae
Subfamily III. Saccharomycoideae
   Tribe 1. Endomycopseae
   Tribe 2. Saccharomyceteae
   Tribe 3. Nadsonieae   ·
Subfamily IV. Nematosporoideae

Most of the budding yeasts were thus classified among the Saccharomycoideae. She placed in the Endomycoideae *Schizosaccharomyces* together with *Endomyces*. The genus *Endomycopsis* was created for yeasts which develop true mycelia as well as budding cells, e.g., for *Endomyces fibuliger* Lindner, *Saccharomycopsis capsularis* Schiönning and *Endomyces javanensis* Klöcker. For the new genus a special tribe was established in the Saccharomycoideae and termed the Endomycopseae (tribe 1).

Earlier Zender (1925) had put forward arguments to abandon fission and budding as a basis for differentiation on the ground that these characters were too dependent upon environmental conditions. As a basis for classification into families he proposed to substitute the morphology of the ascospores for mycelial characteristics and vegetative reproduction while alcoholic fermentation and ester production were accepted as physiological characters appropriate to separate genera as well as suborders. The neglect of vegetative morphology together with the application of the morphology of the ascospores resulted in a more or less arbitrary construction in Zender's system which was criticized by Stelling-Dekker (1931).

In the latter's system the genus *Nematospora* although also reproducing by budding is set apart from the Saccharomycoideae in view of the extraordinary shape of the ascospores (fusiform, provided with a whip). Supported by Guilliermond's (1928) cytological study of the genus, she proposed to bring together in the Nematosporoideae the genera *Nemato-*

spora, Monosporella, and *Coccidiascus.* In other respects, however, Zender's ideas have been abandoned both by Stelling-Dekker and by later workers of the Dutch School.

Guilliermond in general accepted Stelling-Dekker's proposals except for her unification of *Zygosaccharomyces* with *Saccharomyces* and of *Zygopichia* with *Pichia.* In this respect he maintained his opinion concerning the biphyllic descent of the Endomycetaceae.

Whereas Stelling-Dekker (1931) accepted only one family in the order of the Endomycetales, Gäumann (1949) recognized: (1) the Endo-

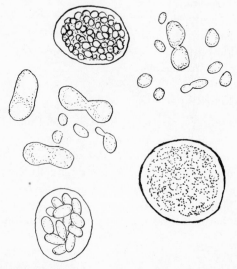

Fig. 9. *Kluyveromyces polysporus.* Vegetative cells, zygotes and asci with spores (×1000).

mycetaceae and (2) the Saccharomycetaceae. Furthermore he introduced into the order (3) the Spermophthoraceae, including the genus *Nematospora.* In the Endomycetales the Dipodascaceae represent his fourth family; actually these comprise only filamentous fungi and no yeasts. According to Gäumann *Dipodascus* is the genus from which the Endomycetaceae can be derived. Conjugation of gametangia in this genus results in a multisporic ascus. Disappearance of gametangia and reduction of the number of ascospores was pictured as leading to the development of fungi approaching *Eremascus* and *Endomyces.* The discovery by van der Walt (1956a) in South Africa of a budding yeast, *Kluyveromyces polysporus* (Fig. 9), which develops multisporic asci provides an attractive contribution supporting Gäumann's views.

For the classification of *Nematospora* together with *Eremothecium,* *Ashbya,* and *Spermophthora* in the Spermophthoraceae Gäumann finds support in Guilliermond's studies (Guilliermond, 1928, 1936). The filamentous fungi *Ashbya* and *Eremothecium* are considered to be equiva-

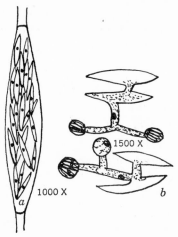

FIG. 10. Life cycle of *Spermophthora gossypii:* a, gametangium (×1000); b, conjugation and ascus formation (×1500). (From A. Guilliermond, 1928.)

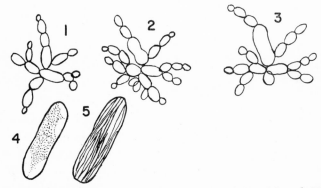

FIG. 11. *Nematospora coryli.* Somatic conjugation. (From Manuel, 1938.)

lent to the gametangious stage of *Spermophthora* (Fig. 10). In the former fungi the "gametes" have no sexuality and represent mere sporangial spores. *Nematospora* (Fig. 11) was found to represent a reduced stage of *Spermophthora,* lacking any sporangial development and in which somatic conjugation replaces a life cycle consisting of 2 complete generations (Manuel, 1938).

Lodder and Kreger-van Rij (1952) could not follow Gäumann in his views and maintained Stelling-Dekker's classification. Names of the subfamilies were corrected and the subgenera in *Saccharomyces, Pichia,* and *Hansenula* abandoned. One genus was added and described. This was *Lipomyces* which was placed provisionally in a separate subfamily. After criticism by Buchanan (1952) the authors changed the name of the family to Saccharomycetaceae which name has priority (Lodder and Kreger-van Rij, 1954).

B. *Anascogenous Yeasts*

After incidental investigation by Turpin (1838), Pasteur (1861), and Hansen (1888) it was Will (1916) who first studied the anascogenous yeasts more extensively. He gathered the genera *Torula, Eutorula,* and *Mycotorula* into the family of the Torulaceae and, in addition, recognized the genera *Pseudomonilia, Monilia* and *Dematium, Mycoderma* and *Pseudomycoderma.* According to him the Torulaceae should differ from the other genera by the complete absence of septate or nonseptate hyphae. Within the Torulaceae, *Mycotorula* was set apart from the other genera on the basis of formation of pseudohyphae, consisting of elongate or cylindrical budding cells. This was an important decision, for the presence or absence of a pseudomycelium, a term introduced by Ciferri and Redaelli (1929), is still maintained as a differential character in the classification of the anascogenous yeasts.

Janke (1924) accepted Saccardo's system in the classification of the Fungi Imperfecti; he brought the anascogenous yeasts into the Hyphomycetes–Mucedinaceae–Hyalosporae. Instead of the Torulaceae he established as a subfamily of the Mucedinaceae the Pseudosaccharomycetes, comprising the majority of the known genera. (The generic name *Pseudosaccharomyces* was created by Klöcker for the apiculate anascogenous yeasts.) *Monilia,* on the other hand, was classified *pro parte* in the Oosporaceae and the budding "Moniliae" isolated from various fermentation industries[2] were transferred to the genus *Oospora* Wallroth, notwithstanding the fact that they had earlier been removed from there by Berkhout (1923) who had established for them the separate genus *Candida.*

Janke accepted Berlese's criticism of the generic name *Torula* for asporogenous yeasts and adopted *Torulopsis* Berlese instead (Saccardo, 1906).

Vuillemin's (1911, 1931) system of the Hyphomycetes was based on differences in the mechanism of vegetative reproduction. Most yeasts are

[2] In German literature called: "Gärungsmonilien."

included in the Thallosporeae, i.e., among these organisms producing "thallospores" by fragmentation of the thallus. Therefore Vuillemin distinguished within the Thallosporeae: (1) the Blastosporeae, reproducing by budding, and (2) the Arthrosporeae, reproducing by fission of the septate mycelium (Fig. 12). Vuillemin, while making an important contribution to classification, nevertheless added to the confusion by separating a pathogenic genus, *Cryptococcus*, from the other asporogenous non-filamentous yeasts. This genus had been originally created by Kützing in 1883.

Furthermore Vuillemin applied the name *Monilia* for yeasts producing both pseudomycelium and budding cells, whereas this name was used

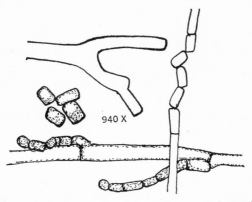

FIG. 12. *Geotrichum candidum*. Arthrospores (×940).

earlier by Gmelin to denominate fungi characterized by true hyphae bearing conidia. For a long time the names *Cryptococcus* and *Monilia* have been mistakenly used by many medical mycologists; during the last decades, however, *Monilia* has abandoned the field to *Candida*.[3]

A new system was published by Ciferri and Redaelli (1929) in which differentiation into genera is based exclusively on morphology. Two families are recognized in the nonsporogenous yeasts:

I. Nectaromycetaceae: developing aerial conidia.
   Genera: *Sporobolomyces* and *Nectaromyces*.
II. Torulopsidaceae: no aerial conidia developed.
   Subfamily 1. Torulopsideae: no hyphae or pseudohyphae.
   Subfamily 2. Mycotoruleae: mycelial developments.

[3] The generic name *Candida* was adopted by the Eighth Botanical Congress at Paris, 1954 as a *nomen conservandum*.

Ciferri and Redaelli supported Guilliermond's opposition against the idea of a close affinity between *Sporobolomyces* and the Basidiomycetes (Guilliermond, 1927). This concept resulted in the classification of *Sporobolomyces* in the group of conidia-forming yeasts. To the genera already recognized by Will they added in the Torulopsidaceae: *Pityrosporum* Sabouraud, *Geotrichum* Link, and *Candida* Berkhout, as well as some others now no longer accepted.

A major attempt to refine the classification of the Mycotorulaceae was made by Langeron and his collaborators whose system was also based on purely morphological characters. The structure called "l'appareil sporifère" was considered to yield sufficient morphological differences for the separation of six genera in the Mycotorulaceae (Langeron and Talice, 1932). Later, after extensive studies on the morphology of the pseudomycelium, applying a modern technique (Rivalier and Seydel, 1932), Langeron and Guerra (1938) in a critical study combined all six genera into one: *Candida* Berkhout.

Langeron and Talice (1932) followed Vuillemin in his conception of 2 subfamilies in the Thallosporeae. They differed from Ciferri and Redaelli who classified the arthrospored genus *Geotrichum* Link in the Torulopsidaceae–Mycotoruleae, in placing it apart in the Arthrosporeae.

In Lodder's system of the anascogenous yeasts the Arthrosporeae have been left aside. A new family, that of the Rhodotorulaceae was erected by the author to comprise the genus *Rhodotorula,* created by Harrison (1928) for yeasts producing red pigments. The genus was redefined by Lodder in this respect in that it includes organisms producing red or yellow carotenoid pigments. The genus *Chromotorula* proposed by Harrison to include yeasts that develop yellow, brown, or black pigments was rejected by Lodder (1934, p. 20) because of the inclusion of "black yeasts" which differ considerably in their morphology from the Torulopsidaceae.

A critical review of classification was published in Chapter III of Diddens' and Lodder's monograph of the Mycotoruloideae (Diddens and Lodder, 1942). This subfamily included the anascogenous yeasts which produce pseudomycelia although, in this group, a true mycelium may be present to a lesser extent. Budding cells (= blastospores) are arranged at the mycelium in a characteristic manner. Arthrospores (resulting from fragmentation of septate hyphae) and chlamydospores may also occur.

In contrast to the conception of Langeron and Guerra who expelled the genus *Trichosporon* from the Mycotoruloideae, Diddens and Lodder included it in this subfamily. The main representative of the Mycotoruloideae was the genus *Candida.* As a third genus, *Brettanomyces* was also accepted.

To Ciferri and Redaelli (1929) it was not yet clear whether the Torulopsidaceae should be placed in the family of the Oosporaceae (Hyphomycetes–Mucedinaceae–Amerosporae) or alongside with it. Diddens and Lodder, however, following Buchwald's classification (Buchwald, 1939) separated the Torulopsidaceae from the Mucedinaceae and arranged them in an order of their own, the Torulopsidales, apart from the Hyphomycetales. The description of the new order was published in Lodder and Kreger-van Rij's monograph (1952, p. 67).

Certain representatives of the Torulopsidales–Torulopsidaceae show much resemblance in morphology to the fungi classified in the Hyphomycetales–Mucedinaceae. It is the presence of *pseudohyphae* which marks the former as a separate group. The arthrospored genus *Geotrichum* (= *Oospora*) is no longer reckoned among the "yeasts" and finds its place smoothly in the Mucedinaceae–Amerosporae.

Lodder and Kreger-van Rij (1952) changed the name of the order into Cryptococcales, in accordance with their recognition of the genus *Cryptococcus*, embracing those nonsporogenous and nonfermenting capsulated yeasts which are capable of producing a starch-like substance under special conditions. The authors accepted a much closer relation between the representatives of the order than had been done by their predecessors. This affinity was emphasized by the classification of all Cryptococcales in one family, the Cryptococcaceae, which was divided into 3 subfamilies. The genera *Trichosporon* and *Rhodotorula* were set apart on their own in 2 subfamilies, the Trichosporoideae and the Rhodotoruloideae, while all other genera were grouped in the Cryptococcoideae.

In the delimitation of subfamilies as well as of genera, Lodder and Kreger-van Rij make a somewhat extensive use of physiological characteristics. The genera *Torulopsis* and *Cryptococcus* are differentiated almost exclusively by means of such characters, while the subfamily of the Rhodotoruloideae is characterized by the conspicuous presence of carotenoid pigments. The last classification has met with much criticism (Wickerham, 1952; Magni, 1953; Peterson *et al.*, 1954; Nakayama *et al.*, 1954) and as carotenoids had been demonstrated by chemical analysis in representatives of the genus *Cryptococcus*, the authors admitted that the classification of *Rhodotorula* offers real difficulties (Lodder and Kreger-van Rij, 1955).

For the dark-colored strains no place was reserved in the Cryptococcales as only hyaline organisms and those producing carotenoid pigments were accepted in the order. The principle not to consider dark-pigmented organisms as "yeasts" was criticized by Mrak and Phaff (1948) who proposed including the genus *Pullularia* in taxonomic yeast studies. Many species have been labeled "black yeasts" of which Langeron discussed several and added a new species to the list, *Torula bergeri*[4] (Berger and Langeron, 1949). He proposed to bring all the dark-colored strains, exhibiting a yeast-like phase in their juvenile stage, succeeded by development of a true mycelium with profusely budding conidia, into the genus *Pullularia* Berkhout (Berkhout, 1923). These were not regarded as true yeasts although Langeron was able to recognize several other organisms as "Levures véritables à colonies noires crémeuses . . . " of which one is *Monilia nigra* Burri et Staub (Maurizio and Staub, 1928). These latter Langeron proposed to bring provisionally into the genus *Torula. Monilia nigra* Burri et Staub, however, had been described earlier by Orla Jensen (1902) as *Cladosporium butyri* and it is noteworthy that De Vries (1952) in his monograph on the genus *Cladosporium* recorded that the species possesses a yeast-like form. It should be added that arthrospores develop in a later stage and that from its morphology the fungus could represent a dark-pigmented analogon of the hyaline yeast-genus *Trichosporon*. De Vries did not feel justified in transferring it to an existing genus and also refrained from creating a new genus for this species.

Quite apart from the above considerations, the existence in nature of dark-pigmented organisms analogous to non- or light-pigmented yeasts cannot *a priori* be denied.

C. *Ballistosporogenous Yeasts*

A third group of yeasts has been distinguished on the basis of the production of so-called ballistospores. This group contains the genera *Sporobolomyces* and *Bullera.*

"Ballistospores" are produced on sterigmata protruding from vegetative cells (Fig. 13) and are ejaculated into the air by a mechanism, the nature of which is as yet not completely understood. Müller, with the aid of a moving picture of the ejaculation of spores by *Sporobolomyces salmonicolor*, reviewed several theories on the subject (Müller, 1954). Although a similar mechanism is active in the discharge of basidiospores of the Hymenomycetes (Buller, 1933), the ballistospore was not generally accepted as a homologon of the basidiospore because (a) the vegetative cells are uninucleate, and (b) no karyogamy was observed preceding ballistospore formation (Guilliermond, 1927; Buller, 1933). For such reasons, Ciferri and Redaelli (1929) classified *Sporobolomyces* as a conidia-bearing yeast in the Nectaromycetaceae, alongside the Torulopsidaceae.

---

[4] A. Trejos considered this species name a synonym of *Phialophora jeanselmei* (Langeron) Emmons (*Mycologia* **45**, 253, 1953).

Derx (1948) created the family of the Sporobolomycetaceae for the known ballistospore-forming genera, including in the family the genera *Tilletiopsis* and *Itersonilia* which however are not yeasts. He supports the opinion of Kluyver and van Niel who suggested that the genus *Sporobolomyces* may be included in the Hemibasidii together with the Uredinales and the Ustilaginales (Kluyver and van Niel, 1925).

Sainclivier (1951, 1952) observed karyogamy in many yeast cells in *Sporobolomyces*. He is of the opinion that in this genus karyogamy

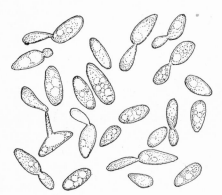

FIG. 13. *Sporobolomyces roseus*. Malt extract culture (×1000). (From Lodder and Kreger-van Rij, 1952.)

(= fusion of nuclei) regularly precedes spore formation. Therefore he regards the ballistospore as a basidiospore and supports the concept of *Sporobolomyces* as a Basidiomycete.

D. New Trends in Classification

As early as 1933, Ramsbottom suggested that heterothallism in fungi, i.e., the existence of two (or more) types of different sex in one species, could give rise to imperfect stages, in those cases where one of the sexes was exceedingly rare or had ceased to exist (Ramsbottom, 1933).

In 1943 Lindegren and Lindegren reported the existence in single-spore cultures of *Saccharomyces cerevisiae* of mating types in the sense that certain cultures produce ascospores when mixed whereas other cultures do not. Whereas these matings demonstrating heterothallism in yeasts were produced in the laboratory, Wickerham and Burton (1952) demonstrated the occurrence of yeast mating types in nature also. It was found that some species exist predominantly as haploid mating types, whereas other yeasts quickly become nonsporogenous under conditions of laboratory cultivation. However, when these strains were cultured together with a complementary mate, ascospores were again produced.

By applying the mating method, mating types have been found in strains of *Candida guilliermondii* isolated recently from nature and also in strains kept for years in collections (Wickerham and Burton, 1954b). In strains of this species and in *Candida melibiosi* in which sexuality is weak, successful mating is considered to demonstrate close relationship and even identity (cf. p. 52).

This introduction of the "mating" method in the study of imperfect yeasts has already disclosed that several of them belong to ascogenous species. This method has, in fact, provided us with a modern means with which to search for natural relationships in these hitherto little understood fields.

E. *Phylogenetic Lines in Yeasts*

It must be emphasized that the mating method represents only part of the modern scheme of classification research, as planned and already put into shape by Wickerham and Burton (Wickerham, 1951; Wickerham and Burton, 1954a). By isolating and examining large numbers of yeasts from nature these authors are working out phylogenetic lines in yeast genera. According to these ideas, haploid yeasts (those that conjugate immediately before ascus formation) are considered to belong to the most primitive species while isolates in which the diploid condition predominates are believed to represent more recently evolved species of yeasts. Another progressive change from primitive to higher developed species is a decrease in the dependence on an external supply of vitamins, and a third trend in this progression is the development of the capacity to cause fermentation of an increasing number of sugars.

Phylogenetic lines have been worked out on such principles in the genus *Hansenula*. This method of classification not only enables identification to be carried out but also reveals relationships which might otherwise remain obscure. A further study might give information on the evolution of the genera and our insight into the connection between sporogenous and asporogenous yeasts may well be widened by these studies which promise to throw light also on the relationships between yeasts and other fungi.

4. Characteristics Used in the Classification of Yeasts

A yeast can be characterized according to its morphological and its physiological properties. The former define the main lines in yeast taxonomy, whereas the differentiation into species is generally effected by means of physiological characters.

The *morphological properties* mainly concern the modes of vegetative and generative reproduction.

Vegetative Reproduction. A yeast may reproduce either by budding or by fission. Budding takes place either over the whole surface (multilaterally) when the buds arise on a narrow base, or it is bipolar and the buds arise on a more or less broad base. The first is a very common way of reproduction and the latter is characteristic of the tribe of the Nadsonieae but also occurs in a few genera belonging to the asporogenous yeasts (*Kloeckera, Pityrosporum*).

Yeasts reproducing exclusively by fission are found in the genus *Schizosaccharomyces* only (Fig. 2). The yeasts of this genus generally occur as single cells, though mycelium formation may also take place. When the mycelium breaks apart, arthrospores, again one-celled, are formed.

The concurrence of budding and fission is mainly found in the genera *Endomycopsis, Candida,* and *Trichosporon.* In these genera the occurrence of arthrospores is restricted to the genus *Trichosporon.* Incidentally the arthrospores are arranged in a typical zig-zag formation (Fig. 4).

Besides occurring as single cells or as a mycelium, yeasts may take the form of a pseudomycelium, e.g., in *Candida* (Fig. 5). The shape of the pseudomycelium[5] may be very much like a true mycelium, but its origin is different. It arises from budding cells, which often elongate while remaining in contact. The yeast cells sprouting at the ends of the elongate cells are called blastospores, the ones in between blastoconidia.

The primitively developed pseudomycelium consists of tree-like formations in which there is little differentiation between hyphal cells and blastospores. In the more highly developed pseudomycelia Langeron and Talice (1932) have recognized different types as follows:

"Mycotorula": Blastospores in compact clusters around the top of the pseudomycelium cells.

[5] This term was introduced by Ciferri and Redaelli (1929) and attributed to Ota (1924). In Ota's publication on the "Morphologie, Biologie und Systematik der pathogenen, asporogenen Sproszpilze," however, neither the term "pseudomycelium" nor its German equivalent "Sproszmycel" is mentioned. Even from this article it cannot be concluded that Ota recognized the mycelial growth in "Sproszpilze" (= fungi producing budding cells) as being different from the normal fungal mycelium. It is perhaps significant that the author did not refer to Will's "Beiträge sur Kenntnis der Sproszpilze ohne Sporenbildung" (Will, 1916, p. 274) which clearly defined the term "Sproszmycel" and placed a mycelium produced by budding sharply apart from true hyphae. Ciferri and Redaelli, having knowledge of Will's publication probably translated the German word "Sproszmycel" by "pseudo-mycelium" and "pseudo-hyphae."

"Mycotoruloides": Blastospores in loose branched verticils.

"Candida": Blastospores in chains at the ends of the pseudomycelium cells.

"Mycocandida": Strongly branched pseudomycelium. Blastospores in small verticils; often only two symmetrically arranged blastospores.

"Blastodendrion": Stalagmoid blastospores arranged in a penicillium-shaped way.

More than one of these types of pseudomycelium may occur in one yeast species.

The mode of vegetative reproduction, i.e., budding (multilateral or bipolar) or fission is of great taxonomic value while the presence of pseudomycelium itself constitutes an important aspect of the differentiation of the asporogenous yeasts.

Closely connected with the mode of vegetative reproduction stands the shape of the cells. Multilaterally budding cells may be round, oval, or elongate but bipolar budding cells are generally lemon-shaped or apiculate. The genus *Trigonopsis* has triangular cells which produce buds at the three angles. Shape and size of the cells are often variable. Nevertheless, in some cases not only the shape but also the size of the cells may be used in the differentiation of species or varieties.

The observation of such characteristics as the vegetative reproduction and shape of the cells may be carried out in liquid as well as on solid media, provided these media allow favorable conditions for growth. Especially the shape and more so the size of the cells should be studied under optimal, and if possible, standard conditions. Malt extract and malt agar may be used as such, but synthetic media can also be employed. The temperature in the experiments may vary from 25–30°C., apart from a few yeasts which have a relatively low optimal temperature of growth and should be grown at 17–20°C.

The formation of pseudomycelium often calls for special conditions. A review of factors stimulating filamentous growth in yeasts has been given by Scherr and Weaver (1953).

A technique often employed involves growth on a slide covered with a thin layer of agar so that a coverslip placed over part of the inoculation streak provides local anaerobic conditions. The slides are incubated in a petri dish on a U-shaped rod, with a little water added to prevent drying out of the agar. Special media like potato-, carrot-potato- or corn-meal agar are used.

The formation of a true mycelium and arthrospores is also easy to observe on slides. Seeliger (1955) found that a semi-solid medium containing Tween-80 was especially suitable for obtaining a rapid development of filaments in *Candida albicans*.

The appearance of the colonies or the streak culture on solid media e.g., malt agar and malt gelatin, is also one of the properties characterizing a yeast but is, however, often subject to variation.

Generative Reproduction. All yeasts belonging to the Saccharomycetaceae form asci which are single cells with ascospores. They may arise from the zygote immediately after conjugation of the haploid vegetative cells, or from a diploid generation in which a cell turns into an ascus. In the diploid generation conjugation has apparently taken place at an earlier stage, occasionally already during the germination of the spores. Two equal cells may conjugate giving rise to what is called isogamous conjugation, but two unequal cells may also fuse, e.g., mother cell and bud, leading to heterogamous conjugation. It is possible that haploid as well as diploid cells may be present side by side in one strain.

In the appearance of the spores there is great variation as they may be round or oval, reniform, bean- or sickle-shaped, Saturn- or hat-shaped hemispherical or angular, fusiform or needle-shaped. The wall of the spores may be either smooth or warty. The color is brown in *Nadsonia* and *Lipomyces* while in most species of the genus *Schizosaccharomyces* the wall is colored blue by iodine.

The number of spores varies from 1 to 16, *Kluyveromyces polysporus* being an exception. Some species have always 1 or exceptionally 2 spores (*Debaryomyces* species) while in others 4 is the usual number (*Saccharomyces cerevisiae*). A higher number is infrequently found; *Schizosaccharomyces octosporus* has 8 spores and *Lipomyces* may have 16.

In some genera the ascus ruptures at maturity and sets the spores free as is the case in many *Pichia* and *Hansenula* species. After being liberated the spores often adhere to each other in clumps.

The way in which asci and spores are formed, taken in conjunction with the shape of the spores, constitute important characters in the subdivision of the Saccharomycetaceae.

Induction of sporulation in a yeast strain is not always easy. Many factors seem to be involved, and these may differ for species and perhaps even for strains (see Chapter III, p. 106; Chapter VI, p. 305).

Adams and Miller (1954) found that oxygen had a stimulating effect while carbon dioxide and ethanol vapor inhibited sporulation. The temperature is also of importance. Tremaine and Miller (1954) studied the influence of vitamins on sporulation in baker's yeast, Oppenoorth (1956) that of light and Miller *et al.* (1955) and Miller and Halpern (1956) that of several chemical compounds.

Before inoculating the yeast on to a sporulation medium it is usually brought into an active condition by growing it in a rich presporulation medium, e.g., malt extract. A great number of actual sporulation media are used, e.g., Gorodkowa agar (peptone agar with 0.1% glucose), vegetable agar, acetate agar (Adams, 1949; Fowell, 1952; Kleyn, 1954), carrot and potato plugs, gypsum blocks, cement blocks (Hartelius and Ditlevsen, 1953), and sterile soil (Hartelius and Ditlevsen, 1956). Fowell (1955) gives a short review of the conditions for sporulation and of sporulation media in connection with hybridization.

Several yeast species lose their spore-forming faculty when cultivated for a longer time. Wickerham and Burton (1952, 1954a) found, on the other hand, that among the nonsporulating strains are yeasts which exist in the haploid stage and are heterothallic. In such cases, when strains of opposite mating type are mixed and spread together on a sporulation medium ascospore formation may be obtained.

Spores can be stained with malachite green (see "Manual of Methods for Pure Culture Study of Bacteria," IV, 13, 1946).

Ballistospores provide a source of controversy in that it is uncertain whether they are sexual spores, namely basidiospores, or conidia. They are formed by the Sporobolomycetaceae and arise on a sterigma on the cell whence they are discharged by a drop-excretion mechanism. This phenomenon can be detected by cultivating the yeast in an inverted petri dish after which the shot-off spores give a mirror image of the colonies in the lid. The ballistospores are asymmetrical, kidney- or sickle-shaped in *Sporobolomyces,* and symmetrical, round, or oval in *Bullera.*

Physiological Properties. Characters of this kind in yeasts which may be used in the first instance as an aid to classification are: pellicle formation on liquid media; fermentation and assimilation of carbohydrates; assimilation of nitrate; and occurrence of carotenoid pigments. Among other properties which generally have only secondary value are: splitting of arbutin; production of acid; vitamin requirements; and splitting of fat.

Pellicle formation by a yeast on a liquid medium is a property partly connected with its oxygen needs.

In several species, a more or less thin, dull, often wrinkled, creeping pellicle, the so-called "Kahmhaut," is formed generally after 1–2 days. In other species only after a longer time, e.g., 1 month, a glistening, wet pellicle or islets appear. In species forming a true mycelium a thick, tough skin is often formed, which gradually fills up the flask. Yeasts forming no pellicle only show bottom growth and in many cases ring formation.

To the early formation of a pellicle much value has been attached in the past and in species differentiation it remains of importance. As an aid in defining genera it is nowadays clearly less informative, since in some genera, like *Hansenula* and *Pichia,* species forming no pellicle or a slightly developed pellicle have been accepted.

Pellicle formation may be observed on any medium yielding favorable conditions for growth, e.g., malt extract or the liquid media for the assimilation tests.

Fermentation of sugars is one of the important characteristics of a yeast and a variety of combinations of fermentable carbohydrates exists to assist in the differentiation of species. Fermentation may be completely lacking but if it takes place at all, glucose is always among the sugars to be fermented. Further Kluyver has given the empirical rule that the fermentation of glucose always carries with it the ability to ferment fructose and mannose.

The carbohydrates generally used in the fermentation tests are: glucose, galactose, sucrose, maltose, lactose, and occasionally raffinose, melibiose, and inulin.

If a carbohydrate is well fermented a substantial amount of carbon dioxide will have accumulated after 1–2 days cultivation in the fermentation vessel. Fermentation is on the other hand judged to be weak when after a longer time of incubation only a slight amount, occasionally a single bubble of gas, is visible. It may be noted that with galactose, and sometimes with maltose and raffinose, it often takes a longer time before fermentation starts.

In order to carry out the fermentation tests, several tubes and vessels have been devised, e.g., Einhorn tubes, Durham tubes, the Winge fermentometer (Winge and Roberts, 1950), the syringe gasometer (Baird *et al.*, 1952) and the fermentation tubes of Morris and Kirsop (1953) and of Lindegren (1956). For routine tests, Durham tubes containing 2% sugar solution are often used.

The *assimilation* of various *carbohydrates* is also determined by growing the yeast under examination in a complete medium containing the carbohydrate in question as the sole source of carbon. A fermentable carbohydrate can also be assimilated but the reverse is not always true and the diversity of behavior assists therefore in the characterization.

Carbohydrates which may be used in assimilation tests include those used in the fermentation tests, but also a considerable number of other compounds come into consideration. These latter include *alcohols:* ethanol, glycerol, adonitol; *pentoses:* rhamnose, xylose; *polysaccharides:* cellobiose and inulin, and others. Wickerham and Burton (1948) and Wickerham (1951) advise the use of as many as 38 different carbon compounds in such assimilation tests to obtain a comprehensive picture of the yeast. For differentiating purposes in a certain genus a selected number of them may however be sufficient.

The assimilation tests may be carried out on solid media, the so-called auxanograms, or in liquid media. The auxanographic method was first described by Beijerinck. Barnett and Ingram (1955) have recently made a study of the factors involved in this technique. The liquid medium test was devised by Wickerham and Burton (1948).

In both cases the yeast is grown in a basal medium containing minerals, growth factors, and ammonium sulfate. The carbohydrates are either added on the surface of the agar or incorporated in the liquid medium. The auxanographic method has the advantage of being technically simple and of giving quick results in 1–2 days. The liquid medium test may be prolonged to 3 weeks and is very suitable for slow-growing yeasts and for compounds for which adaptation is required.

Shifrine, Phaff and Demain (1954) used the replica method of Lederberg and Lederberg (1952) when testing a large number of yeast strains. In this method, the solid medium consists of the basal medium with one of the potentially assimilable compounds added. Up to 25 yeasts are inoculated on the surface of a plate containing glucose. When grown, the off-print of the pinpoint colonies on a velveteen cloth is transferred to plates containing the other sugars.

The *assimilation of nitrate* may be tested in similar ways, either by the auxanographic method or in liquid medium. It has appeared (Wickerham, 1946) that the assimilation of other nitrogen compounds like urea and ammonium sulfate depends on the presence of growth factors.

The faculty of assimilating nitrate is an important taxonomic characteristic. For instance, in the genus *Hansenula* all species are nitrate positive whereas in other genera, especially among the asporogenous yeasts, both nitrate-positive and nitrate-negative species occur.

The *formation of starch-like compounds* by capsulated yeasts in the capsule, the cell wall, or in the medium was first studied by Aschner, *et al.* (1945). Later this property was used in yeast systematics, notably as one of the most important characters of the genus *Cryptococcus*. This genus is, in fact, separated partly on this basis from *Torulopsis*.

"Starch" is only produced if the yeast is grown on a medium of a pH lower than 5. In a medium containing ammonium sulfate as sole source of nitrogen during growth, the pH drops sufficiently following the disappearance of the ammonia.

Again, the examination may be carried out either on a solid or in a liquid medium. For the latter, Wickerham (1951, 1952) uses the medium for the carbon assimilation tests containing 0.5 or 3% of glucose and if necessary, the cultures are shaken. The results are observed after 1–2 weeks by adding a few drops of an iodine solution. For the solid medium an analogous synthetic medium may be used containing 1% of glucose and 0.1% ammonium sulfate, together with necessary minerals and growth factors, the production of "starch" again being noted after 1–2 weeks.

The faculty of starch production is not confined to the genus *Cryptococcus*. It is also present in the genus *Bullera*, in *Candida curvata*, and *Candida humicola*, in strains of *Trichosporon cutaneum*, in *Lipomyces*, and in some *Rhodotorula* strains. Indeed, it should be mentioned that *Cryptococcus laurentii*, *Bullera alba*, *Candida curvata*, and *C. humicola*, and also *Trichosporon cutaneum* show a great similarity in physiological properties although Aschner and Cury (1951) state that starch production in the *Trichosporon* strains is usually weaker than in *Cryptococcus*. It is noteworthy that in *Lipomyces*, Lodder and Kreger-van Rij (1952) could not detect starch on a solid medium, while Wickerham (1952) and Connell *et al.* (1954) were able to observe it in liquid medium. Finally, as regards *Rhodotorula*, the strains in question also give the starch reaction when grown on a medium with a higher pH (Slooff, unpublished).

The property of starch production certainly deserves closer investigation in view of its importance in yeast taxonomy.

The *occurrence of carotenoid pigments* in the cells may give the yeast a red to yellow appearance. It is possible to extract the pigment from the cells with acetone and light petroleum, and then identify it chromatographically and spectroscopically (Nakayama *et al.*, 1954; Peterson *et al.*, 1954).

The color is clearly pronounced in the genus *Rhodotorula* and in most *Sporobolomyces* strains. There are, however, a few cases when the strains in question show only a vague yellow or red color. It appears from the above-mentioned analytical method that here too carotenoid pigments may be present although of different nature or in smaller amounts. Indeed Nakayama *et al.* (1954) could even demonstrate such pigments in strains classified in the genus *Cryptococcus*.

Lodder and Kreger-van Rij (1952) restricted the taxonomic use of the presence of carotenoid pigments for the genus *Rhodotorula* to its expression in a distinct red or yellow color. The doubtful cases could be identified with *Cryptococcus* species with which they had another important characteristic in common, namely, the ability to form starch under special conditions.

Several yeast strains are able to *split* the *β-glucosides* arbutin and aesculin into glucose and a phenolic aglucone of which the latter gives a dark brown color with ferric salts.

The test is usually carried out on a solid medium of yeast-agar containing 0.5% arbutin or aesculin and a trace of ferric chloride. Barnett and

Swain (1956) use a different method, first growing the yeasts on a rich medium, namely malt-yeast-glucose-peptone agar, and then introducing the harvested yeast into a synthetic liquid medium containing 0.025% aesculin as sole source of carbon. After shaking the culture for 20 hours the aesculetin is extracted and measured spectrophotometrically. It appeared that all strains tested by the authors in this way were able to split aesculin, including many species which were negative by the plate method. Barnett et al. (1956) similarly employed other β-glucosides in their investigations, i.e., arbutin, salicin, and cellobiose. It appeared that a yeast capable of splitting one β-glucoside, did not necessarily hydrolyze another.

The *production of acid* is one of the characteristics of the genus *Brettanomyces*, though not exclusively belonging to this genus. Custers (1940) who made a special study of *Brettanomyces* gave a standard method for testing this property by which the yeast is grown on yeast-agar containing calcium carbonate. The production of a substantial amount of acid after 10 days' cultivation is made evident by the solution of the calcium carbonate.

Efforts have been made to use the *vitamin requirements* of a yeast in taxonomy especially in the species *Saccharomyces cerevisiae*. It appears, however, that the need for different vitamins has perhaps more value for the differentiation of strains than for separating species although Wickerham (1951) employs the inability to grow in a synthetic medium without vitamins as a characteristic for separating species.

Urease activity in yeast was used by Seeliger (1956) for differentiation. He employed Christensen's medium (1946), a solid medium including urea, peptone, and phenol red as indicator. The original pH is 6.8 and when urea is split the color turns deep red. Seeliger found that yeasts of the genera *Cryptococcus* and *Rhodotorula*, with the exception of *R. flava*, gave a positive reaction. Further urease activity was demonstrated in *Candida humicola, C. curvata, Bullera alba, Trichosporon cutaneum* and *T. pullulans* but all other genera and species tested by Seeliger were found to be negative.

Serological tests as a means for differentiating species have also been applied. The results, however, have not been promising so far.

For the identification of a yeast a preliminary microscopic observation is indispensable. Then a study of the following properties is recommended: the ability to form ascospores or ballistospores, the formation of mycelium, arthrospores, and pseudomycelium on slide cultures, the shape and size of the cells as well as the formation of a pellicle in liquid media. Further, fermentation and assimilation tests should be made.

In many cases the results of these tests will give enough information to identify the culture but when necessary other tests should be added. Wiles (1953) has elaborated a scheme according to which it should be possible to accomplish the identification of twenty yeast strains within two weeks.

5. Discussion of the Genera and Species Belonging to the Yeasts

Genera which belong to the three groups of ascosporogenous, ballistosporogenous, and asporogenous yeasts will be discussed and some of the more important species will be dealt with in some detail.

A. *Ascosporogenous Yeasts*

The ascosporogenous yeasts belong to the family of the Saccharomycetaceae (see Table I) and include five subfamilies: Eremascoideae, Endomycetoideae, Saccharomycetoideae, Nematosporoideae, and Lipomycetoideae.

In the first two of these subfamilies vegetative reproduction proceeds entirely by fission but only the genus *Schizosaccharomyces* of the Endomycetoideae is considered to belong to the yeasts. The species of this genus generally occur in the one-cell phase, though one of them forms also filaments. The genus *Eremascus* of the Eremascoideae, and *Endomyces* of the Endomycetoideae, are molds and will not be discussed here.

The genus *Schizosaccharomyces.* The single cells of this genus may be regarded as arthrospores. They reproduce by fission, and the mycelium also breaks up into arthrospores. Ascus formation is immediately preceded by isogamous conjugation. The spores are round, oval or reniform, 4–8 per ascus. In the spore wall, starch is usually formed and can be demonstrated with iodine.

S. pombe is most frequently found. Strains have been isolated from cane sugar, cane sugar molasses, and palm wine. Leupold (1950) made a special study of the genetics of this species.

S. octosporus has been described by Beijerinck who isolated it from Greek raisins. Typical of this species is the occurrence of 8 spores in the ascus (Fig. 14). Strains have been isolated from honey from British Columbia and from raw cane sugar.

S. versatilis has been isolated from fermenting fruit juice and from Portuguese wine. It is the only species in the genus which is filamentous.

The third subfamily of the Saccharomycetaceae (see Table II) comprises most of the sporogenous genera. It is characterized by budding and although occasionally septa may be formed in the hyphae arthrospores are never found. Spore formation occurs after iso- or hetero-gamous conjugation; 1–4 spores per ascus, spores of various shapes, but not fusiform or needle-shaped; vigorous fermentation to no fermentation at all.

The subfamily has three tribes. The first are the Endomycopseae with a single genus *Endomycopsis*.

The genus *Endomycopsis* has, besides a true mycelium with septa, budding cells. The spores are hat-, sickle- or Saturn-shaped, round or oval. Fermentation is absent or very weak.

The *Endomycopsis* species are somewhat uncommon. One of the species of more frequent occurrence is *E. fibuliger* which has been isolated from spoiled bread, from flour used in the manufacture of macaroni,

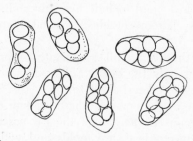

Fig. 14. *Schizosaccharomyces octosporus*. Spores (×1000). (From Lodder and Kreger-van Rij, 1952.)

from compressed yeast and from "Chinese Yeast" used for the production of an alcoholic beverage from rice starch. Wickerham *et al.* (1944) found that this species can produce an extracellular amylase and it is one of the few yeast species capable of fermenting starch.

An organism originally described by Nechitch as *Dematium chodati* was classified by Wickerham and Burton (1952) as *Endomycopsis chodati*, according to which authors it is widely distributed. It generally occurs as a haploid mating type. Teunisson (1954) gives a more complete description of the physiological properties.

Two species which also appear to be heterothallic and occur in the haploid phase are *E. ohmeri* Etchells et Bell and *E. guilliermondii* Wickerham et Burton. They have their imperfect stage in the genus *Candida*, i.e., *C. guilliermondii* var. *membranaefaciens* and *C. guilliermondii* respectively. In both cases Wickerham and Burton (1954b) were able to prove the connection by mating appropriate strains and obtaining spores. Mycelium formation in these species is, however, either completely lacking or very scant. Therefore the latter authors placed the species *guillier-mondii* provisionally in the genus *Endomycopsis* with the remark that a redefinition of this genus will be given later.

Strains which are very similar to *Endomycopsis javanensis* have been isolated by Phaff and Knapp (1956) from the slime flux of an oak. According to these authors, budding was not apparent in their strains nor in the original strain from Klöcker, and so these strains do not fit in the definition of the genus *Endomycopsis*. For these reasons, Phaff and Knapp prefer to rename this species *Endomyces javanensis*.

The genus *Saccharomyces* comprises yeast species which generally ferment a variety of sugars well. The cells are round to oval with multilateral budding. Pseudomycelium occurs in some species, but is primitive or missing in most of them. Sporulation takes place immediately after iso- or heterogamous conjugation, or there is a diploid generation between conjugation and ascus formation.

This genus includes many species, the most important of which is *Saccharomyces cerevisiae*. Strains of this species are used as baker's yeast, brewer's yeast, or wine yeast, in the manufacture of alcohol and for other fermentation purposes. This species has been the subject of numerous morphological, cytological, physiological and genetical studies. The variety *ellipsoideus* comprises many wine yeasts. Among the strains of the species there exists a great variability which is often difficult to express according to the usual taxonomic properties. Nevertheless, for industrial purposes it is desirable to be able to recognize the so-called wild yeasts which may cause spoilage. Wiles (1954) used for the characterization of strains encountered in the brewing process a combination of morphological properties and of vitamin requirements.

Gilliland (1956) found that among 54 strains of S. *cerevisiae* and variety *ellipsoideus* 12 strains were not able to ferment maltotriose. He suggested classifying these nonfermenting strains in a new species.

A species found as an infection in wort appears to cause superattenuation of beer. It has the same physiological and morphological properties as S. *cerevisiae*, but appears also to be able to ferment dextrin and starch and Andrews and Gilliland (1952) named it therefore S. *diastaticus*.

Saccharomyces willianus, isolated from grapes and other fruits, also resembles S. *cerevisiae*, but the cells are much longer.

Another important brewery yeast is S. *carlsbergensis* (Fig. 1) which is differentiated from S. *cerevisiae* by the fermentation of melibiose. Beer-spoiling strains occur in this species also.

Saccharomyces uvarum like S. *carlsbergensis* can ferment melibiose and the two are also similar in other respects but are distinguished by the longer cells of the former. Most strains have been isolated from fruit juices and fruit wines.

The species *Saccharomyces rouxii* and *S. mellis* are both osmophilic, and have been isolated from media with high sugar or salt content. *S. rouxii* ferments glucose and maltose, *S. mellis* glucose only. In the former species Pappagianis and Phaff (1956) detected a delayed fermentation of sucrose, i.e., after 3 weeks or longer. The beginning of fermentation depended on the age of the cells, since in Durham tubes inoculated with 3-week-old cultures gas formation appeared already after 2 days. The authors suggested that after sufficient ageing a rather abrupt change in the permeability of the cell occurs. The vegetative cells of *S. rouxii* and *S. mellis* are predominantly haploid.

Saccharomyces rosei and *S. fermentati* both have round to oval cells which often form protuberances resembling conjugation tubes (Fig. 15).

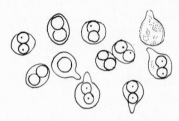

Fig. 15. *Saccharomyces rosei.* Spores (×1000). (From Lodder and Kreger-van Rij, 1952.)

No pseudomycelium is formed. Generally the asci contain 1–2 spores. Originally these species were classified in the genus *Torulaspora*. One of the main properties of this genus is that the cells may form conjugation tubes, although no conjugations occur. Krumbholz (1933) rejected this genus when he discovered iso- and heterogamous conjugations in strains of *Torulaspora* species.

Saccharomyces delbrueckii and *S. pretoriensis* van der Walt et Tscheuschner (1956a) resemble the two above-mentioned species in many respects.

Saccharomyces chevalieri has been studied by Winge and Roberts (1948) for its remarkable fermentation of galactose which commences only after a long time of incubation. The authors called this phenomenon long-term adaptation and suggested that a special gene is responsible for it. Strains of this species have been isolated from palm juice and palm wine.

Peynaud and Domercq (1956a) proved *Saccharomyces steineri* and

S. *italicus* to be identical and chose the name S. *steineri* for this species. Since, however, the species was first described as S. *italicus* this name has priority over S. *steineri*.

To the yeasts capable of fermenting lactose belong *Saccharomyces fragilis*, S. *lactis*, and S. *sociasi* (Ramirez, 1954). The first mentioned species is characterized by reniform spores (Fig. 16) which are easily liberated from the ascus, and by a well-developed pseudomycelium. S. *lactis* and S. *sociasi* have round spores and a very reduced or no pseudomycelium. They differ in the assimilation of maltose.

Strains of S. *fragilis* and S. *lactis* have been found in milk and milk products. S. *fragilis*, like S. *sociasi*, has also been isolated from human sources. Luh and Phaff (1951) found that the former is capable of attacking pectin.

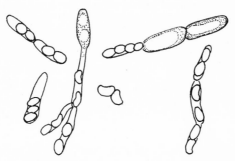

Fig. 16. *Saccharomyces fragilis*. Spores (×1000). (From Lodder and Kreger-van Rij, 1952.)

Saccharomyces marxianus closely resembles S. *fragilis*, but is unable to ferment lactose although it can assimilate this sugar. Both can grow at a temperature of 40°C. and ferment inulin.

Other yeast species having reniform-, bean-, or sickle-shaped spores, of which the ascus readily ruptures at maturity have been described as follows: S. *wickerhamii* by Phaff *et al.* (1956), S. *phaselosporus*, S. *dobzhanskii*, and S. *drosophilarum* by Shehata *et al.* (1955), and S. *delphensis* by van der Walt and Tscheuschner (1956b).

In this connection it may be mentioned that Wickerham (1955) and Wickerham and Burton (1956) intend to separate certain species from the genus *Saccharomyces* in a new genus *Dekkeromyces*, of which no clear definition has as yet been given, but in which will also be classified the species S. *lactis*, S. *fragilis*, and S. *marxianus*. Most of these species can produce a red pigment related to pulcherrimin. The asci rupture on the medium on which they are formed. *Dekkeromyces* species use a larger number of carbon sources than *Saccharomyces* species and most species produce ethyl acetate. They fail to hybridize with the other *Saccharomyces* species, but are able to do so with each other.

Some other yeast species previously described as *Saccharomyces* species have now been removed from this genus. For example, Ramirez and Boidin (1953) isolated from tanning liquid three species which they named S. *rhodanensis*, S. *chambardi*, and S. *strasburgensis*. Later, however, Boidin and Abadie (1954) brought these species into the new genus *Petasospora* which is defined as follows: cells round, oval, or elongate; multipolar budding; pseudomycelium present or absent; hat- or Saturn-shaped spores which are easily liberated from the ascus; conjugation may precede ascus formation. In liquid media, bottom growth, ring, and after a longer time a mucous pellicle. Fermentation variable, may be absent. Nitrate is not assimilated.

It differs from *Saccharomyces* in the shape of the spores and in the reduced fermentative ability. Boidin and Abadie also brought the species S. *pastori* and S. *pini* into this same genus. The authors did not point out the difference between their genus and the genus *Pichia* which lies chiefly in the mode of pellicle formation.

The genus *Pichia* has been characterized by the following properties: cells oval to long-cylindrical, pseudomycelium, spores hat-shaped, angular or round, 1–4 per ascus, pellicle formation on liquid media.

Shifrine and Phaff (1956), Phaff and Knapp (1956) and Phaff *et al.* (1956) isolated and described new species which showed much resemblance to the existing *Pichia* species, but lacked the ability to form either a pellicle, or pseudomycelium, or both. Phaff (1956) thereupon amended the genus *Pichia* and also accepted in it species forming no pellicle and species without or with a reduced pseudomycelium.

It then became possible also to classify the *Saccharomyces* species with hat-shaped spores, S. *pastori* and S. *pini*, in this genus. It seems obvious, moreover, that the *Petasospora* species described by Boidin and Abadie should fit in the genus *Pichia* as amended by Phaff. Phaff brought a third species which had previously presented difficulties in classification into the amended genus *Pichia*, namely, *Debaryomyces vini*. This organism deviated from other *Debaryomyces* species by the formation of a well-developed pseudomycelium and by the number of spores, namely, 1–4 per ascus. It does not form a pellicle.

One of the results of the amendment of *Pichia* is that the difference between the genera *Pichia* and *Debaryomyces* has become somewhat more difficult to express. It lies chiefly in the number and the shape of the spores.

One of the species of *Pichia* which is frequently encountered is *Pichia membranaefaciens* which may occur as a contaminant of beers or wines on which it forms a pellicle. Ethanol can be used as source of carbon. Glucose is occasionally very weakly fermented.

Pichia fermentans also forms a pellicle but ferments glucose rapidly. The spores are hat-shaped. Strains have been isolated from buttermilk and from fermenting cocoa.

The species *P. farinosa, P. polymorpha,* and *P. pseudopolymorpha* and *P. vini* all have round spores. Heterogamous conjugation precedes ascus formation.

The species described by Phaff and co-workers have been isolated from bark beetles and from slime flux of trees.

The genus *Hansenula* comprises all those ascosporogenous yeasts which can assimilate nitrate.

Wickerham (1951) made an extensive study of this genus including several new species which all had in common the ability to assimilate nitrate, but in which other properties like the formation of a pellicle, of pseudomycelium, and fermentation, were either weakly developed or missing. In the properties both of the new species and of the older ones Wickerham recognized certain lines of development, from completely haploid to completely diploid, from vitamin dependence to independence, from no fermentation to vigorous fermentation, from no pellicle to pellicle formation, and others. The author stated that organisms which show a possible relationship expressed by such so-called phylogenetic lines should be classified in one genus or group of genera. Accordingly, he redefined the genus *Hansenula* and extended its limits.

The definition runs in short: yeasts which reproduce asexually by budding, or by budding accompanied by the formation of pseudohyphae or true hyphae, form 1–4 ascospores per ascus, and assimilate nitrate. The spores in the genus *Hansenula* are mainly hat-shaped or Saturn-shaped. The ascus usually ruptures at maturity to liberate the spores.

Since the formation of true hyphae is included in this definition, there exists no longer any difference between *Hansenula* species and nitrate-assimilating *Endomycopsis* species. Accordingly Wickerham placed *Endomycopsis bispora,* the only nitrate-assimilating species of the genus *Endomycopsis* in *Hansenula* as *H. beckii.*

If in future the formation of true hyphae should be accepted as a property of other genera of the Saccharomyceteae, e.g., in *Pichia,* the genus *Endomycopsis* is doomed to disappear.

Wickerham and Burton (1954a) developed a technique for obtaining cultures from single spores by using the difference in heat resistance between vegetative cells and spores. If the yeast is heterothallic a single spore culture may be used as mating type in mating experiments.

The first species described is *Hansenula anomala* (Fig. 17). It is the prototype of the genus *Hansenula* in the old sense, exhibiting pellicle formation, fermentation, pseudomycelium formation, ester production, and splitting of arbutin. The species is very common and has been isolated from various sources. Single spore cultures of this species could be mated with strains of *Candida pelliculosa* which is the imperfect stage of *Hansenula anomala*.

Hansenula wingei is a nonfermenting, heterothallic species with hat-shaped spores described by Wickerham (1956). It shows a remarkable feature in that cells of opposite sex, when mixed, may immediately agglutinate. This agglutination does not occur in all strains.

FIG. 17. *Hansenula anomala.* Spores (×1000). (From Lodder and Kreger-van Rij, 1952.)

An osmophilic, nitrate-positive yeast species was described by Santa Maria (1956) as *Hansenula matritensis.* The spores in this species, one or seldom two per ascus, are round, warty, with an oil drop inside. No conjugation is observed immediately before ascus formation. The sporulating culture turns brown while the shape of the spores in this species is conspicuous and different from that occurring in the genus *Hansenula.* It seems, therefore, conceivable that it should belong in the tribe Saccharomyceteae to a different genus, incidentally, a new one. *Torulopsis globosa* shows such a close resemblance to this species that it might be regarded as the imperfect stage.

Of the genus *Schwanniomyces* only one species, S. *occidentalis,* is known, of which few strains are mentioned in the literature. They have been isolated from soil of St. Thomas and of South Africa. Fermentation occurs in this genus. Before ascus formation the cells form protuberances but no actual conjugation takes place. The spores are round or oval, with a warty wall and a ledge in the middle (Fig. 18). There is an oil drop inside.

The genus *Debaryomyces* was created by Klöcker for yeasts with spores having one membrane the surface of which is warty. He originally described one species in the genus, *D. globosus* which ferments both glucose and sucrose. Later other species were described, some fermenting and others nonfermenting but the main property characterizing the genus was still the warty spore wall. Lodder and Kreger-van Rij (1952), studying the genus, were of the opinion that this characteristic, as already mentioned by other authors, was often difficult to observe. Since they also found that the genus on this basis was rather heterogeneous in composition they proposed to amend it as follows. The fermenting species were eliminated as they could be classified as *Saccharomyces* species. The nonfermenting species were retained in the genus, the im-

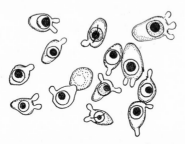

Fig. 18. *Schwanniomyces occidentalis.* Spores (×1000). (From Lodder and Kreger-van Rij, 1952.)

portant properties of which are now: cells round or short-oval, haploid, multilateral budding; pseudomycelium absent or very primitive; a pellicle may be formed on liquid media; fermentation very weak or absent; spores are generally formed after conjugation between mother cell and bud and may have a warty wall; usually one, sometimes two spores per ascus (Fig. 19). The species can be distinguished by the carbon assimilation and the pellicle formation.

Debaryomyces hansenii has been isolated from cheese and sausage. *D. kloeckeri* has been obtained from diseased nails and fingers, from sausage and cheese. Costilow *et al.* (1954) isolated 89 yeast strains from meat brines, all of which were *Debaryomyces* species withstanding a high salt concentration. Phaff and Knapp (1956) isolated a strain which they named *D. fluxorum* from slime flux of an oak.

Fig. 19. *Debaryomyces hansenii.* Spores (×1000). (From Lodder and Kreger-van Rij, 1952.)

The single species tentatively retained in the genus *Saccharomycopsis*, *S. guttulata*, is still a subject for investigation. Its conditions of growth are still insufficiently known, and its cultivation therefore difficult. It occurs in the stomach of rabbits where it may be found in great numbers adhering to the wall and among the stomach contents. It is present in the feces of rabbits where it is still viable. The cells are large, long-oval to cylindrical, generally arranged in branched chains. The spores are oval, 1–3 per ascus. The temperature of growth is 35–40°C. Glucose is fermented. The organism may be cultivated in a liquid medium, consisting of the extract of stomach contents according to Parle (1956), or in a peptone-glucose medium with vitamins added and at pH 1–5 (Kreger-van Rij, unpublished).

The tribe of the Nadsonieae has bipolar budding cells, generally lemon shaped. All genera belonging to it cause fermentation.

Of the first genus *Saccharomycodes*, a study has been made by Hjort (1954). It has diploid cells which may turn into asci in which usually four round spores are formed (Fig. 20). The spores conjugate in pairs with or without conjugation tubes or, more seldom, they germinate without conjugation.

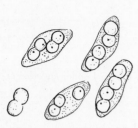

Hjort recognizes one species, *Saccharomycodes ludwigii*, with the variety *bisporus*. Various strains have been isolated from must. A genetical study of the species has been made by Winge and Laustsen (1939) and by Winge (1947).

FIG. 20. *Saccharomycodes ludwigii.* Spores (×1000). (From Lodder and Kreger-van Rij, 1952.)

The genus *Hanseniaspora* has hat-shaped, Saturn-shaped, or round spores. The spore-forming faculty is easily lost on cultivation.

A frequent species is *H. valbyensis*. It has hat-shaped spores. Shehata *et al.* (1955) isolated apiculate yeast strains with spherical spores and this would answer to the description of the genus *Kloeckeraspora* by Niehaus (1932). Since, however, the difference in the shape of the spores was not considered important enough to separate the genera, the yeasts were described as *Hanseniaspora* species, namely *H. uvarum.* Glucose is fermented and assimilated by this species and *H. valbyensis*.

Yeasts of this genus are often found in the early fermentation of fruit juices, especially of grape must. Castelli (1952) found in grape musts from North and Middle Italy generally asporogenous apiculate yeasts of the genus *Kloeckera;* in the warmer south of Italy the sporogenous *Hanseniaspora* species predominated.

The genus *Nadsonia* is the last in the tribe of the Nadsonieae. It has large lemon-shaped cells. The spores are formed in a peculiar way (Fig. 21). A cell forms a bud at one of the poles and conjugation between mother cell and bud takes place. Then a second bud is formed at the other pole of the mother cell. The contents of the zygote move into the second bud which turns into an ascus. Usually one, seldom two, round light-brown warty-walled spores are formed.

Two species are known, *N. elongata* and *N. fulvescens,* differing in fermentation and assimilation reactions. They have been isolated from exudations of trees.

Yeast species with fusiform or needle-shaped spores are classified in the subfamily of the Nematosporoideae.

Strains of the genera *Monosporella* and *Coccidiascus* are parasites which have not yet been cultivated. *Monosporella* parasitizes in *Daphnia magna* and *Dasyhelea obscura,* while *Coccidiascus* is found in *Drosophila funebris.*

The genus *Nematospora* has one species, *N. coryli,* the strains of which

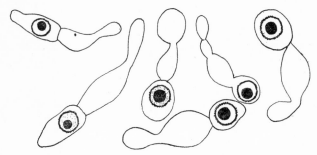

FIG. 21. *Nadsonia elongata.* Spores (×1000). (From Lodder and Kreger-van Rij, 1952.)

are plant parasites. The cells of this species vary from almost round to oval and elongate, while pseudomycelium and mycelium are also formed. The asci are very large and contain eight spindle-shaped spores, arranged in bundles of four (Fig. 11), each having a whip. These yeasts bring about fermentation and cause various diseases in fruits. They have been isolated from hazelnuts, cotton bolls, coffee beans, tomatoes, and oranges.

The last subfamily the Lipomycetoideae is classified with one genus, *Lipomyces,* of which the outstanding character is the typical way in which ascus and ascospores arise (Fig. 22). This peculiarity was first observed and described by Starkey (1946) while the genus was described by Lodder and Kreger-van Rij (1952).

The ascospore formation proceeds as follows. On one or more sides of a cell a sac-like protuberance is formed. The contents of the sac are at first granular, but after some time spores may be distinguished varying in number from 4 to 16, and perhaps more. The ascus remains attached to the mother cell. The spores are oval and have a smooth wall which is amber colored. This is the cause of the brown color assumed by an actively sporulating culture. The spores may be stained by malachite green. Nitrogen-deficient media with ethanol, glycerol, or lactose as sources of carbon are suitable for obtaining sporulation.

The genus *Lipomyces* is further characterized by round to oval capsulated cells, in older cultures containing a large fat globule, and by the absence of fermentation.

Two species have been recognized by Lodder and Kreger-van Rij (1952), *L. lipofer* and *L. starkeyi* differing in the assimilation of lactose

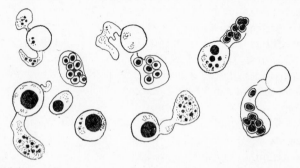

Fig. 22. *Lipomyces lipofer*. Spores (×1000). (From Lodder and Kreger-van Rij, 1952.)

and ethanol as well as in the size of the cells. Connell *et al.* (1954) did not agree with the separation of these species as the strains of neither were able to assimilate lactose, ethanol could be assimilated by both, while the difference in the size of the cells is very slight. Therefore they considered *L. lipofer* a synonym of *L. starkeyi*.

Wickerham (1952) and also Connell *et al.* (1954) found that a starch-like compound could be formed by *Lipomyces* under suitable conditions. This was not noted by the authors of the genus and may be due to a difference in method. Wickerham employs the test in liquid medium, Lodder and Kreger-van Rij the plate method, the former probably being more sensitive. Strains of the genus have been isolated from soil from various countries and also from human skin (Connell and Skinner, 1953).

Recently yeasts have been described which cannot be included in any of the above mentioned genera and which call for special attention.

As has been briefly mentioned, an important contribution to a better understanding of the phylogeny of the ascosporogenous yeasts has been made by van der Walt (1956a) with the discovery of a yeast for which he created the genus *Kluyveromyces*. The most striking character of this budding yeast is the formation, generally preceded by isogamous or heterogamous conjugation of unusually large multispored asci; hence the name *Kluyveromyces polysporus*. It has a strong fermentative ability; nitrate is not assimilated; it forms a pellicle in malt extract. The vegetative cells are uninucleate. Van der Walt supposes that *K. polysporus* might be derived from *Dipodascus* and especially from *D. uninucleatus* by a retrogression of mycelium formation and gametangial sexuality on the one hand, and a gain of blastospore formation and fermentative dissimilation on the other hand. In a second publication van der Walt (1956b) described another *Kluyveromyces, K. africanus* isolated from soil in South Africa like *K. polysporus*. It resembles the latter in many respects but differs in that the spores in the ascus number 1 to 16. Van der Walt admits that this difference in spore number makes the inclusion of the species *africanus* in the genus *Kluyveromyces* rather doubtful and, therefore, he only provisionally classified it in this genus. He further brought forward the relationship between *K. africanus* and the genus *Dekkeromyces* since *K. africanus* has long-oval to slightly reniform spores which are soon liberated from the ascus, fermentative ability, and no ability to assimilate nitrate, characters all found in the genus *Dekkeromyces*. In this way *Dekkeromyces* might be derived from *Dipodascus uninucleatus* via *K. polysporus* and *K. africanus*. By the number of spores in the ascus, *Kluyveromyces* takes a special position among the ascosporogenous yeasts which cannot yet be determined.

B. *Ballistosporogenous Yeasts*

The ballistosporogenous yeasts belong to the family of the Sporobolomycetaceae (see Table III). Derx (1948) placed four genera into this family: *Sporobolomyces, Bullera, Tilletiopsis*, and *Itersonilia*. Only the first two are considered as yeasts. Another genus closely related is *Sporidiobolus* Nyland (1949) which differs from *Sporobolomyces* only by its formation of a well-developed mycelium with clamp connections and chlamydospores. The ballistospores and vegetative yeast-like cells are uninucleate while the mycelium is binucleate. A fusion of nuclei takes place in the chlamydospores indicating a sexual phase. Sainclivier (1952) observed a fusion of nuclei in a mutant strain of *S. salmoneus* which is perhaps an indication that the supposition that *Sporobolomyces* and *Bullera* belong to the Basidiomycetes may be correct.

The genus *Sporobolomyces* is characterized by red to salmon-pink organisms, with oval, elongate, or hyphal cells. Vegetative reproduction is mainly by budding and true mycelium as well as pseudomycelium may be present. Ballistospores develop on sterigmata and are discharged by a drop-excretion mechanism. The spores may germinate and form yeast cells, or further sterigmata on which a new ballistospore develops. The metabolism is strictly oxidative.

Sporobolomyces species occur on plants and in the air. *S. salmonicolor* is one of the few mycelium-forming species. It can assimilate nitrate.

Sporobolomyces roseus (Fig. 13) forms no true mycelium and nitrate is not assimilated.

The genus *Bullera* differs from *Sporobolomyces* by its symmetrical ballistospores and the pale-yellow or cream color of the cultures. Neither true mycelium nor pseudomycelium are formed.

In the species *B. alba* the cells are round to oval, surrounded by a capsule, in which under appropriate conditions starch may be formed. *Bullera* strains were isolated from plants and from the air.

C. *Asporogenous Yeasts*

The asporogenous yeasts are grouped in the family of the Cryptococcaceae (see Table IV) in which three subfamilies are distinguished: Cryptococcoideae, Trichosporoideae, and Rhodotoruloideae.

In the Cryptococcoideae, reproduction proceeds by multilateral or bipolar budding, although budding on three angles of a triangular cell also occurs (*Trigonopsis*). Pseudomycelium is formed in the genus *Candida* where also true hyphae may be found. To a lesser extent pseudomycelium is developed in most species belonging to *Brettanomyces*. Extraordinary cell morphology is exhibited by *Pityrosporum* (bottle-shaped), *Kloeckera* (apiculate), and *Trigonopsis* (triangular). None of the members of this subfamily exhibits distinct red or yellow color due to the presence of carotenoid pigments.

The genus *Cryptococcus*. Here the species exist exclusively in the one-cell stage, exhibit round or oval cells, and multilateral budding. Further characteristics are: the mucous appearance of the colony and of the streak on solid media owing to the development of a slimy capsule, the production of a starch-like compound on acid media, and the lack of fermentative capacity.

An extensive review of the difficulties that had arisen around the generic name was published by Lodder (1938). Lodder and Kreger-van Rij (1952) proposed a modern conception of the genus from which the characteristics given above have been extracted, and Connell and Skinner (1953), in a survey of organisms isolated from the human body and from the air, adopted this modern diagnosis. In this sense *Cryptococcus* has been separated from *Torulopsis* generally on the bases of lack of fermentative capacity, development of a mucous capsule and, on acid media, of a starch-like compound.

The capsular substance has been analyzed chemically among others by Mager and Aschner (1947) and by Einbinder *et al.* (1954). It contains soluble carbohydrates and a high percentage of pentose was demonstrated. The actual composition of the capsule in a given culture of *Cryptococcus* will probably depend on the medium. A starch-like substance could only be found on media, liable to acidification during the cultivation of the organism and Mager and Aschner suggested that the appearance of "starch" in the medium of capsulated yeasts represents a pathological deviation of the metabolism.

Di Menna (1955a) found that *Cryptococcus* is highly resistant toward ultraviolet radiation and drying.

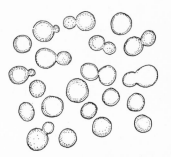

Cryptococcus neoformans (Fig. 23) is a very pathogenic representative of the genus. Cryptococcosis is an infection, in most cases limited to the central nervous system although other organs may be involved. Though only in a few cases has the yeast been isolated from other than human or animal sources, Emmons (1951) supposed it to have a widespread distribution as a saprophyte in nature. He succeeded, indeed, in repeatedly isolating the yeast from soil by inoculating soil suspensions into rats.

FIG. 23. *Cryptococcus neoformans.* Malt extract culture (×1000). (From Lodder and Kreger-van Rij, 1952.)

Ascospore formation has been intermittently reported in *Cryptococcus neoformans*. Todd and Herrmann (1936) stated to have observed cell conjugation and ascospore formation in young broth cultures inoculated from an old culture and they named their strain *Debaryomyces hominis*, because the ascus resulted from heterogamic conjugation and contained one spore. These observations were confirmed by Redaelli *et al.* (1937), but not by Lodder and De Minjer (1947) nor by Langeron (1945), Langeron and Luteraan (1947) or Emmons (1947). A quite different mode of sporulation was, however, reported by Benham (1955a), who, in a newly isolated strain of the species, found 2–8 spores in "sacs" which had budded out from normal cells. On account of these structures and of similarity of vegetative properties she supposed a relationship existed between the ascogenous species *Lipomyces starkeyi* and *C. neoformans* but clearly these findings require closer investigation. She further published an account of the genus and its differentiation into species (Benham 1956), using beside other characters the form of the colony, the ability to grow at 37° C., agglutination reactions, and pathogenicity for mice.

Besides mucous forms, smooth or dry cultures are encountered among strains of *Cryptococcus neoformans*. They have been classified in the variety *uniguttulatus*.

The species has attracted much attention from medical workers on account of its pathogenicity; accordingly an extensive synonymy has arisen for which reference may be made to Lodder and Kreger-van Rij (1952).

In *Cryptococcus laurentii* a weak carotenoid pigmentation has frequently been observed (Nakayama *et al.*, 1954) and strains originally described as *Torula aurea* Saito and *Torulopsis carnescens* Verona et Luchetti are now considered to find their proper place here.

Cryptococcus albidus is, like *C. laurentii*, widespread. An interesting feature in some strains of *C. albidus* is the property of producing a pectinase. Wieringa was able to isolate many strains from dew-retted flax and demonstrated the hydrolysis of pectin by applying a special technique (Wieringa, 1947, 1956).

Cryptococcus luteolus is distinguishable from *C. neoformans* by its elongate cells, and by a maximum temperature which is below 37°C. Moreover, this species possesses no pathogenic properties for mice (Benham, 1955b). It has been isolated only once, from the air in Japan.

C. diffluens differs from *C. neoformans* in that the former species is capable of assimilating potassium nitrate.

C. terreus has been isolated from soil samples in New Zealand by di Menna (1954). It holds a unique position in *Cryptococcus* by its inability to assimilate sucrose.

As regards the relationship of *Cryptococcus* to other organisms, Wickerham (1952) suggested that the genus could be related to the ascogenous yeast *Lipomyces*, in which organism "starch" could also be demonstrated, and Benham (1955a), observing plurispored asci in one strain of *Cryptococcus neoformans*, supported these views. Furthermore Wickerham pointed to a similarity to *Taphrina*, in which genus, also, some species produce "starch," although in small amounts, and multispored asci. Lodder and Kreger-van Rij (1955), without rejecting other possibilities laid stress on the resemblance of *C. laurentii* to *Bullera alba*, a nonpigmented "starch"-producing ballistospore-forming yeast.

The genus *Torulopsis* differs from *Cryptococcus* in lacking the property of "starch" formation on special media and in showing fermentative capacity. Divergences from the fermentation rule remain in the cases of *T. aeria, T. pinus,* and *T. inconspicua.* As "starch" could be demonstrated in none of these species when tested according to the classical method (Mager and Aschner, 1947) they were classified in *Torulopsis* by Lodder and Kreger-van Rij (1952).

Connell and Skinner (1953) removed *T. aeria* to *Cryptococcus* following their demonstration of "starch" in the authentic strain after having tested this yeast in a liquid medium according to Wickerham (1951).[6] They record having isolated considerable numbers of strains belonging to this species from the human body.

T. pinus is remarkable because of the capsulated spherical cells which, however, lack the property of "starch" production. Only glucose is assimilated. Recently a strain was isolated from *Drosophila* by Phaff *et al.* (1956) in California.

T. inconspicua is another species of poor activity. In contrast to *T. pinus* and *T. aeria* it has frequently been isolated from various substrates, Boidin and Abadie (1954) culturing the species repeatedly from tannery liquids.

The last representative of the nonfermenting group in *Torulopsis* was recently described from the gut of the bark beetle of *Pinus ponderosa* by Shifrine and Phaff (1956). They named it *T. melibiosum* to stress its remarkable ability to utilize melibiose but neither the trisaccharide raffinose nor sucrose.

Several species of *Torulopsis* have been either incidentally or regularly isolated from highly osmotic substrates, e.g., dates yielded *T. dattila,* a species which ferments glucose, sucrose, and raffinose strongly. Under aerobic conditions maltose and galactose are also utilized (Kluyver and Custers, 1939–1940).

T. glabrata, originally isolated by Anderson (1917) from human feces, was considered to be exclusively connected with human sources until Phaff *et al.* (1952) cultured it from shrimps and Recca and Mrak (1952) found this species in a sample of concentrated orange juice. Strains belonging to *T. glabrata* have proved to be pathogenic towards rats and white mice (Black and Fisher, 1937; Lopez-Fernandez, 1952). In 1956 it was isolated from garden soil in Holland (E. H. Battley, personal communication). A related species is *T. pintolopesii,* isolated from the liver and the spleen of mice (van Uden, 1952).

T. lactis-condensi has been cultured frequently from spoiled sweetened condensed milk (Olson and Hammer, 1935). A yeast, causing spoilage

[6] An extremely weak "starch" reaction was found by the present authors when applying the same method.

in pickled cucumbers and termed *T. caroliana* (Etchells and Bell, 1950) could be identified with the former species. It was reported to tolerate concentrations of 15–20% salt. Recently *T. lactis-condensi* was isolated by van der Walt in Pretoria from pickled onions containing 17% of sodium chloride (personal communication). All strains belonging to this species are difficult to maintain on solid media; the scanty growth produces a filiform streak and the cultures die off rapidly. A typical characteristic is the assimilation of potassium nitrate.

T. globosa was also isolated by Olson and Hammer from a similar source (Olson and Hammer, 1935). It is very different, however, in its morphology, as it possesses large round cells. It is also capable of assimilating potassium nitrate.

T. magnoliae represents one more species capable of nitrate assimilation. It is commonly associated with flowers and insects and may be found in nectar. It has also been isolated from orange concentrates in South Africa (van der Walt, personal communication).

Several species, isolated by Etchells and Bell from highly salted media are capable of utilizing potassium nitrate as the only source of nitrate (Etchells and Bell, 1950). Originally they have been described by the generic name *Brettanomyces*. Lodder and Kreger-van Rij (1952, p. 429), however, objected to this classification and transferred these yeasts to the genus *Torulopsis*. The species concerned are: *B. versatilis, B. sphaericus,* and a variety of *B. versatilis,* renamed, respectively, *T. versatilis, T. etchellsii,* and *T. anomala.* When compared with authentic strains belonging to the genus *Brettanomyces* the newly named species did not show the complex of characters typical for this genus; for instance, the production of acids for which *Brettanomyces* is renowned was found to be rather low. Wickerham (1952), on the other hand, disagreed with the Dutch authors being of the opinion that gradations in acid production may occur among the species in the genus *Brettanomyces* and that the strains discussed might represent such deficient species.

T. stellata and *T. bacillaris* form a group of yeasts associated with liquids of high sugar concentration such as concentrated grape musts. Recently isolates were reported from *Drosophila* (Phaff *et al.,* 1956) and from alphalpha honey containing about 55% of sugars (Shifrine and Schade, personal communication).

In the genus *Torulopsis,* species are to be found which might be sporogenous yeasts apart from the ascospore formation and such species are looked upon as imperfect forms. Some of them, however, after mixing similar strains produced ascospores and are now considered to represent haploid strains of heterothallic ascogenous yeasts. This is the case with:

(1) *T. molischiana:* a haploid strain of *Hansenula capsulata* (Wickerham, personal communication); and

(2) *T. sphaerica:* a haploid strain of *Saccharomyces lactis* (Wickerham and Burton, 1952).

Although *T. molischiana* had been described as a yeast not capable of utilizing potassium nitrate, Wickerham in applying his liquid medium test, demonstrated that nitrate was in fact assimilated by the authentic strain.

The following species may represent imperfect stages of ascogenous yeasts:

T. colliculosa: imperfect form of *Saccharomyces fermentati.*

T. holmii: imperfect form of *Saccharomyces exiguus.*

T. candida: imperfect form of *Debaryomyces subglobosus.*

T. famata: imperfect form of *Debaryomyces kloeckeri.*

T. osloensis:[7] imperfect form of *Saccharomyces rouxii.*

The genus *Pityrosporum* comprises a number of peculiar yeasts which are easily recognizable by the bottle shape of the budding cells. After budding on a broad base, a partition wall develops by cleavage of which the young cell is subsequently liberated. Growth on regular media is very scanty and addition of fatty substances is needed for vigorous development and prolonged cultivation (Benham, 1947).

P. ovale (Fig. 3) can be regularly cultivated from scales of the human scalp, and *P. pachydermatis* was isolated by Weidman (1925) from the inflamed skin of an Indian rhinoceros.

Gordon (1951a) isolated a spherical organism, for which yeast he proposed the name *P. orbiculare,* from tinea versicolor scales as well as from apparently normal skin. It proved amenable to cultivation only under a layer of a fatty substance. In order to permit classification of this isolate in the genus *Pityrosporum,* Gordon (1951b) proposed to redefine the genus to include anascosporogenous lipophilic yeast-like organisms of various shapes. This procedure of substitution of morphologic characters by biochemical properties in the differentiation between groups on the generic level is, however, somewhat hazardous.

Gustafson (1955) isolated cultures, from otitis externa in Swedish dogs, of yeasts named *P. canis* and similar strains have been isolated in Holland.

The genus *Brettanomyces.* In most species of this genus, pseudomycelium is developed on suitable solid media. In its differentiation from

[7] Dietrichson, 1954.

Candida, stress is laid on the "ogive" shape of the cells (= shape of a pointed arch) but this characteristic is not always easy to verify. Further the genus *Brettanomyces* is distinguished by its biochemical properties. Thus strains belonging to the genus produce unusually high amounts of acid, inhibiting growth and causing the culture to die off early, while a very characteristic odor is developed. The biochemical properties of the genus were studied by Custers (1940) whose thesis, written in Dutch, was reviewed by Skinner (1947b) and by Shimwell (1947).

The classic source of isolation of many members of the genus is the late fermentation in the manufacture of Belgian lambic beer and of English beers. *B. bruxellensis* and *B. lambicus* have both been isolated by Kufferath (1920) from lambic beer in Belgium and only differ in the appearance of the cultures on malt agar. *B. anomalus* was isolated by Custers from the sediment in lambic beer. It was so named because it ferments lactose, but not maltose, indeed a remarkable characteristic in a beer yeast. *B. claussenii* ferments vigorously all six sugars applied in the routine tests. Pseudomycelium development in Kufferath's strain, isolated probably by Schiönning (1907–1909), is only scanty. In a second strain received from Andersen and isolated from green beer in Denmark a characteristic *Brettanomyces* pseudomycelium is developed abundantly.

Isolation of strains related to *Brettanomyces bruxellensis* has been reported from acid spoilage in the manufacture of certain French wines and these were described with the name *B. bruxellensis* var. *vini* (Barret *et al.,* 1955). Peynaud and Domercq (1956b) compared the properties of these yeasts with those of isolates from other sources, including the authentic strain of *Brettanomyces bruxellensis.* They considered the differences of enough importance to establish two new species: *Brettanomyces vini* and *B. schanderlii.*

Earlier Etchells and Bell (1950) isolated several species from fermentation of cucumbers in salt brines which were described with the generic name *Brettanomyces.* For a short account of the subject the reader is referred to the heading *Torulopsis* above.

The genus *Candida.* In this genus the development of pseudohyphae is the most outstanding feature. True hyphae showing partition walls, however, are also found in many species, e.g., in *C. albicans, C. tropicalis, C. krusei,* and *C. mesenterica.* In most cases budding cells or blastospores are formed in abundance on the filaments. The blastospores can be arranged on the filaments in different ways, for the description of which the reader is referred to Section 4 above. On nitrogen-deficient media, chlamydospores, large cells provided with a thick membrane and containing one or more oil drops, frequently develop. Chlamydospores have proved to be acid fast on staining (Langeron and Luteraan, 1949) and are encountered in *C. albicans, C. parapsilosis, C. pseudotropicalis, C. reukaufii, C. pulcherrima,* and also in other genera (van der Walt, 1952).

C. albicans is undoubtedly the most studied species and Conant *et al.* (1944) state that 172 binomial synonyms exist in the literature. The species is a common saprophyte on human and animal mucous membranes and on the skin. When conditions are unfavorable for the host and especially in patients treated with antibiotics, *C. albicans* may become pathogenic. Generally the species develops a pseudomycelium of the "Mycotorula" type (Langeron and Talice, 1932) on the joints of which blastospores accumulate in clusters. In most strains chlamydospores develop on maize agar. However, the organism shows a great variability even to the extent that chlamydospores or filaments may be lacking although a low oxygen tension and a poor medium stimulate development of both structures. Drouhet and Couteau (1954) recommend a potato-carrot medium preceded by a passage through 10–20% of carbon dioxide; Nickerson and Mankowski (1953) applied a purified soluble-starch medium containing trypan blue which accumulates in the chlamydospores and so provides vital staining. Seeliger (1955) secured development of pseudomycelium in *C. albicans* by making use of stab cultures in a semi-solid medium containing Tween 80. Furthermore *C. albicans* appears in a smooth and a rough form (S and R form). In contrast to the S form, the R form is very filamentous and develops a pellicle on liquid media, whereas development of blastospores is only scanty. Freshly isolated cultures generally show the S form although R forms in new isolates have been reported by di Menna (1952). Recently the species has been cultured in New Zealand from soil samples (di Menna, 1955b) and in Portugal it has been isolated from leaves of *Myrtus communis* and from a flower of *Ulex* species (van Uden *et al.,* 1956). These occasional isolations from soil and from vegetable matter provide evidence that *C. albicans* is able to maintain itself on extra-human or extra-animal substrates but is not likely to flourish on them. *Candida stellatoidea* differs from *C. albicans* mainly in not being capable of sucrose assimilation and of fermentation of galactose. Strains of this species have been reported exclusively from the vagina. Winter and Foley (1955) report transitions between the two species as regards the properties of acid production from sucrose and of pathogenicity towards rabbits. The authors did not apply sucrose assimilation reactions. Their conclusion that the existence of intermediate forms provides a reason to reject one of the species is, according to the opinion of the present authors, not warranted.

Other species in the genus, repeatedly isolated from human and animal sources but generally not considered to be pathogenic are *C. tropicalis*, *C. pseudotropicalis*, *C. guilliermondii*, and *C. parapsilosis*.

C. tropicalis is characterized by very large cells and an abundance of coarsely developed pseudomycelium (Fig. 5). In contrast to *C. albicans* it is a good fermenter of sucrose, whereas raffinose is only weakly fermented. Strains of this species, capable of utilization of xylose (Windisch, 1948) have been used in the German fodder yeast manufacture. *C. pseudotropicalis* ferments lactose whereas maltose is not attacked at all. But for the lack of ascospores it is identical with *Saccharomyces fragilis*, and just as the last yeast it is often encountered in milk products. *C. guilliermondii* is outstanding for its small-sized cells and the development of pseudomycelium in elegant, elongate, branched plumes. Chains of stalagmoid cells are typical of this species and sucrose and raffinose are fermented by it. It is found to be a common inhabitant of frass and tree gums (Wickerham and Burton, 1954b). The same authors found in certain strains, when mixed with the suitable mating type, conjugations and ascospores. They concluded from results of assimilation reactions and from mating experiments that *C. guilliermondii* and *C. melibiosi* were identical. *C. parapsilosis* ferments the least vigorously among those of this group. A branched pseudomycelium bearing small verticils with very few blastospores is common. Lipolytic activity has been demonstrated in strains, isolated from fatty substances, i.e., the residues of olives.

Other species of *Candida* capable of production of lipase are *C. lipolytica* and *C. rugosa*. These species can be regularly isolated from such fatty substances as margarine, butter, and olives. They are also often associated with infections of the skin and the nails. Both yeasts develop early pellicles on malt extract, both lack fermentative capacity, while assimilation of sugars is restricted to glucose, or glucose and galactose. Morphologically *C. lipolytica* is distinguished by profuse development of coarse pseudohyphae and true mycelium, in contrast to *C. rugosa* where a pseudomycelium is only primitive, consisting of branched chains of cylindric or elongate cells. *C. lipolytica* is also remarkable for its capacity for reproduction on higher carbohydrates as a source of carbon (Just *et al.*, 1951, 1952).

C. mycoderma and *C. krusei* are very common species, known as spoilage yeasts in many industries, where they have been isolated from beer, wine, pickled cucumbers, dough, fermenting cocoa, tannery liquids, etc. Both species produce dry pellicles on liquid media, which creep up the vessel wall. The former possesses very little fermentative ability, whereas the latter ferments glucose vigorously. Many species of the former genus

Mycoderma have been renamed *C. mycoderma* (Lodder and Kreger-van Rij, 1952). Walker and Wiles (1952) in an effort to differentiate strains of *Mycoderma* used 35 different carbon sources. Among these substances, succinic acid and mannitol or sorbitol may prove to be useful for taxonomic purposes. *C. sorbosa* is a closely related species, isolated from feces of a fruit fly by Hedrick and Burke (1951).

Interesting are *C. pulcherrima* and *C. reukaufii*. They have very much in common, both morphologically and as regards physiological characters, and find their natural habitat on similar substrates, such as stomachs of bees and bumblebees, flowers, and fruits. *C. pulcherrima* is distinguishable by its large, fat-containing cells, formed on nitrogen-deficient media. Most strains produce a red pigment on iron-containing media (Roberts, 1946). The chemical structure of the red substance was studied by Kluyver *et al.* (1953) and by Cook and Slater (1954, 1956). In *C. reukaufii*, on the other hand, no red pigment has ever been observed. Martin (1954) isolated 46 strains from 5 species of flowering plants by micromanipulation of the "aeroplane-structures" from drops of nectar. These structures are formed by *C. reukaufii* on highly osmotic media. Rippel-Baldes *et al.* (1948) reported that considerable amounts of fat could be produced by certain strains of this species on aerated media. In this connection it seems noteworthy that Beijerinck applied the name "fat yeast" to *C. pulcherrima,* on account of the large oil-containing globules occurring in the cells at a certain stage (Beijerinck, 1912). The latter species was studied extensively by van der Walt (1952).

Many species in the genus *Candida* utilize lactose, and one actually ferments this sugar. They may be listed as follows:

C. pseudotropicalis: lactose is fermented, no assimilation of maltose.

C. macedoniensis: fermentation, except for lactose and maltose; maltose not assimilated.

C. intermedia: lactose is not fermented, good fermentation of maltose.

C. tenuis: fermentation of glucose and galactose only: a very thin pseudomycelium is developed.

C. curvata: no fermentation; pseudomycelium predominates.

C. humicola: no fermentation; true mycelium is abundantly developed. The nonfermenting lactose-assimilating species are differentiated mainly by the appearance of the pseudomycelium and by cell morphology. Among the fermenting lactose assimilators, some may represent imperfect strains of ascogenous species, e.g., *C. pseudotropicalis* is indistinguishable from the vegetative stage of *Saccharomyces fragilis,* whereas *C. macedoniensis* could represent a nonsporulating strain of *Saccharomyces marxianus. C. tenuis* has been reported to be isolated from bark beetles in the United States; the other strains listed above were originally described from human or animal sources. Recently, however, 2 strains of *C. intermedia* were isolated from brewing operations and Shifrine and Phaff (1956) reported 15 strains of *C. curvata* from the guts of bark beetles in California.

Other species are outstanding because of their ability to utilize potassium nitrate as a source of nitrogen. In this group *C. utilis* (syn. *Torula utilis*) is by far the best known, as it has been applied in food- and fodder-yeast manufacture, especially in wartime. Another nitrate assimilating species is *C. pelliculosa*. Originally several strains were isolated from human sources, mostly cases of disease of the pulmonary tract. Strains of this species, mated with a mating type of *Hansenula anomala*, produced typical hat-shaped ascospores and Wickerham and Burton (1954a) have thus demonstrated that *C. pelliculosa* represents a haploid stage of *Hansenula anomala*. *C. melinii* was isolated from woodpulp in Sweden. Recently Shifrine and Phaff (1956) cultured from bark beetles in California 70 strains which belong to a hitherto unknown species, named *Candida silvicola* and also found to exist in mating types of a species of *Hansenula*. Another interesting yeast assimilating potassium nitrate is *C. scottii*, which can be regularly isolated from chilled beef and prefers low temperatures for growth. Recently it was isolated from the air in Norway. From tannery liquids in France, Boidin isolated a species designated by Ramirez (1954) as *C. boidini*. This species was also capable of utilizing potassium nitrate (Boidin and Abadie, 1954).

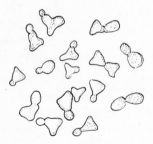

Fig. 24. *Trigonopsis variabilis*. Malt extract culture (×1000). (From Lodder and Kreger-van Rij, 1952.)

Dietrichson (1954) studied a strain named *C. trigonopsoides* isolated from sputum in a case of asthma. It develops triangular cells, uncommon in *Candida* and in this respect it may represent a transitional form of the genus *Trigonopsis*.

The genus *Trigonopsis* is remarkable for its triangular cells, although oval cells are also present. As yet the genus is represented by 2 strains of *Trigonopsis variabilis* only, both isolated from beer (Fig. 24).

In the genus *Kloeckera* are gathered the nonsporogenous apiculate or lemon-shaped yeasts (Fig. 25). As such it comprises the imperfect forms of *Hanseniaspora*. All species are good fermenters, at least of glucose. They are differentiated according to their morphology and to their fermentation and assimilation of sugars, potassium nitrate not being utilized. *K. apiculuta* is the most common species, found on fruits, flowers, and in soil samples. Only glucose is fermented and assimilated. *K. magna* has also been frequently isolated. Both species were repeatedly obtained from *Drosophila* by Phaff *et al.* (1956).

The genus *Schizoblastosporion* was originally isolated by Starkey and Henrici from soil samples and described by Ciferri (1930b). Its salient features are the budding of the cells on a very broad base, the subsequent development of a partition, by the fission of which the bud is detached from the mother cell. It is still questionable whether this property will not disappear on prolonged cultivation. The validity of the genus is therefore contestable. Recently Lund (1954) isolated a strain which he considered identical with *Schizoblastosporion starkeyi-henricii* from soil samples in Sweden. As the similarity of reproduction with that of *Pityrosporum* is obvious he suggested that *Schizoblastosporion* should be considered a synonym of the former generic name. *Schizoblastosporion,* unlike *Pityrosporum,* is easily cultured on regular media, needs neither fatty substances for growth, nor elevated temperatures.

Fig. 25. *Kloeckera jensenii.* Malt extract culture (×1000). (From Lodder and Kreger-van Rij, 1952.)

The second subfamily in the Cryptococcaceae is named Trichosporoideae (see Table IV). This subfamily includes only one genus: *Trichosporon* (Fig. 4). Reproduction proceeds by budding as well as by means of arthrospores. In the filaments, developed after budding on a more or less broad base, cross-walls appear at a later stage. By splitting at the cross-wall the filaments disintegrate into arthrospores. From the filaments as well as from the arthrospores, cells again develop by budding. Dissimilation is strictly oxidative in most species and a pellicle is formed on liquid media. *Trichosporon pullulans* is outstanding because of its preference for low temperatures for growth. Most strains known are derived from northern Europe and originate from breweries, exudations of trees or woodpulp. An exceptional case is represented by the strains, isolated by Scott (1936) in Australia from cooled beef. In contrast to *T. cutaneum, T. pullulans* is capable of nitrate utilization. Well known for fat production is the strain formerly designated *Endomycopsis vernalis.* Lipase activity has been demonstrated in all yeasts belonging to the species *T. pullulans. T. cutaneum* is the most studied species in the genus on account of infections of the human skin, from which cases it has frequently been isolated. It was, however, also isolated from sewage and waste water in dairies, from woodpulp, and from orange peel. The last isolates are capable of "starch" production (Aschner and Cury, 1951), as is described for the genus *Cryptococcus*. Species capable of fermentation are *T. fermentans* and *T. behrendii*. The former species seems to be connected with trees and with substances derived from them; isolations are known from woodpulp and tannery liquids; Phaff *et al.* (1956) cultured the species from *Drosophila*. These authors also isolated a species with typical needle-shaped cells, which they named *T. aculeatum*.

The Rhodotoruloideae represent the third and last subfamily in the Cryptococcaceae. It includes only one genus: *Rhodotorula* (see Table IV). In morphology and vegetative reproduction *Rhodotorula* is indistinguishable from *Cryptococcus*, but it is characterized by the production of distinct red or yellow carotenoid pigments. The genus exhibits a strictly oxidative dissimilation. Nakayama *et al.* (1954), considering the fact that separation of *Cryptococcus* and *Rhodotorula* on the basis of manifest carotenoid production is arbitrary, suggest that it could better be based on "starch" production. This is, in fact, the practice followed by Lodder and Kreger-van Rij (1952) as in doubtful cases the strains capable of "starch" production were classified in *Cryptococcus*. Wickerham, on the contrary, is of opinion that "starch" production will not serve well as a principal characteristic in differentiation of genera (Wickerham, 1952). Recently it was found that all the strains of *Rhodotorula* that responded positively to the "starch" reaction could develop the substances without cultivation on a medium at a low pH. Among them was *R. glutinis* var. *infirmo-miniata*.

Species of *Rhodotorula* are of very common occurrence and strains have frequently been isolated from the air. Connell and Skinner (1953) in a survey of yeasts cultured from the air, demonstrated that some 47% of the isolates belonged to this genus. Several other strains were identified with *Sporobolomyces*. Lodder (1934, p. 27) discussed the relationship of these genera when it became obvious that strains of *Sporobolomyces*, examined after the loss of their capacity for ballistospore formation will automatically be classified in *Rhodotorula*. Lodder and Kreger-van Rij are of opinion that whereas *Rhodotorula* could be related to *Sporobolomyces*, *Cryptococcus* may be associated with *Bullera*, in which genus "starch" has already been demonstrated.

Skinner and Huxley (1956) considered difficulties which arose from using 29 carbon-sources for differentiating species of *Rhodotorula*. They found differences in morphology and color, as well as in physiological characters, which, however, were not useful taxonomically. They suggested that it would be best to postpone classifying *Rhodotorula* until more work has been done to make a phylogenetic classification possible. They go as far as to say that *Rhodotorula* should be considered monotypic, the only species being *Rhodotorula glutinis*. In their system, *Rhodotorula flava* is excluded from the genus.

Common species are *Rhodotorula glutinis* and *R. mucilaginosa;* the former has the larger cells and is able to utilize potassium nitrate unlike the latter. *R. aurantiaca* and *R. flava* produce yellow carotenoids. Apart from the nature of carotenoids the latter species is related to *R. texensis*, isolated from shrimp and described by Phaff *et al.* (1952). From the same source, the authors described two more species: *R. marina* and *R. peneaus*, of which the latter is a yellow, "starch"-producing yeast. Hedrick and Burke (1951) isolated *R. pilimanae* from the larva of *Drosophila*. Recently *R. crocea* was isolated from bark beetles and studied by Shifrine and Phaff (1956). Sonne Frederiksen in Denmark studied yeasts associated with pectin hydrolysis in dew-retted flax. He isolated a species producing carotenoids and capable of assimilating lactose as well as potassium nitrate. The organism was named *R. macerans* (Sonne Frederiksen, 1956). This species, like *R. glutinis* var. *infirmominiata* has no need of media at a low pH to give a positive "starch" reaction.

References

Adams, A. M. (1949). *Can. J. Research* **C27**, 179.
Adams, A. M., and Miller, J. J. (1954). *Can. J. Botany* **32**, 320.
Anderson, H. W. (1917). *J. Infectious Diseases* **21**, 341.
Andrews, J., and Gilliland, R. B. (1952). *J. Inst. Brewing* **58**, 189.
Aschner, M., and Cury, A. (1951). *J. Bacteriol.* **62**, 350.
Aschner, M., Mager, J., and Leibowitz, J. (1945). *Nature* **156**, 295.
Baird, V., Hestrin, S., and Lindegren, C. C. (1952). *Wallerstein Labs. Communs.* **15**, 213.
Barnett, J. A., and Ingram, M. (1955). *J. Appl. Bacteriol.* **18**, 131.
Barnett, J. A., Ingram, M., and Swain, T. (1956). *J. Gen. Microbiol.* **15**, 529.
Barnett, J. A., and Swain, T. (1956). *Nature* **177**, 133.
Barret, A., Bidan, P., and André, L. (1955). Acad. Agric. France, Extr. du procès-verbal de la Séance du 18 mai 1955.
Beijerinck, M. W. (1912). *Folia Microbiol.* (*Delft*) **1**, 75.
Benham, R. W. (1947). *Ann. Cryptogam. Phytopathol.* **6**, 63.
Benham, R. W. (1955a). *Proc. Soc. Exptl. Biol. Med.* **89**, 243.
Benham, R. W. (1955b). *Trans. N.Y. Acad. Sci.* Ser. II, **17**, 418.
Benham, R. W. (1956). *Bacteriol. Rev.* **20**, 189.
Berger, L., and Langeron, M. (1949). *Ann. parasitol. humaine et comparée* **24**, 574.
Berkhout, C. M. (1923). "De Schimmelgeslachten Monilia, Oidium, Oospora en Torula." Edauw & Johannissen, Scheveningen.

Black, R. A., and Fisher, C. V. (1937). *Am. J. Diseases Children* **54**, 81.

Boidin, J., and Abadie, F. (1954). *Bull. soc. mycol. France* **70**, 353.

Buchanan, R. E. (1952). *Ann. Cryptogam. Phytopathol.* **6**, 63.

Buchwald, N. F. (1939). "Fungi Imperfecti (Deuteromycetes)." Royal Veterinary and Agricultural School, Copenhagen.

Buller, A. H. R. (1933). "Researches on Fungi," Vol. 5, p. 171. Longmans, New York.

Castelli, T. (1952). *Rev. fermentations et aliment.* **7**, 35.

Christensen, W. B. (1946). *J. Bacteriol.* **52**, 461.

Ciferri, R. (1930a). *Ann. Mycol. (Berlin)* **28**, 372.

Ciferri, R. (1930b). *Arch. Protistenk.* **71**, 448.

Ciferri, R., and Redaelli, P. (1929). *Ann. Mycol. (Berlin)* **27**, 243.

Ciferri, R., and Redaelli, P. (1953). *Atti VIth Cong. Intern. Microbiol.* **5**, 111.

Conant, N. F., Martin, D. S., Smith, D. T., Baker, R. D., and Callaway, J. L. (1944). "Manual of Clinical Mycology." Saunders, Philadelphia (cited after Skinner, 1947b).

Connell, G. H., and Skinner, C. E. (1953). *J. Bacteriol.* **66**, 627.

Connell, G. H., Skinner, C. E., and Hurd, R. C. (1954). *Mycologia* **46**, 12.

Cook, A. H., and Slater, C. A. (1954). *J. Inst. Brewing* **60**, 213.

Cook, A. H., and Slater, C. A. (1956). *J. Chem. Soc.* pp. 4130, 4133.

Costilow, R. N., Etchells, J. L., and Blumer, T. N. (1954). *Appl. Microbiol.* **2**, 300.

Custers, M. T. J. (1940). "Onderzoekingen over het gistgeslacht Brettanomyces." Thesis, Delft.

Derx, H. G. (1948). *Bull. botan. Gardens Buitenzorg*, Ser. III, **17**, 465.

Diddens, H. A., and Lodder, J. (1942). "Die anaskosporogenen Hefen, II Hälfte." North Holland Publ., Amsterdam.

Dietrichson, E. (1954). *Ann. parasitol. humaine et comparée* **29**, 271.

Drouhet, E., and Couteau, M. (1954). *Ann. inst. Pasteur* **86**, 602.

Einbinder, J. M., Benham, R. W., and Nelson, C. T. (1954). *J. Invest. Dermatol.* **22**, 279.

Emmons, C. W. (1947). *In* Henrici's "Molds, Yeasts and Actinomycetes," 2nd ed. Wiley, New York.

Emmons, C. W. (1951). *J. Bacteriol.* **62**, 685.

Etchells, J. L., and Bell, T. A. (1950). *Farlowia* **4**, 87.

Fowell, R. R. (1952). *Nature* **170**, 578.

Fowell, R. R. (1955). *J. Appl. Microbiol.* **18**, 149.

Gaümann, E. (1949). "Die Pilze." Birkhäuser, Basel.

Gilliland, R. B. (1956). *Compt. rend. trav. lab. Carlsberg Sér. physiol.* **26**, 139.

Gordon, H. A. (1951a). *J. Invest. Dermatol.* **17**, 267.

Gordon, H. A. (1951b). *Mycologia* **43**, 524.

Guilliermond, A. (1912). "Les Levures." Octave Doin, Paris.

Guilliermond, A. (1927). *Bull. soc. mycol. France* **43**, 245.

Guilliermond, A. (1928). *Rev. gén. botan.* **40**, 609.

Guilliermond, A. (1936). *Rev. mycol.* **1**, 115.

Guilliermond, A. (1937). *Ann. fermentations* **2**, 129.

Guilliermond, A., and Tanner, F. W. (1920). "The Yeasts." Wiley, New York.

Gustafson, B. A. (1955). "Otitis Externa in the Dog." Gernandts Boktryckeri, Stockholm.

Hansen, E. C. (1888). *Compt. rend. trav. lab. Carlsberg* **2**, 149.

Hansen, E. C. (1904). *Zentr. Bakteriol. Parasitenk. Abt. II,* 12, 529.

Harrison, F. C. (1928). *Trans. Roy. Soc. Can.* 22, 187.

Hartelius, V., and Ditlevsen, E. (1953). *Compt. rend. trav. lab. Carlsberg Sér. physiol.* 25, 213.

Hartelius, V., and Ditlevsen, E. (1956). *Compt. rend. trav. lab. Carlsberg Sér. physiol.* 25, 369.

Hedrick, L. R., and Burke, G. C. (1951). *Mycopath. et Mycol. Appl.* 6, 92.

Hjort, A. (1954). *Compt. rend. trav. lab. Carlsberg Sér. physiol.* 25, 259.

Janke, A. (1924). "Allgemeine technische Mikrobiologie." Theodor Steinkopff, Dresden and Leipzig.

Just, F., Schnabel, W., and Ullmann, S. (1951). *Brauerei, Wissenschaftl. Beil.* 5, 57, 71, 100.

Just, F., Schnabel, W., and Ullmann, S. (1952). *Brauerei, Wissenschaftl. Beil.* 6, 8.

Kleyn, J. G. (1954). *Wallerstein Labs. Communs.* 17, 91.

Klöcker, A. (1924). "Die Gärungsorganismen in der Theorie und Praxis der Alkoholgärungsgewerbe." Urban und Schwarzenberg, Berlin.

Kluyver, A. J., and Custers, M. T. J. (1939–1940). *Antonie van Leeuwenhoek, J. Microbiol. Serol.* 6, 121.

Kluyver, A. J., and van Niel, C. B. (1925). *Zentr. Bakteriol. Parasitenk. Abt. II,* 63, 1.

Kluyver, A. J., Walt, J. P. van der, and Triet, A. J. van (1953). *Proc. Natl. Acad. Sci. U.S.* 39, 583.

Krumbholz, G. (1933). *Arch. Mikrobiol.* 4, 167.

Kufferath, H. (1920). *Compt. rend. soc. biol. belge,* 185.

Langeron, M. (1945). "Précis de mycologie." Masson, Paris.

Langeron, M., and Guerra, P. (1938). *Ann. parasitol. humaine et comparée* 16, 36, 162, 429, 481.

Langeron, M., and Luteraan, P. J. (1947). *Ann. parasitol. humaine et comparée* 22, 254.

Langeron, M., and Luteraan, P. J. (1949). *Compt. rend.* 229, 382.

Langeron, M., and Talice, R. V. (1932). *Ann. parasitol. humaine et comparée* 10, 1.

Lederberg, J., and Lederberg, E. M. (1952). *J. Bacteriol.* 63, 399.

Leupold, U. (1950). *Compt. rend. trav. lab. Carlsberg Sér. physiol.* 24, 381.

Lindegren, C. C. (1956). *Wallerstein Labs. Communs.* 19, 49.

Lindegren, C. C., and Lindegren, G. (1943). *Ann. Missouri Botan. Garden* 30, 453.

Lodder, J. (1934). "Die anaskosporogenen Hefen, I Hälfte," *Verhandel. Koninkl. Akad. Wetenschap. Afdel. Natuurk. Sect. II,* 32, 1.

Lodder, J. (1938). *Mycopathologia* 1, 62.

Lodder, J., and Kreger-van Rij, N. J. W. (1952). "The Yeasts." North Holland Publ., Amsterdam.

Lodder, J., and Kreger-van Rij, N. J. W. (1954). *Lab. Practice* 3, 483.

Lodder, J., and Kreger-van Rij, N. J. W. (1955). *Lab. Practice* 4, 53.

Lodder, J., and Minjer, A. de (1947). *In* "Biology of Pathogenic Fungi" (W. J. Nickerson, ed.). Chronica Botanica, Waltham, Mass.; *Ann. Cryptogam. Phytopathol.* 6, 7.

Lopez Fernandez, J. R. (1952). *Anales fac. med. Montevideo* 37, 470.

Luh, B. S., and Phaff, H. J. (1951). *Arch. Biochem. and Biophys.* 33, 312.

Lund, A. (1954). "Studies on the ecology of yeasts." Thesis. Munksgaard, Copenhagen.

Mager, J., and Aschner, M. (1947). *J. Bacteriol.* 53, 283.

Magni, G. E. (1953). *Ist. botan. univ. Lab. crittogam. Pavia, Atti* [5] **10**, 201.

Manuel, J. (1938). *Compt. rend.* **207**, 1241.

Martin, H. H. (1954). *Arch. Mikrobiol.* **20**, 141.

Maurizio, A., and Staub, W. (1928). *Zentr. Bakteriol. Parasitenk. Abt. II*, **75**, 375.

Menna, M. E. di (1952). *Nature* **169**, 550.

Menna, M. E. di (1954). *J. Gen. Microbiol.* **11**, 195.

Menna, M. E. di (1955a). *Trans. Brit. Mycol. Soc.* **38**, 119.

Menna, M. E. di (1955b). *J. Gen. Microbiol.* **12**, 54.

Meyen, J. (1838). *Wiegmann's Arch. Naturgeschichte* **4**, II, 98.

Miller, J. J., Calvin, J., and Tremaine, J. H. (1955). *Can. J. Microbiol.* **1**, 560.

Miller, J. J., and Halpern, C. (1956). *Can. J. Microbiol.* **2**, 519.

Morris, E. O., and Kirsop, B. (1953). *J. Inst. Brewing* **59**, 486.

Mrak, E. M., and Phaff, H. J. (1948). *Ann. Rev. Microbiol.* **2**, 1.

Müller, D. (1954). *Friesia* **5**, 65.

Nakayama, T., Mackinney, G., and Phaff, H. J. (1954). *Antonie van Leeuwenhoek J. Microbiol. Serol.* **20**, 217.

Nickerson, W. J., and Mankowski, Z. T. (1953). *J. Infectious Diseases* **92**, 20.

Niehaus, Ch. J. G. (1932). *Zentr. Bakteriol. Parasitenk. Abt. II*, **87**, 97.

Nyland, G. (1949). *Mycologia* **41**, 686.

Olson, H. C., and Hammer, B. W. (1935). *Iowa State Coll. J. Sci.* **10**, 37.

Oppenoorth, W. F. F. (1956). *Nature* **178**, 992.

Orla Jensen, S. (1902). *Zentr. Bakteriol. Parasitenk. Abt. II*, **8**, 311.

Ota, M. (1924). *Dermatol. Wochschr.* **78**, 216.

Pappagianis, D., and Phaff, H. J. (1956). *Antonie van Leeuwenhoek J. Microbiol. Serol.* **22**, 353.

Parle, J. N. (1956). *Antonie van Leeuwenhoek J. Microbiol. Serol.* **22**, 237.

Pasteur, L. (1861). *Ann. sci. nat. Zool.* [4] **16**, 5.

Peterson, W. J., Bell, T. A., Etchells, J. L., and Smart, W. W. F. (1954). *J. Bacteriol.* **67**, 708.

Peynaud, E., and Domercq, S. (1956a). *Ann. inst. Pasteur* **91**, 574.

Peynaud, E., and Domercq, S. (1956b). *Arch. Mikrobiol.* **24**, 266.

Phaff, H. J. (1956). *Antonie van Leeuwenhoek J. Microbiol. Serol.* **22**, 113.

Phaff, H. J., and Knapp, E. P. (1956). *Antonie van Leeuwenhoek J. Microbiol. Serol.* **22**, 117.

Phaff, H. J., Miller, M. W., and Shifrine, M. (1956). *Antonie van Leeuwenhoek J. Microbiol. Serol.* **22**, 145.

Phaff, H. J., Mrak, E. M., and Williams, O. B. (1952). *Mycologia* **44**, 431.

Ramirez, C. (1954). *Rev. mycol.* **19**, 98.

Ramirez, C., and Boidin, J. (1953). *Rev. mycol.* **18**, 149.

Ramsbottom, J. (1933). *J. Quekett Microscop. Club* [2] **16**, 261.

Recca, J., and Mrak, E. M. (1952). *Food Technol.* **6**, 450.

Redaelli, P., Ciferri, R., and Giordano, A. (1937). *Boll. sez. ital. soc. intern. microbiol.* **1**, 2.

Reess, M. (1870). "Botanische Untersuchungen über die Alkoholgärungspilze." Arthur Felix, Leipzig.

Rippel-Baldes, A., Pietschmann-Meyer, K., and Kochler, W. (1948). *Arch. Mikrobiol.* **14**, 113.

Rivalier, E., and Seydel, S. (1932). *Compt. rend. soc. biol.* **40**, 181.

Roberts, C. (1946). *Am. J. Botany* **33**, 237.

Saccardo, P. A. (1906). *Sylloge Fungorum* 18, 495.

Sainclivier, M. (1951). *Bull. soc. botan. France* 98, 165, 254.

Sainclivier, M. (1952). *Bull. soc. botan. France* 99, 147.

Santa Maria Ledochowski, J. (1956). *Anales invest. Agron.* 5, 151.

Scherr, G. H., and Weaver, R. H. (1953). *Bacteriol. Revs.* 17, 51.

Schiönning, H. (1907–1909). *Compt. rend. trav. lab. Carlsberg Sér. physiol.* 7, 138.

Schröter, J. (1889). *In* "Die natürlichen Pflanzenfamilien," Vol. I, Part 1. Engelmann, Leipzig.

Scott, W. J. (1936). *J. Council Sci. Ind. Research* 9, 177.

Seeliger, H. P. R. (1955). *Z. Hyg. Infektionskrankh.* 141, 488.

Seeliger, H. P. R. (1956). *J. Bacteriol.* 72, 127.

Shihata, A. M. El-Tabey A, Mrak, E. M., and Phaff, H. J. (1955). *Mycologia* 47, 799.

Shifrine, M., and Phaff, H. J. (1956). *Mycologia* 48, 41.

Shifrine, M., Phaff, H. J., and Demain, A. L. (1954). *J. Bacteriol.* 68, 28.

Shimwell, J. L. (1947). *Am. Brewer* 80, 21, 56.

Skinner, C. E. (1947a). *In* Henrici's "Molds, Yeasts and Actinomycetes," 2nd ed., Chapter IX, Wiley, New York.

Skinner, C. E. (1947b). *Bacteriol. Revs.* 11, 227.

Skinner, C. E., and Huxley, M. J. (1956). *Mycologia* 48, 371.

Sonne Frederiksen, P. (1956). *Friesia* 5, 234.

Starkey, R. L. (1946). *J. Bacteriol.* 51, 33.

Stelling-Dekker, N. M. (1931). "Die sporogenen Hefen." *Verhandel. Koninkl. Akad. Wetenschap. Afdel. Natuurk. Sect. II,* 28, 1.

Teunisson, D. J. (1954). *Appl. Microbiol.* 2, 215.

Todd, R. L., and Herrmann, W. W. (1936). *J. Bacteriol.* 32, 89.

Tremaine, J. H., and Miller, J. J. (1954). *Botan. Gaz.* 115, 311.

Turpin, P. J. F. (1838). *Compt. rend.* 7, 369.

Uden, N. van (1952). *Arch. Mikrobiol.* 17, 199.

Uden, N. van, Matos Faia, M. de, and Assis-Lopes, L. (1956). *J. Gen. Microbiol.* 15, 151.

Vries, G. A. de (1952). "Contribution to the knowledge of the genus *Cladosporium* Link ex Fr." Uitgeverij Hollandia, Baarn.

Vuillemin, P. (1911). *Bull. soc. mycol. France* 27, 137.

Vuillemin, P. (1931). "Les Champignons Parasites et les Mycoses de l'Homme." Lechevalier, Paris.

Walker, T. K., and Wiles, A. E. (1952). *J. Inst. Brewing* 58, 140.

Walt, J. P. van der (1952). "On the Yeast *Candida pulcherrima* and its pigment." Thesis, Delft.

Walt, J. P. van der (1956a). *Antonie van Leeuwenhoek J. Microbiol. Serol.* 22, 265.

Walt, J. P. van der (1956b). *Antonie van Leeuwenhoek J. Microbiol. Serol.* 22, 321.

Walt, J. P. van der, and Tscheuschner, I. T. (1956a). *J. Gen. Microbiol.* 14, 485.

Walt, J. P. van der, and Tscheuschner, I. T. (1956b). *Antonie van Leeuwenhoek, J. Microbiol. Serol.* 22, 162.

Weidman, F. D. (1925). *In* H. Fox, *Rept. Lab. Museum Comp. Pathol. Zool. Soc. Phila.*

Wickerham, L. J. (1946). *J. Bacteriol.* 52, 293.

Wickerham, L. J. (1951). *U.S. Dept. Agr. Tech. Bull. No.* 1029.

Wickerham, L. J. (1952). *Ann. Rev. Microbiol.* 6, 317.

Wickerham, L. J. (1955). *Nature* 176, 22.

Wickerham, L. J. (1956). *Compt. rend. trav. lab. Carlsberg Sér. physiol.* 26, 423.

Wickerham, L. J., and Burton, K. A. (1948). *J. Bacteriol.* 56, 363.

Wickerham, L. J., and Burton, K. A. (1952). *J. Bacteriol.* 63, 449.

Wickerham, L. J., and Burton, K. A. (1954a). *J. Bacteriol.* 67, 303.

Wickerham, L. J., and Burton, K. A. (1954b). *J. Bacteriol.* 68, 594.

Wickerham, L. J., and Burton, K. A. (1956). *J. Bacteriol.* 71, 290, 296.

Wickerham, L. J., Lockwood, L. B., Pettijohn, O. G., and Ward, G. E. (1944). *J. Bacteriol.* 48, 413.

Wieringa, K. T. (1947). *Intern. Congr. Microbiol. Rept. Proc. 4th Congr. Copenhagen* p. 482.

Wieringa, K. T. (1956). *Neth. J. Agr. Sci.* 4, 203.

Wiles, A. E. (1953). *J. Inst. Brewing* 59, 265.

Wiles, A. E. (1954). *Wallerstein Labs. Communs.* 17, 259.

Will, H. (1916). *Zentr. Bakteriol. Parasitenk. Abt. II,* 46, 226.

Windisch, S. (1948). *Brauwelt* 3, 203.

Winge, Ö. (1935). *Compt. rend. trav. lab. Carlsberg Sér. physiol.* 21, 77.

Winge, Ö. (1947). *Compt. rend. trav. lab. Carlsberg Sér. physiol.* 24, 223.

Winge, Ö., and Laustsen, O. (1937). *Compt. rend. trav. lab. Carlsberg Sér. physiol.* 22, 99.

Winge, Ö., and Laustsen, O. (1939). *Compt. rend. trav. lab. Carlsberg Sér. physiol.* 22, 357.

Winge, Ö., and Roberts, C. (1948). *Compt. rend. trav. lab. Carlsberg Sér. physiol.* 24, 263.

Winge, Ö., and Roberts, C. (1950). *Compt. rend. trav. lab. Carlsberg Sér. physiol.* 25, 36.

Winter, W. D., and Foley, G. E. (1955). *J. Infectious Diseases* 97, 227.

Wolf, F. A., and Wolf, F. T. (1948). "The Fungi," Vol. I. Wiley, New York.

Zender, J. (1925). "Sur la classification des Endomycétacées." Imprimerie Jent S.A., Genève.

CHAPTER II

Ecology of Yeasts

A. Lund

1. Introduction

Yeasts are widely distributed in nature, generally living saprophytically. They thrive on various parts of plants, such as sweet fruits and the fruit bodies of fleshy fungi. They also occur in the alimentary tracts of man and herbivorous animals; further, there are indications that skin surfaces in man serve as a habitat for certain yeasts (Connell and Skinner, 1953). Some of these organisms are common in insects and sometimes they play an important role in their nutrition; in addition, certain yeasts are known to live symbiotically in insects. Finally, the soil forms an important reservoir for yeasts, where they can survive unfavorable periods.

Only occasionally do yeasts live parasitically in plants and animals including man. These are treated more fully in Chapter XI, but it seems useful to mention at the present point the few yeasts which are pathogenic to plants and insects.

From their natural habitats yeasts are often carried into the fermentation and food industries, where they may act as spoilage organisms. Often a special flora is found, e.g., the lactose-fermenting yeasts in dairy products, and osmophilic types in honey, sweetened condensed milk, and brines. Some fermentation products are manufactured by means of the natural yeast flora of the raw materials, others by means of specially cultivated yeasts.

Yeast flora examinations have often been made by means of enrichment methods; these, however, can make it difficult to estimate the greater or smaller value of a particular substrate as a habitat for yeasts and so, for this purpose, plate counts are better suited. Usually, only the predominant yeasts are isolated from platings and, on the whole, different methods can easily produce different pictures of the yeast content of a substrate.

Only recently has more reliable information been obtained on the numbers of yeast cells which occur in various substrates in nature, thanks to the use of selective plating media which inhibit the growth of accompanying organisms, especially of molds. For this purpose agar media containing 0.01% of diphenyl (Hertz and Levine, 1942; Beech and Carr, 1955), 0.25–0.35% of sodium propionate (Hertz and Levine, 1942; Mrak and Phaff, 1948; Lund, 1954; Etchells *et al.*, 1954), 1% of ox-gall (Miller *et al.*, 1951; Miller and Webb, 1954), or 0.003% of rose bengal (Miller and Webb, 1954) have been used.

In the following, the yeast designations follow the nomenclature by Lodder and Kreger-van Rij (1952) (see also Chapter III).

2. Yeast Content of Substrates Occurring in Nature

Leaves. Extraneous matter may collect on leaves and these may exude substances which favor the propagation of fungi. *Sporobolomyces* has been shown to occur commonly on old leaves of cereals (Derx, 1930; Last, 1955). The latter author, for instance, examining the surfaces of old and dead leaves of wheat and barley, found many *Sporobolomyces* colonies, up to about 50–70 per sq. cm. of leaf blade although, on the other hand, this yeast occurred in but small amounts on young leaves.

On leaves of various herbs and deciduous trees, Lund (1954) found yeasts fairly frequently though in very small numbers. The leaves examined may possibly have been so young that no appreciable growth occurred on them but a few species belonging to *Torulopsis* and *Candida* were isolated.

Flowers. Yeasts in flowers have commonly been reported from European countries, and have also been found in investigations from the United States, Canada, and Japan. The enrichment methods commonly employed for such examinations often make it difficult or impossible to decide whether flowers are actually habitats for yeasts or whether the occurrence of yeast cells is merely accidental.

However, Schuster and Úlehla (1913) drew the conclusion from their investigations in the vicinity of Prague that flower nectar is a normal habitat of yeasts and, indeed, infection experiments have shown that various yeasts, e.g., *Candida reukaufii* and *Sporobolomyces roseus* grow well in the nectars of various flowers (Schöllhorn, 1919; Hautmann, 1924; Grüss, 1926). In 25% of 65 flower samples from the neighborhood of Copenhagen, Lund (1954) counted quite considerable numbers of yeast cells, ranging from 100 to about 1,500,000 in which cases yeasts undoubtedly grew in the flowers. The majority of the samples examined, however, contained only a few yeast cells or none at all. Yeasts occur in flowers of plants that are widely different systematically and it is a common view that no relation exists between the yeast and flower types.

Visits by insects are an important factor in the occurrence of yeasts in flowers. Schöllhorn (1919) found that nectar in hothouse plants was nearly always sterile in the month of January, owing to the absence of insects. Yeasts were observed more frequently in summer, i.e., in 60–70% of the samples examined, than earlier in the year, when only 20–30% of the samples were infected (Hilkenbach, 1911; Jimbo, 1926; Lund, 1954).

By far the greatest number of yeasts isolated from flowers are asporogenous types. *Candida reukaufii* and 10 "Torulae" were found in Schöllhorn's investigations (1919) near Geneva; and Hilkenbach (1911) isolated 12 yeasts, all of them asporogenous, near Kiel. Also, only asporogenous types were found in other investigations from Germany, Japan, Russia, and California. Recently Capriotti (1953, 1955a) isolated numerous species of *Candida* and *Torulopsis* from flowers of various cultivated plants in Italy, while *Kloeckera* and *Rhodotorula* were more rarely represented. The most common species belonged to *Candida*, e.g., *C. reukaufii* and *C. guilliermondii*.

In some investigations, however, sporogenous yeasts, too, have been found. Etchells *et al.* (1953) isolated such types from flowers of *Cucumis sativus*, but asporogenous genera, especially *Rhodotorula*, were again most frequently represented. Two sporogenous types, belonging to *Saccharomyces* and *Hansenula*, were isolated by Lund (1954), but on the other hand asporogenous yeasts were represented by 25 species, especially by types of *Torulopsis* and *Candida*, forms of *Cryptococcus*, *Kloeckera*, and *Rhodotorula* being less frequent. In investigations of sugar-tolerant yeasts in flowers in Canada 11 types were found, including both asporogenous and sporogenous ones. In these cases, species of *Saccharomyces* (*Zygosaccharomyces*) were common (Lochhead and Heron, 1929).

Sweet Fruits. Pasteur (1876, 1878) demonstrated the presence of yeasts on ripe grapes, but not on the unripe fruits. Hansen (1881) in his investigations into the occurrence of *Kloeckera apiculata* found that the same thing applied to fruits of various plants. He demonstrated that this particular yeast is common on ripe strawberries, cherries, plums, gooseberries, and grapes and that it multiplies on them. He likewise found it to occur, though less commonly, on red currants, raspberries, rowanberries, and barberries although still only in very rare cases did it occur on unripe fruits.

In investigations into osmophilic yeasts on grapes in Germany, Kroemer and Krumbholz (1931) and Krumbholz (1931) in particular found species of *Saccharomyces* (*Zygosaccharomyces*), which grew at a concentration of 40–50% sugar. From grapes in California, the yeasts most commonly isolated were *Saccharomyces* (especially *S. cerevisiae*), *Candida, Torulopsis,* and *Kloeckera,* in that order, while other genera, *Hanseniaspora, Hansenula, Pichia, Debaryomyces,* and *Rhodotorula* were more rarely represented (Mrak and McClung, 1940). In this connection, too, a reference should be made to the discussion of yeasts in grape must and wine on p. 78.

De Migoya (1950) isolated 97 cultures of sporogenous yeasts and 49 strains of asporogenous yeasts from ripe plums in Argentina. *Hansenula anomala* was the type that occurred most frequently; more or less common were representatives of *Saccharomyces, Hanseniaspora, Debaryomyces, Schizosaccharomyces,* and *Kloeckera,* as well as *Candida mycoderma.* From dates, Mrak *et al.* (1942a) isolated 67 cultures most of which consisted of species of *Saccharomyces, Hansenula,* and *Candida. Saccharomyces* (*Zygosaccharomyces*) showed the highest tolerance to sugar, but *Hanseniaspora valbyensis* (termed *H. melligeri*) and a new species of *Torulopsis, T. dactylifera,* were also capable of fermenting 50° Brix date syrup. In souring fresh figs a great number of yeast genera have been found, *Saccharomyces* and *Candida* being especially frequent (Mrak *et al.,* 1942b).

In counts of yeasts on the epidermis of apples, Marshall and Walkley (1951) found greatly varying numbers of yeast cells on the healthy fruits, ranging from 100 to about 1,500,000 per fruit. On damaged and mold-infected apples much greater numbers of cells occurred, up to some 60,000,000 per fruit. From apples, exclusively asporogenous yeasts were isolated by Clark *et al.* (1954), the predominating species being a *Candida,* termed *C. malicola.* In samples of ripe fruits, such as strawberries, gooseberries, and raspberries, Lund (1954) counted greatly varying numbers of yeast cells, 14 out of 27 samples containing large amounts of yeast cells, from 1000 up to several millions, the greatest numbers being present in decomposing fruits. Most of the yeasts so isolated were asporogenous types belonging to *Candida, Torulopsis, Cryptococcus, Kloeckera,* and *Rhodotorula,* only one sporogenous type, a species of *Saccharomyces,* being found.

The theory has been proposed that yeasts are normally present in the interior of undamaged fruits. From the flesh of healthy fruits such as gooseberries and red currants, Romwalter and Király (1939) isolated *Saccharomyces cerevisiae* var. *ellipsoideus* and some forms of *Torulopsis* and Niethammer (1942) demonstrated the presence of various asporogenous yeasts in the flesh of raspberries, pears, apples and other fruits. These findings, however, could not be confirmed by Marcus (1942). In an examination of gooseberry tissues taken under sterile conditions he demonstrated the presence of yeasts only in a few cases while in other fruits, too, yeasts were only rarely found. Nor do yeasts occur in the flesh of healthy apples; however, they were found to be present in the core though in much smaller numbers than on the skin (Marshall and Walkley, 1951).

Grain. On grains of wheat, barley, and oats in the vicinity of Prague, Derx (1930) demonstrated the presence of *Sporobolomyces*. This genus, together with *Rhodotorula*, was found to be predominant on grains of barley in Denmark in the hot, dry summer of 1955, whereas species of *Hansenula, Torulopsis,* and *Candida* occurred less frequently (Lund, 1956). Grains taken from the barley plants just before harvest time often housed large amounts of yeast cells on the surface, up to about 3000 yeast cells per grain, or about 70,000 per gram. Again, in samples of rough rice which were stored in sealed bins, large amounts of yeast cells up to 76,000 per gram have been reported (Teunisson, 1954). The species isolated belonged to *Endomycopsis, Hansenula, Pichia,* and *Candida.*

Root Crops. In damaged mangelwurzels, yeasts occur frequently (Lund, 1954). Often, few yeast cells were found, but some samples contained larger amounts, up to about 14,000 cells per gram. Most of the yeasts isolated were species of *Candida* and *Torulopsis,* while only one isolation belonged to *Hansenula.*

Fleshy Fungi. Fleshy fungi have proved to be excellent habitats for yeasts. Anderson and Skinner (1947), using an enrichment method, found in Minnesota yeasts to occur commonly on decaying forms of mushrooms and of *Boletus, Clavaria, Phallus, Tremella,* and *Peziza.* Yeasts were frequent in decaying mushrooms which had an acid reaction while they occurred rarely in mushrooms with a pH above 7. The majority of the yeasts isolated belonged to *Saccharomyces,* while only a few asporogenous types occurred, including species of *Torulopsis* (*Cryptococcus*) and *Rhodotorula.*

Lund (1954), examining the yeast content of mushrooms in Denmark, found by counts on agar plates that old decaying and decomposing fruit bodies almost always contain yeast cells in large amounts up to 4 million per gram. On the other hand, no or few yeast cells were found in young fresh fruit bodies. As distinct from the investigations by Anderson and Skinner, practically the only yeasts isolated were asporogenous types belonging to *Candida*, *Torulopsis*, and *Kloeckera*, whereas the presence of *Saccharomyces* was demonstrated only once. This difference between the two investigations may reasonably be attributed to the different methods employed.

Exudates of Trees. The presence of yeasts in sap and slime flux from trees was first demonstrated many years ago. Ludwig (1886) described fermentation in slime flux from oaks in which he found, among others, the yeast subsequently described as *Saccharomycodes ludwigii*. This species was also isolated by Hansen (1889) from slime flux of oaks, elms, horse chestnuts, and limes, together with other yeasts, both sporogenous and asporogenous types.

From exudates of elms, horse chestnuts, and hornbeams, a species of *Nadsonia* and some types of *Torulopsis* have been reported (Kostka, 1927) while *Schizosaccharomyces octosporus* has been isolated from the sap of maples and *Nadsonia fulvescens* from the sap of birches (Sherwin, 1948).

In addition, some species of *Hansenula* have been isolated from saps and gums of trees (Wickerham, 1951) while the exudates of pine trees were found to contain *Torulopsis* and *Rhodotorula* (Shihata and Mrak, 1952). In exudates of various deciduous trees, Lund (1954) observed yeasts in the majority of the samples examined, often in large amounts, up to 3 million per gram. Here, only asporogenous yeasts belonging to *Candida* and *Torulopsis* were isolated.

Insects. For a long time, great importance has been attributed to insects as bearers of yeasts to fruits and other substrates. *Drosophila* flies have been observed carrying yeasts to grapes in French vineyards and dissemination of the plant-pathogenic yeast *Nematospora* by insects has been reported (Steinhaus, 1946).

Berlese (1896) held the opinion that yeasts propagate in the alimentary tract of Diptera and De Kruyff (1908) demonstrated that yeasts were always found in ants in Java. A *Saccharomyces pastori* strain (described as *Zygosaccharomyces pini*) was isolated from the bark beetles *Dendroctonus* and *Ips* on pine (Holst, 1936), and a new species of *Hansenula*, *H. wingei*, recently described by Wickerham (1956) was isolated from *Ips* on spruce. *Endomycopsis bispora* was found in *Ips typographus* and in a species of *Platypus*. From the interior of various species of *Ips* and *Dendroctonus* collected from pines in California Shifrine and Phaff (1956) isolated a number of yeasts belonging to various genera.

Several new species were described, namely, *Pichia haplophila, Candida silvicola, Torulopsis nitratophila, T. melibiosum,* and *Rhodotorula crocea.* The most commonly occurring yeasts were *Candida silvicola, Hansenula capsulata,* and a species identical with *Zygosaccharomyces pini* Holst, which is regarded as a strain of *S. pastori* by Lodder and Kreger-van Rij (1952). Shifrine and Phaff described the species as *Saccharomyces pini* (Holst) comb. nov. A new species of *Torulopsis,* named *T. acidophila,* has been isolated from the cockroach *Periplaneta americana,* the digestive tract of which was considered the normal habitat of the yeast (Owen and Mobley, 1948). From the dried-fruit beetle, *Carpophilus hemipterus,* Miller and Mrak (1953) isolated *Hanseniaspora valbyensis* and *Candida krusei* as predominant yeasts. Several isolates belonged to the genus *Torulopsis,* one of them a new species, *T. carpophila* while a few cultures proved to be species of *Saccharomyces, Pichia, Kloeckera,* and *Rhodotorula.*

From Hawaiian fruit flies, species of *Hansenula, Candida,* and *Rhodotorula,* including two new species, *C. sorbosa* and *R. pilimanae,* have been isolated by Hedrick and Burke (1950, 1953). The intestinal yeast flora of *Drosophila* were examined by Shihata and Mrak (1952) in California and many species belonging to *Saccharomyces, Pichia, Torulopsis, Candida, Rhodotorula,* and *Kloeckera* were found. Honeybees, bumblebees, and wasps captured during their visits to flowers in Denmark very frequently housed yeasts (Lund, 1954). The presence of considerable amounts of yeast cells was often demonstrated, up to 200,000 per insect while in bees from hives up to about 1 million yeast cells per bee were counted. Most of the species isolated belonged to *Candida* and *Torulopsis; Kloeckera* occurring less frequently and only one sporogenous yeast, a species of *Hansenula,* was encountered.

Yeasts are essential to the nutrition of certain insects. Several authors have reported that *Drosophila melanogaster* does not grow on fresh sterile media of bananas unless a yeast extract or a live yeast has been added. Wagner (1944) found that several species of *Drosophila* breed in decaying fruits of *Opuntia lindheimeri* in Texas, and that yeasts and other microorganisms were present in all cases. Eight yeasts (not identified) were isolated from the fruits. When these yeasts were added to a cactus agar, all of them gave complete development of *D. mulleri* larvae, while only five of them were found complete for *D. aldrichi.* These two species of *Drosophila* could not be grown on cactus fruit tissue without yeasts. In experiments with attraction of *Drosophila* to banana bait fermented with strains of *Candida krusei* and *Kloeckera apiculata* which had been isolated from species of *Drosophila* in Brazil, Dobzhansky and

Da Cunha (1955) stated that species of *Drosophila* often showed clear preferences for one or the other of the yeast strains. When autoclaved banana not fermented with yeast was used, *Drosophila* flies were not attracted at all. Miller and Mrak (1953) found that *Candida krusei* was more attractive to *Carpophilus hemipterus* than were *Hanseniaspora valbyensis* and *Torulopsis carpophilus*. The rate of digestion of yeasts by the insects was rapid, most cells being destroyed at 25°C. within 1–4 hours after feeding. Digestion of yeast by *Drosophila pseudoobscura* also occurs very rapidly. Thus, 24 hours after feeding on a paste of baker's yeast at room temperature the crops of the flies were almost empty (Shihata and Mrak, 1951).

Many scientists have observed intracellular symbionts in Homoptera and Coleoptera and have often considered them to be yeasts. In most of the cases no pure cultures were isolated so that very little is known of the nature and the systematic position of any yeasts concerned (Steinhaus, 1946). They are believed to be important for the nutrition of insects, perhaps as a source of vitamin.

The symbionts in the intestinal epithelium in the weevil, *Anobium paniceum*, and other Anobiidae were considered by Buchner (1921) to be asporogenous yeasts; later, various asporogenous yeasts which were not closely identified were isolated from species of Anobiidae and Cerambycidae, the larvae of which live in wood (Müller, 1934). Gräbner (1954) isolated species of *Candida* from Cerambycidae and species of *Torulopsis* from Anobiidae, and described a new species, *T. buchnerii*. In general, those cerambycid larvae which live in fresh wood of deciduous trees seem to be without symbionts while those living in live or dead coniferous trees may contain yeasts (Schomann, 1937).

Only in a few cases have yeasts been known to cause diseases in insects. It has been reported that corn borer larvae (*Pyrausta nubilalis*) were destroyed by "*Mycoderma clayi*"; and "*Blastodendrion pseudococci*" was found to parasitize the fat body and the muscular system of the mealy bug, *Pseudococcus citri*. *Monosporella bicuspidata* has been found parasitizing *Daphnia magna*, and *M. unicuspidata* parasitizes the body cavity of a dipterous larva, *Dasyhelea obscura*. *Coccidiascus legeri* was described by Chatton (1913) as being a parasite in the cells of the intestine of *Drosophila funebris*.

Dung. Yeasts occur commonly in the alimentary tracts of higher animals, which ingest them with their food. Several authors have demonstrated the presence of yeasts, especially asporogenous types, in human feces. Feeding experiments with saprophytic yeasts such as *Rhodotorula glutinis* and *Hansenula anomala* showed that such yeasts pass through the alimentary tract without being damaged by the digestive juices. While these yeasts are not retained longer than the ingested food, the pathogenic *Candida albicans* is able to remain and seemingly to multiply in the alimentary tract (Anderson, 1917). Other investigations have shown, on the other hand, that virtually all cells of baker's yeast are destroyed in the alimentary tract (Rettger *et al.*, 1924).

In examinations of 10 samples of dung from horses and cows from fields and dunghills, yeasts were found in all of the samples though in relatively small amounts, maximally amounting to 6000 cells per gram. The yeasts isolated belonged to the genera *Hansenula, Cryptococcus,* and *Candida* (Lund, 1954). Such yeasts seem to pass the alimentary canal in an undamaged condition. Thus, a relatively high number of yeast cells, 4400 per gram, were found in a sample of horse feces which had just been dropped, while as many as 200,000 yeast cells per gram have been counted in freshly discharged bovine feces (Empey and Scott, 1939).

Soil. From flowers, fruits, and other substrates in which yeasts multiply, yeasts are conveyed to the soil which functions as an important reservoir in which they can be maintained and thence disseminated. Hansen (1881, 1903) in his classical investigations found *Kloeckera* and also Saccharomycetes to be especially common in orchard soil in Denmark and also in vineyard and orchard soil in Italy.

In the vicinity of Kiel, too, yeasts occurred most frequently in soil samples from orchards and in a materially smaller number of samples from other localities (Nissen, 1930). On the other hand, the analyses by Bouthilet (1953) of uncultivated soils in Minnesota showed that all of the 84 samples examined contained yeasts; further, Lund (1954) demonstrated the presence of yeasts in 90% of 136 samples from both cultivated and uncultivated lands in Denmark. Sugar-tolerant yeasts were found regularly in Ottawa in soil in apiaries, but not in soil from gardens, orchards, and fields (Lochhead and Farrell, 1930).

Only recently has information been provided on the extent to which yeasts occur in the soil, so making it possible to reach a more reliable view of the yeast content of various types of soils at different seasons and of their importance in such cases. In different localities in Ontario, Miller and Webb (1954) found an average number of 3300 yeast cells per gram of soil. The highest number of yeast cells, 55,000 per gram of soil, occurred in an old apple orchard while in other localities such as grassland, meadows, and forests, 2000–6000 yeast cells per gram of soil were not infrequently counted. Examinations of the same localities at three different times often disclosed greatly varying numbers of yeast cells in the same locality. Thus, in an apple orchard, 55,000, 6000, and 900 yeast cells, respectively, were found per gram of soil, while in meadow soil 910, 0, and 5000 yeast cells, respectively, were counted.

In Danish soil, also, great differences were frequently found in the yeast content at different times in the same locality at the same depth (Lund, 1954). Thus, in a beech wood at a depth of 5 cm., 16,200 and 12 yeast cells per gram of soil were counted; in a spruce wood at a depth of 10 cm., 10,000 and 10 yeast cells; and in a peat bog at a depth of 5 cm., 300 and 74,000 yeast cells were counted on different occasions. At one and the same time, moreover, the number of yeast cells can vary considerably in the same locality. Such samples, taken at the same depth only a few centimeters from each other on uncultivated grassland, contained, e.g., per gram of dry soil 1800, 950, and 800 yeast cells at one sampling site; at another sampling site the variation was even greater, being from 150 to 5000 yeast cells per gram.

The greatest numbers of yeast cells are present on the surface or in the upper layers down to a depth of about 5–10 cm. At greater depths the number of yeast cells in most cases decreases rapidly, few being found at depths of 20 to 30 cm. (see Table I).

The greatest number of yeast cells found by Lund was in an orchard, where 245,000 were counted per gram of dry soil, although the maximum number in another orchard was only 1350 per gram. It is hardly possible to draw any general conclusion to the effect that certain types of soil contain appreciably greater amounts of yeast cells than other types (see Table I), apart from the fact that yeasts have been found to occur in only very small amounts in dune and beach sand. Generally, the number of yeast cells in the soil is much lower than what may be found on sweet fruits, fleshy fungi, etc. The amount of yeast cells in the soil doubtless depends primarily on the supply of substrates which contain yeasts in large quantities, and which provide the soil with substances especially favorable to yeast reproduction.

The number of yeasts below the surface of the ground largely remains the same in the same locality at different seasons if allowance is made for the variation that can occur at one and the same time. It appears from Table I that, in a number of localities, the amounts of yeast cells were largely of the same order in late summer and in the early spring of the following year. In other localities, however, especially on uncultivated lands, the volume of yeast population fluctuated considerably and no relation between yeast quantity and season could be established. In samples from the surface of the ground, on the other hand, a seasonal difference was found. In the month of March, surface samples usually contained a greater number of yeast cells than did similar samples taken in August when sunshine and drought produced an inhibiting effect on the yeast flora.

In earlier investigations based on the proportion between the number of samples which contained yeasts and the number in which no yeasts

TABLE I

SURVEY OF ANALYSES OF SOIL AT DIFFERENT DEPTHS[a,b]

Locality	August						March					
	Surface	5 cm.	10 cm.	15 cm.	20 cm.	30 cm.	Surface	5 cm.	10 cm.	15 cm.	20 cm.	30 cm.
Cultivated soil												
1. Orchard mold, pH 7.7	174,900	23,500	17,700	9,500	7,700	250	244,500	41,600	17,500	5,900	600	370
2. Orchard mold, pH 7.5	500	950	950	44	<11	—	1,350	650	650	550	—	—
3. Field, light mold, pH 6.9	700	1,350	1,000	600	—	—	3,700	900	1,200	1,350	1,850	170
4. Field, sandy mold, pH 7.9	10	320	170	160	—	—	110	240	420	120	120	—
5. Meadow mold, pH 7.9	1,750	<16	310	2,500	—	—	80	34	0	17	<18	<18
Uncultivated soil												
6. Grassy terrain mold, pH 7.9	1,100	6,200	3,900	700	—	—	5,800	7,900	3,300	2,400	22	45
7. Common, light mold, pH 5.8	<12	89	<11	<11	—	—	36,800	1,700	700	120	46	—
8. Littoral meadow sandy mold, pH 6.7	590	<13	<13	<12	—	—	—	—	—	—	—	—
9. Seashore sand, pH 7.6	0	54	<11	—	—	—	260	<13	25	—	—	—
10. Bog peat soil, pH 3.5	100	300	40	—	—	—	0	11	<11	—	—	—
11. Beech wood mold, pH 5.9	4,300	16,200	40	<11	—	—	7,900	74,000	700	11,300	—	—
12. Beech wood raw humus, pH 5.0	<10	<10	<10	—	—	—	1,050	12	0	12	0	—
13. Spruce forest raw humus, pH 4.3	10	1,000	10,000	—	<10	—	150	0	10	60	40	0

[a] Number of yeast cells per gram of dry soil (per gram of moist soil in nos. 12 and 13 and in no. 10 from August).

[b] From Lund (1954).

were found, seasonal variations were occasionally found; in these cases, however, the depths at which the samples were taken was not recorded. Wortmann (1897–98) found yeasts to occur commonly in vineyard soil in November–December. Thereafter they became increasingly rare until grape-ripening time when they suddenly became very common again. Nissen (1930) and Starkey and Henrici (1927) found yeasts in more samples in the autumn than in samples taken earlier in the year and in winter.

Often, asporogenous yeasts have been found to be predominant in soil, e.g., by Nissen (1930), who demonstrated the presence of many asporogenous types but only a few species of *Saccharomyces* and *Hansenula*. Bouthilet (1953) mostly isolated species of *Hansenula, Candida,* and *Rhodotorula*, although *Debaryomyces, Saccharomyces, Pichia, Torulopsis,* and *Trichosporon* were also represented. Lund (1954) found 17 asporogenous yeasts, mostly belonging to *Candida* and *Torulopsis*, more rarely to *Cryptococcus, Schizoblastosporion, Kloeckera,* and *Rhodotorula,* as well as 10 sporogenous types especially belonging to *Hansenula,* whereas *Saccharomyces, Pichia, Hanseniaspora,* and *Lipomyces* were rarer. Capriotti (1955b, 1955c) observed that asporogenous yeasts were the most commonly occurring types in soil in Holland, whereas species of *Saccharomyces*, in particular *S. cerevisiae* var. *ellipsoideus*, were predominating in Italian soils. Recently some new sporogenous yeasts were isolated from soil in South Africa, namely a new genus *Kluyveromyces* with two species *K. polysporus* and *K. africanus* in addition to *Saccharomyces transvaalensis, S. pretoriensis,* and *Pichia vanrijii* (van der Walt, 1956; van der Walt and Tscheuschner, 1956). It is worth special mention that the pathogenic yeast *Cryptococcus neoformans* has been isolated from soil (Emmons, 1951), and that the organism of thrush, *Candida albicans* also has been found in soil (Di Menna, 1955).

It seems that propagation of yeasts takes place in rich mold especially in the presence of remnants of fruits or other favorable growth substrates, whereas they hardly grow in poorer soils. Thus some authors have observed a more or less distinct multiplication, especially in soil rich in humus from gardens and orchards (Lund, 1954). Others have found that yeasts, particularly in experiments with pure cultures, remain alive in soil for a short time only.

3. Plant-Pathogenic Yeasts

The subfamily of the Nematosporoideae comprises parasitic yeasts, the genera *Monosporella* and *Coccidiascus*, which live in invertebrates, together with the plant-pathogenic genus *Nematospora*. The last-mentioned, according to Lodder and Kreger-van Rij (1952), contains only one species, *N. coryli* (syn. *N. lycopersici* ?, *N. phaseoli, N. nagpuri*).

Nematospora coryli causes diseases in fruits and seeds of various plants. Thus it is known from hazelnuts, tomatoes, cotton bolls, coffee beans, pecan nuts, Lima beans, soybeans, citrus fruits, and pomegranates. It has been found in California, Florida, Virginia, Brazil, Cuba, Mexico, Jamaica, the Lesser Antilles, India, Belgian Congo, Tanganyika, the Philippine Islands, Japan, and China. In Europe, *N. coryli* seems to be known only from Peglion's original description of it from diseased hazelnuts in Italy and insect infested maize.

Nematospora causes discoloration and collapse of the infected tissues which consequently dry out. Fawcett (1929) described the disease in citrus as a collapsing and desiccation of the juice sacs immediately inside the rind, resulting in a gradual drying out of part of the pulp.

Ashbya gossypii (syn. *Nematospora gossypii*), though not belonging to the yeasts, in certain respects is very similar to *Nematospora*. It attacks the fruits and seeds of plants similar to those attacked by *Nematospora;* and both fungi have almost identical geographical distribution.

According to Pridham and Raper's survey (1950), *Ashbya gossypii* and related organisms belonging to *Nematospora, Spermophthora,* and *Eremothecium* infect the young lint fibers of cotton, which assume a yellowish color and mat on to the seeds. The latter develop a brown, spotty discoloration and as the bolls grow older, the locks become totally retarded and the lint is reduced to a papery membrane. The infection causes desiccation or premature dropping of the bolls. In coffee and in leguminous plants the disease causes desiccation and shrinking of the seeds.

It has often been reported that diseases caused by *Ashbya gossypii* and related organisms are transferred to the hosts by means of certain Hemiptera, such as species of *Dysdercus* (cotton stainers), *Leptoglossus* (leaf-footed tomato bug), *Nezara* (green bug), and *Antestia* (coffee bug).

4. Cycle of Yeasts in Nature

Taking a wide view of the foregoing findings, it is possible to perceive a cycle of yeasts in nature. Hansen, on the basis of his very extensive investigations drew up such a cycle, finding mainly the same conditions in colder and warmer climates (Denmark–Italy). He distinguished between primary habitats, such as ripe juicy fruits, where yeasts grow and multiply, and secondary habitats, i.e., the soil. He found that yeasts propagate to some extent in the soil, and that they hibernate there.

Later, large quantities of yeasts, often as many as several million cells per gram were found in sweet fruits, exudates of trees, fleshy fungi, and insects; moreover, larger or smaller quantities of yeast cells have been found in flowers, on leaves and grains, in damaged sugary roots, and in dung from herbivorous animals. Dissemination of yeast cells from flower to flower, from fruit to fruit, etc., takes place especially through insects.

Yeasts are conveyed to the soil from the aforementioned substrates, and as these are widely distributed it is not strange that yeasts have been found in almost all types of soil. The greatest numbers of yeast cells have been found in orchard soil, maximally 245,000 per gram of dry soil, though large quantities of yeast cells have also been noticed in entirely different localities. From the surface of the ground, yeast cells are carried some distance into the soil by seeping water and by the tilling of the soil. The amount of yeast cells decreases with increasing depth, few cells being left at a depth of 20–30 cm.

Several authors hold the view that yeasts are capable of reproducing in the soil, at any rate under certain conditions. Probably, however, the greatest significance of the soil in this connection lies in its provision of a reservoir in which yeasts can survive adverse periods. For instance, it has been demonstrated in Denmark and Canada that the organisms may survive the winter in the soil and on the whole similar numbers of yeast cells have been found in subsurface soil in the same localities in late summer and in the early spring of the following year. Laboratory tests, too, have shown that yeasts withstand low temperatures and can remain viable in soil for at least six months.

During the hot season, the sun may exercise a harmful effect on yeasts on the surface of the ground. As will appear from Section 6, p. 84, their thermal death points are rather low and ultraviolet light has a pronounced destructive effect on them. Desiccation, too, has a strongly inhibiting effect on yeasts, most cells being destroyed in soil if the moisture content drops below about 7%. In most cases, therefore, larger quantities of yeast cells have been found on the surface of the ground in spring than in summer.

Just as yeasts can survive the winter in the soil, so they appear to be capable of hibernating in dung and in beehives. In spring, and of course later in the year as well, yeast cells are carried from soil and dung with the wind, by animals, and following heavy showers, to substrates where they can grow and multiply; bees obviously convey yeasts to sugary substrates. With the wind and with currents in lakes and seas, yeasts can be carried over long distances. Yeasts have been found in the oceans far from the shore, often in surprisingly large amounts (ZoBell's survey, 1946).

5. Yeasts in Industrial Products

Beer. For the production of bottom-fermented beer (lager) and top-fermented beer (ale), strains of *Saccharomyces carlsbergensis* and *S. cerevisiae*, respectively, are used. Since E. C. Hansen developed his method for pure cultivation, pure cultures of these yeasts are commonly employed for beer fermentations in almost all countries except in Great Britain where the practice has never found much acceptance.

Through the air or in other ways, the so-called wild yeasts can easily be carried into breweries and some of them, through their growth in beer, can cause beer "diseases" which are manifest in changes in its flavor or appearance.

The wild yeasts especially known as beer spoilage yeasts are Hansen's classical species, which in modern systematics according to Lodder and Kreger-van Rij (1952) are termed *Saccharomyces cerevisiae* var. *ellipsoideus, S. pastorianus, S. willianus,* and *S. uvarum.* Recently, Andrews and Gilliland (1952) isolated from wort, yeast, and beer in Ireland a new species named *S. diastaticus,* which causes so-called superattenuation in beer.

Species of *Torulopsis* are frequent in breweries and sometimes they can grow in beer, especially those of low alcoholic content. For instance, they were responsible for imparting an alien flavor to the weak beer brewed in Germany during the War (Janensch, 1941). *Torulopsis cylindrica,* described from Australia by Walters (1943), is characterized as an exceedingly virulent beer-disease organism.

In British stock beers and in Belgian Lambic, species of *Brettanomyces* have frequently been found (Custers' monograph, 1940). They impart a particular flavor to beer, and in England formerly were of importance during the secondary fermentation. They still play a part in the manufacture of Lambic, whereas in Great Britain today, where weaker beers are brewed which are stored for a shorter time than formerly, they are rarer and, like other wild yeasts, are often reckoned as undesirable.

Several film-forming species belonging to *Pichia* and *Hansenula* as well as *Candida mycoderma* occur commonly in breweries and can frequently be isolated from beer, but they are only able to grow and form a film in beers with ample oxygen.

In more recent investigations in England, species of many different genera such as *Endomycopsis, Saccharomyces, Pichia, Torulopsis, Candida,* and *Kloeckera* have been isolated from brewer's yeast and beer (Wiles, 1953; Hemmons, 1954).

For a more detailed discussion of brewer's yeast see Chapter XI.

Wine and Cider. During the spontaneous fermentation of grape must a number of yeasts take part, including both sporogenous and asporogenous types, which originate from the grapes. From Castelli's survey (1952a) of investigations in Italy it seems that *Saccharomyces cerevisiae* var. *ellipsoideus* and apiculate yeasts are predominant in fermenting grape must. Apiculate yeasts are conspicuous in the early stage of the fermentation, and these, in northern and central Italy, are asporogenous types belonging to *Kloeckera*, *Hanseniaspora* being moreover common in southern Italy. On the whole, sporogenous yeasts are becoming increasingly widespread in musts as we go farther south in Italy. Among the numerous other yeasts occurring in musts may be mentioned *Saccharomyces rosei*, *S. oviformis*, *S. bayanus*, *S. chevalieri* (*S. mangini*), *S. italicus*, and *Candida pulcherrima*.

Florenzano (1949) isolated from musts and the lees in Tuscano *S. cerevisiae* var. *ellipsoideus*, *S. rosei*, *S. florentinus*, and species of *Kloeckera*, *Candida pulcherrima* and *Torulopsis bacillaris* ? (termed *Brettanomyces italicus*) among others. In Israel, the yeast flora in fermenting musts was found to be similar to that in southern Italy, *S. cerevisiae* var. *ellipsoideus* and *Hanseniaspora* being predominant (Castelli, 1952b).

In investigations from Médoc, *S. cerevisiae* var. *ellipsoideus* and *Kloeckera apiculata* are also common in musts; in addition, other species of *Saccharomyces* were encountered, such as *S. bayanus*, *S. uvarum*, *S. chevalieri*, and species of *Pichia*, *Torulopsis*, and *Rhodotorula* (Peynaud and Domercq, 1954). In California musts and wines, mostly species of *Saccharomyces* occur and in these cases representatives of *Hanseniaspora*, *Pichia*, *Hansenula*, *Torulopsis*, *Candida*, and *Kloeckera* have been isolated much less frequently (Mrak and McClung, 1940).

The yeasts forming the film in the "flor" process in the production of sherry in the Jerez region and of certain wines in the Arbois district were examined by Hohl and Cruess (1939). They found certain types similar to *S. cerevisiae* var. *ellipsoideus*, which form a film on completion of the fermentation, as well as species of *Pichia*, *Hansenula*, and *Torulopsis*. These yeasts, incidentally, are capable of forming films on wines containing up to 16–17% of alcohol by volume.

Saccharomyces mellis, according to Phaff and Douglas (1944) caused a turbidity or sediment in wines containing about 19–21% alcohol. Other spoilage yeasts from wines include species of *Pichia* and *Candida mycoderma* (Scrivani, 1939) while *S. pastorianus*, species of *Torulopsis*, and *Kloeckera apiculata* have also been reported as infecting organisms during fermentations (Perotti, 1951). In Europe, grape wines are mostly made by spontaneous fermentation by means of yeasts occurring naturally on the grapes although fermentation by means of pure-cultured yeasts is employed in some areas. In California, pure-cultured strains of *S. cerevisiae* var. *ellipsoideus* are commonly employed while in Italy, attempts have been made to use also other pure-cultured yeasts than *S. cerevisiae* var. *ellipsoideus*, e.g., *S. rosei* (Castelli, 1952a).

For the production of *fruit wines* from juices of various berries and fruits, pure-cultured strains of *S. cerevisiae* var. *ellipsoideus*, isolated from grape must and grape wine, are commonly used. Many different yeasts have been found in fruit must in addition to *S. cerevisiae* var. *ellipsoideus;* these include *S. pastorianus, S. microellipsodes*, types of *Saccharomycodes, Pichia* and *Hansenula, Candida mycoderma, Kloeckera apiculata*, species of *Torulopsis* and *Rhodotorula* (Kroemer and Krumbholz, 1932). Many of these organisms can cause diseases in fruit wine by adversely affecting its flavor and by causing turbidity or a slimy consistency in the case of species of *Torulopsis*, or by forming a film on the surface in the presence of ample oxygen, this applying to *Pichia, Hansenula* and *Candida mycoderma*.

Cider is manufactured mostly by spontaneous fermentation of apple juice by means of the yeasts occurring naturally in the juice, though some factories use pure-cultured yeast for the fermentation. Little is known of the yeasts occurring in apple juices and still less of those which are of importance for the fermentation. Barker (1949, 1950) demonstrated that the predominant yeasts in apple juices were sporogenous types which could best be referred to *S. cerevisiae, S. cerevisiae* var. *ellipsoideus*, or *S. pastorianus*, together with apiculate yeasts. In the matured ciders, *Saccharomyces* and *Torulopsis*-forms were found.

Beech (1954) observed a number of yeasts in apple juices, including species of *Saccharomyces*, species probably of *Torulopsis*, together with apiculate and film-forming organisms (presumably *Pichia* and *Candida mycoderma*), as well as pigmented yeasts similar to *Candida pulcherrima*. During the fermentation, the *Saccharomyces*-forms become predominant, the presumable *Torulopsis*-forms being also numerous. It appears from the investigations of Clark *et al.* (1954) that numerous isolates from cider belonged to *Saccharomyces, Debaryomyces*, and *Pichia*, whereas only asporogenous types were isolated from apples (see p. 66).

For yeasts concerned in other alcoholic beverages see also Chapter XII.

Honey and Syrup. Honey can undergo fermentation due to the growth of sugar-tolerant species of *Saccharomyces*. In Italian honey, Sacchetti (1931–32) found such yeasts (*Zygosaccharomyces*) almost exclusively while species of the same genus were also isolated from honey in the United States and Canada by Fabian and Quinet (1928). These authors found *S. rouxii* (*Z. japonicus*), *S. rouxii* var. *polymorphus* (*Z. barkeri*) and a new species, S. *mellis*, as well as a new species of *Torulopsis*, *T. mellis*. They believe that absorption of moisture causes the sugar concentration on the surface of honey to decrease so much that certain yeasts are able to grow there and are gradually inured to the higher sugar concentrations below the surface.

S. *mellis* (designated as Z. *richteri*) was isolated together with other species of *Saccharomyces* (*Zygosaccharomyces*) from Canadian honeys by Lochhead and Heron (1929), who noticed that osmophilic yeasts from fermenting honey grow best in agar media containing 60–67% honey. On the other hand, nonosmophilic yeasts such as S. *cerevisiae* and S. *cerevisiae* var. *ellipsoideus* do not grow at such high concentrations, media containing about 30% honey being the most favorable. Interestingly enough, certain yeasts in fermented honey were identical with yeasts isolated from flowers.

The most common yeast in the investigations by Lochhead and Farrell (1931) was S. *mellis* (Z. *richteri*). Only species of *Saccharomyces* (*Zygosaccharomyces*) were capable of causing fermentation in honey whereas other isolates from honey, belonging to *Schizosaccharomyces* and *Torulopsis*, caused no fermentation.

The amounts of sugar-tolerant yeasts occurring in normal honeys were examined in Canada by Lochhead and McMaster (1931), who found, per gram of honey, up to 100,000 yeast cells with a median count of 1000 per gram. In a subsequent investigation Lochhead (1933) demonstrated the presence of sugar-tolerant yeasts in all of the 128 samples of normal honey examined by him. The number of yeast cells, however, fluctuated considerably, from only a few up to a million cells per gram of honey.

In maple syrup Fabian and Hall (1933) found various spoilage-causing species of *Saccharomyces*, e.g., S. *carlsbergensis*, S. *rouxii* var. *polymorphus* (Z. *barkeri*), and *Hansenula anomala* (named S. *aceris-sacchari*). Fermentation of *malt extract* was found to be caused by *Saccharomyces rouxii* (English, 1953).

Milk and Milk Products. While lactose-fermenting yeasts are rare in most substrates, such yeasts occur commonly, along with nonlactose-fermenting types, in milk, cream, and milk products. In sour cream butter, the presence of yeasts was demonstrated in 98% of the samples examined (Kellermann, 1950). Macy *et al.* (1932) found from 50 to 14,500 yeast cells per milliliter of raw cream. A yeast cell number of > 1000 per milliliter occurred in 90% of the examined raw cream samples in summer, but in only 33% of the samples in spring. In fresh butter, up to 1180 yeast cells were counted per milliliter; during storage, the amount of yeast increases in unsalted butter whereas it decreases in salted butter.

Yeasts can cause objectionable odor and flavor as well as fermentation in milk products. In the preparation of fermented milk beverages, certain lactose-fermenting species produce a beneficial effect. On the other hand, the pathogenic yeast *Cryptococcus neoformans* was recently isolated from milk samples and from a biopsy of udder tissue (Emmons, 1953), being in fact the cause of an unusual and severe outbreak of bovine mastitis.

The yeasts most common in milk products are asporogenous types. The lactose-fermenting *Candida pseudotropicalis* var. *lactosa* has been isolated from buttermilk. In French soft cheeses, Macé (1903) demonstrated the presence of 10 lactose-fermenting "Torulae"; Dombrowski (1910) found both lactose-fermenting and nonfermenting types of *Torulopsis* in milk and milk products.

"Yeasty" or "foamy" fermentation may occur in cream to be made into butter, which cream is often shipped over long distances. From samples of "yeasty" cream, and from other samples of cream and milk, Hammer and Cordes (1920) isolated 45 cultures of lactose-fermenting yeasts. They were distributed among two species, *Candida pseudotropicalis* (termed *Torula cremoris*) and a new species, *Torulopsis sphaerica*.

Nonlactose-fermenting yeasts have also been found frequently in dairy products. Thus Nelson (1928) isolated 160 cultures of "white" yeasts from milk, cream, butter, and cheese. They were divided into four types which were all nonlactose-fermenting but which otherwise were not identified. In later investigations by Chinn and Nelson (1946), many isolates of nonlactose-fermenting yeasts from cream and butter belonged to *Candida*, *Torulopsis*, *Rhodotorula*, and *Trichosporon* whereas sporogenous yeasts were rare.

According to Nissen (1930), red yeasts are especially harmful in that they peptonize the milk and decompose the butter fat. Miklik (1953) found a *Rhodotorula* in butter, in which it caused early rancidity; *Sporobolomyces salmonicolor* also has been isolated from fermented cream (Olson and Hammer, 1937).

Sweetened condensed milk permits growth of such yeasts as can withstand a high percentage of sucrose. Hammer (1919) described *Torulopsis lactis-condensi*, which caused gas formation in sweetened condensed milk. This species, together with a new species, *Torulopsis globosa*, was found in a sweetened condensed milk undergoing gas formation and possessing a yeasty odor (Olson and Hammer, 1935).

Of ascospore-forming yeasts, the lactose-fermenting *Saccharomyces lactis* (which is regarded as the perfect form of *Torulopsis sphaerica*), has been isolated from both milk and butter. In the course of investigations into rancidity in butter, Jensen (1902) found two Saccharomycetes; and Sacchetti (1932, 1933) isolated *S. lactis* (termed *Z. casei* and *Z. versicolor*) and *S. fragilis* (the perfect form of *Candida pseudotropicalis*) from Italian soft cheeses. He moreover demonstrated the presence of several nonlactose-fermenting species of *Saccharomyces*, e.g., *S. chevalieri* (*S. mangini* var. *casei*) and *S. delbrueckii* (*S. unisporus*). Finally, *Debaryomyces hansenii* (*D. tyrocola*) has been isolated from cheese.

Yeasts have been found in a number of fermented milks where, in several cases, together with the bacterial flora, they play a part in the fermentation. "Kephir" is prepared by the inhabitants of the Caucasus by the admixture to milk of "kephir grains." These consist mostly of bacteria though yeasts, e.g., *Candida pseudotropicalis* var. *lactosa*, and *S. fragilis*, have also been isolated from this source.

In "Leben," a kephir-like beverage from Egypt, a "*Mycoderma*" and other yeasts are said to be involved in the fermentation. In the preparation of "Kumiss" in Russia and Asia, yeasts are considered necessary for the fermentation and types of *Torulopsis* and *S. fragilis* have been shown to be present.

In "Mazun," prepared in Armenia, various yeasts have been found, among them a lactose-fermenting *Saccharomyces*, in addition to bacteria. In the case of "Busa," coming from Turkistan, it has been demonstrated that a *Torulopsis*-type is always associated with the lactic acid bacteria while from yoghurt, species of *Torulopsis* have been obtained (Soulides, 1955) and *Saccharomyces fragilis* and *S. lactis* have likewise been detected.

Meats. According to Jensen (1954), red yeasts apparently identical with *Rhodotorula glutinis* (*Cryptococcus glutinis*) and *Candida pulcherrima* (*Saccharomyces pulcherrimus*) may occur in fats.

Debaryomyces has been isolated from slimy sausages by Mrak and Bonar (1938) and from other meat products such as ham, bacon, and pickled meats (Mrak and Phaff, 1948). Empey and Scott (1939) found that spoilage of chilled beef in the abattoir was caused not only by bacteria and molds but also by various yeasts including types belonging to *Candida* and *Rhodotorula* which came chiefly from the hide and hairs of the slaughtered animals.

Brines. It is known, especially from American investigations, that yeasts occur commonly in brines used for storing vegetable and meat products. Such yeasts are frequently film-forming species of *Debaryomyces, Pichia, Hansenula,* and *Candida*. Species of *Debaryomyces* seem to be the most widely distributed yeasts associated with brines. They possess high tolerance to salt and organic acids and grow well at low temperatures down to 1–2°C.

Costilow *et al.* (1954) isolated from brined meat, such as hams, beef tongues, and bacon, 89 cultures all of which belonged to *Debaryomyces*, especially *D. nicotianae* (*D. membranaefacians* var. *hollandicus*). From different types of food brines Mrak and Bonar (1939) likewise commonly isolated species of *Debaryomyces*. *D. nicotianae* (*D. membranaefaciens* var. *hollandicus*), and *D. hansenii* (*D. membranaefaciens, D. guilliermondii* var. *nova-zeelandicus*) could be induced to grow in cucumber brine containing 24% salt. In addition, they isolated *Pichia membranaefaciens* and *Candida mycoderma* (*Mycoderma decolorans*).

Torulopsis holmii and *Saccharomyces rosei* were reported to be the predominant yeasts in cucumber fermentations (Costilow and Fabian, 1953). Among the film-forming yeasts in cucumber brines Etchells *et al.* (1953) report species of *Debaryomyces* as being the most widely distributed, followed by types of *Saccharomyces* (*Zygosaccharomyces*), *Endomycopsis, Candida, Hansenula,* and *Pichia. Debaryomyces* is the most salt tolerant of these while *Candida krusei, Pichia membranaefaciens,* and *Hansenula anomala* grow poorly if at all at concentrations of salt above 10%.

Subsurface brine yeasts which cause gaseous fermentation in the brine were found to comprise species of *Saccharomyces, Hansenula,* and *Torulopsis.* In brines with higher concentrations of salt, the fermentation lasts longer than in more dilute solutions for the lactic acid bacteria are inhibited as the brine strength increases and more food remains for those yeasts which are more salt tolerant.

Wood Pulp. Wood pulp used for paper manufacture contains large quantities of asporogenous yeasts. Rennerfelt (1937) counted in Swedish paper mills, per gram of dry pulp, about 1500 to about 100,000 cells of "Torulopsidaceae," among which, however, *Geotrichum candidum* was included for practical reasons. Species of *Rhodotorula, Torulopsis, Candida,* and *Trichosporon* were also isolated.

In wood pulp in Italy, species of *Torulopsis, Candida, Trichosporon,* and *Sporobolomyces* were observed (Goidánich *et al.,* 1939). According to Melin (1933), types of *Candida* and *Torulopsis* exert an inhibiting influence on the development of the blueing fungi, among which *Cadophora* and *Pullularia* are the most common, in the pulp.

Sundry Products. Yeasts are able to grow in soft drinks. In the writer's experience these are chiefly types of *Torulopsis* and *Candida.* McKelvey (1926) found that spoilage of carbonated beverages was frequently due to yeast growth and indeed from this source he isolated sporogenous yeasts (not identified) for use in thermal death point determinations.

In the manufacture of baker's yeast, pure-cultured strains of *Saccharomyces cerevisiae* are employed. The wild yeasts most commonly found in such yeast are *Candida mycoderma* and types of *Torulopsis,* infection with the former sometimes adversely affecting the flour-raising power of the yeast. *Saccharomyces exiguus* and *Pichia membranaefaciens* have also been reported to occur in yeast, and Windisch (1940) isolated *Candida pulcherrima* and *C. tropicalis* from the compressed material. *Candida utilis* is often used as food and fodder yeast.

Yeasts can cause spoilage of mayonnaise, salad dressing, French dressing, and related products. Species of *Saccharomyces* (*Zygosaccharomyces*) have been isolated from such products, e.g., *S. rosei* (*Z. globiformis*) according to Williams and Mrak (1949). Sugar-tolerant types of *Saccharomyces* from concentrated orange juice can grow in solutions containing up to 70% sugar, and of pH 3 (Ingram, 1950).

In sake, Japanese rice wine, species of *Saccharomyces* and *Hansenula* have been observed while in rum fermentation in Jamaica, *Schizosaccharomyces pombe* is used. In fermentations of cocoa beans, *Kloeckera apiculata* and *Hansenula anomala* are found at first, the initial stage being followed by an alcoholic fermentation with species of *Saccharomyces*. In addition to these, a *Schizosaccharomyces* and *Candida mycoderma* have also been isolated. From tobacco, species of *Debaryomyces* have been isolated which grow vigorously during the fermentation while in this case *Rhodotorula*-types have also been found (Giovannozzi, 1948).

More particular technological and food spoilage aspects of various yeasts are considered in Chapters X and XII, respectively.

6. Importance of External Factors to Yeasts

This discussion is primarily concerned with those factors which have particular importance for the growth of yeasts and their survival of unfavorable conditions. The findings of different authors may of course differ somewhat, either because of variations in the methods used or because of the fact that within the same species there may occur strains which react differently to outside influences. In the discussion of yeasts in industrial products certain environmental factors were mentioned such as concentrations of alcohol, sugar, and salt.

Influence of Temperature on Growth. Table II lists the cardinal points of temperature with regards to the growth of representative species of a number of genera, as found in the experiments of various authors.

The minimum temperature for growth is often in the neighborhood of 0°C., but for some species may be somewhat higher, up to 5°C. However, growth below zero is occasionally reported. For example, Smart (1935) observed slow yeast growth on agar medium at about −9°C. and a pink *"Torula"* (presumably a species of *Rhodotorula*) was found to multiply at −4°C. (Berry and Magoon, 1934).

TABLE II

Minimum, Optimum, and Maximum Temperatures for the Growth of Yeasts[a]

Species	Minimum (°C.)	Optimum (°C.)	Maximum (°C.)
Saccharomyces carlsbergensis	0	25	33.5
Saccharomyces cerevisiae var. *ellipsoideus*	0.5	30–35	40–41
Saccharomyces marxianus	0.5	—	46–47
Hansenula suaveolens	3	30	30–35
Hanseniaspora valbyensis	5	—	32–33
Torulopsis candida	5	22	32
Torulopsis molischiana	5	22	>42
Candida parapsilosis	0	20–25	30
Kloeckera apiculata	3	30	35
Rhodotorula gracilis	5	27	37–42

[a] From various authors.

The optimum temperature is in most cases around 20–25°C., but is sometimes rather higher, 30–35°C. The maximum temperature varies between 30 and 46–47°C.

Thermal Death Points. The temperature at which a yeast is destroyed depends on a number of factors, such as the composition of the heating medium, the duration of the thermal action, and the condition of the test organism. Thus, yeasts show higher resistance in a dry state than when moist.

Thermal death points between 50 and 60°C. for vegetative cells of various yeasts have often been reported and in these cases the investigations were made by heating yeast suspensions over a short period. Thus, Epstein and Snell (1940) found that *Saccharomyces cerevisiae* var. *ellipsoideus* would withstand up to 58°C. for 10 minutes in beer while Lund (1951) stated that a particular strain of the same species was destroyed after heating for 20 minutes in beer at 50°C., a second strain at 56°C., and a third strain (termed *S. odessa*, strain G) only at 60°C. under the same conditions.

Heating in honey caused destruction of vegetative cells of species of *Saccharomyces* (*Zygosaccharomyces*) and of *Torulopsis mellis* after

5–10 minutes at 60°C. (Fabian and Quinet, 1928); in cream, yeasts were usually killed at 63°C. after 30 minutes (Lund, 1918).

By exposing young agar cultures to various temperatures for 48 hours, Lund (1954) found relatively low thermal death points, e.g., 43°C. for S. cerevisiae var. ellipsoideus and 35°C. for Hansenula suaveolens.

Spores are more resistant to heating than are vegetative cells. Vegetative cells of a certain strain of S. cerevisiae var. ellipsoideus were killed by heating in beer for 20 minutes at 56°C., while 58°C. was required for destruction of sporulating cells of the same strain. Again, vegetative cells of another strain of the same species (termed S. Odessa, strain F) were destroyed under identical conditions at 52°C., although its spores were not killed until 64°C. had been reached (Lund, 1951). Vegetative cells of species of Saccharomyces were killed in maple syrup after 5–10 minutes at 60°C. whereas 75°C. for 5 minutes was required to destroy the spores (Fabian and Hall, 1933). Castelli (1935) showed that suspensions of vegetative cells of S. cerevisiae var. ellipsoideus in grape juice were killed in 5 minutes at 60°C., while spore suspensions withstood a maximum of 15 minutes at the same temperature.

Resistance to Cold. Yeasts are very resistant to low temperatures. For instance, Hansen (1881, 1903, 1905) found that Kloeckera as well as Saccharomycetes can survive the winter in the soil in Denmark, while Lochhead and Farrell (1930) noticed that sugar-tolerant yeasts can remain viable in the soil during the Canadian winter.

Young agar cultures of Saccharomyces, Hansenula, Schizoblastosporion, Candida, and Kloeckera survived −15°C. for 48 hours apparently without being impaired (Lund, 1954); and it has been reported that yeasts survived freezing in grape juice for several months without detriment to their vitality.

Stille (1950) found that 29.2% of the cells in Saccharomyces cerevisiae were killed after freezing at −24°C., while only 18.4% of them were destroyed at −193°C. The difference is attributed to the higher rate of cooling as the temperature falls below a critical range. This point is passed at −24°C., a further drop in temperature to −193°C. causing no further destruction of cells.

In experiments with yeast cells which had been frozen at −24°C., prolonged storage of the cells at −4°C. caused a much more pronounced and rapid decrease in the number of live cells than at a lower temperature (−15°C.). The lower the temperature, the more slowly are the cells destroyed and further, rapid freezing and slow thawing is less detrimental to yeast cells than is slow freezing and rapid thawing. The environment has, however, an important bearing on the rate of destruction.

Thus, yeast cells were destroyed much more rapidly when frozen at an acid reaction than when the reaction was neutral or alkaline. When frozen in saline solution, the cells were destroyed more rapidly than when frozen in a sugary nutrient solution.

Light. Several investigations have shown that ultraviolet light destroys yeasts in a very short time even if they seem somewhat more resistant than bacteria. Buchta (1914) noticed that ultraviolet rays inhibit reproduction after 10 seconds, and that the cells are killed by irradiation for more than 3 minutes.

Feuer and Tanner (1920), by exposing aqueous suspensions of various sporogenous and asporogenous yeasts in open petri dishes to ultraviolet light, found that more yeasts were killed within 1 minute, and that even the most resistant types were destroyed after 7 minutes. Tanner and Ryder (1923) state nevertheless that, to achieve destruction of yeast cells, somewhat longer exposure of aqueous suspensions in thin layers to the irradiation is occasionally required. The most resistant yeast of all was a red-pigmented yeast which was destroyed only after irradiation for 20 minutes, whereas the other yeasts examined including species of *Endomyces, Saccharomyces,* and *Torulopsis,* were killed after irradiation for periods between 1.5 and 15 minutes.

By subjecting species of *Saccharomyces, Hansenula, Schizoblastosporion,* and *Kloeckera* on the surface of wort agar in open petri dishes to irradiation with ultraviolet light, Lund (1954) found that all yeast cells were destroyed within the exposure time employed (30 minutes). It was scarcely surprising therefore to find that exposure to sunlight for 1 hour had a detrimental effect on several yeasts although diffuse daylight for 1 hour failed to inhibit the yeasts. It is worth noting, however, that Buchta (1914) found diffuse daylight inhibits the reproduction of *S. cerevisiae* and *Saccharomycodes ludwigii.* The influence of light on spore-formation of brewer's yeast was examined by Oppenoorth (1956), who found that daylight stimulates sporulation in some strains, whereas in other strains the sporulation is unaffected or even inhibited by daylight.

Oxygen. Both Saccharomycetaceae and Cryptococcaceae comprise types which are aerobic, thriving poorly or not at all at low oxygen pressure, whereas other types are facultatively anaerobic.

Certain yeasts, e.g., *Pichia* and *Candida mycoderma,* rapidly form, as an expression of their need for oxygen, a film on the surface of liquid media. However, even yeasts with an entirely oxidative dissimilation do not invariably form a film.

Oxygen also promotes the growth of facultatively anaerobic types;

thus, *Saccharomyces cerevisiae* multiplies more rapidly in the presence of ample oxygen. Oxygen is also a factor of great importance to the formation of ascospores.

Desiccation. Hansen (1885, 1898) found that yeasts died rapidly when distributed in thin layers on the sides and bottoms of glass flasks. However, if they occurred as thicker layers in filter paper or cotton they would remain alive for a long time. In soil containing 14–17% moisture yeasts grew well in Barthel's experiments (1918) and plainly worse at a moisture content of 7%, and, indeed, the cells died in soil containing only 2.5% moisture.

References

Anderson, H. W. (1917). *J. Infectious Diseases* **21**, 341.

Anderson, K. W., and Skinner, C. E. (1947). *Mycologia* **39**, 165.

Andrews, J., and Gilliland, R. B. (1952). *J. Inst. Brewing* **58**, 189.

Barker, B. T. P. (1949). *Ann. Rept. Agr. Hort. Research Sta. Long Ashton, Bristol.* p. 137.

Barker, B. T. P. (1950). *Ann. Rept. Agr. Hort. Research Sta. Long Ashton, Bristol.* p. 178.

Barthel, C. (1918). *Zentr. Bakteriol. Parasitenk. Abt. II*, **48**, 340.

Beech, F. W. (1954). Unpublished. (Cf. Challinor, S. W. *J. appl. Bact.* **18**, 212, 1955.)

Beech, F. W., and Carr, J. G. (1955). *J. Gen. Microbiol.* **12**, 85.

Berlese, A. (1896). *Riv. Patol. Vegetale* **5**, 211, 295, 354.

Berry, J. A., and Magoon, C. A. (1934). *Phytopathology* **24**, 780.

Bouthilet, R. J. (1953). *Mycopathol. et Mycol. Appl.* **6**, 79.

Buchner, P. (1921). *Arch. Protistenk.* **42**, 319.

Buchta, L. (1914). *Centr. Bakteriol. Parasitenk. Abt. II*, **41**, 340.

Capriotti, A. (1953). *Riv. Biol.* [N.S.] **45**, 369.

Capriotti, A. (1955a). *Riv. Biol.* [N.S.] **47**, 343.

Capriotti, A. (1955b). *Antonie van Leeuwenhoek J. Microbiol. Serol.* **21**, 145.

Capriotti, A. (1955c). *Riv. Biol.* [N.S.] **47**, 209.

Castelli, T. (1935). *Boll. sez. ital. soc. intern. microbiol.* **7**, 123; see also Phaff, H. J., and Mrak, E. M. (1948). *Wallerstein Labs. Communs.* **11**, 261.

Castelli, T. (1952a). *Rev. fermentations et ind. aliment.* **7**, 35.

Castelli, T. (1952b). *Bull. Research Council Israel* **1**, 4.

Chatton, E. (1913). *Compt. rend. soc. biol.* **65**, 117.

Chinn, S. H. F., and Nelson, F. E. (1946). *J. Dairy Sci.* **29**, 507.

Clark, D. S., Wallace, R. H., and David, J. J. (1954). *Can. J. Microbiol.* **1**, 145.

Connell, G. H., and Skinner, C. E. (1953). *J. Bacteriol.* **66**, 627.

Costilow, R. N., Etchells, J. L., and Blumer, T. N. (1954). *Appl. Microbiol.* **2**, 300.

Costilow, R. N., and Fabian, F. W. (1953). *Appl. Microbiol.* **1**, 314.

Custers, M. T. J. (1940). "Onderzoekingen over het Gistgeslacht Brettanomyces." Proefschrift. Delft.

De Kruyff, E. (1908). *Centr. Bakteriol. Parasitenk. Abt. II*, **21**, 616.

De Migoya, A. E. (1950). *Rep. Agr. Ministerio. agr. y ganaderia Publ. téc. No. 4*; see also *Food Sci. Abstr.* **25**, 577 (1953).

Derx, H. G. (1930). *Ann. mycol.* **28**, 1.

Di Menna, M. E. (1955). *J. Gen. Microbiol.* **12**, 54.

Dobzhansky, T., and Da Cunha, A. B. (1955). *Ecology* **36**, 34.

Dombrowski, W. (1910). *Centr. Bakteriol. Parasitenk. Abt. II*, **28**, 345.

Emmons, C. W. (1951). *J. Bacteriol.* **62**, 685.

Emmons, C. W. (1953). *Mycopathol. et Mycol. Appl.* **6**, 231.

Empey, W. A., and Scott, W. J. (1939). *Australia Council Sci. Ind. Research Bull. No. 126*; see also Ayres, J. C. (1955). *Advances in Food Research* **6**, 109.

English, M. P. (1953). *J. Gen. Microbiol.* **9**, 15.

Epstein, S. S., and Snell, F. D. (1940). *J. Inst. Brewing* **46**, 175.

Etchells, J. L., Bell, T. A., and Jones, I. D. (1953). *Farlowia* **4**, 265.

Etchells, J. L., Costilow, R. N., Bell, T. A., and Demain, L. (1954). *Appl. Microbiol.* **2**, 296.

Fabian, F. W., and Hall, H. H. (1933). *Zentr. Bakteriol. Parasitenk. Abt. II*, **89**, 31.

Fabian, F. W., and Quinet, R. I. (1928). *Mich. Agr. Expt. Sta. Tech. Bull. No.* **92**, 1.

Fawcett, H. S. (1929). *Phytopathology* **19**, 479.

Feuer, B., and Tanner, F. W. (1920). *J. Ind. Eng. Chem.* **12**, 740.

Florenzano, G. (1949). *Ann. sper. agrar.* (*Rome*) [N.S.] **3**, 887; *Food Sci. Abstr.* **24**, 359 (1952).

Giovannozzi, M. (1948). *Mycopathol.* **4**, 260.

Goidánich, G., Ciferri, R., and Redaelli, P. (1939). *Mycopathol.* **2**, 48.

Gräbner, K. E. (1954). *Z. Morphol. Ökol. Tiere* **41**, 471.

Grüss, J. (1926). *Jahrb. wiss. Botan.* **66**, 109.

Hammer, B. W. (1919). *Iowa Agr. Expt. Sta. Research Bull. No.* **54**, 209.

Hammer, B. W., and Cordes, W. A. (1920). *Iowa Agr. Expt. Sta. Research Bull. No.* **61**, 1.

Hansen, E. C. (1881). *Medd. Carlsberg Lab.* **1**, 293.

Hansen, E. C. (1885). *Botan. Centr.* **21**, 183.

Hansen, E. C. (1889). *Centr. Bakteriol. Parasitenk. Abt. II*, **5**, 632.

Hansen, E. C. (1898). *Medd. Carlsberg Lab.* **4**, 198.

Hansen, E. C. (1903). *Centr. Bakteriol. Parasitenk. Abt. II*, **10**, 1.

Hansen, E. C. (1905). *Centr. Bakteriol. Parasitenk. Abt. II*, **14**; *Medd. Carlsberg Lab.* **9**, 54 (1911).

Hautmann, F. (1924). *Arch. Protistenk.* **48**, 213.

Hedrick, L. R., and Burke, G. C. (1950). *J. Bacteriol.* **59**, 481.

Hedrick, L. R., and Burke, G. C. (1953). *Mycopathol.* **6**, 92.

Hemmons, L. M. (1954). *J. Inst. Brewing* **60**, 288.

Hertz, M. R., and Levine, M. (1942). *Food Research* **7**, 430.

Hilkenbach, R. (1911). "Neue Beiträge zur Kenntnis der wilden Hefen in der Natur." Dissertation, Kiel; see also Lockhead and Heron (1929).

Hohl, L. H., and Cruess, W. V. (1939). *Zentr. Bakteriol. Parasitenk. Abt. II*, **101**, 65.

Holst, E. C. (1936). *J. Agr. Research* **53**, 513.

Ingram, M. (1950). *J. Gen. Microbiol.* **4**, 9.

Janensch, I. (1941). *Wochschr. Brau.* **58**, 227.

Jensen, L. B. (1954). "Microbiology of Meats." Garrard Press, Champaign, Ill.

Jensen, O. (1902). *Centr. Bakteriol. Parasitenk. Abt. II*, **8**, 1.

Jimbo, T. (1926). *Science Repts. Tôhoku Imp. Univ. Fourth Ser.* **2**, 161.

Kellermann, R. (1950). *Milchwissenschaft* **5**, 216.

Kostka, G. (1927). *Verhandl. naturforsch. Ver. Brünn* **59**, 14; see also *Wochschr. Brau.* **44**, 128.

Kroemer, K., and Krumbholz, G. (1931). *Arch. Mikrobiol.* **2**, 352.

Kroemer, K., and Krumbholz, G. (1932). "Obst- und Beerenweine." Serger & Hempel, Braunschweig.

Krumbholz, G. (1931). *Arch. Mikrobiol.* **2**, 411.

Last, F. T. (1955). *Trans. Brit. Mycol. Soc.* **38**, 221.

Lochhead, A. G. (1933). *Zentr. Bakteriol. Parasitenk. Abt. II*, **88**, 296.

Lochhead, A. G., and Farrell, L. (1930). *Can. J. Research* **3**, 51.

Lochhead, A. G., and Farrell, L. (1931). *Can. J. Research* **5**, 665.

Lochhead, A. G., and Heron, D. A. (1929). *Dom. Can. Dept. Agr. Bull. No. 116 N.S.*

Lochhead, A. G., and McMaster, N. B. (1931). *Sci. Agr.* **11**, 351.

Lodder, J., and Kreger-van Rij, N. J. W. (1952). "The Yeasts. A Taxonomic Study." North Holland Publ., Amsterdam.

Ludwig, F. (1886). *Ber. deut. botan. Ges.* **4**, 17.

Lund, A. (1951). *J. Inst. Brewing* **57**, 36.

Lund, A. (1954). "Studies on the Ecology of Yeasts." Munksgaard, Copenhagen.

Lund, A. (1956). *Friesia* **5**, 297; *Wallerstein Labs. Communs.* **19**, 221.

Lund, T. H. (1918). *N.Y. Produce Rev. and Am. Creamery* **48**, 282; see also Tanner, F. W. (1941). "The Microbiology of Foods." Garrard Press, Champaign, Ill.

Macé, P. (1903). *Ann. inst. Pasteur* **17**, 11.

Macy, H., Coulter, S. T., and Combs, W. B. (1932). *Univ. Minn. Agr. Expt. Sta. Tech. Bull. No.* **82**, 1.

Marcus, O. (1942). *Arch. Mikrobiol.* **13**, 1.

Marshall, C. R., and Walkley, V. T. (1951). *Food Research* **16**, 448.

McKelvey, C. E. (1926). *J. Bacteriol.* **11**, 98.

Melin, E. (1933). *Arch. Mikrobiol.* **4**, 509.

Miklik, E. (1953). *Milchwissenschaft* **8**, 23.

Miller, J. J., Peers, D. J., and Neal, R. W. (1951). *Can. J. Botany* **29**, 26.

Miller, J. J., and Webb, N. S. (1954). *Soil Sci.* **77**, 197.

Miller, M. W., and Mrak, E. M. (1953). *Appl. Microbiol.* **1**, 174.

Mrak, E. M., and Bonar, L. (1938). *Food Research* **3**, 615.

Mrak, E. M., and Bonar, L. (1939). *Zentr. Bakteriol. Parasitenk. Abt. II*, **100**, 289.

Mrak, E. M., and McClung, L. S. (1940). *J. Bacteriol.* **40**, 395.

Mrak, E. M., and Phaff, H. J. (1948). *Ann. Rev. Microbiol.* **2**, 1.

Mrak, E. M., Phaff, H. J., and Vaughn, R. H. (1942a). *J. Bacteriol.* **43**, 689.

Mrak, E. M., Phaff, H. J., Vaughn, R. H., and Hansen, H. N. (1942b). *J. Bacteriol.* **44**, 441.

Müller, W. (1934). *Arch. Mikrobiol.* **5**, 84.

Nelson, J. A. (1928). *J. Dairy Sci.* **11**, 397.

Niethammer, A. (1942). *Arch. Mikrobiol.* **13**, 45.

Nissen, W. (1930). *Milchwirtsch. Forsch.* **10**, 30.

Olson, H. C., and Hammer, B. W. (1935). *Iowa State Coll. J. Sci.* **10**, 37.

Olson, H. C., and Hammer, B. W. (1937). *Iowa State Coll. J. Sci.* **11**, 207.

Oppenoorth, W. F. F. (1956). *Nature* **178**, 992.

Owen, W. L., and Mobley, R. L. (1948). *Food Research* **13**, 281.

Pasteur, L. (1876). "Études sur la bière." Gauthier-Villars, Paris.

Pasteur, L. (1878). *Compt. rend.* **87**, 813.

Perotti, R. (1951). "Biologia vegetale applicata all'Agricoltura IV, B. Microbiologia delle Industrie." Rosenberg and Sellier, Torino.
Peynaud, E., and Domercq, S. (1954). 8me Congr. Intern. botan. Paris Sect. 19, Mycol. p. 117.
Phaff, H. J., and Douglas, H. C. (1944). Fruit Products J. 23, 332.
Pridham, T. G., and Raper, K. B. (1950). Mycologia 42, 603.
Rennerfelt, E. (1937). Svenska Skogsvårdsför. Tidskr. 35, 47.
Rettger, L. F., Reddish, G. F., and McAlpine, J. G. (1924). J. Bacteriol. 9, 327.
Romwalter, A., and Király, A. v. (1939). Arch. Mikrobiol. 10, 87.
Sacchetti, M. (1931–32). Mem. reale accad. sci. ist. Bologna Classe sci. fis. [8], Part 9. (Cf. Mrak and Phaff, 1948.)
Sacchetti, M. (1932). Arch. Mikrobiol. 3, 650.
Sacchetti, M. (1933). Arch. Mikrobiol. 4, 427.
Schomann, H. (1937). Z. Morphol. Ökol. Tiere 32, 542.
Schuster, P., and Úlehla, V. (1913). Ber deut. botan. Ges. 31, 129.
Schöllhorn, K. (1919). Bull. soc. botan. Genève II, 11, 154.
Scrivani, P. (1939). Arch. Mikrobiol. 10, 446.
Sherwin, H. S. (1948). J. Elisha Mitchell Sci. Soc. 64, 267.
Shifrine, M., and Phaff, H. J. (1956). Mycologia 48, 41.
Shihata, A. M. El-Tabey Awad, and Mrak, E. M. (1951). Am. Naturalist 85, 381.
Shihata, A. M. El-Tabey Awad, and Mrak, E. M. (1952). Evolution 6, 325.
Smart, H. F. (1935). Science 82, 525.
Soulides, D. A. (1955). Appl. Microbiol. 3, 129.
Starkey, R. L., and Henrici, A. T. (1927). Soil Sci. 23, 33.
Steinhaus, E. A. (1946). "Insect Microbiology," Chapter 6. Comstock Publ., Ithaca, New York.
Stille, B. (1950). Arch. Mikrobiol. 14, 554.
Tanner, F. W., and Ryder, E. (1923). Botan. Gaz. 75, 309.
Teunisson, D. J. (1954). Appl. Microbiol. 2, 215.
van der Walt, J. P. (1956). Antonie van Leeuwenhoek J. Microbiol. Serol. 22, 190, 265, 321.
van der Walt, J. P., and Tscheuschner, I. T. (1956). J. Gen. Microbiol. 14, 485; 15, 459.
Wagner, R. P. (1944). Univ. Texas Publ. No. 4445, 104.
Walters, L. S. (1943). J. Inst. Brewing 49, 253.
Wickerham, L. J. (1951). U.S. Dept. Agr. Washington, D.C. Tech. Bull. No. 1029.
Wickerham, L. J. (1956). Compt. rend. trav. lab. Carlsberg, Sér. physiol. 26, 423.
Wiles, A. E. (1953). J. Inst. Brewing 59, 265.
Williams, O. B., and Mrak, E. M. (1949). Fruit Products J. 28, 141; see also Tanner, F. W. "The Microbiology of Foods." Garrard Press, Champaign, Ill. (1944).
Windisch, S. (1940). Arch. Mikrobiol. 11, 368.
Wortmann, J. (1897–98). Ber. Lehranst. Weinb. Geisenheim p. 75; see also Klöcker, A. "Die Gärungsorganismen," p. 248. Berlin, Wien (1924).
ZoBell, C. E. (1946). "Marine Microbiology." Chronica Botanica, Waltham, Mass.

CHAPTER III

Life History and Cytology of Yeasts

Ö. WINGE AND C. ROBERTS

1. Historical Introduction

Yeasts are found in nature most often on sweet juicy fruits on which they are carried to the soil where they survive unfavorable periods. Most of the yeasts occurring in soil are asporogenous, while those employed in baking, brewing, wine-making, and in alcohol production belong to the spore-forming species. Lund (1954, 1956), who studied the ecology of yeasts, has cited the older literature concerning the occurrence of yeasts in nature.

Although yeasts had been observed under a microscope by Leeuwenhoek as far back as 1680 and Persoon had made the first recorded descriptions of them a hundred years later, it was not until the twentieth century that their life cycles were elucidated. It could hardly have been otherwise, however, for these early investigators were unaware of the significance of a pure culture. On the basis of observations on mixtures of organisms, some of the most authoritative voices of nineteenth-century biology asserted that the yeasts were merely phases in the complicated life cycles of molds, bacteria, or even algae. De Bary and Rees, it is true, considered the yeasts as a group apart and recognized their similarities to other Ascomycetes, while Pasteur clearly realized that different forms of yeasts exist, although he did not succeed in isolating any pure cultures. The isolation of a single yeast cell was, in fact, first accomplished by the Danish investigator, Emil C. Hansen. The view that yeasts lacked any form of sexuality was prevalent, however, and persisted even after Hansen in 1891 had observed that the ascospores of *Saccharomycodes ludwigii* were able to fuse together at germination. Indeed, at this time it was generally assumed that the propagation of yeasts was exclusively vegetative.

In 1895 Schiønning, assistant to Emil C. Hansen, demonstrated the occurrence of cellular copulation prior to ascus formation in *Schizosaccharomyces octosporus*. He regarded this phenomenon as being indicative of sexuality, although Beijerinck (1894) who had originally erected the species, had stated at the time: "Nirgendwo ist es klarer wie hier, dass der Ascus und die Ascosporen ohne einen Sexualakt entstehen."

In 1900 Schiønning's observation of cellular copulation in yeasts was confirmed by Hoffmeister, who further claimed that plasmogamy was followed by caryogamy. In 1901 Barker and Guilliermond independently reported the occurrence of caryogamy in yeasts, and although this was subsequently confirmed by other investigators, many years were to pass before the existence of an alternation of haploid and diploid generations was acknowledged. It was not known that some yeasts propagate themselves vegetatively in the haplophase while others do so in the diplophase. For example, *Schizosaccharomyces* is a haploid yeast, for its diplophase is normally limited to the ascus alone, while *Saccharomycodes* and some species of *Saccharomyces* represent diploid yeasts in which the haplophase is limited to the ascospores alone, or to a few haploid cells originating from ascospore germination. In these diploid yeasts, copulation may occur between the ascospores themselves, their haploid cell derivatives, or even between a spore and cell. In each case a vegetative diploid generation is initiated since intercellular copulation is followed by intracellular nuclear fusion.

This failure to recognize the existence of an alternation of generations in yeasts was in part due to the views of one of the leading yeast investigators of the time, Alexandre Guilliermond, who maintained (1910) that the nucleus of the yeast cell divided amitotically and later (1928) put forward the view that the majority of yeasts have lost all traces of sexuality. It is true that Guilliermond in 1928 speaks of a meiosis in connection with spore formation but he apparently did not realize that a combination of amitotic and mitotic division in the life cycle of an organism would hardly be expected to occur.

Even Stelling-Dekker's otherwise excellent treatise on the sporulating yeasts (1931) bears the imprint of the then prevailing uncertainty as to the life cycle of yeasts. It was not until the researches of Winge (1935), Winge and Laustsen (1937, 1939a), and the Lindegrens (1943a, 1945a) that the existence of an alteration of generations in yeasts was unequivocally established; the consequence of these investigations is evident in the important taxonomic work of Lodder and Kreger-Van Rij, which in 1952 succeeded that of Stelling-Dekker.

It should be mentioned that the discussion which follows concerns only the Endomycetaceae, the ascosporogenous yeasts exhibiting both sexual and asexual reproduction. The imperfect yeasts (Cryptococcaceae) which reproduce solely vegetatively have not been considered.

2. Haplophase and Diplophase

A. *General Considerations*

In the absence of cytological abnormalities, the ascospores of yeasts always belong to the haplophase portion of the life cycle. In certain yeasts, the cells arising as a result of the germination of these spores remain haploid, while in others, as will be discussed later, the diplophase is initiated at this point in the life cycle.

In the genus *Saccharomyces*, a clear morphological differentiation of haploid and diploid cells is frequently apparent. The former are most often round or spherical and smaller than the elongated, oval, diploid cells. Figure 1 shows this characteristic difference between haploid and

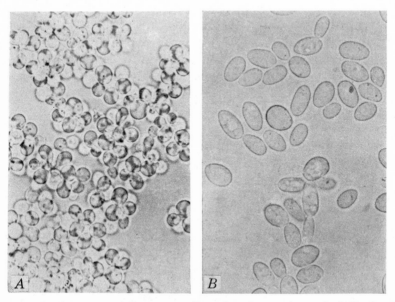

FIG. 1. *Saccharomyces cerevisiae* var. *ellipsoideus* (×1000). A: Haploid cells of a single-spore culture. B: Diploid cells of a single-spore culture. (From Winge and Laustsen, 1937.)

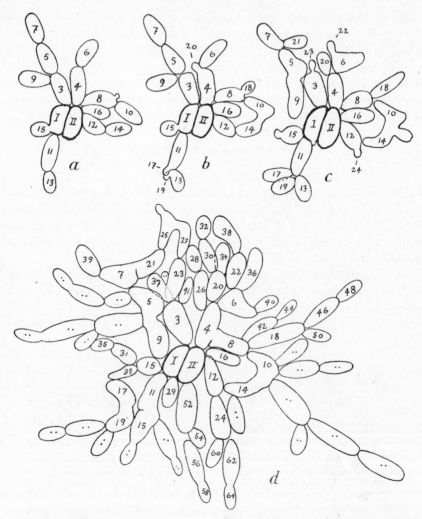

FIG. 2. *Saccharomyces cerevisiae* var. *ellipsoideus*. Two spores, I and II, producing haploid cells, which fuse in pairs to form diploid zygotes. (From Winge, 1935.)

diploid cells of *S. cerevisiae* var. *ellipsoideus*. It should be noted, however, that this morphological differentiation may be much less evident in other species or varieties.

It is worthy of note that the presence or absence in some forms of *Saccharomyces* of a single gene, *D* (Winge and Roberts, 1949), determines whether an ascospore will grow out into a diploid or a haploid colony. In the presence of the *D* gene compulsory diploidization takes place, usually soon after spore germination and most often by the fusion in pairs of the haploid cells derived from the germination of single spores (Fig. 2). When the ascospore lacks the *D* gene and consequently carries the recessive allelomorph, *d*, it grows out into a stable haploid colony in which diploidization normally does not occur. It is possible, therefore, for a single genus or even species to comprise forms which reproduce vegetatively in the haplophase, as well as forms reproducing vegetatively in the diplophase. In this connection it is worth noting that the investigations of Lindegren and his school in the United States have been undertaken on haploid forms of *Saccharomyces*, while at the Carlsberg

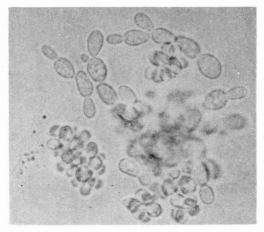

FIG. 3. *Saccharomyces priorianus* ($\times 700$). A single-spore culture showing a mixture of haploid and diploid cells. (From Winge and Laustsen, 1939b.)

Laboratorium in Copenhagen it has been, for the most part, diploid forms of *Saccharomyces* which have been studied.

The fact should be stressed that the normal vegetative growth of yeasts, both in nature and in laboratory cultures, takes place either by haploid cells, diploid cells, or even by a mixture of both (Fig. 3), and that the sporulating stage occurs only when suitable conditions are present. Yeasts are, however, generally designated as either haploid or diploid organisms, depending upon which phase takes part in vegetative growth. Figure 4 illustrates the life cycles of a haploid and a diploid yeast. In the former, the diploid zygote gives rise to the vegetative phase, and in the latter, diploidization through zygote formation occurs immediately before sporulation. Since both types of vegetative growth are found in the genus *Saccharomyces*, the former distinction between the haploid genus *Zygosaccharomyces* and the diploid genus *Saccharomyces* cannot be valid. This view has been stressed by several investigators, including Phaff and Mrak (1948), who made their point clear in a diagram of the manner in which *Zygosaccharomyces* may revert to *Saccharomyces* and vice versa (Fig. 5). Finally, Lodder and Kreger-van Rij,

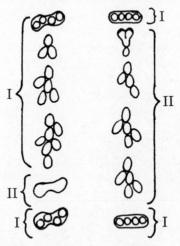

FIG. 4. Diagram of the life cycle of a haploid yeast (left) and a diploid yeast (right). The haplophase is indicated by I and the diplophase by II. (Redrawn from Winge, 1942.)

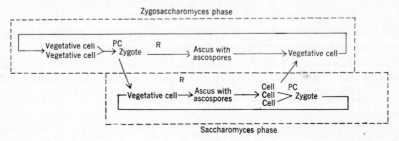

FIG. 5. Diagram showing how a haploid yeast (*Zygosaccharomyces*) may shift to a diploid yeast (*Saccharomyces*) and vice versa. (From Phaff and Mrak, 1948.)

in their recent work on taxonomy (1952), have relegated all species of *Zygosaccharomyces* to the genus *Saccharomyces*. Hjort (1956) has shown that the vegetative growth of *Saccharomyces rouxii* also alternates between the haplophase and the diplophase, and that under certain conditions of cultivation, S. *paradoxus* lacks normal vegetative growth but continually oscillates between the diploid and haploid phases. In nature,

Hansenula wingei has been shown to grow vegetatively both in the haplophase and diplophase (Wickerham 1956).

In 1902, Emil C. Hansen investigated the temperature range which permitted growth of the diploid vegetative phase of eleven species and varieties belonging to the genera *Saccharomyces, Hansenula, Pichia,* and *Saccharomycodes.* The minimum temperature for all forms was found to be about 0.5–1.0°C., with very scanty or scarcely perceptible growth occurring at this temperature. The maximum temperature was found to be more variable: for *Saccharomyces pastorianus* it was 34°C., while for *S. marxianus* it was between 46 and 47°C. Intermediate temperature maxima were found in *Pichia membranaefaciens* (35–36°C.), *Hansenula anomala,* and *Saccharomycodes ludwigii* (37–38°C.), and *Saccharomyces cerevisiae* and *S. willianus* (39–40°C.).

B. *Mating Type*

In 1936, Guilliermond discussed the possibility of *Saccharomycodes* being heterothallic, and this view was confirmed by the discovery by Winge and Laustsen in this genus in 1939 of a gene for mating type (or compatibility). It was Lindegren and Lindegren (1943a,b) who, 4 years later, first demonstrated a mating type system in *Saccharomyces.* These authors made use of this discovery in crossing haploid yeast cells; it will be remembered that before this time yeast crossings had been carried out only with spores (Winge and Laustsen, 1938).

The mating system in *Saccharomyces* is a simple bipolar one. When 4 single-spore cultures from 1 ascus of Lindegren's material are cultivated, 4 haploid colonies arise, of which 2 belong to one mating type called *a* and 2 to the opposite mating type called *α.* Only by mixing together an *a* culture with an *α* culture can a mating reaction be obtained: the round haploid cells form a small copulatory protuberance and cellular fusion takes place when 2 such protuberances arising from cells of opposite mating type are in contact. Copulation leads directly to the formation of a zygote. The zygotes (or their daughter cells) remain diploid, and when they are transferred to a sporulation medium, asci are formed, the spores of which again segregate out 2 *a* types and 2 *α* types.

In 1951 Fowell improved Lindegren's method of hybridizing yeasts by making serial transfers of the mixture of two haploid cultures of opposite mating type in which copulation had occurred. In this way a vigorous growth of diploid cells was obtained and, since their rate of growth was higher than that of the unmated haploid cells, the culture finally consisted of nearly all diploid cells. From such a culture single cells were isolated with the aid of a micromanipulator; these were cultivated on suitable substrata and could be considered as pure hybrid material, uncontaminated by the haplophase.

The two mating types are not always constant in their mating reaction (Lindegren and Lindegren, 1944a), for through mutation one or both types can easily lose the ability to mate, and it is by such behavior that *Torula* forms originate. It is also possible for a mating type to mutate to the opposite mating type ($a \rightarrow \alpha$ or $\alpha \rightarrow a$). Leupold (1950) has convincingly demonstrated this behavior in *Schizosaccharomyces pombe*, and Ahmad has reported the same phenomenon in *Saccharomyces* (1952, 1953a,b).

As previously mentioned on p. 96, the peculiar condition exists in *Saccharomyces* in which the mating type system is abolished if the diploidization gene, *D*, is present; in other words, an *a* or *α* single spore containing the *D* gene will automatically diploidize either at germination or during the subsequent growth of the colony, and the cells from such a diploid culture will normally not copulate with cells of the opposite mating type. A yeast which is heterozygous with respect to the *D* gene (*Dd*) will segregate out in each of its asci two spores which will give rise to diploid colonies and two spores which will give rise to haploid colonies (Winge and Roberts, 1949).

Furthermore, it should be mentioned that the mating system in yeasts may actually be more complex than appears from the foregoing discussion. In particular, it seems that the mating type does not express itself in all stages of the life cycle. A single spore of mating type *a* containing the *D* gene will give rise to a diploid homozygous culture of the formula *DD aa*, whose spores will in turn be of only one formula, *Da*. These can, however, be crossed with the spores from all 4 single-spore cultures from a *DD aα* ascus (Winge and Roberts, 1950; Thorne, 1951), even though *DD aa* cells are normally unable to copulate with either *DD aα* or *DD aa* cells. It is not yet known whether it is the *D* gene alone which here abolishes the expression of the mating system, since so far it has not been established whether copulation of *d* spores of the same mating type may also take place, although Lindegren (1949) has demonstrated the fusion of *d* cells of presumably the same mating type.

It has been established (Winge and Roberts, unpublished data) that when two spores of the same mating type are crossed, the diploid material which arises as a result of copulation is in no way abnormal but possesses a vigorous growth rate and gives rise to spores with a high percentage of germination. Investigations were carried out on a self-diploidized and therefore completely homozygous yeast culture, which produced normal 4-spored asci. From one of these asci, the 4 single-spore diploid cultures (nos. 1–4) were allowed to sporulate, and when the spores were mature, spore crossings were attempted in all 6 possible combinations: 1×2, 1×3, 1×4, 2×3, 2×4, and 3×4. It will be remembered that all 4 diploid single-spore cultures must have been homozygous and identical, both with respect to the mating type gene, *aa*, and to the diploidization gene, *DD*. Nearly all the 6 crossing combinations were successful; 8 crossings were undertaken for each combination, and a total of 8 hybrids were obtained from 4 of the 6 combinations. In addition, a hybrid was obtained by crossing No. 1×No. 1. All of the hybrids arising from these crosses were in every way normal and possessed excellent sporulating ability. The spores possessed a high percentage of germination, ranging from 87.5 to 100% and averaging 95.7%. But, as mentioned previously, whether the presence of the *D* gene can explain the compatibility encountered in this investigation is as yet unknown.

A recent study of mating reaction in *S. cerevisiae* by Levi (1956) is of considerable interest. His preliminary results suggest that the mating reaction may be controlled by chemical substances capable of diffusing through a solid nutrient medium, since a mating response in the form of copulatory processes was observed between separated colonies of opposite mating type. On solid medium copulatory processes were formed only by *α* cells, whereas in liquid medium they were formed by both *a* and *α* cells.

It is interesting to note that in *Hansenula wingei* some haploid strains of opposite mating type agglutinate intensely when they are mixed, while other strains of opposite mating type have no ability to agglutinate whatsoever (Wickerham 1956). If a strong agglutinative and a nonagglutinative haploid of opposite mating type are mixed, the diploid hybrid is not agglutinative, but nearly all ascosporic haploid offspring from the hybrid are more or less agglutinative. Agglutination markedly increases zygote formation, and nonagglutinative strains will not mate at all immediately after their isolation from the ascus but will do so after some months have elapsed.

C. Initiation of the Diplophase

The transition from haplophase to diplophase may take place in various ways which are illustrated in Fig. 6. They may be regarded as falling into 5 main groups, as follows:

(1) *Fusion of Daughter Nuclei* (Fig. 6A). A haploid spore (A 1) germinates, and at the conclusion of the first mitotic division (A 2), the

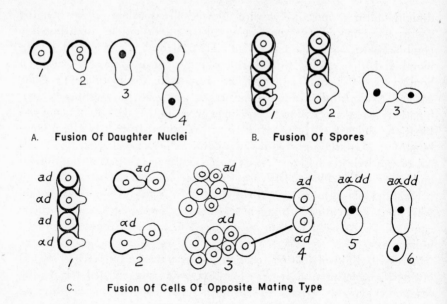

A. **Fusion Of Daughter Nuclei**   B. **Fusion Of Spores**

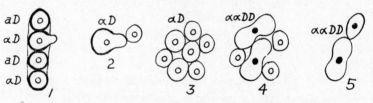

C.   **Fusion Of Cells Of Opposite Mating Type**

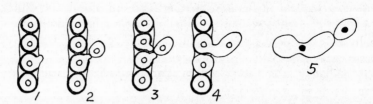

D.   **Fusion Of Cells Of Identical Mating Type**

E   **Fusion Of A Cell And A Spore**

Fig. 6. Diagrammatic representation of the various modes of origin of the diplo-phase from the haplophase in the life cycles of yeasts. (Haploid nuclei, white; diploid nuclei, black.)

two daughter nuclei fuse, resulting in the diplophase being initiated within the germinating spore (A 3, 4). This process, first reported in a Danish baking yeast, is known as "direct diploidization" (Winge and Laustsen, 1937). It seems to lead invariably to serious inbreeding degeneration, which is evident from the very low germinating ability of the spores arising from such a diploid yeast (Winge and Laustsen, 1940). It is possible that Lindegren's phenomenon of "illegitimate copulation" which he found in *Saccharomyces* and which also leads to degeneration, may arise, in part, in this way, although the phenomenon had been described as the copulation of haploid cells originating from a single spore of a heterothallic species.

(2) *Fusion of Spores* (Fig. 6B). Two haploid spores lying next to one another, but not necessarily within an ascus, germinate simultaneously (B 1) and, in doing so, fuse to form a zygote (B 2). Caryogamy occurs at the completion of plasmogamy, the zygote then giving rise to the diploid vegetative generation (B 3). This type of diploidization occurs in *Saccharomycodes ludwigii* (Winge and Laustsen, 1939a; Lindegren, 1945a; Winge, 1947), the obligate diploid yeast in which heterothallism was first reported, and although it occurs primarily in heterothallic organisms it may also be found in homothallic forms. It is known to occur in the genus *Saccharomyces*.

(3) *Fusion of Cells of Opposite Mating Type* (Fig. 6C). Haploid *d* spores of opposite mating type, *a* and *α*, germinate to form stable haploid colonies (C 1, 2, 3). This has been demonstrated in heterothallic forms of *Saccharomyces cerevisiae* by Lindegren and Lindegren (1943a) and in heterothallic forms of *Schizosaccharomyces pombe* by Leupold (1950). The initiation of the diplophase in such organisms by the production of a zygote can take place only when haploid *d* cells of opposite mating type come together (C 4, 5, 6); cells belonging to the same mating type will not copulate. In the absence of cells of opposite mating type, cells of a heterothallic yeast may remain permanently in the haplophase, giving rise to stable vegetative growth. It is possible that yeasts which have been identified as belonging to the anascosporogenous *Torula* may actually be these stable haploid forms of *Saccharomyces* (Winge and Laustsen, 1937; Lindegren and Lindegren, 1944a). Over twenty years ago Satava (1934) called attention to the fact that sporulating yeasts could give rise to nonsporulating, round *Torula* cells, the so-called "reduced forms."

It may be noted here that Lindegren and Lindegren (1954a) maintain that in *Saccharomyces*, when haploid cells of opposite mating type fuse, the two nuclei which are thus brought together in the zygote do not fuse directly. They claim that each nucleus first divides mitotically, and the two daughter nuclei then migrate out into the first bud of the zygote where caryogamy takes place and the true diplophase is initiated. According to the authors, this assertion is based upon evidence obtained from a film. In this connection we can state that in the homothallic material employed for study at the Carlsberg Laboratorium the fusion of the two haploid nuclei takes place directly within the zygote before the first bud has been formed. This has been verified cytologically by the observation of uninucleate zygotes formed as the result of spore copulation (Winge 1935, Plate 2, Figs. 11–16).

(4) *Fusion of Cells of Identical Mating Type* (Fig. 6D). A haploid D spore (D 1) of a homothallic yeast germinates to form a haploid colony (D 2, 3). Under suitable conditions the colony is able to diploidize by the fusion in pairs of its constituent cells, each fusion resulting in the formation of a diploid zygote (D 4). Fusion of cells of the same mating type, as well as fusion of a cell and a spore of the same mating type (see 5 below), may occur at spore germination, resulting in the formation of twin zygotes (Fig. 7). The diploid generation thus initiated continues to propagate itself vegetatively (D 5) until conditions permit the transformation of the diploid cells into asci.

The two haploid cells which fuse together may be identical in appearance (isogamy) as in *Schizosaccharomyces* and some species of *Saccharomyces* or morphologically differentiated (heterogamy) as in *Debaryomyces* and *Nadsonia*. In *Debaryomyces*, for example, two sister cells of unequal size may copulate to form a zygote which is directly transformed into an ascus. Again, copulation in *Nadsonia* takes place between a mother cell and its smaller daughter cell; the daughter cell nucleus migrates into the larger cell, where nuclear fusion occurs. Following caryogamy, the diploid nucleus migrates out into a bud which has formed on the mother cell opposite to the point of attachment of the daughter cell. This bud becomes the ascus.

(5) *Fusion of a Cell and a Spore* (Fig. 6E). A single spore germinates and forms a bud (E 1, 2, 3) which copulates with an adjacent germinating spore (E 4). As mentioned above, modifications of this process may occur. From the derivatives of one single spore, both spore × cell fusion and cell × cell fusion (see above) may take place (Fig. 7). It is also possible for a germinating spore to fuse with one of the many haploid cells derived from a single spore from another ascus.

Thus the transition from haplophase to diplophase in the life cycle of the yeast fungi may take place in five different ways, as outlined above. That variations of these principal types exist has already been alluded to, and it should also be mentioned that the mode of initiation of the diploid generation has not been elucidated for all yeasts suspected of having an alternation of generations. As an example can be mentioned *Torulopsis pulcherrima* (= *Candida pulcherrima*, according to Lodder and Kreger-van Rij). Large "pulcherrima cells" are produced by this organism which appear to give rise to a small bud in which bodies resembling spores have been observed. Both Windisch (1938, 1940) and

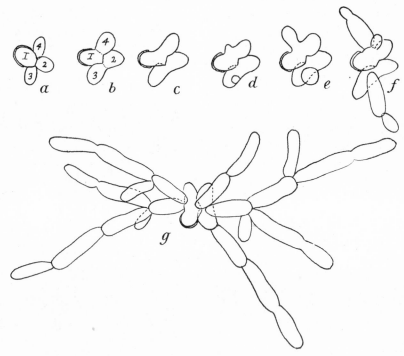

FIG. 7. *Saccharomyces validus*. A single spore (I) germinating and giving rise to twin zygotes. (From Winge, 1935.)

Roberts (1946), without working out details of the life cycle, interpreted these buds as asci containing spores, while other investigators do not accept the existence of sporulation in *T. pulcherrima*. Van der Walt (1952), in particular, considers that the "ascus" is simply a remnant of the cell wall which has trapped within itself a small number of vegetative cells. Further details on the life cycle of this organism, especially cytological demonstrations of its ploidy, are clearly desirable, although it can be mentioned that Magni (1953a) on the basis of x-ray survival curves, concluded that *T. pulcherrima* is a diploid yeast.

3. Sporulation

With regard to sporulating yeasts, certain environmental factors must naturally be present in order for these organisms to abandon the vegetative growth phase.

In the first place, temperature plays an important role in the shift to the sporulating phase. This was first demonstrated as early as 1883 by Emil C. Hansen. He grew some species of *Saccharomyces* in beer wort at room temperature and then transferred them to the same medium, in which they were incubated for about 24 hours at 26–27°C. The species were then transferred to gypsum blocks which were maintained at temperatures ranging from 0.5–37.5°C. The results he obtained with respect to sporulating ability are shown in Table I.

TABLE I

EFFECT OF TEMPERATURE ON THE SPORULATING ABILITY OF VARIOUS SPECIES
OF *Saccharomyces*[a]

Yeast	Sporulation Temperatures, (°C.)		
	Minimum	Optimum	Maximum
Saccharomyces cerevisiae (Saccharomyces cerevisiae I)	11	30	37
Saccharomyces cerevisiae var. *ellipsoideus (Saccharomyces ellipsoideus* I)	7.5	25	31.5
Saccharomyces cerevisiae var. *ellipsoideus (Saccharomyces ellipsoideus* II)	11	29	34
Saccharomyces pastorianus (Saccharomyces pastorianus I)	3	27.5	30.5
Saccharomyces willianus (Saccharomyces pastorianus II)	3	25	28
Saccharomyces willianus (Saccharomyces pastorianus III)	8.5	25	28

[a] Results of Emil C. Hansen's investigations at the Carlsberg Laboratorium in 1883. His original species designations are given in parentheses immediately following the present-day nomenclature of Lodder and Kreger-van Rij.

Since the time of Hansen, the importance of an adequate supply of oxygen and sufficient humidity during yeast sporulation has been recognized. It has also been established that the pH of the sporulating medium is of relatively minor significance, but that it is highly important that the cells are young, well nourished, and in vigorous growth at the time that they are transferred to the sporulating medium.

Stantial (1928, 1935) found that various fruit juices had a beneficial effect in promoting sporulation and that mannose and maltose were particularly effective. It was also found that a high content of sugar was detrimental, but that organic acids, especially acetates, together with the sugars promoted sporulation. Adams (1949, 1950) found that good sporulation in baker's yeast was obtained by first growing the organism on tomato juice or glucose-agar and then transferring it to a medium containing 0.04% of glucose, 0.14% of anhydrous sodium acetate, and 2% of agar. Fowell (1952) employed sodium acetate-agar of a different composition incorporating 0.4% of anhydrous sodium acetate and 1.5% of agar at pH 6.5–7.0, the medium being sterilized at 122°C. for 20 minutes. From our own experience with the genus *Saccharomyces*, we can state that Fowell's medium gives excellent results.

In general, it can be said that many different methods have been described for inducing good sporulation, but it should be remembered that the organisms are not identical in their requirements. Many investigators prefer to grow the yeast on a solid medium and then to transfer it to sterilized Gorodkowa agar slants (1% of peptone, 1% of meat extract, 0.25% of glucose, 0.5% of sodium chloride, and 2% of agar). Others grow the yeast in liquid media and then transfer it to a sterilized gypsum block standing in water. Gypsum blocks, which have been employed for many years in inducing sporulation, have the fault that they cannot stand a temperature which is sufficiently high to ensure their sterility, and bacterial spores, especially those of *Bacillus subtilis*, are difficult to kill with dry heat. Hartelius and Ditlevsen (1953) remedied this deficiency by producing a sporulation block consisting of 3 parts of super-rapid Portland cement and 2 parts of diatomaceous earth. The block was hardened in carbon dioxide and sterilized for 1 hour at 121°C. Such a preparation was found to give better sporulation and more 4-spored asci than gypsum blocks.

The use of a special presporulation medium before the yeast is transferred to the final sporulation medium has been suggested. Lindegren and Lindegren (1944b) proposed such a medium consisting of extracts of beet leaves and beet roots together with fruit juices.

A vegetable sporulation medium (carrots, beets, cucumbers, and potatoes) which gives satisfactory results for many different yeasts was that proposed by Mrak, Phaff, and Douglas (1942). Mrak and Phaff have, in addition discussed the techniques for inducing sporulation in yeasts in an excellent review (1949).

Adams and Miller (1954) studied the inhibitory effect of carbon dioxide and the stimulatory effect of oxygen on sporulation, as well as the effect of temperatures ranging from 3 to 33.3°C. Kirsop (1954) also studied the effect of various environmental factors, including pH, on sporulation and concluded that there is a maximum level of sporulation which can be attained in the presence of an optimum quantity of nutrient or at the optimum cell concentration, and this cannot be exceeded by combining the two factors. Tremaine and Miller (1954) found that pantothenate increases sporulation, while Miller *et al.* (1955) reported that assimilable sugars stimulated sporulation. Further studies on the metabolism of sporulation by Miller and Halpern (1956) showed that the presence of glucose in the sporulation medium results in a low proportion of 3- and 4-spored asci but that the "early stages in spore formation determining the number per ascus are not inhibited by glucose as are the later stages that result in the development of visible spores."

The form and number of the ascospores in the yeast fungi may vary considerably according to the organism, but the prototype consists of four round hyaline spores per ascus. Very often less than four spores are found in the ascus since spore degeneration is a common occurrence and, moreover, the development of the maximum number may depend upon the presence of specific environmental conditions. Certain species, despite seemingly ideal conditions for sporulation, have never been known to form more than one spore per ascus, as for example, *Saccharomyces unisporus* and *Monosporella* while in *Debaryomyces* two, and in *Nadsonia* even three spores may occasionally be formed in an ascus, although the usual number is one. In the ascus of *Saccharomycodes* there are four ascospores in pairs, the members of each pair being closely adherent. Eight spores per ascus are produced in *Schizosaccharomyces octosporus* and in *Nematospora coryli;* in the latter organism the elongated spores are arranged in two groups of four. Certain yeasts are characterized by their ability to produce a large number of ascospores. In *Lipomyces,* for example, 16 spores per ascus seems to be a common number. Recent attempts to induce germination of these spores has been successful (Roberts, 1957), but no genetic segregation was found among the subsequent single-spore isolates. Van der Walt (1956a, b) has recently erected a new genus, *Kluyveromyces,* characterized by the formation of multispored asci. In *K. polysporus* asci were observed containing more than 50 spores, while the asci of *K. africanus* were never observed to contain more than 16 spores. The ability of the ascus to rupture on the medium on which it is produced has been regarded by Wickerham (1956a, b) as a significant taxonomic character, and a tentative genus, *Dekkeromyces* was proposed by him to comprise those yeasts exhibiting this character. It is of interest, therefore, that the asci of *Kluyveromyces spp.* also rupture on the medium on which they are produced. Some of the yeasts which Wickerham considers to belong to the yet undescribed genus *Dekkeromyces* possess crescent-shaped spores, 1–4 per ascus, and most of them produce a red diffusible pigment which is possibly identical with pulcherrimin (van der Walt, 1952).

The form of the spore in many genera and species deviates considerably from the round or spherical type. For the most part, *Saccharomyces* has round spores, but S. *fragilis* possesses reniform spores, and in those species formerly regarded as comprising the genus *Zygosaccharomyces* hemispherical, reniform, or hat-shaped spores are found. A hat-shaped spore is characterized by the formation on one side of a brim-like extension of the wall. In some yeasts this brim may be in an equatorial position, resulting in a saturn-shaped spore (e.g., *Hansenula saturnus*). Usually the ascospore wall is smooth, but a warty surface can also occur, as in the spores of *Debaryomyces* and *Nadsonia*. Quite different from the normal round spores are the sickle-shaped spores of *Endomycopsis selenospora* which have given rise to the name of the species and the fusiform spores of *Nematospora coryli*, which are equipped with a needle-like appendage and which have given rise to the name of the genus.

4. Cytology

It is probably correct to say that of all organisms yet investigated, the yeasts are those which have occasioned most disagreement among cytologists. Especially with respect to the nucleus and the chromosomes the cytological interpretations are widely divergent. The basis for this lack of agreement is first to be found in the fact that the yeast nucleus is extremely small (the diameter of the stained chromatin in a resting nucleus is only about 0.5–1.5 μ) and also because it is a most difficult task to elucidate the actual structure of the nucleus.

Since the investigations of Janssens, who undertook cytological observations on yeasts at the Carlsberg Laboratorium under Emil C. Hansen and who published the results of his studies in 1893 and later, together with Leblanc, in 1898, progress in the field of yeast cytology has been meager. Janssens and Leblanc observed the division of the nucleus and realized that this phenomenon comprised a mitosis; they observed the two nuclear divisions in an immature ascus, but here they were not aware that a meiosis was involved; they established that each spore in an ascus contained one nucleus. They did not, however, observe chromosomes.

Some years later both Swellengrebel (1905) and Fuhrmann (1906) studied the mechanism of nuclear division; the former found that there were 4 chromosomes in baking yeast (*Saccharomyces cerevisiae*), and the latter author found the same number in the variety, *ellipsoideus.* Thus, these findings would indicate that this species possessed 4 chromosomes in the diplophase and two in the haplophase. Nuclear division was also studied by Kater (1927) and Rochlin (1933), while a particularly noteworthy investigation was that of Badian (1937). This author believed that he had shown that yeast chromosomes conjugate in pairs following fertilization, so that the diplophase contains the same number of chromosome units (2) as does the haplophase. Four chromosomes were also observed in the cells of the vegetative diploid phase of S. *cerevisiae* by Sinotô and Yuasa (1941), who also showed that chromosome abnormalities arose as a result of treating the yeast with colchicine.

Lindegren (1949) claimed to have observed four or five pairs of chromosomes in S. *bayanus* and five or six pairs in S. *cerevisiae,* but these assumed chromosomes, which are situated in the "nuclear vacuole," are at times pictured as small rods and at other times as giant complexes extending throughout the length of the cell.

Lindegren and his collaborators have carefully investigated the structure of the yeast cell and the budding process and have compared their findings with those of earlier investigators. In this connection, we can best refer to the cytological publications of Lindegren (1945b, 1949, 1952), Lindegren and Rafalko (1950), Townsend, Sarachek, and Lindegren (1954) and Lindegren and Townsend (1954). The confusion that prevails regarding the interpretation of the intracellular structures is well illustrated in a scheme erected by Lindegren (1949) in which it is seen that what Wager and Peniston (1910) called the nucleolus, Guilliermond called the cell nucleus, and Lindegren, the centrosome. Furthermore, what Wager and Peniston called the nuclear vacuole, Janssens and Leblanc called the nucleus, and what Wager and Peniston called the central volutin granule in the vacuole, Janssens and Leblanc and Lindegren called the nucleolus. Figure 8 shows Lindegren's conception of the structure of a yeast cell.

It is clear that this wide divergency of opinion makes it at present very difficult, if not impossible, to form a clear generally acceptable picture of the structure of the nucleus of a yeast cell and the identity and function of the other intracellular structures. For example, it is doubtful whether Lindegren's centrosome is actually such, since it is represented as a body of considerable size which neither in its appearance nor in its behavior during mitoses has much similarity with the cellular structure which is traditionally designated the centrosome.

It also does not seem possible to accept the chromosomes of Lindegren, and much less those of Subramaniam and his colleagues (1945, 1946,

1948a, 1951). These authors picture the chromosomes as bodies which considerably exceed the chromosome dimensions expected in a nucleus of about 1 μ in diameter; when yeast cells are correctly hydrolyzed and stained according to Feulgen's technique or with azure, such large intracellular structures are not observed. In particular, the large chromosomes of Subramaniam are pictured as being extremely variable in number, a mother and daughter cell often having varying numbers. Subramaniam claims that his diploid yeast has 2 chromosomes (the haploid therefore should have only 1), and, contrary to expectation, he

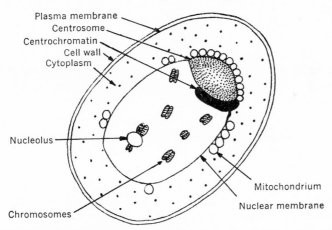

FIG. 8. The structure of the yeast cell, according to Lindegren. (Redrawn from Lindegren, 1952.)

often pictures these bodies as being unequal in size. It appears that Subramaniam has not demonstrated the existence of only 1 chromosome in a haploid yeast, and his tetraploid yeasts show a great variation in number of chromosomes. Ganesan's results (1956) suggest that the bodies identified as chromosomes by Subramanian and co-workers may be fixation artifacts or complex cytoplasmatic inclusions. Endopolyploidy as claimed by Subramaniam (1947) could not be detected. Ganesan found no difference between the nuclei of aerobically and anaerobically growing cultures, or between young and old cultures.

The cytological investigations of Levan (1947) on a brewing yeast are rather convincing. By using for the most part the Feulgen technique, this author found quite small chromosomes and is of the opinion that the number is larger than would be expected—ten or more. In addition, he studied the effect of camphor and related substances on nuclear division and concluded that they cause abnormal nuclear divisions as well as an increase in chromosome number.

DeLamater (1950), also using the Feulgen stain, found that in S. cerevisiae there are normally two pairs of chromosomes, one being long and the other more rounded. He rejects Lindegren's views as to the structure of the yeast nucleus and maintains that what Lindegren called the centrosome is actually the whole nucleus. DeLamater's photomicrographs of his cytological preparations are for the most part quite satisfactory except for the fact that their sharpness is reduced due to excessive enlargement.

In 1951 Winge criticized Lindegren's and Subramaniam's views on yeast cytology, particularly with regard to the chromosomes. In a hematoxylin-stained preparation of cells of S. cerevisiae he observed and photographed two small centrosomes at mitosis and in S. cerevisiae var. ellipsoideus four chromosome-like bodies in what was assumed to be the anaphase.

An excellent cytological investigation on the haplophase, diplophase, and sporulating phase of Saccharomyces priorianus was carried out by Lietz (1951) who employed the Feulgen technique. This species is especially suited to such a study, since its single spore cultures are composed of haploid cells together with a continually increasing number of diploid cells (Fig. 3). Lietz believed he had observed three chromosomes in the haplophase, six in the diplophase, and three gemini in the immature ascus. He was of the opinion that mitosis is intranuclear.

In 1954 Winge and Roberts undertook a cytological investigation of cells of Saccharomyces in which Azure I was employed. The nuclei of both haploid and diploid cells were well stained, and instances of 5- and 6-nucleate asci and binucleate spores were observed. The significance of this observation is discussed in Chapter IV. The chromosomes in this material were not, however, so clearly evident as in the material investigated by Lietz, in spite of the fact that these authors had employed the best optical equipment available to them.

The electron microscope was used in the investigations of Bartholomew and Mittwer (1954) on the structure of the yeast cell, but no significant results were obtained by employing this technique.

By way of summary, it can be said that the most convincing cytological studies with especial reference to nuclei and chromosomes have been undertaken by Levan, DeLamater, and especially Lietz, who undoubtedly has observed the actual chromosomes both in mitosis and meiosis. The frequent occurrence of a double structure in nuclear-stained preparations of yeast cells has been explained by Lietz by assuming that the transition from anaphase to telophase involves a considerable period of time.

Since the researches of Guilliermond (1902 and later), numerous cytologists have studied the chondriosomes (mitochondria) of yeasts. These bodies are easily recognizable when vital stains such as methylene blue or neutral red are employed or by fixation and staining with basic blue or violet aniline dyes or with hematoxylin. Chondriosomes are observable in all cells but are especially abundant in young asci just before sporulation. Among the most recent investigations on chondriosomes are those of Bautz and Marquardt (1953, 1954) who, employing Altmann's staining method and the Nadi reaction, found approximately 13 chondriosomes per cell, but a smaller number in buds; they also found a positive correlation between the number of chondriosomes and the size of the cell. Sarachek and Townsend (1953) investigated the effect of ultraviolet light on the chondriosomes, and Bartholomew and Levin (1955) undertook electron microscope examinations of ultra-thin sections of yeast cells, in which the chondriosomes were observed.

An interesting observation was made by Barton in 1950, who demonstrated the presence of both "bud scars" and "birth scars" on the yeast cell. He found in *S. cerevisiae* var. *ellipsoideus* that a newly detached cell possesses a birth scar at the point at which it is joined to its mother cell. When this cell itself produces buds, which gradually become detached, each of the daughter cells leaves a bud scar upon the cell. The first bud produced is situated diametrically opposite to the birth scar. One cell was studied which produced 23 successive buds, all of which gave rise to macroscopically identical cultures. The electron microscope was employed in the study of these bud scars by Bartholomew and Mittwer (1953) who found that the reproductive age of a cell is limited, but that a cell is potentially capable of producing about 100 daughter cells, since a bud is always formed at a new point on the cell. They were, however, unable to find any cells with more than 20 actual bud scars.

Finally, brief mention of the staining of yeast cells in general may be appropriate. Methods for vital staining may be found in the publications of Buchy (1944) and Lindegren (1949), while Shimwell (1938), Arnold (1938), McClung (1943), and Lindegren (1949) have all described reliable methods for the staining of spores. For the determination of whether a yeast cell is living or dead, a dilute aqueous solution of methylene blue (e.g., 0.01%) has been the standard procedure for many years, although it has not always given satisfactory results. More recently, however, acridine orange, in connection with a fluorescent microscope, has been successfully employed by Strugger (1943) for this purpose.

5. Polyploidy

That polyploidy may occur in the yeast fungi must be regarded as being highly possible, but proof of its existence has not yet embraced chromosome counts.* As a matter of fact, as discussed earlier, even an unambiguous demonstration of the difference in chromosome number between haploid and diploid yeasts is still lacking. In this connection the investigations of Subramaniam and his co-workers referred to in the preceding section must be left out of consideration, for it seems likely that actually the chromosomes were confused with other stainable bodies within the cell. Otherwise no cytological proof of the ploidy of yeast cells has been offered; the work of Levan (1947) on cells treated with camphor comes nearest, but even this author has not been able to show that haploid, diploid, triploid, and tetraploid yeasts have successively increasing chromosome counts.

Proof of the existence of polyploidy could theoretically be obtained from sources other than cytological ones, and investigations on this aspect of the problem have involved the following approaches:

(1) Measurement of the size of the cell and of the nucleus, both of which would be expected *a priori* to increase with increasing degrees of ploidy.

(2) Determination of genetic segregations, which, in the presence of polyploidy, must necessarily involve deviations from Mendelian segregation.

(3) Investigations on the frequency of lethal mutations induced by radiation, the effect of which is expected to decrease with increasing degrees of ploidy.

(4) Quantitative determination of the nucleic acid content and other chemical constituents of the cell.

The results of applying these four methods for investigating the ploidy of a yeast cell are briefly as follows:

(1) *Measurement of the Size of the Cell and of the Nucleus.* Duraiswami and Subramaniam (1950) measured the size of yeast cells which, according to them, were haploid, diploid, and tetraploid, and had originated from the same source. These authors were led to the

---

* Note *added in press.*

It has recently been claimed that chromosome counts have been made in a polyploid series of *Saccharomyces* and that the diploid number is eight (McClany, D. O., Williams, M. A., Lindegren, C. C., and Ogur, M., *J. Bact.*, 1957, **73**, 360).

unexpected conclusion that their haploid cells measured about 10.6 × 7.2 μ, their diploid cells, 7.0 × 5.9 μ, and their tetraploid cells, 6.9 × 6.6 μ; in other words, the cells decrease in size as the degree of ploidy increases. Subramaniam and his colleagues (1945, 1948b) and Duraiswami and Subramaniam (1950) reported the occurrence of a mutant, which through appropriate treatment with acenaphthene, was able to increase its chromosome number to the octoploid state, but, as mentioned earlier, the so-called chromosomes of these investigators cannot be accepted as such. They believe it possible to recognize the diploid on the basis of the radial structure of its giant colony, the tetraploid being nearly completely smooth, and moreover that the cells of each recognizable sector in a giant colony possess either one-half or double the number of chromosomes found in the cells of the mother colony. Genetic proof of these assumptions is, however, lacking, since the authors did not undertake segregation analyses, single spore isolations, or hybridizations. It would have been highly significant if it had been possible to demonstrate cytologically that the diploid yeast had two chromosomes and the haploid one, but unfortunately this was not attempted; instead, they merely stated that the slow growth rate of one of the giant colonies "suggested that it ought to be haploid." The assumption that the degree of ploidy of a yeast is incessantly shifting must be rejected.

In 1951 Lindegren and Lindegren discussed and illustrated yeast cells which increased in size in proportion to the increase in the degree of ploidy from the haploid to the tetraploid. Two years later Lindegren's material was reinvestigated by Mundkur (1953) with especial reference to the cellular and nuclear dimensions after freeze-drying of cultures in vigorous growth. His results may be summarized as follows:

	Haploid	Diploid	Triploid	Tetraploid
Cell size in μ	2.81 × 2.81	5.338 × 2.658	7.041 × 3.591	7.964 × 4.23
Nuclear diameter in μ	0.84	1.35	1.73	2.01
Standard deviation in μ	0.0195	0.0663	0.055	0.0833
Mean volume in μ^3	0.31	1.288	2.711	4.252

It is at once apparent that these results show a trend which is diametrically opposed to that observed by Subramaniam if the two series are indeed comparable with regard to polyploidy.

(2) *Segregation Analyses.* In various attempts to demonstrate the existence of polyploidy in yeasts, many reports of genetic segregations not in accord with the laws of Mendel have appeared. Among the first of these was an account of an investigation by Roman, Hawthorne, and

Douglas (1951) in which 1 irregular ascus out of 64 normal asci was assumed to be tetraploid; in this connection, the cytological studies of Winge and Roberts (1954) have shown that an extra mitosis may often occur in a young ascus, leading to the production of binucleate spores. If 4 binucleate spores had been found in this irregular ascus, a segregation identical to that observed could result. It thus does not seem that this investigation necessarily furnishes conclusive proof of the existence of polyploidy in yeasts.

Lindegren and Lindegren (1951) reported the occurrence of tetraploid yeast cells based upon the same argument as that of Roman *et al.*, namely, that diploid spores were formed in a presumably tetraploid ascus. The so-called diploid spores undoubtedly were also binucleate in this case, i.e., containing 2 haploid nuclei. This seems to be confirmed by the authors' tables. But in spite of differences of interpretation, the phenomenon observed remains of much interest. If a spore contains two haploid nuclei of the same mating type, it is possible that a diploid cell which preserves its gametic character will result; this may be dependent upon the absence of the diploidization gene, *D*. A diploid *αα* cell could conceivably take part in the sexual act with a diploid *aa* cell or with a haploid *a* cell. The authors reported to have obtained tetraploid and triploid yeasts, but it is not to be expected that tetraploid asci should segregate out only diploid spores, as claimed; normally, a tetraploid will give rise to aneuploid products of segregation, which assumedly would be abnormal. Lack of knowledge regarding the nature of yeast chromosomes makes it impossible to elucidate this point cytologically, but if only 1 chromosome exists in the haplophase, then the existence of aneuploid types would of course be out of the question.

Pomper (1952, 1954) also reported the occurrence of polyploid yeasts by the prototroph recovery method. Gene-controlled biochemical deficiencies were used as markers in the parent strains, and by mixing haploids with diploids and diploids with diploids, small numbers of prototrophic colonies on minimal media were obtained which were assumed to be triploids or tetraploids. The diploid strain employed (1952) in the production of the triploid was not, however, normal, as it was unable to sporulate. The assumed triploid was capable of producing viable spores and of segregating out two haploid and two diploid spores from a single ascus, but "the aberrant ratios encountered in the triploid analyses cannot be explained with our present knowledge of the meiotic processes of these isolates." An assumed tetraploid (1954) was found to yield 4 sporulating diploid spores from one ascus, and here also evidence of peculiar meioses were obtained.

Roman and Sands (1953) undertook a genetic analysis of the offspring of a *Saccharomyces* hybrid and obtained 3 types of colonies composed of: (1) small round haploid cells of either mating type α or a, (2) large diploid cells, αα or aa, which will copulate but will not form spores, and (3) large diploid cells αa, which will not copulate but will form spores and whose asci segregate out as 2α:2a. The latter category is assumed to have arisen by mutation of the mating type. The cross 1×1 (opposite mating type) yields a hybrid with diploid segregation. The cross 1×2 yields a hybrid with triploid segregation. The cross 2×2 yields a hybrid with tetraploid segregation. In 1955, Roman, Phillips, and Sands describe a tetraploid segregation with respect to the mating type alleles. They obtained 4:0, 3:1, and 2:2 ratios from an αααa type, and 2:2 and 1:3 ratios from an αaaa type. They assume that both bivalent and tetravalent chromosome pairing takes place in this material but cytological investigations were not carried out.

Investigating firstly mating type, secondly adenine, methionine, uracil, and tryptophan deficiency and thirdly galactose fermentation in *Saccharomyces*, Leupold and Hottinguer (1954) observed a type of segregation which they assumed to be tetraploid. Cytological support is lacking, however, and the possibility exists that their observations could be explained on the basis of supernumerary mitoses and binucleate spores. Leupold (1956) found in *Schizosaccharomyces pombe* two exceptional asci, which he considered to be triploid. Such asci must be expected, *a priori*, to segregate out aneuploid types, but the author found that both tetrads consisted of 2 diploid and 2 haploid spores. Tetraploid asci were also investigated, and Leupold considers that he has demonstrated segregations typical of triploid as well as tetraploid asci. The majority of immature asci, both diploid and tetraploid, which were investigated cytologically were found to contain 4 nuclei; these appeared to be diploid in the tetrapolid asci and haploid in the diploid asci. However, binucleate spores were also found in both types of asci, and it is assumed that they arose through extra mitoses resulting in the formation of more than 4 nuclei per ascus.

By irradiating a culture of *Schizosaccharomyces pombe* Ditlevsen and Hartelius (1956) obtained a "gigas" type (mating type —) which was regarded as a diploid; this culture was successfully crossed with a haploid of opposite mating type. The spores from the assumed triploid hybrid germinated poorly but it was possible to obtain the following types segregated out: (a) sterile single-spore cultures which lacked the ability to mate with any other type; (b) single-spore cultures of mating type +; (c) single-spore cultures of mating type —; and (d) single-spore cultures of +— mating type. The +— cultures were able to form small-spored asci without preceding cellular copulation, as well as large-spored asci following cellular copulation. In the latter case a mutation in mating type was probably involved.

Ahmad and Khan (1954) reported that they had observed three "gametes" (presumably haploid cells) in S. *cerevisiae* fuse together and assumed that triploid yeasts may originate in this way. In their material, however, the zygotes in question were not viable.

Townsend and Lindegren (1954) describe and illustrate in *Saccharomyces* (Carbondale Breeding Stock) the different degrees of ploidy with respect to both cell size and growth characteristics.

(3) *Irradiation Experiments.* An increasing degree of ploidy in yeast cells is correlated with a decreasing frequency in the production of lethal mutations, since a gene mutation occurring in a haploid may be fatal to the cell, but the damage arising from the same mutation in a diploid or polyploid will be masked by the allelomorphs of the other chromosome set(s). Thus in the induction of mutation by irradiation, 1 hit is sufficient to destroy a gene in a haploid, while in a diploid, 2 hits are necessary to destroy both alleles. On this theoretical basis, experiments have been carried out with both Röntgen and ultraviolet irradiation on the frequency of mutation to be found in yeast types of assumedly varying degrees of ploidy. In general, it can be said that the results which have been obtained in the form of irradiation survival curves have agreed quite well with expectation.

Latarjet and Ephrussi (1949) obtained a 1-hit survival curve when they investigated the effect of Röntgen irradiation on the frequency of mutation in a haploid strain of S. *cerevisiae* var. *ellipsoideus,* while the effect of the same treatment of a diploid strain could be expressed as a sigmoid curve (2-hit survival curve). De Long and Lindegren (1951) claimed to have demonstrated a triploid and a tetraploid condition in yeasts on the basis of survival curves. Magni (1951, 1953a,b) employed Röntgen irradiation in an attempt to determine the degree of ploidy of various yeasts, and his results have formed the basis of some interesting considerations regarding yeast taxonomy. He found a 1-hit survival curve for each of 19 different yeasts belonging to the genera *Rhodotorula, Torulopsis,* and *Candida,* while the species *Torulopsis pulcherrima* and *T. neoformans* yielded a sigmoid survival curve. The author is therefore led to the conclusion that these two yeasts actually belong to the Endomycetaceae rather than the Cryptococcaceae, a view which has been held previously on the basis of other lines of evidence (see p. 105). Magni (1956) has recently summarized the extent of our knowledge regarding the sensitivity of yeast cells to irradiation and has concluded that the complex theoretical survival curves derived from a mathematical approach to the problem are not satisfactory for a quantitative evaluation of the observed survival curves, especially in view of the fact that both biological variability and a large number of unknown constants are involved. The induction of lethal mutations and irradiation survival curves have also been studied by Sarachek and Lucke (1953), Sarachek (1954), and by Pomper, Daniels, and McKee (1954). The latter authors, however, warned against concluding, without genetic confirmation, that a yeast giving an exponential survival curve is a haploid, since some of their diploid material yielded such survival curves.

(4) *Chemical Means.* Ogur *et al.* (1952) showed that the cellular content of nucleic acid corresponds to the degree of ploidy and Ogur (1955) listed several other criteria for determining increasing degrees of ploidy in yeast cells, including dry weight per cell, ultraviolet budding retardation, nitrogen content, and turbidity.

Weinfurtner and Voerkelius (1955a) and Weinfurtner, Uhl, and Wullinger (1955b) have described a peculiar dependence of polyploid degree upon cellular tolerance with respect to varying concentrations of toxic substances. This dependence is claimed to be capable of expression as either 1-hit or 2-hit survival curves, but it is not known whether the phenomenon is explicable in terms of differences in chemical constitution of cells or nuclei, depending upon the degree of ploidy.

Even though many investigators claim to have demonstrated the existence of polyploidy in yeasts, it should be remembered that so-called polyploid segregation may be explicable on the basis of supernumerary mitoses and binucleate spores. Therefore not all claims seem sufficiently justified, but the great amount of evidence that has accumulated in recent years leaves no doubt of the existence of polyploidy in the yeast fungi.

A widespread misconception, however, regarding the segregation of polyploid asci seems to prevail. It cannot be expected that a tetraploid ascus should regularly give rise to four diploid spores or that a triploid ascus should regularly segregate out two haploid and two diploid spores. On the contrary, aneuploid chromosome counts should be frequent, just as in other polyploid organisms. Of course, if the haploid chromosome number was one, then regular segregations may be expected, but it should be stressed that the most careful observations so far carried out indicate that haploid yeasts possess a higher chromosome number than one.

References

Adams, A. M. (1949). *Can. J. Research* **C27**, 179.
Adams, A. M. (1950). *Can. J. Research* **C28**, 413.

120   Ö. WINGE AND C. ROBERTS

Adams, A. M., and Miller, J. J. (1954). *Can. J. Botany* **32**, 320.

Ahmad, M. (1952). *Nature* **170**, 546

Ahmad, M. (1953a). *Cellule* **55**, 235.

Ahmad, M. (1953b). *Scientist Pakistan* **1**, 1.

Ahmad, M., and Khan, A. (1954). *Nature* **173**, 133.

Arnold, C. R. (1938). *J. Bacteriol.* **36**, 655.

Badian, J. (1937) *Bull. intern. acad. polon. sci. Sér. B, I* **5**, 61.

Barker, B. T. P. (1901). *Phil. Trans. Roy. Soc.* **B194**, 467.

Bartholomew, J. W., and Mittwer, T. (1953). *J. Bacteriol.* **65**, 272.

Bartholomew, J. W., and Mittwer, T. (1954). *Stain Technol.* **29**, 121.

Bartholomew, J. W., and Levin, R. (1955). *J. Gen. Microbiol.* **12**, 473.

Barton, A. A. (1950). *J. Gen. Microbiol.* **4**, 84.

Bautz, E., and Marquardt, H. (1953). *Naturwiss.* **40**, 531.

Bautz, E., and Marquardt, H. (1954). *Naturwiss.* **41**, 121.

Beyerinck, M. W. (1894). *Centr. Bakteriol. Parasitenk. Abt.* **16**, 49.

Buchy, A. (1944). *Ann. sci. nat. Botan, et biol. végétale* [11], **4**, 119.

DeLamater, E. D. (1950). *J. Bacteriol.* **60**, 321.

DeLong, R., and Lindegren, C. C. (1951). *Bacteriol. Proc.* **63**.

Ditlevsen, E., and Hartelius, V. (1956). *Compt. rend. trav. lab. Carlsberg, Sér, physiol.* **26**, 41.

Duraiswami, S., and Subramaniam, M. K. (1950). *Cellule* **53**, 215.

Fowell, R. R. (1951). *J. Inst. Brewing* **57**, 180.

Fowell, R. R. (1952). *Nature* **170**, 578.

Fuhrmann, F. (1906). *Centr. Bakteriol. Parasitenk. Abt, II,* **15**, 169.

Ganesan, A. T. (1956). *Cytologia* **21**, 124.

Guilliermond, A. (1901). *Compt. rend.* **133**, 1252.

Guilliermond, A. (1902). Thèse doctorat ès sciences, Sorbonne.

Guilliermond, A. (1910). *Centr. Bakteriol. Abt. II,* **26**, 577.

Guilliermond, A. (1928). "Titres et travaux scientifiques (1900–1928)," 162 pp., Laval.

Guilliermond, A. (1936). *Rev. gén. botan.* **48**, 403.

Hansen, E. C. (1883). *Medd. Carlsberg Lab.* **2**, 29.

Hansen, E. C. (1891). *Medd. Carlsberg Lab.* **3**, 53.

Hansen, E. C. (1902). *Medd. Carlsberg Lab.* **5**, 65.

Hartelius, V., and Ditlevsen, E. (1953). *Compt. rend. trav. lab. Carlsberg Sér. physiol.* **25**, 213.

Hjort, A. (1956). *Compt. rend. trav. lab. Carlsberg, Sér. physiol.* **26**, 161.

Hoffmeister, C. (1900). *Sitzber. Deut. Naturw.-med. Ver. (Lotos), No.* **5**.

Janssens, F. A. (1893). *Centr. Bakteriol. Parasitenk.* **13**, 639.

Janssens, F. A., and Leblanc, A. (1898). *Cellule* **14**, 203.

Kater, J. McA. (1927). *Biol. Bull.* **52**, 436.

Kirsop, B. H. (1954). *J. Inst. Brewing* **60**, 393.

Latarjet, R., and Ephrussi, B. (1949). *Compt. rend.* **229**, 306.

Leupold, U. (1950). *Compt. rend. trav. lab. Carlsberg, Sér. physiol.* **24**, 381.

Leupold, U., and Hottinguer, H. (1954). *Heredity* **8**, 243.

Leupold, U. (1956). *Compt. rend. trav. lab. Carlsberg, Sér. physiol.* **26**, 221.

Levan, A. (1947). *Hereditas* **33**, 457.

Levi, J. D. (1956). *Nature* **177**, 753.

Lietz, K. (1951). *Arch. Mikrobiol.* **16**, 275.

Lindegren, C. C., and Lindegren, G. (1943a). *Ann. Missouri Botan. Garden* **30**, 453.
Lindegren, C. C., and Lindegren, G. (1943b). *Proc. Natl. Acad. Sci. U.S.* **29**, 306.
Lindegren, C. C., and Lindegren, G. (1944a). *Ann. Missouri Botan. Garden* **31**, 203.
Lindegren, C. C., and Lindegren, G. (1944b). *Botan. Gaz.* **105**, 304.
Lindegren, C. C. (1945a). *Bacteriol. Rev.* **9**, 111.
Lindegren, C. C. (1945b). *Mycologia* **37**, 767.
Lindegren, C. C. (1949). "The Yeast Cell, Its Genetics and Cytology." Educational Publ., St. Louis.
Lindegren, C. C., and Rafalko, M. M. (1950). *Exptl. Cell Research* **1**, 169.
Lindegren, C. C., and Lindegren, G. (1951). *J. Gen. Microbiol.* **5**, 885.
Lindegren, C. C. (1952). *Symposia Soc. Exptl. Biol.* **6**, 277.
Lindegren, C. C., and Lindegren, G. (1954a). *Cytologia* (*Tokyo*) **19**, 45.
Lindegren, C. C., and Townsend, G. F. (1954b). *Cytologia* (*Tokyo*) **19**, 104.
Lodder, J., and Kreger-van Rij, N. J. W. (1952). "The Yeasts. A Taxonomic Study." North Holland Publ., Amsterdam.
Lund, A. (1954). "Studies on the Ecology of Yeasts," 132 pp. Munksgaard, Copenhagen.
Lund, A. (1956). *Wallerstein Labs. Communs.* **19**, 221.
McClung, L. S. (1943). *Science* **98**, 159.
Magni, G. E. (1951). *Nuovo ann. igiene microbiol.* **2**, 240.
Magni, G. E. (1953a). *Ist. botan. univ. Lab. crittogam. Pavia Att.* [5] **10**, 89.
Magni, G. E. (1953b). *Ist. botan. univ. Lab. crittogam. Pavia Att.* [5] **10**, 201.
Magni, G. E. (1956). *Compt. rend. trav. lab. Carlsberg, Sér. physiol.* **26**, 273.
Miller, J. J., Calvin J., and Tremaine, J. H. (1955). *Can. J. Microbiol.* **1**, 560.
Miller, J. J., and Halpern, C. (1956). *Can. J. Microbiol.* **2**, 519.
Mrak, E. M., Phaff, H. J., and Douglas, H. C. (1942). *Science* **96**, 432.
Mrak, E. M., and Phaff, H. J. (1949). *Wallerstein Labs. Communs.* **12**, 29.
Mundkur, B. D. (1953). *Experientia* **9**, 373.
Ogur, M., Minckler, S., Lindegren, G., and Lindegren, C. C. (1952). *Arch. Biochem. and Biophys.* **40**, 175.
Ogur, M. (1955). *J. Bacteriol.* **69**, 159.
Phaff, H. J., and Mrak, E. M. (1948). *Wallerstein Labs. Communs.* **11**, 261.
Pomper, S. (1952). *Nature* **170**, 892.
Pomper, S., Daniels, K. M., and McKee, D. W. (1954). *Genetics* **39**, 343.
Roberts, C. (1946). *Farlowia* **2**, 345.
Roberts, C. (1957). *Nature* **179**, 1199.
Rochlin, E. (1933). *Zentr. Bakteriol. Parasitenk. Abt. II*, **88**, 304.
Roman, H., Hawthorne, D. C., and Douglas, H. C. (1951). *Proc. Natl. Acad. Sci. U.S.* **37**, 79.
Roman, H., and Sands, S. M. (1953). *Proc. Natl. Acad. Sci. U.S.* **39**, 171.
Roman, H., Phillips, M. M., and Sands, S. M. (1955). *Genetics* **40**, 546.
Sarachek, A., and Townsend, G. F. (1953). *Science* **117**, 31.
Sarachek, A., and Lucke, W. H. (1953). *Arch. Biochem. and Biophys.* **44**, 271.
Sarachek, A. (1954). *Cytologia* (*Tokyo*) **19**, 77.
Satava, J. (1934). *Congr. intern. Tech. et chim. ind. agr. compt. rend. 3rd Congr. Paris, 1934*, 8 pp.
Schiönning, H. (1895). *Medd. Carlsberg Lab.* **4**, 77.
Shimwell, J. L. (1938). *J. Inst. Brewing* **44**, 474.
Sinotô, Y., and Yuasa, A. (1941). *Cytologia* (*Tokyo*) **11**, 464.

Stantial, H. (1928). *Trans. Roy. Soc. Canada III* **22**, 257.

Stantial, H. (1935). *Trans. Roy. Soc. Canada III* **29**, 175.

Stelling-Dekker, N. M. (1931). "Die Sporogenen Hefen," I Teil. Drukkerij Holland, Amsterdam.

Strugger, S. (1943). *Flora (Ger.)* **37**, 73.

Subramaniam, M. K., and Ranganathan, B. (1945). *Current Sci. (India)* **14**, 131.

Subramaniam, M. K. (1946). *Proc. Natl. Acad. Sci. India* **12**, 143.

Subramaniam, M. K. (1947). *Current Sci. (India)* **16**, 157.

Subramaniam, M. K., and Ranganathan, B. (1948a). *Proc. Natl. Acad. Sci. India* **14**, 279.

Subramaniam, M. K., Ranganathan, B., and Krishna Murthy, S. N. (1948b). *Cellule* **52**, 39.

Subramaniam, M. K. (1951). *Nature* **168**, 427.

Swellengrebel, M. (1905). *Ann. inst. Pasteur* **19**, 503.

Thorne, R. S. W. (1951). *Compt. rend. trav. lab. Carlsberg Sér. physiol.* **25**, 101.

Townsend, G. F., and Lindegren, C. C. (1954). *J. Bacteriol.* **67**, 480.

Townsend, G. F., Sarachek, A., and Lindegren, C. C. (1954). *Cytologia (Tokyo)* **19**, 130.

Tremaine, J. H., and Miller, J. J. (1954). *Botan. Gaz.* **115**, 311.

Wager, H., and Peniston, A. (1910). *Ann. Botany (London)* **24**, 45.

Walt, J. P. van der (1952). Ph.D. thesis, Delft.

Walt, J. P. van der (1956a). *Antonie van Leeuwenhoek J. Microbiol. Serol.* **22**, 265.

Walt, J. P. van der (1956b). *Antonie van Leeuwenhoek J. Microbiol. Serol.* **22**, 321.

Weinfurtner, F., and Voerkelius, G. A. (1955). *Naturwiss.* **42**, 20.

Weinfurtner, F., Uhl, A., and Wullinger, F. (1955). *Naturwiss.* **42**, 213.

Wickerham, L. J. (1956). *Compt. rend. trav. lab. Carlsberg, Sér. physiol.* **26**, 423.

Wickerham, L. J., and Burton, K. A. (1956a). *J. Bacteriol.* **71**, 290.

Wickerham, L. J., and Burton, K. A. (1956b). *J. Bacteriol.* **71**, 296.

Windisch, S. (1938). *Arch. Mikrobiol.* **9**, 551.

Windisch, S. (1940). *Arch. Mikrobiol.* **11**, 368.

Winge, Ö. (1935). *Compt. rend. trav. lab. Carlsberg Sér. physiol.* **21**, 77.

Winge, Ö. (1947). *Compt. rend. trav. lab. Carlsberg Sér. physiol.* **24**, 223.

Winge, Ö. (1951). *Compt. rend. trav. lab. Carlsberg Sér. physiol.* **25**, 85.

Winge, Ö., and Laustsen, O. (1937). *Compt. rend. trav. lab. Carlsberg Sér. physiol.* **22**, 99.

Winge, Ö., and Laustsen, O. (1938). *Compt. rend. trav. lab. Carlsberg Sér. physiol.* **22**, 235.

Winge, Ö., and Laustsen, O. (1939a). *Compt. rend. trav. lab. Carlsberg Sér. physiol.* **22**, 357.

Winge, Ö., and Laustsen, O. (1939b). *Compt. rend. trav. lab. Carlsberg Sér. physiol.* **22**, 337.

Winge, Ö., and Laustsen, O. (1940). *Compt. rend. trav. lab. Carlsberg Sér. physiol.* **23**, 17.

Winge, Ö., and Roberts, C. (1949). *Compt. rend. trav. lab. Carlsberg Sér. physiol.* **24**, 341.

Winge, Ö., and Roberts, C. (1950). *Compt. rend. trav. lab. Carlsberg Sér. physiol.* **25**, 35.

Winge, Ö., and Roberts, C. (1954). *Compt. rend. trav. lab. Carlsberg Sér. physiol.* **25**, 285.

CHAPTER IV

Yeast Genetics

Ö. WINGE AND C. ROBERTS

1. Introduction

Emil C. Hansen's pioneer researches on yeasts at the turn of the century led to the observation that a pure culture of a bottom yeast may be transferred into a top yeast and vice versa, i.e., what we now call a mutational change, but it was not until the existence of the alternation of haploid and diploid generations had been established (Winge, 1935) that any serious genetic investigations on the yeast fungi could begin. Since that time a vast literature on yeast genetics has accumulated: a large number of individual genes have been investigated, chromosome maps have been constructed on the basis of linkage calculations, and the existence of inbreeding degeneration, hybrid vigor, mutation, and cytoplasmatic inheritance has been demonstrated. All in all, the field of yeast genetics has made surprisingly rapid progress in the course of twenty years, and from a genetic point of view the yeasts may now be regarded as among the most thoroughly investigated microorganisms.

For theoretical genetic investigations the yeasts, with their many advantages, are often to be preferred to other organisms. With the rapid development of micromanipulative technique, it is now a comparatively simple matter to isolate single yeast cells, to isolate the single spores from an individual ascus, and to carry out artificial hybridizations. Here the rapid vegetative growth of a yeast fungus in culture is a distinct advantage; in a very short time yeast hybrids can be produced and their offspring analyzed genetically. In the laboratory approximately one week transpires between the isolation of a single haploid spore and the appearance of the next spore generation; during this time, an alternation of generations has taken place, involving diploidization, ascus formation, and meiosis. In addition to rapid growth in culture, many yeasts possess the advantage of producing ascospores in groups of four so that tetrad analyses are possible, and in some species linear asci are produced so that ordered tetrads may be studied. From a practical point of view, the study of yeast genetics may lead to significant results, for it is possible through artificial hybridization to produce a yeast possessing selected characters. In the brewing industry, however, such possibilities with bottom yeasts are limited, for their sporulating ability is often very poor; this most probably is due to the accumulation during the course of centuries of a large number of mutations which have resulted in the loss of ability to produce viable spores. Most of the genetic investigations on yeasts have been carried out on species belonging to the genus *Saccharomyces,* but studies on *Saccharomycodes, Schizosaccharomyces,* and *Nadsonia* have also resulted in interesting additions to our knowledge of yeast genetics.

2. Spore Isolation and Hybridization Techniques

Emil C. Hansen isolated individual yeast cells by means of the dilution method as well as by marking cells under the microscope, but now it is the common practice to undertake cell isolation with a micromanipulator and for spore isolation and hybridization work such an instrument is a necessity. Various types of micromanipulators are available but for yeast work the most expensive types are not required. A trained technician can easily isolate 20–24 tetrads during the course of a morning, and a larger number is usually not required if analyses of all of these single spore cultures are to be undertaken within the following days.

Various types of isolation chambers are also available, all of which, of necessity, are constructed in such a way that accidental airborne infection is prevented. The present authors employ a chromium-plated copper chamber which is held fast to a sterile slide by means of a mixture of wax and vaseline. The mounting of the chamber is done in a sterile box in which hands and arms are inserted into two openings supplied with rubber sleeves. Nutrient droplets as well as a droplet containing cells or asci are arranged in a definite pattern on the undersurface of a glass coverslip by means of a very small loop (Fig. 1A). The actual micromanipulation is carried out with the aid of one or two glass needles attached to the micromanipulator which are inserted into the side arms of the copper chamber. Details of the construction of this chamber (previously of glass) as well as of the sterile box used in mounting the chamber have been described by Winge (1935).

A single ascus is withdrawn from the large nutrient droplet and transported with the needle through the droplets of condensed water which have formed between the nutrient droplets on the undersurface of the coverslip. At a point somewhere between the large nutrient drop and the 2 rows of small nutrient drops, the area is cleared of water droplets, and the actual dissection of the ascus is carried out on the dry glass. The 4

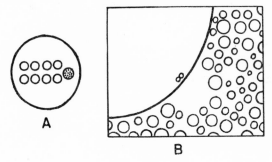

Fig. 1. A: Diagram of the undersurface of a glass coverslip with 8 sterile wort droplets and a larger droplet containing a suspension of the asci to be dissected. B: Diagram of a hybridization experiment carried out on the undersurface of a glass coverslip. The two spores, in contact, have been placed within a sterile wort droplet. Drawn to a much larger scale than A. (From Roberts, 1950.)

spores from 1 ascus are placed in the 4 nutrient droplets composing 1 row, and the other row receives the spores from a second dissected ascus. In hybridization work, 2 large nutrient droplets containing asci from the 2 yeasts to be crossed are employed, and after dissection, two different spores are paired just inside the edge of an empty nutrient droplet (Fig. 1B).

When an ascospore is placed in an empty nutrient droplet, it germinates usually within 24 hours and thereby gives rise to a colony of yeast cells. After about 2 days this colony is sufficiently large to be transferred from the copper chamber to a flask of nutrient material with the aid of a small sterile triangle of filter paper, which absorbs the droplet of liquid containing the cells. This transferring is of course carried out in the sterile box.

There are two main techniques employed in artificial hybridization work. When sporulating, self-diploidizing yeasts are employed (see

Chapter III, p. 96), one spore from each of the two types to be crossed are paired in a nutrient droplet with the aid of a micromanipulator on the undersurface of the coverslip (Fig. 1B). The copper chamber is incubated at 30–32°C. and often within the course of 3–4 hours, the spores will germinate and copulate to form a diploid zygote. It is necessary to observe the formation and subsequent germination of the zygote under the microscope, in order to be certain that the spores had not put out a bud preceding fusion—in such a case, the "hybrid" culture would actually consist of a mixture of genotypes (Winge and Roberts, 1948). Approximately 48 hours after the formation of the zygote, the colony derived from it is large enough to be transferred, as a new hybrid, to fresh nutrient material. On the other hand, if the material to be hybridized is haploid, the spore-crossing technique can obviously not be employed; instead, two young cultures of opposite mating type are mixed together, and after about 24 hours, at room temperature, zygotes are formed in the mixture in large numbers. These zygotes may either be transformed directly into asci, as in *Schizosaccharomyces*, or they propagate themselves vegetatively in the diplophase until the mixture is transferred to a medium suitable for sporulation.

Both those yeasts whose single spore cultures grow vegetatively in the haplophase as well as those whose single spore cultures automatically diploidize possess certain advantages and disadvantages for genetic investigations. In the first place, a haploid yeast often possesses the tendency to lose its ability to mate; secondly, when two haploids of opposite mating type are mixed together, the mixture eventually consists of the two haploid parents and the diploid hybrids. When the fact that the mating type gene may mutate to its allelomorph ($a \rightarrow \alpha$, or vice versa) is taken into consideration, it is at once evident that in the isolation of a hybrid cell from the mixture, there is the risk that it actually is one of the parent types which has diploidized following the mutation of the mating type gene.

A diploid yeast which is homozygous may be genetically stable for generations; in such a yeast, overlapping of generations may take place without the genotype being changed, for even if sporulation and spore germination should occur in the culture flask, segregation is not possible because of the homozygous nature of the organism. The disadvantage of employing diploid yeasts in hybridization work is that the two parent spores are "used up" during the crossing, but it is an advantage that the single spore cultures of diploid yeasts will automatically diploidize and thereby become homozygous. Diploid yeasts, furthermore, usually have a higher growth rate than the haploids. In Chapter III (p. 100) the D gene in *Saccharomyces* and its effect was discussed: the presence of this gene determines whether a single-spore culture will diploidize or not. The single spore cultures of yeasts containing the *D* gene are analyzed in the diplophase, while those containing the *d* gene are analyzed in the haplophase.

With respect to the qualitative determination of fermentative ability, it is convenient to grow the yeasts to be investigated in Freudenreich flasks containing beer wort or in yeast-water to which has been added one or more sugars (2–4%) to promote vigorous vegetative growth. The cells from a 1- or 2-day-old culture on such a substratum are washed in sterile tap water, centrifuged, and placed in the Winge fermentometer together with a 2 or 4% solution in yeast water of the sugar to be investigated; the time required for the first appearance of CO_2 is noted, as well as the time elapsing between the beginning and completion of fermentation (Roberts, 1950; Winge and Roberts, 1950a). The determination of the ability to ferment galactose, however, is carried out in Einhorn tubes or Durham tubes, since it has been found that galactose fermentation progresses better under more aerobic conditions than are possible in the sealed Winge fermentometer. Another rapid method of determining fermentative ability using large inocula in small volumes of substrate was described by Morris and Kirsop in 1953. For quantitative determination of fermentative ability the van Iterson-Kluyver fermentometer may be employed with satisfactory results.

For the cultivation of yeasts on a synthetic medium, that of Nielsen and Hartelius (1940) can be recommended. It contains: 0.7 g. of $MgSO_4 \cdot 7H_2O$, 1.0 g. of KH_2PO_4, 0.5 g. of NaCl, 0.4 g. of $CaCl_2$, 0.6 g. of $(NH_4)_2SO_4$, 0.5 cc. of 1% $FeCl_3 \cdot 6H_2O$, and 50 g. of sucrose per liter to which 2γ biotin, 200γ calcium D-pantothenate, 200γ thiamine, 200γ pyridoxine, 200γ nicotinic acid, and 200γ inositol are added. In addition, the following trace elements (Burkholder, 1943) (in p.p.m.) are employed: B, 0.01; Mn, 0.01; Zn, 0.07; Cu, 0.01; Mo, 0.01; and Fe, 0.05. If a solid substratum is desired, 2% of Difco agar is added to the above.

For determining the macroscopic appearance of giant colonies of yeasts, beer wort gelatin is recommended as a substrate; the inoculated plates should be incubated at 15°C. in order to bring out the best possible surface structure.

3. Mendelian Segregation

The first successful isolations of ascospore tetrads in yeasts were carried out on a baking yeast, *Saccharomyces cerevisiae* var. *ellipsoideus* (Winge and Laustsen, 1937). The appearance of the giant colonies derived from these spore tetrads was studied by transferring each of the 4 single-spore cultures from one ascus on to the surface of wort-gelatin in a petri dish maintained at 15°C. It was found that each of the 4 colonies was different from the others with respect to morphological structure. The ascus from which they originated must therefore have been heterozygous, and the fact that the colonies were not identical in pairs and that no two tetrads were alike proved that the asci were heterozygous in more than 1 pair of genes. It was moreover clear that crossing-over took place at the re-duction division of the diploid nucleus of the young asci.

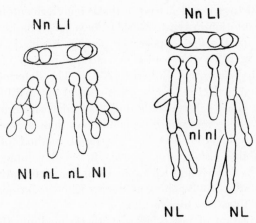

FIG. 2. Diagram of the two types of segregation in the asci of the doubly hetero-zygous *Saccharomycodes ludwigii*. (From Winge and Laustsen, 1939a.)

Mendelian segregation could not, however, be demonstrated by these preliminary morphological studies and the first instance of this kind in yeasts was found in *Saccharomycodes ludwigii* (Winge and Laustsen, 1939a), in which the four spores in the cylindrical ascus are adherent in pairs. Two pairs of genes were discovered, which, by combined action, are responsible for the balanced heterozygous condition of this yeast. The diploid ascus was of the formula *Nn Ll*. Here *N* designates normal cell growth and *n*, abnormal growth which is limited to the formation of one or two hyphal-like cells; *L* designates long-celled growth and *l*, short-celled growth. The two pairs of genes segregate out to produce either two *Nl* and two *nL* spores or two *NL* and two *nl* spores (Fig. 2). The two spores comprising each pair in the ascus always have opposite ge-netic formulas and since at germination they always fuse together, the zygotes, which germinate vegetatively, are always of the formula *Nn Ll*.

The results of this investigation may be summarized as follows: (*a*) the occurrence of Mendelian segregation with respect to *N-n* and *L-l*, (*b*) the occurrence of a balanced heterozygous condition, and (*c*) the occurrence of heterothallism in the haplophase. Haploid single-spore cultures with long-celled growth (*NL*) produced lobed giant colonies, while single spore cultures with short-celled growth (*Nl*) produced smooth giant colonies. Lobed giant colonies were also formed by the diploid zygotes (*Nn Ll*). Lindegren (1945) explained this behavior by assuming that both pairs of genes are situated so near the centromere that no crossing-over between it and the genes takes place, and that both gene pairs undergo prereduction during the first meiotic division. This explanation was accepted by Winge (1947). Meanwhile Ditlevsen (1944) demonstrated a simple Mendelian segregation with regard to colonial morphology in *S. italicus*. This yeast was found to be heterozygous with respect to a gene for elongated cells which was dominant over a gene for short-cell growth. Homozygous short-celled types produced relatively smooth giant colonies, while both homozygous and heterozygous long-celled types produced giant colonies with radial and concentric sculpture.

Winge and Laustsen, who had demonstrated in 1938 that it was possible to hybridize yeasts under the microscope, found (1939a) that when a successful crossing was made between two yeasts differing in their ability to ferment a particular sugar, the hybrid was always a fermenter. This observation has since been confirmed many times, and it seems to be a general rule that the presence of a fermentative or hydrolyzing enzyme is dominant over its absence. Winge and Laustsen could not go farther in their studies, however, since the spores of their interspecific hybrids germinated very poorly and tetrad analyses were thus excluded. They did find, however, an excess of the dominant type in the spore cultures at their disposal, but it was not known whether these were actually representative of the true segregation. Later, Kudriavtsev and Kosikov, in their work on artificial hybridization of yeasts (1947), also found the occurrence of a similar dominance with respect to fermentative ability as well as segregation in the F_2. It should also be noted that as early as 1939–1940, the Japanese investigators, Takizawa (1939) and Yamamoto (1940) were successful in producing artificial yeast hybrids.

The first tetrad analyses with respect to fermentative ability were carried out by Lindegren *et al.* in 1944 on the offspring of a hybrid between *S. cerevisiae* (nonfermenter of melibiose) and *S. carlsbergensis* (fermenter of melibiose). Although simple Mendelian segregation was not observed, this study served to initiate a long series of genetic investigations by Lindegren and his school and by Winge and his collaborators with the aim of elucidating the inheritance of fermentative ability in yeasts. In addition, Lindegren and his co-workers as well as other investigators, have studied the inheritance of further biochemical characters in yeasts; these will be discussed later.

In 1945 Spiegelman *et al.* investigated the segregation with respect to melibiose fermentation in another S. *cerevisiae* × S. *carlsbergensis* hybrid: this time simple Mendelian segregation was obtained, since each of the 10 asci analyzed yielded 2 fermenters and 2 nonfermenters. Of even greater interest, however, was the authors' claim that when the crossing, sporulation, and transfers were carried out in the presence of melibiose, all of the single-spore progeny of the hybrid were capable of fermenting this sugar—in other words, only 4:0 segregation ratios were obtained; but when melibiose was omitted from the substrate, the 4:0 ratios reverted to the normal 2:2 ratios. Their explanation of this phenomenon was that the cytoplasm of the hybrid asci contained enzyme-forming factors which were transferred to *all* 4 spores. This experiment led to a significant conclusion, namely, that this was an example of the maintenance and synthesis of an enzyme in the absence of the gene. Lindegren's cytogene theory was proposed in order to account for the observed behavior, but in view of the fact that later attempts to repeat the melibiose experiment were unsuccessful, the cytogene theory has at present only historic interest. Lindegren himself abandonded it, but introduced new theoretical concepts as, for example, masked recessiveness (Lindegren and Lindegren, 1946) to account for his irregular fermentation ratios.

The inheritance of the ability to synthesize vitamins was also investigated by Lindegren and Lindegren (1947a; Lindegren, 1945) with particular reference to the synthesis of pantothenic acid, pyridoxin, thiamin, and *p*-aminobenzoic acid. They found monofactorial segregation for each of these characters.

With regard to pantothenate requirements, Raut (1950b) found in a pantothenate-dependent strain a spontaneous mutant which was capable of synthesizing the vitamin in question. The new gene, however, was not identical with the original gene, for it was found to occur at a different locus.

Pomper and Burkholder (1949), who investigated the inheritance of a series of biochemical mutants in yeasts (thiamineless, methionineless, and tryptophanless), found simple Mendelian segregation for these characters. They also demonstrated that S. *cerevisiae* requires two complementary genes in order to synthesize uracil, the absence of one of these genes presumably blocking the synthesis. These authors also discuss a gene pair responsible for "disperse" and "non-disperse" growth and state that "disperse" is dominant. This same character, which may also be designated as "non-flocculent" and "flocculent," and which is of considerable practical significance in the brewing industry, has been studied in great detail by Thorne (1951). His investigations, however, led to a different result, since he conclusively established that polymeric genes are responsible for the inheritance of this character and that the dominant genes for flocculence mutate with high frequency to their nonflocculent allelomorphs. Gilliland (1951) also obtained simple Mendelian segregation for flocculence, but the character was found in some hybrids to be dominant and in others to be recessive. In 1953 Pomper and McKee showed that the manner of cultivation of the yeast cultures played a role in the determination of the flocculent character in heterozygotes.

The Lindegrens' study (1947b) of the inheritance behavior of a red adenineless mutant which has been observed and studied by several yeast investigators supported their view of the frequent occurrence of non-Mendelian inheritance and led them to set forth their remarkable concept of "depletion mutation." The present authors obtained in 1948 the same mutant by means of Röntgen irradiation (Winge and Roberts, 1950a); it was then found that the red type behaved quite normally as a recessive to the mother type. The hybrid white × red was itself white and regularly segregated out 2 white:2 red in each of 35 asci investigated. A single ascus yielded 2 white:2 yellow, but further investigations were not undertaken, as the yellow type unfortunately grew poorly and was not suitable for hybridization experiments.

With regard to the characters "top yeast" versus "bottom yeast," it can be said that the former character is usually dominant (Winge and Laustsen, 1939b), although simple Mendelian inheritance is not involved. These characters are quantitative and influenced by several different genes, although the hybrid resulting from a cross between two bottom yeasts will always itself be a bottom yeast. On the other hand, Winge and Laustsen found that such a hybrid could segregate out types with a marked tendency toward top fermentation, and by crossing a Danish baking yeast (bottom yeast) with S. cerevisiae Rasse II (top yeast) both top-fermenting and bottom-fermenting hybrids were produced. Oppenoorth (1956) has recently put forth the hypothesis that 2 pairs of genes, A-a and B-b are involved in top and bottom fermentation. The diploidized single-spore cultures AA BB and AA bb are top yeasts, whereas aa bb is a bottom yeast and aa BB an intermediate type. However, the different yeast types may vary as to the number of allelomorphic pairs they contain. It was found, for example, that one variety, as mentioned above, had 2 genes for top fermentation, while another had 3.

Winge and Roberts (1948, 1950a, 1952, 1954a) investigated the genes responsible for fermentative and hydrolytic phenomena in various species of *Saccharomyces*. In 1948 the occurrence of three polymeric genes for maltose fermentation was demonstrated in S. *cerevisiae*, but as the result of later studies in this genus this number has since been increased to six (M_1, M_2, M_3, M_4, M_5, M_6). Gene M_4 arose as a spontaneous mutation and also as a result of Röntgen irradiation (1950a) while M_5 was isolated by Gilliland from S. *diastaticus* (1953, 1954a,b) and M_6 from S. *carlsbergensis* (Winge and Roberts, 1956). These 6 genes are not biochemically identical: M_1 and M_4, for example, ferment both maltose and sucrose, while M_2, M_5, and M_6 ferment only maltose and M_3 can be adapted, although with difficulty, to the fermentation of sucrose. The M gene present in S. *italicus* was identified as M_1 (Winge and Roberts, 1950b), and Lindegren's MA gene (Carbondale breeding stock) and Hawthorne's *Ma-1 gene* (Roman *et al.* 1951) were also found to be identical with M_1 (Winge and Roberts, 1955). Gilliland (1954a) identified one of the two M genes in his S. *diastaticus* as M_1, while the other (M_5) was a new gene. M_1 appears, therefore, to be widely distributed in yeasts.

At present the existence of 3 raffinose-fermenting genes is known; actually these genes, R_1, R_2, and R_3, hydrolyze the raffinose molecule into melibiose and fructose, the latter being fermented by all yeasts which bring about fermentation. It was the work of Gilliland (1949) which first showed that three polymeric genes must be present in S. *chevalieri*, and they were later isolated in individual yeast types (Winge and Roberts, 1952). It has since been shown that the R gene present in the Yeast Foam strain of S. *cerevisiae* is identical with R_2 (Winge and Roberts, 1953), and Gilliland (1954b) showed that the R gene in S. *diastaticus* is also R_2.

From the crossing S. *cerevisiae* (rapid galactose fermentation) × S. *microellipsodes* (slow galactose fermentation), Lindegren and Lindegren (1946) isolated a single spore culture which was completely unable to ferment galactose; this culture was crossed with a rapid fermenter and the hybrid (Gg) regularly segregated out 2 rapid fermenters to 2 non-fermenters in each ascus. On the other hand, Winge and Roberts (1948) crossed S. *cerevisiae* with S. *chevalieri* of which the later species, according to the literature, is unable to ferment galactose. These authors were led to the conclusion that the difference in the galactose-fermenting ability of these two species was of a quantitative nature. S. *cerevisiae* possesses the G gene, which brings about rapid (1–2 days) fermentation of galactose, while S. *chevalieri* possesses the g_s-gene, which is responsible for a slow fermentation of galactose following a period of adaptation of approximately 1 week. It is noteworthy that when g_s types are first adapted they are able to ferment just as vigorously as the G types. This phenomenon was called "long-term adaptation." In the material then examined, when a GG type was crossed with a $g_s g_s$ type, the hybrid obtained was always a rapid fermenter of galactose and the asci of the hybrid always segregated out 2 rapid fermenters and 2 slow fermenters. As already mentioned, when a g_s type is grown in a galactose-containing medium, it becomes adapted to rapid fermentation, but if it is then maintained on a medium lacking galactose, it will become deadapted, i.e., it will ferment galactose only slowly. After deadaptation, the yeast may be readapted by growth on a galactose medium. It is not known whether G or g_s are allelomorphs, but it seems most probable that the majority of *Saccharomyces* species are homozygous with respect to g_s, while some of them have, in addition, the nonallelomorphic gene G. As mentioned above, the fact that Lindegren and Lindegren obtained a nonfermenter from the hybrid rapid-fermenter $\times$ slow-fermenter also supports this view.

Lindegren (1949) and Mundkur and Lindegren (1949) claimed that in *Saccharomyces* the g_s type arises from a nonfermenter, g, which mutates to G. According to this view, adaptation to rapid fermentation consists simply in a higher rate of growth in the presence of galactose of cells which have mutated from $g \to G$ than of the unmutated g cells. Lindegren claimed that there were varying degrees of mutability of g types and that therefore some adapt, i.e., mutate from $g \to G$, more rapidly than others. This explanation of the phenomenon was criticized by Spiegelman (1951) who stated that with regard to long-term adaptation to galactose fermentation by *S. chevalieri*, the "possibility that it is based on mutation and selection has been eliminated by a variance analysis which indicates that the induced heritable modification does not occur in the absence of the adaptive substrate and by the further demonstration that reversion to the original type is a mass phenomenon." The mutation explanation was also criticized by Winge (1952).

An interesting experiment on long-term adaptation was reported by Spiegelman and DeLorenzo in 1952. Using Winge and Roberts's Hybrid 55 (Gg_s), they found that prior adaptation to galactose resulted in $4G:0g_s$ and $3G:1g_s$ segregations, whereas the same hybrid, grown in the absence of galactose, yielded only $2G:2g_s$ ratios. The segregation ratios of the tetrads from the adapted material reverted to 2:2 in the absence of galactose. These results are in accord with Winge and Roberts's explanation of long-term adaptation involving the slow synthesis of the enzyme by the g_s-gene in the presence of galactose, but

Spiegelman and DeLorenzo's further experiments indicated that cytoplasmatic elements are probably involved as well. They found that it was impossible to obtain any segregation in a $g_s g_s$ single-spore culture by prior adaptation to galactose, since all of the tetrads analyzed yielded only $0G:4g_s$ ratios. They concluded therefore that long-term adaptation requires the presence of cytoplasmatic particles produced by the action of the dominant allele, G. These results, however, are not in accord with the fact (Winge and Roberts, 1948) that long-term adaptation is involved in the fermentation of galactose by S. *chevalieri* ($g_s g_s$), and consequently the $g_s g_s$ type used by Spiegelman and DeLorenzo cannot be identical with S. *chevalieri* with respect to galactose-fermentative ability, in spite of the fact that Hybrid 55 was produced by crossing a G type with S. *chevalieri*.

Mundkur (1952), in studying long-term adaptation, came to the conclusion that differences in the material accounted for the differences in results. He found that a nonfermenter became adapted to rapid galactose fermentation through its ability to mutate to rapid-fermenter cells which were incapable of reversion in the absence of galactose. A slow fermenter (S. *chevalieri*), on the other hand, became adapted to rapid galactose fermentation through contact with galactose (long-term adaptation), and he was of the opinion that this species possesses a gene for slow galactose fermentation. In contrast to the results of the present authors, however, he found that in S. *chevalieri* mutation of $g_s \rightarrow G$ could also occur, since such rapid fermenters arising in a culture were incapable of deadaptation upon the removal of galactose from the substratum.

In 1954, Pittman and Lindegren studied long-term adaptation in S. *chevalieri* and concluded that " . . . a major mechanism in 'long-term' adaptation is mutation and selection, complicated by suppression; but, specific experiments were not devised which would exclude the possibility that mechanisms involving cytoplasmatic particles or slow genes may co-exist."

The results of the investigations on long-term adaptation are thus conflicting but this may be due, in part, to the different material employed. Yeasts completely unable to ferment galactose have, for example, never been found in the yeast material which we have studied. See also Section 4.

The genetics of melibiose fermentation was investigated by Lindegren *et al.* (1944), Spiegelman *et al.* (1945), and Lindegren (1949). It was first reported that S. *carlsbergensis* contains two independent nonallelic genes for the fermentation of melibiose, but later (1949) it was claimed that non-Mendelian segregation with respect to this character was frequent. This problem will be discussed more fully in the next section.

Oppenoorth (1956) found a peculiar type of inheritance involved in melibiose fermentation. A hybrid $Me+ \times Me-$ failed to ferment melibiose but nevertheless melibiose fermenters were found in the progeny of this hybrid. Another hybrid (also $Me+ \times Me-$), which he designated K 5, was capable of fermenting melibiose but of 30 single-spore cultures derived from it, all were nonfermenters. It seems probable that these results may have been due to technical difficulties.

Leupold (1950), working with *Schizosaccharomyces pombe,* conclusively demonstrated the presence of multiple allelomorphs. He found (a) a gene, H^{90}, for homothallism and 90% sporulation, (b) a gene, $h+$, for heterothallism, mating type $+$, and (c) a gene, $h-$, for heterothallism, mating type $-$. Another gene, H^{40}, was also found, but the author was unable, on the basis of his experiments, to determine whether it belonged to this series of allelomorphs. All four genes showed simple Mendelian segregation.

The existence of lethal genes in yeasts has been demonstrated in *Saccharomycodes* (Winge and Laustsen, 1939a) and in *Saccharomyces diastaticus* (Gilliland, 1954b). In each case only 2 of the 4 spores within an ascus are capable of normal germination and development.

4. Complementary Gene Action

Several instances of complementary gene action have been described in yeasts. In 1949 Pomper and Burkholder found regular Mendelian segregation in a gene pair, Ur_1 and Ur_2, which governed the synthesis of uracil and it was found that both genes must be present in order to initiate and complete the synthesis. In the same year certain results obtained with *Saccharomyces* by Magni (1949) appeared to indicate that the type of growth form of giant colonies was dependent upon the presence of two complementary genes.

Gilliland (1953, 1954a,b) demonstrated that in the new dextrin-fermenting species, *Saccharomyces diastaticus,* which he had described complementary gene action exists between M_1 (α-glucosidase synthesis) and a gene called S_1 (amylase synthesis). Gene M_1 together with S_1 bring about a rapid fermentation of dextrin. It was also found that there was complementary action between M_5 (maltase) and the S gene which resulted in slow dextrin fermentation. With respect to galactose fermentation in *Saccharomyces,* Leupold and Hottinguer (1954) obtained from a $G+ \times G-$ hybrid nine 1:3 asci and one 0:4 ascus and concluded that these results could be explained in terms of two complementary genes, both of which were required for the fermentation of galactose. These two investigations constitute the first recorded instances of the existence of complementary genes governing fermentative characters in yeasts. Douglas and Condie (1954) have suggested that two genes may be involved in the fermentation of galactose: it is believed that a gene G_1 controls the formation of an enzyme required for the conversion of galactose into glucose-6-PO$_4$, while another gene, G_2, is involved in the transport of galactose into the cell. Lindegren (1955a) justly criticized these authors in calling a G_1g_2 type a nonfermenter, for it actually is capable of fermenting galactose, but only after 7 days or more. The above-mentioned work of Leupold and Hottinguer calls for the same criticism; according to them, "strains which do not fill the inverted tube with gas within one week are classified as nonfermenters (g)."

Hawthorne (1956) has also contributed to our knowledge of the genetics of galactose fermentation. He found in *Saccharomyces* that 3 dominant G genes are necessary for rapid fermentation of galactose. The recessive allelomorphs are designated g-1, g-2, and g-3, and the last-named he considers to be identical[1] with the g_s-gene of Winge and Roberts (1948) which is responsible for the slow fermentation of galactose. This means that S. *chevalieri* (a slow fermenter of galactose) would have the formula G_1G_1 G_2G_2 g_3g_3. It is, however, difficult to distinguish between slow-fermenters and non-fermenters in this investigation, for Hawthorne states that after 7 days fermentation is visible in fermentometers inoculated with G_1 g_2 types (with or without G_3?).

Winge and Roberts (1956, 1957) demonstrated that the raffinose molecule is fermented not only by the R genes (β-h-fructosidase synthesis), whereby fructose is liberated and fermented, but also by the complementary action of a melibiase gene, Me, and a galactozymase gene, G. The Me gene hydrolyzes the raffinose into sucrose and galactose, the latter being fermented by the activity of the G gene. In both cases, only ⅓ of the raffinose molecule is fermented, the fructose portion being involved when one of the R genes is present, and the galactose portion being involved when $Me + G$ are present.

Losada (1957) showed, in addition, that the complementary action of M_1 and Me brings about the fermentation of the raffinose molecule. Gene M_1 brings about the synthesis of an α-glucosidase which is capable of fermenting both maltose and sucrose (Winge and Roberts, 1952). When Me has hydrolyzed the raffinose molecule into sucrose and galactose, M_1 then hydrolyzes the sucrose into fructose and glucose, both

---

[1] Hawthorne writes that g-3 is "allelic with" g_s, but from his text it appears that he means "identical with."

of which are fermented. If G is also present, then the liberated galactose is likewise fermented. Thus, $Me + M_1$ cause $\frac{2}{3}$ fermentation and $Me + M_1 + G$, $\frac{3}{3}$ fermentation of the raffinose molecule.

The subject of irregular or non-Mendelian segregation which is assumed to be due to polyploidy has been discussed in Chapter III.

5. On the Importance of Identifying Genotypes

Genes M_1 and M_4 produce α-glucosidase which brings about the fermentation of maltose and sucrose while M_2 and M_6 produce maltase, which ferments maltose alone. Because these polymeric maltose-fermenting genes do not possess the same biochemical activity, it is at once evident that the *in vitro* isolation of the enzyme causing maltose fermentation should not be undertaken with any yeast merely with reference to the simple fact that it possesses the ability to ferment this sugar. In *Saccharomyces cerevisiae*, the species most commonly studied by biochemists (usually under the sole epithet, "yeast"), three M genes, M_1, M_2, and M_3, are known to be present and, if enzyme extracts responsible for maltose fermentation be prepared, the result can hardly be otherwise than a mixture of enzymes. It is therefore of utmost importance that cooperative investigations of geneticists and biochemists be initiated; the yeast geneticist is now in a position to produce a yeast type containing only one fermentation gene as well as to determine the genetical constitution of the yeast type the biochemist wishes to investigate. In *Saccharomyces chevalieri* the existence of 3 polymeric raffinose-fermenting genes (R_1, R_2, R_3) has been demonstrated, and it is reasonable to expect that all 3 genes synthesize β-h-fructosidase, but it is not by any means certain that they are all identical. In general, biochemical investigations of yeasts which contain only one gene for the synthesis of the fermentative enzyme in question are to be preferred; in such cases, the biochemist is assured that his extracted enzyme preparation will be pure in the sense that it will not consist of a mixture of different enzymes.

6. Irregular Segregation

It is clear that the occurrence of mutation can cause deviations from simple Mendelian segregation, and also that tetrad analyses may show a deficiency in recessive types if spores carrying the recessive gene germinate poorly. Nevertheless, yeast literature abounds in reports of deviations from Mendelian segregation, which are assumed to arise from causes other than the two mentioned above. Neither the existence of polymeric genes nor the overlapping of generations, both of which can also bring about segregation ratios other than the normal 2:2, have been taken into consideration by those investigators who have claimed that non-Mendelian segregation is of relatively common occurrence in yeasts. They claim that a hybrid, *Aa*, should be able to segregate out not only 2*A*:2*a* tetrads, but also 3*A*:1*a* or 1*a*:3*A* tetrads. Mundkur (1949, 1952) and Lindegren (1949, 1953) supported Winkler's hypothesis (1930) that "gene conversion," which may also be called gene contamination, occurs in a heterozygote, whereby *A* is transformed into *a*, or vice versa. Other instances of irregular ratios have been explained on the basis of polyploidy.

The fact that in some cases more than 4 spores may be found in 1 ascus shows that an extra mitosis must have occurred (Winge and Roberts, 1950c), but, as was pointed out by Mundkur (1950), this explanation

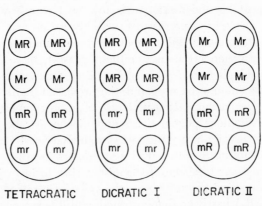

TETRACRATIC   DICRATIC I   DICRATIC II

Fig. 3. Diagram of the three types of asci which may arise from a doubly heterozygous hybrid. The eight nuclei in each ascus have arisen though supernumerary mitosis. (From Winge and Roberts, 1954a.)

may not hold for certain instances of irregular segregation occurring in material containing various marker genes. A cytological and genetic investigation of yeast material in which irregular segregation was evident showed, however, that the occurrence of supernumerary mitoses in association with the formation of binucleate spores could actually explain the phenomenon (Winge and Roberts, 1954a,b).

When an extra mitosis occurs with respect to all 4 nuclei in an immature ascus of a double heterozygote, *Mm Rr*, the ascus will become 8-nucleate and the following tetrad segregations are possible (see also Fig. 3):

   (a) 4 different nuclear types, 2*MR*:2*Mr*:2*mR*:2*mr* (tetracratic)

   (b) 2 different nuclear types, 4*MR*:4*mr* (dicratic)

   (c) 2 different nuclear types, 4*Mr*:4*mR* (dicratic)

If 2 nuclei of different genotypes come to lie in the same spore of a dicratic ascus, this spore will always give rise to a doubly heterozygous culture. This theoretical expectation was confirmed by observation. If, for example, a tetrad yielded a 3:1 segregation with respect to the ability to ferment maltose, it could be shown that the formulas of the 4 single spore cultures were: (a) *mm RR* (b) *Mm Rr* (c) *MM rr* (d) *MM rr*. Spore was formed around 2 nuclei, *mR* and *Mr,* while the cultures derived from spores 1, 3, and 4 had diploidized in the usual way.

Winge and Roberts also showed that binucleate spores occurred in Lindegren's material, in which normally the single-spore cultures remain haploid. Analyses of deviating tetrads, as, for example, one segregating as 3*Ma*:1*ma,* showed without exception that one of the 3 fermenters was always diploid and heterozygous. This was due to the occurrence of an extra mitosis in the ascus, which resulted in the formation of a binucleate heterocaryotic spore. It should also be noted that in the material employed by Mundkur which contained gene markers and which yielded irregular ratios, the occurrence of binucleate spores could theoretically explain the results observed.

Fowell (1956) demonstrated a peculiar type of segregation in a yeast hybrid which was heterozygous with respect to the synthesis of tryptophan. Instead of the expected 2:2 ratio, he found most asci segregating out as 4 Try:0 try, a few 2 Try:2 try, and no 3 Try:1 try. Since the hybrid showed a tendency to produce supernumerary spores, Fowell explained the segregation behavior as the result of an intra-ascal competition between genotypes in which the recessive type would be eliminated.

So far, no proof of the existence of gene conversion in yeasts has been obtained, although Lindegren (1955b) continues to express belief in its occurrence. However, the fact that he analyzed 2500 asci before he found an ascus giving a 3:1 segregation (with respect to pink and white), indicates that this particular deviation could have been due to a mutation. In this material, Lindegren took precautions to ensure that the cultures were haploid.

7. Linkage

Lindegren (1949) and Lindegren and Lindegren (1950) erected the first chromosome map of *Saccharomyces,* which embraced 4 chromosomes. The distance of the genes from the centromere was calculated, as well as their reciprocal distances, by ordinary recombination analyses. Eight genes were placed on the 4 chromosomes, as follows:

Chromosome I: *PN* (pantothenate), *AD* (adenine), *IN* (inositol)
Chromosome II: *G* (galactozymase), *ME* (melibiase)
Chromosome III: *PB* (*p*-aminobenzoic acid)
Chromosome IV: *a* (mating type)

The strongest linkage was found between G and the centromere; this gene was located 6 centimorgans from the centromere. The weakest linkage was found between G and ME, which were found to be 46 units apart. This shows that the chromosome map cannot be regarded as final, for the 46 units between G and ME lie so close to 50 that "false linkage" may have been mistaken for true linkage, i.e., the ability of spores to germinate may depend upon their genetic constitution, and if a certain spore genotype germinates poorly, linkage may well be imagined even though it actually does not exist in the material.

With regard to chromosome I, PN is situated 26 units to the left of the centromere, while the other genes in the order listed above are situated to the right.

Later Lindegren and Lindegren (1951) added a gene for adenine synthesis, AD 2, to chromosome II, so that the gene arrangement of this chromosome is Centromere—G–AD 2—ME. In addition, the same authors have found the gene UR (uracil) situated on a new chromosome (V) only 5 centimorgans from the centromere. They state, however, that chromosomes IV and V could be identical, since linkage relations between UR and PB have not been investigated. It is also stated that HI (histidine) and AN (anthranilic acid) are linked (25 centimorgans) but that it is not known on which chromosomes they are situated.

In 1952 the same authors further found that the genes MA (maltase), MZ (melizitase), MG (α-methylglucosidase), and SU (β-fructofuranosidase) were linked. They found, though, that MG and SU are strongly linked in certain families while in others they are freely segregating. They assume that this difference is due to the occurrence of crossover suppressors, arising in an inverted region. Several other purely hypothetical explanations of unexpected tetrads are proposed, as, e.g., crossing-over in the inverted region, reduction division in tetraploid zygotes, conversion of genes and subsequent back mutation of the converted gene, etc. All of these explanations, however, lack a sound basis. When one considers that the existence of a series of independent, polymeric genes have been demonstrated (as, for example, the 3 nonallelic R genes, designated SU by Lindegren), it is only to be expected that they will exhibit linkage in some material while in other material they will be freely segregating. Jinks (1953) studied this problem and criticized Lindegren's results; he himself investigated the linkage relations in certain families and the free segregation of the same characters in other families.

It is relatively infrequent that ordered tetrads can be analyzed in the yeasts for the spores do not commonly lie in a single row in an elongated ascus. However, as previously mentioned, exceptions are to be found in the genera *Saccharomyces, Schizosaccharomyces,* and *Saccharomycodes.* Even though special skill is required in spore-isolation work, it is possible to isolate the spores in the order in which they occur in the ascus and therefore possible to determine whether prereduction or postreduction has taken place. This problem has been dealt with by Winge and Laustsen (1939a) and Lindegren (1945, 1949) with respect to *Saccharomycodes,* while Hawthorne (1955) has studied the problem in *Saccharomyces.* Later Hawthorne (1956) identified Lindegren's galactozymase gene, G, which was closely linked to the centromere, with his G-1. The G-2 gene had no centromere linkage, while the third galactozymase gene, G-3, showed close centromere linkage and also very close linkage to a gene for tryptophan dependence; G-3 was found to be allelic with the g_s gene of Winge and Roberts (1948) and with the recessive gene of James and Lee-Whiting (1955).

Winge and Roberts (1952) demonstrated the existence of very strong linkage between M_1 (hydrolysis of maltose) and R_1 (hydrolysis of raffinose), in which the crossover percentage was 1.3, and later (1953) a similar linkage between M_3 and R_3. On the basis of these results, Winge (1955) proposed his hypothesis of "interallelic crossing over," interpreting the observed results as being due to the activity of complex genes. He considered, for example, that the genes M_1 and R_1 actually consisted of 4 allelomorphs, (1) M^R, (2) M^r, (3) m^R, and (4) m^r which determined the hydrolysis of (i) maltose + raffinose, (ii) maltose, (iii) raffinose, and (iv) neither sugar. He assumed that the exchange of portions of the complex gene molecule could result in interallelic crossing-over, in which the chromatid axis may or may not be involved (axial or nonaxial).

On the basis of his considerations of the origin of prototrophic colonies in *Schizosaccharomyces pombe,* Leupold (1955) also discussed pseudoallelism and the possibility of the existence of complex genes.

Lindegren's theoretical considerations (1952) of the origin of a fermentation gene from a common gene and the assumption that the number of genes increases during the course of time through unequal crossing-over and mutation should also be mentioned in this connection.

It should finally be mentioned that Gilliland (1954b) also found evidence for strong linkage between the maltose-fermenting gene (M_5) and the gene for amylase production (S) occurring in S. *diastaticus.*

8. Mutation and Variation

In the first decade of this century Emil C. Hansen (1905, 1907) observed that it was possible to isolate from a culture of a bottom yeast single cells which gave rise to top yeast cultures. The reverse—bottom yeasts arising from top yeasts—was also observed but much more rarely. This phenomenon was most probably caused by mutation.

In the years that followed much interest was aroused in the occurrence of mutations, both spontaneous and induced, in a large number of different organisms, including the yeast fungi.

When giant colonies of any yeast are allowed to develop on the surface of a solid medium, they are rather often provided with sectors. This sectoring occurs both in haploid and diploid strains. A single-spore or single-cell isolate of either a haploid or a homozygous diploid yeast which is maintained in culture for one or two years will in that time undergo so many mutations that the surface of a new giant colony will be covered by a very large number of sectors of such widely different appearance that it is sometimes difficult to believe that the culture originally was genotypically pure (Winge, 1944).

It might be expected that this high frequency of mutation would make the yeasts unsuited for genetic investigations, but experience has shown that practically any mutation will influence the macroscopic appearance of the colony, whereas the relatively few genes for the characters which are most often analyzed are normally not involved.

The phenomenon of "dissociation" has been known for many years in the bacteria, whose different forms have been characterized as R(rough), S(smooth), M(mucoid), etc. Similar dissociation has also been found in the yeasts, as well as transformation from one form or another and then back again to the original form.

Fabian and McCullough (1934), employing various chemical substances (lithium chloride, brilliant green, alcohol), were able to produce in normal single-cell cultures of the S form of Saccharomyces cerevisiae (and five other species) R forms as well as so-called G forms (gonidial forms), which were stable during the course of many months. Some single-cell cultures of the R and G forms could revert to the S form by repeated transfers to malt extract. They found that the various forms did not always possess identical fermentative ability. With regard to sporulation, it was found that both the S and R forms produced ascospores, while the small-celled G form was unable to do so. In consideration of the fact that these investigations were carried out before the discovery of alternation of generations in yeasts, it is tempting to consider that the G forms arose at spore germination and were haploids, and that in general many instances of so-called mutation may have actually been instances of segregation.

Bauch carried out some investigations on the effect on yeasts of camphor (1941) and of irradiation (1943) and later (1954) on the effect of a number of different carcinogens. He was able to produce in this way constant races with modified cell size termed "gigas," "supergigas," and "minor." The last-mentioned are completely constant but the gigas races, on the other hand, are capable of segregating out normal cells, and in competition with normal cultures, some of these gigas cells are successful while others are not. The supergigas types, which are relatively constant, also segregate out types with smaller cells. Bauch considered the gigas races to be polyploid genome mutants and therefore that those types with smaller cells which were segregated out from them had an aneuploid chromosome number. Colchicine was found to have no effect on the mutation frequency in the yeasts employed.

Thaysen and Morris (1943) produced with the aid of camphor a gigas race of *Torulopsis utilis*, which was designated var. *major*. As *T. utilis* is employed as a food yeast, this new race was of practical significance since the increased cellular volume made it possible to filter off the cells more easily.

Several investigators have employed camphor and related substances in studying mutation and mitotic disturbances in yeasts. The so-called "camphor reaction" consists in the production of hyphal-like growth as well as involution forms in *Saccharomyces* (Levan and Sandwell, 1943; Levan, 1944, 1947). These last-named investigators agreed with Bauch in being unable to find that colchicine produced an effect similar to the "camphor reaction" and they found that acenaphtene was also without effect. The camphor reaction is reversible when the concentration of the mutagen is not sufficiently high, or when the cells have gradually become adapted to its presence. Levan, who is one of the few investigators who appears to have actually observed the chromosomes of yeasts, found a large increase in the number of mutated cells and of endomitotic processes in the presence of camphor. He employed many other chemical substances including aliphatic, alicyclic, and aromatic compounds (1947) and found that their degree of solubility in water was of significance. Some appeared to be very effective at high concentrations (up to the saturation point) although the author did not come to any general conclusions in this respect.

Skovsted (1948) also employed camphor in investigating mutations in a haploid strain of *Saccharomyces cerevisiae*. He found that after camphor treatment there was an increase in the number of mutations over the untreated control, the induced mutants giving rise to dwarf growth of the "giant" colonies. In contrast to Bauch, Skovsted did not obtain large-celled mutants indicative of polyploid types. He pointed out that if

Levan's views as to chromosome disturbances being caused by camphor treatment are correct, then one should expect to find a large number of different mutant types after treatment. On the other hand he did not deny that the diploid brewing yeast he treated could have had such chromosome disturbances since he found many mutant sectors in its giant colonies.

An interesting study of induced mutation in *Saccharomyces cerevisiae* has recently been reported by Srb (1956), who worked with the effect of β-propiolactone in the induction of canavanine resistance. The growth of normal yeasts (*C*) is strongly inhibited by the presence of canavanine, but treatment with lactone induces canavanine resistance (*c*). The results of hybridizations between *C* and *c* yielded a 1-gene segregation, and, as would be expected, treatment of a haploid strain (*C*) yielded a far greater number of canavanine-resistant colonies than did treatment of a diploid strain (*CC*). Quite unexpectedly, however, β-propiolactone treatment resulted in a much higher frequency of mutation of heterozygous diploids than of haploids. No explanation of this phenomenon is given, the author wisely stating that "speculation . . . will not be justified until the material is better known genetically."

Subramaniam and his colleagues have undertaken a long series of experiments on the induction of mutations in yeasts (Subramaniam and Krishna Murthy, 1948; Subramaniam *et al.*, 1948; Ranganathan and Subramaniam, 1950; Subramaniam and Rao, 1950; Ranganathan, 1950; Krishna Murthy and Subramaniam, 1950; Krishna Murthy and Subramaniam, 1951; Duraiswami and Subramaniam, 1950). In brief, the following can be said of these investigations: (a) even though it is stated (Ranganathan and Subramaniam, 1950) that "one has to dismiss as inexact all genetic observations on yeast strains of unknown chromosome constitution," these workers have themselves not studied the chromosomes (see also Chapter III), for the large-stained bodies which they call chromosomes cannot be regarded as such; (b) it is claimed that the transition from diplophase to haplophase and vice versa does not occur in the ascus but rather in vegetative cells; (c) neither spore isolations, hybridizations, nor biochemical analyses of mutants have been undertaken; (d) the only method employed for identification of mutant types is observation of the sectors of giant colonies which, in the absence of proof of any kind and in spite of discrepancies in cell size, are considered to have varying degrees of ploidy (see also Chapter III and Winge, 1951). These investigators employed camphor, ultraviolet irradiation, and temperature shock in their mutation experiments, but, as already mentioned, their analyses of the mutant forms leave much to be desired.

Winge and Roberts (1950a), after treating a nonfermenter of maltose (*Saccharomyces*) with Röntgen irradiation, obtained a mutant capable of fermenting this disaccharide. This was the origin of the maltase gene, M_4, which, subsequently arose spontaneously in the material. The authors describe an experiment in which a M_3m_3 hybrid, possessing no other M genes, was Röntgen-irradiated with 22,500 r.; as a result of this treatment, 5 nonfermenting mutants arose (ca. 1%) while in the non-irradiated control, none appeared. The fact that the giant colonies of all 5 mutants were identical in appearance is of interest, for it indicates that a point mutation was involved. Another M_3m_3 hybrid also yielded 5 nonfermenters after Röntgen irradiation, and the control gave none. Here again, the giant colonies of all 5 mutants were macroscopically identical. This mutation frequency of ca. 1% is surprisingly high.

These authors also obtained an adenine-deficient red mutant following Röntgen irradiation of a haploid *Saccharomyces*. This recessive mutant has been observed several times in yeasts by other investigators and, according to Lindegren and Lindegren (1947b), was first reported by Tatum and Reaume, who obtained it by treatment with mustard gas. Ephrussi (1953) has also worked with this red mutant and found that it, too, frequently gave rise to vegetative "littles," which will be discussed later.

The genetic basis for adenine synthesis in *Saccharomyces* has been thoroughly investigated by Roman (1956). Types deficient in synthetic ability (*ad*) produce a red pigment but are quite unstable, giving rise to pale pink or white sectors in the colony which are regarded as mutants. In all, 81 mutant types distributed among five loci were obtained. Proof of close linkage between two loci, *ad* 5 and *ad* 7, was found, and it is interesting to note that Roman's genetic analyses indicate that somatic crossing over may exist in this material.

In an investigation of 56 adenineless mutants from haploid cultures of *Schizosaccharomyces pombe*, Leupold (1955) showed that they could be classified into 8 main groups corresponding to 8 recessive nonallelic genes, each of which was responsible for adenine deficiency. By crossing mutants belonging to different groups, prototroph hybrids arose. All the mutations belonging to one group would be expected to arise through mutation of the same gene; notwithstanding, certain hybridizations between mutants belonging to the same group resulted in the production of prototroph types. The author attributes this phenomenon to pseudoallelism, in which a complex gene may mutate at different regions within a single locus.

Raut (1950a) obtained a cytochrome-deficient mutant by treating a haploid *Saccharomyces* with ultraviolet irradiation; this mutant was not able to absorb oxygen. A heterozygous hybrid segregated out the normal and the mutant type in 2:2 ratios. For further discussion of cytochrome-deficient mutants the reader is referred to the next section on cytoplasmatic inheritance, which deals primarily with the important contributions of Ephrussi and his colleagues.

Raut (1950b) also studied a pantothenate-dependent culture and obtained by mutation a normal pantothenate-synthesizer, but back mutation of the original mutant gene *a* was not involved. It was rather a mutation of a gene, *b*, for dependency, to a pantothenate-synthesizing gene, *B*. The original wild type synthesizer, *Ab*, thus gave rise to the nonsynthesizing mutant, *ab*, and by irradiation of this mutant arose the synthesizer, *aB*. *AB* may be termed a "double synthesizer," and *A* and *B* may be regarded as polymeric genes.

Pomper also obtained both purine and pyrimidine mutants (1952a) and methionine-deficient mutants (1953) in *Saccharomyces* by ultraviolet irradiation. A pH-sensitive multiple mutant (1952b), which had requirements for *p*-aminobenzoic acid, adenine, histidine, and methionine was also obtained. A complex gene system must be involved here which is difficult to elucidate.

Pomper and McKee (1953) and, as mentioned in Chapter III, Leupold (1950) and Ahmad (1953) have found mutation in the mating type genes, and Leupold also reported mutation in the genes controlling heterothallism and homothallism in *Schizosaccharomyces pombe*. In this organism was found an instance of triple allelomorphism involving (1) a gene for heterothallism, mating type +, (2) an allelomorphic gene for heterothallism, mating type —, and (3) an allelomorphic gene for homothallism. These allelomorphs were transformed into one another by mutation. Microscopically it was possible in hanging drop cultures to observe the occurrence of sporulating mutant sectors which were identified as the following:

(a) heterothallism + → homothallism
(b) heterothallism — → homothallism
(c) heterothallism — → heterothallism +

James (1954, 1955) employed ultraviolet light for the production of mutant types from a heterozygous galactose fermenter; this mutation was explained in terms of somatic crossing-over and disjunction of homologous chromosomes, for the number of sectors of homozygous dominant was correlated with the number of homozygous recessive cells. It appears strange that nearly all visible mutant sectors should be concerned with just that gene which was being investigated, for, as previously mentioned, a mutation in any gene will most probably be expressed as a change in the mascroscopic structure of the giant colony. In 1954 James demonstrated the occurrence of mutation with respect to 1 or 2 lethal genes, but both his method for determining whether the assumed Gg heterozygotes actually were of this formula as well as his proof of the existence of tetraploid sectors and asci seem to rest on a rather insecure basis.

Most of the mutation investigations discussed above were undertaken on *Saccharomyces,* but Skovsted (1943) employed *Nadsonia richteri* as a test organism, in which he described the occurrence of "successive" mutations. The vegetative phase is haploid and homothallic, and the experiments were initiated with the isolation of a single uninucleate spore, which gave rise to a colony capable of sporulation, but, unfortunately, the very low percentage of spore germination precluded any attempt at hybridization work. The main character which was studied was the morphologic structure of the giant colony. It was found that the original furfuraceous type, T.1, produced only two mutant types, one mealy (T.2) and the other squamulose (T.4). From T.2, which was isolated, a number of further mutant sectors of a waxy type (T.5) were obtained as well as a brown-freckled type (T.6), etc. It was shown that a given mutant tended to mutate in a limited number of ways: when single cells or single spores were isolated from a mutant, the subsequent culture gave rise to the same new mutants again. In some cases, more than 30 single cells were isolated from a mutant type, and each of the subsequent cultures showed a tendency to mutate in the same limited number of ways. It was of course impossible to determine whether gene mutations were involved because of the impossibility of making crossings, so the possibility remains that these mutations involved cytoplasmic elements rather than genes.

9. Cytoplasmatic Inheritance

The first report of a cytoplasmatic effect in yeasts involved inbreeding degeneration (Winge and Laustsen, 1940). *Saccharomyces* is able to propagate itself through spore formation in three principal ways (Winge and Laustsen, 1937, 1940):

Scheme 1. Two spores or two haploid cells each originating from a different spore can copulate (plasmogamy + caryogamy).

Scheme 2. A spore germinates and produces haploid cells which fuse in pairs (plasmogamy + caryogamy). The diploid culture arising in this way is always homozygous.

Scheme 3. A spore germinates and at the same time its nucleus divides mitotically, after which the daughter nuclei fuse, forming a diploid nucleus (direct diploidization). Here also the resultant diploid is homozygous.

With regard to *Saccharomyces cerevisiae* var. *ellipsoideus* typical inbreeding degeneration occurs when the diplophase is initiated according to Scheme 1 and when inbreeding is carried out for several generations. This degeneration is assumed to be of ordinary genetic nature, for it is a well-known fact that inbreeding in most organisms is accompanied by deterioration. In *Saccharomyces* inbreeding degeneration manifests itself by a lowering of spore germination ability from generation to generation, but probably cytoplasmatic inheritance is not involved here.

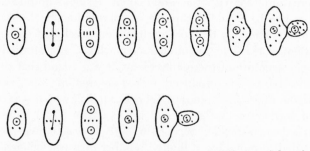

FIG. 4. Diagram of zygote formation following cell fusion (above) and direct diploidization (below), illustrating a hypothetical difference in chondriosome number. (From Winge and Laustsen, 1940.)

When continued inbreeding through several generations is carried out with cultures of S. *cerevisiae* which diploidize according to Schemes 2 and 3, the degeneration is so pronounced that the spore germination percentage falls to a very low value. It is most evident when direct diploidization is involved, and it has been observed that in the course of one or two generations the spores have completely lost their ability to germinate.

The difference between Scheme 2 and Scheme 3 is only that in the former, cell fusion, and in the latter, nuclear fusion, occurs. This led the authors to propose the hypothesis that the propagation of cytoplasmatic elements, assumedly chondriosomes, played a role in the phenomenon. Figure 4 illustrates more clearly than words the proposed hypothesis. It will be seen that in direct diploidization the zygote contains only half the number of chondriosomes contained in a cell × cell zygote.

The fact that a pure homozygous line degenerates with continued inbreeding is not without interest, but not all *Saccharomyces* species behave in this way. For instance, *S. validus,* which may diploidize in any of the three ways listed above, does not suffer from inbreeding degeneration (Winge and Laustsen, 1940). Even after direct diploidization its spore germination percentage was about 85, and if the hypothesis on the role of the chondriosomes is correct, it becomes necessary to assume that the chondriosomes of this species divide at about the same time as the cell nucleus.

Again, no inbreeding degeneration has been observed in *S. priorianus.* The fact that this species is homothallic and was formerly classified under the genus *Zygosaccharomyces* because its vegetative reproduction may take place in the haplophase, implies *eo ipso* that it can be inbred without suffering deterioration. Direct diploidization has not, however, been observed in this species.

A long series of publications on cytoplasmatic inheritance in yeasts by Ephrussi and his collaborators has appeared in recent years (Ephrussi, 1948; Ephrussi *et al.*, 1949 a, b, c; Slonimski, 1949; Slonimski and Ephrussi, 1949; Tavlitzki, 1949; Ephrussi, 1950; Ephrussi and Hottinguer, 1950; Chen *et al.*, 1950; Ephrussi and Hottinguer, 1951; Slonimski and Hirsch, 1952), and in his book "Nucleo-cytoplasmatic Relations in Microorganisms" (1953) Ephrussi devotes a special chapter to a discussion of the results obtained.

He observed that when a haploid or diploid baking yeast is plated out on solid medium in petri dishes, most of the colonies develop at the same rate but ca. 1–2% have a much lower growth rate and remain small; these were designated as "littles." If transfers from the large colonies are again plated out, the phenomenon repeats itself, but if transfers from the small colonies are plated out, only small colonies will develop: the "littles" were therefore constant. Strangely enough, it was found that under anaerobic conditions, during which the yeast derives its energy solely from carbohydrate fermentation, the baking yeast when plated out gave rise to only one type of colony. This indicated that the "littles" possessed some abnormal respiratory mechanism, and by painstaking experiments, it was demonstrated that the "littles" actually lacked certain respiratory enzymes belonging to the cytochrome system. It was possible through spectroscopic investigations to show that the normal cells exhibited different spectra from those of the "littles," the latter lacking two bands for the cytochromes a and b. Moreover, with regard to the respiratory quotient, the "littles" were found to deviate from the normal and furthermore they gave a negative Nadi reaction.

It was found that in addition to this spontaneous mutation from normal → "little," a much greater frequency of "littles" could be induced by the action of certain acridines, e.g., acriflavine, and in the presence of pure euflavine, nearly 100% of the cells were transferred into "littles."

Since more than one enzyme was lacking in the "littles," it appeared improbable that a simple gene mutation was involved; at least, this would not be in accord with the 1 gene–1 enzyme hypothesis.

Hybridization experiments between haploid normals and "littles" confirmed the assumption that the phenomenon was not explicable in terms of a gene mutation, but rather that cytoplasmatic mutation was involved.

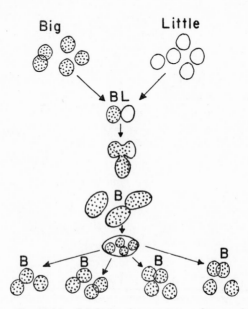

FIG. 5. Diagram illustrating the lack of segregation from a hybrid between a normal yeast and a "vegetative little" strain. Normal cytoplasm is stippled. (Redrawn from Ephrussi, 1953.)

When normal (large) is crossed with "little," the hybrid is normal and segregation of the two types is not obtained by isolating spores from the hybrid (Fig. 5). On the other hand, marker genes for the synthesis of thiamine and adenine segregated out regularly from the hybrid (Ephrussi *et al.*, 1949b), indicating that the hybrid was genuine.

The proposed explanation of these findings was that "certain particles with genetic continuity in the cytoplasm were required for synthesis of certain respiratory enzymes." The authors assume that the number of particles per cell is approximately 10. The acridines are believed to have a damaging effect upon these particles (chondriosomes?) in the cytoplasm.

Not less interesting was the observation that a French baking yeast contained a mutant gene for "littles" involving a similar respiratory abnormality but which segregated out quite normally in crosses (Chen *et al.* 1950). The interaction of the cytoplasmatic deficiency, whereby vegetative "littles" originate, and the mutant gene, whereby segregational "littles" originate, seems to involve the fact that both normal cytoplasm and the normal gene must be present in order for normal respiration to take place.

If the cytoplasmatic factor for normal respiration is designated R and the deficient factor r, and if the gene for normal respiration is designated N and the gene for abnormal respiration n, then a hybrid ascus, $Nn\ Rr$, would transmit to its four spores the cytoplasmatic factor R, while N would be transmitted to two spores and n to the other two. Thus a tetrad would yield the following spores: $2NR$ (normal) and $2nR$ ("little").

Later Ephrussi *et al.* (1955) reported the occurrence of a new respiratory factor which was called "suppressiveness" for vegetative "littles," and which assumedly is biochemically identical with the earlier vegetative "littles" but which can be distinguished by its behavior in crosses with normal yeasts.

Raut and Simpson (1955) produced vegetative "littles" by Röntgen irradiation and alternatively by ultraviolet light, finding that the latter was the most effective in the production of mutations. At 2600 Å, the absorption maximum for nucleic acids, a good effect was obtained, which led the authors to propose the hypothesis that nucleic acid-containing elements, which probably are identical with the self-duplicating elements in the cytoplasm (see above), are destroyed by irradiation. It is possible that the self-duplicating particles are actually PNA-containing mitochondria.

Skovsted (1956) regarded the vegetative mutations which caused submerged growth of the giant colonies of *Saccharomyces cerevisiae* and of certain red-colored mutants as due to unstable cytoplasmatic factors.

Spiegelman *et al.* (1951) and Spiegelman (1951) undertook some noteworthy experiments with *Saccharomyces chevalieri*. In this species there occurs a "long-term adaptation" to galactose fermentation (Winge and Roberts, 1948), to which we have already alluded in the section on Mendelian Segregation. When this yeast is grown in galactose yeast-water, approximately 6 days elapse before fermentation is visible, while certain other *Saccharomyces* species ferment galactose in the course of 1–2 days. The rapidly fermenting types possess the gene G, while S. *chevalieri* has g_s. However, when a g_s type has been adapted by growth on a galactose-containing medium, it is able to ferment just as rapidly as a G type. Spiegelman agrees with Winge and Roberts in their views (opposed to that of Lindegren) that mutation of $g_s \rightarrow G$ is not involved in long-term adaptation. The adapted g_s type can be easily deadapted by growth in a galactose-free medium. This process of deadaptation has been studied in detail by Spiegelman and his collaborators.

They transferred single cells of an adapted g_s type on to a galactose-free substrate and from a given mother cell they isolated and grew the successive buds which it produced. The cultures arising from these individual cells were plated out on eosin-methylene blue galactose test plates, and it was found that those arising from the daughter cells first isolated were all adapted, i.e., galactose fermenters (positives), but the culture arising from the fifth bud isolated was composed of both positives and negatives (deadapted), while the sixth and seventh buds yielded cultures with an increasing number of negative colonies. They also found that the culture arising from a mother cell which had produced ca. 7 daughter cells can itself be negative, although the cultures arising from the daughter-cell may be positive.

The explanation proposed was that an adapted g_s cell contains approximately 100 cytoplasmatic particles which produce galactozymase. When an adapted g_s cell is transferred to a galactose-free medium, the formation of these particles ceases and therefore each successive bud produced by the adapted cell will obtain a smaller number of particles than its predecessor; it is assumed that a daughter cell receives approximately 50% of the particles contained in the mother cell at the time of bud liberation. Thus the number of particles will be halved for each succeeding cell generation until complete deadaptation or lack of particles is attained. The authors are of the opinion that a solitary particle is sufficient for the development of an adapted culture.

From these interesting investigations it can be concluded that the gene g_s in the presence of galactose produces a first particle, capable of synthesizing galactozymase. This particle is autocatalytically able to propagate itself in the presence of galactose more rapidly than cell division can take place, and therefore the new cells formed during adaptation will receive increasingly larger numbers of these enzyme-synthesizing particles until full adaptation is attained. It must naturally be assumed that the g_s gene constantly produces new particles in the presence of galactose, but that this particle formation is surpassed by the particle formation due to the autocatalytic process. The view that these particles are themselves the enzyme molecules cannot be supported, for as Spiegelman rightly maintains (personal communication to O. Winge), the number of enzyme molecules in an adapted cell must greatly exceed

100. It should be mentioned, however, that it is possible that the enzyme molecule is broken down in the absence of galactose so that the calculated number of 100 particles may be doubtful.

According to Campbell and Spiegelman's hypothesis (1956) the "autocatalyst involved in enzyme formation is a complex of three entities, a template, an inducer, and the enzyme itself. Autocatalytic activation of the enzyme-forming system is then achieved as a result of the production of new enzyme molecules."

References

Ahmad, M. (1953). *Scientist Pakistan* **1**, 1.

Bauch, R. (1941). *Naturwissenschaften* **29**, 503.

Bauch, R. (1943). *Arch. Mikrobiol.* **13**, 352.

Bauch, R. (1954). *Wiss. Z. Univ. Greifswald* **3**, 123.

Burkholder, P. R. (1943). *Am. J. Botany* **30**, 206.

Campbell, A. M., and Spiegelman, S. (1956). *Compt. rend. trav. lab. Carlsberg, Sér. physiol.* **26**, 13.

Chen, S. Y., Ephrussi, B., and Hottinguer, H. (1950). *Heredity* **4**, 335.

Ditlevsen, E. (1944). *Compt. rend. trav. lab. Carlsberg, Sér. physiol.* **24**, 223.

Douglas, H. C., and Condie, F. (1954). *J. Bacteriol.* **68**, 662.

Duraiswami, S., and Subramaniam, M. K. (1950). *Cellule* **53**, 215.

Ephrussi, B. (1948). *Colloq. intern. centre nat. recherche sci.* (*Paris*) **8**, 165.

Ephrussi, B. (1950). *Pubbl. staz. zool. Napoli* Suppl. **22**, 50.

Ephrussi, B. (1953). "Nucleo-cytoplasmic Relations in Microorganisms: Their Bearing on Cell Heredity and Differentiation." Oxford Univ. Press, London and New York.

Ephrussi, B., and Hottinguer, H. (1950). *Nature* **166**, 956.

Ephrussi, B., and Hottinguer, H. (1951). *Cold Spring Harbor Symposia Quant. Biol.* **16**, 75.

Ephrussi, B., Hottinguer, H., and Chiménes, A. (1949a). *Ann. inst. Pasteur* **76**, 351.

Ephrussi, B., Hottinguer, H., and Tavlitzki, J. (1949b). *Ann. inst. Pasteur* **76**, 419.

Ephrussi, B., L'Héretier, P., and Hottinguer, H. (1949c). *Ann. inst. Pasteur* **77**, 64.

Ephrussi, B., de Margerie-Hottinguer, H., and Roman, H. (1955). *Proc. Natl. Acad. Sci. U.S.* **41**, 1065.

Fabian, F. W., and McCullough, N. B. (1934). *J. Bacteriol.* **27**, 583.

Fowell, R. R. (1956). *Compt. rend. trav. lab. Carlsberg, Sér. physiol.* **26**, 117.

Gilliland, R. B. (1949). *Compt. rend. trav. lab. Carlsberg Sér. physiol.* **24**, 347.

Gilliland, R. B. (1951). *European Brewery Conv. Proc. 3rd Congr. Brighton 1951*, p. 35.

Gilliland, R. B. (1953). *European Brewery Conv. Proc. 4th Congr. Nice 1953*, p. 121.

Gilliland, R. B. (1954a). *Nature* **173**, 409.

Gilliland, R. B. (1954b). *Wallerstein Lab. Communs.* **17**, 165.

Hansen, E. C. (1905). *Centr. Bakteriol. Parasitenk. Abt. II* **15**, 353.

Hansen, E. C. (1907). *Centr. Bakteriol. Parasitenk. Abt. II* **18**, 577.

Hawthorne, D. C. (1955). *Genetics* **40**, 511.

Hawthorne, D. C. (1956). *Compt. rend. trav. lab. Carlsberg, Sér. physiol.* **26**, 149.

James, A. P. (1954). *J. Bacteriol.* **67**, 237.

James, A. P. (1955). *Genetics* **40**, 204.

James, A. P., and Lee-Whiting, B. (1955). *Genetics* **40**, 826.

Jinks, J. L. (1953). *Compt. rend. trav. lab. Carlsberg, Sér. physiol.* **25**, 252.

Krishna Murthy, S. N., and Subramaniam, M. K. (1950). *J. Indian Inst. Sci.* **A32**, 1.

Krishna Murthy, S. N., and Subramaniam, M. K. (1951). *Current Sci. (India)* **20**, 17.

Kudriavtsev, V. I., and Kosikov, K. V. (1947). *Microbiologiya.* **16**, 477.

Leupold, U. (1950). *Compt. rend. trav. lab. Carlsberg, Sér. physiol.* **24**, 381.

Leupold, U. (1955). *Arch. Julius Klaus-Stift. Vererbungsforsch. Sozialanthropol. u. Rassenhyg.* **30**, 506.

Leupold, U., and Hottinguer, H. (1954). *Heredity* **8**, 243.

Levan, A., and Sandwell, C. G. (1943). *Hereditas* **29**, 164.

Levan, A. (1944). *Hereditas* **30**, 255.

Levan, A. (1947). *Hereditas* **33**, 457.

Lindegren, C. C. (1945). *Bacteriol. Revs.* **9**, 111.

Lindegren, C. C. (1949). "The Yeast Cell. Its Genetics and Cytology." Educational Publ., St. Louis.

Lindegren, C. C. (1953). *J. Genet.* **51**, 625.

Lindegren, C. C. (1955a). *J. Bacteriol.* **70**, 127.

Lindegren, C. C. (1955b). *Science* **121**, 605.

Lindegren, C. C., and Lindegren, G. (1946). *Cold Spring Harbor Symposia Quant. Biol.* **11**, 115.

Lindegren, C. C., and Lindegren, G. (1947a). *Ann. Missouri Botan. Garden* **34**, 95.

Lindegren, C. C., and Lindegren, G. (1947b). *Proc. Natl. Acad. Sci. U.S.* **33**, 314.

Lindegren, C. C., and Lindegren, G. (1950). *Genetics* **35**, 675.

Lindegren, C. C., and Lindegren, G. (1951). *Indian Phytopathol.* **4**, 11.

Lindegren, C. C., and Lindegren, G. (1952). *Nature* **170**, 965.

Lindegren, C. C., Spiegelman, S., and Lindegren, G. (1944). *Proc. Natl. Acad. Sci. U.S.* **30**, 346.

Losada, M. (1957). *Compt. rend. trav. lab. Carlsberg, Sér. physiol.* **25**, 460.

Magni, G. E. (1949). *Compt. rend. trav. lab. Carlsberg, Sér. psysiol.* **24**, 357.

Morris, E. O., and Kirsop, B. (1953). *J. Inst. Brewing* **58**, 486.

Mundkur, B. D. (1949). *Ann. Missouri Botan. Garden* **36**, 259.

Mundkur, B. D. (1950). *Current Sci. (India)* **19**, 84.

Mundkur, B. D. (1952). *Genetics* **37**, 484.

Mundkur, B. D., and Lindegren, C. C. (1949). *Am. J. Botany* **36**, 722.

Nielsen, N., and Hartelius, V. (1940). *Compt. rend. trav. lab. Carlsberg, Sér. physiol.* **23**, 93.

Oppenoorth, W. F. F. (1956). *Brauwissenschaft* **9**, 106.

Pittman, D. C., and Lindegren, C. C. (1954). *Nature* **173**, 408.

Pomper, S. (1952a). *J. Bacteriol.* **63**, 707.

Pomper, S. (1952b). *J. Bacteriol.* **64**, 353.

Pomper, S. (1953). *J. Bacteriol.* **65**, 666.

Pomper, S., and Burkholder, P. R. (1949). *Proc. Nat. Acad. Sci. U.S.* **35**, 456.

Pomper, S., and McKee, D. W. (1953). *Science* **117**, 62.

Ranganathan, B. (1950). *J. Indian Inst. Sci.* **A32**, 91.

Ranganathan, B., and Subramaniam, M. K. (1950). *J. Indian Inst. Sci.* **A32**, 51.

Raut, C. (1950a). *Genetics* **35**, 686.

Raut, C. (1950b). *Genetics* **35**, 381.

Raut, C., and Simpson, W. L. (1955). *Arch. Biochem. and Biophys.* **57**, 218.

Roberts, C. (1950). *Methods Med. Research* **3**, 37.

Roman, H. (1956). *Compt. rend. trav. lab. Carlsberg, Sér. physiol.* **26**, 299.

Roman, H., Hawthorne, D. C., and Douglas, H. C. (1951). *Proc. Natl. Acad. Sci. U.S.* **37**, 79.

Skovsted, A. (1943). *Compt. rend. trav. lab. Carlsberg, Sér. physiol.* **23**, 409.

Skovsted, A. (1948). *Compt. rend. trav. lab. Carlsberg, Sér. physiol.* **24**, 249.

Skovsted, A. (1956). *Compt. rend. trav. lab. Carlsberg, Sér. physiol.* **26**, 335.

Slonimski, P. P. (1949). *Ann. inst. Pasteur* **76**, 510.

Slonimski, P. P., and Ephrussi, B. (1949). *Ann. inst. Pasteur* **77**, 47.

Slonimski, P. P., and Hirsch, H. M. (1952). *Compt. rend.* **235**, 741.

Spiegelman, S. (1951). *Cold Spring Harbor Symposia Quant. Biol.* **16**, 87.

Spiegelman, S., and De Lorenzo, W. F. (1952). *Proc. Natl. Acad. Sci. U.S.* **38**, 583.

Spiegelman, S., Lindegren, C. C., and Lindegren, G. (1945). *Proc. Natl. Acad. Sci. U.S.* **31**, 95.

Spiegelman, S., De Lorenzo, W. F., and Campbell, A. M. (1951). *Proc. Natl. Acad. Sci. U.S.* **37**, 513.

Srb, A. M. (1956). *Compt. rend. trav. lab. Carlsberg, Sér. physiol.* **26**, 363.

Subramaniam, M. K., and Krishna Murthy, S. N. (1948). *Current Sci. (India)* **17**, 92.

Subramaniam, M. K., and Sreepathi Rao, S. K. (1950). *Research (London)* **3**, 49.

Subramaniam, M. K., Ranganathan, B., and Krishna Murthy, S. N. (1948). *Cellule* **52**, 39.

Takizawa, R. (1939). *Japan. J. Genet.* **15**, 351.

Tavlitzki, J. (1949). *Ann. inst. Pasteur* **76**, 497.

Thaysen, A. C., and Morris, M. (1943). *Nature* **152**, 526.

Thorne, R. S. W. (1951). *Compt. rend. trav. lab. Carlsberg, Sér. physiol.* **25**, 101.

Winge, Ö. (1935). *Compt. rend. trav. lab. Carlsberg, Sér. physiol.* **21**, 77.

Winge, Ö. (1944). *Compt. rend. trav. lab. Carlsberg, Sér. physiol.* **24**, 79.

Winge, Ö. (1947). *Compt. rend. trav. lab. Carlsberg, Sér. physiol.* **24**, 223.

Winge, Ö. (1951). *Compt. rend. trav. lab. Carlsberg, Sér. physiol.* **25**, 85.

Winge, Ö. (1952). *Wallerstein Labs. Communs.* **15**, 21.

Winge, Ö. (1955). *Compt. rend. trav. lab. Carlsberg, Sér. physiol.* **25**, 341.

Winge, Ö., and Laustsen, O. (1937). *Compt. rend. trav. lab. Carlsberg, Sér. physiol.* **22**, 99.

Winge, Ö., and Laustsen, O. (1938). *Compt. rend. trav. lab. Carlsberg, Sér. physiol.* **22**, 235.

Winge, Ö., and Laustsen, O. (1939a). *Compt. rend. trav. lab. Carlsberg, Sér. physiol.* **22**, 357.

Winge, Ö., and Laustsen, O. (1939b). *Compt. rend. trav. lab. Carlsberg, Sér. physiol.* **22**, 337.

Winge, Ö., and Laustsen, O. (1940). *Compt. rend. trav. lab. Carlsberg, Sér. physiol.* **23**, 17.

Winge, Ö., and Roberts, C. (1948). *Compt. rend. trav. lab. Carlsberg, Sér. physiol.* **24**, 263.

Winge, Ö., and Roberts, C. (1950a). *Compt. rend. trav. lab. Carlsberg, Sér. physiol.* **25**, 35.

Winge, Ö., and Roberts, C. (1950b). *Nature* **166**, 1114.

Winge, Ö., and Roberts, C. (1950c). *Nature* **165**, 157.

Winge, Ö., and Roberts, C. (1952). *Compt. rend. trav. lab. Carlsberg, Sér. physiol.* **25,** 141.

Winge, Ö., and Roberts, C. (1953). *Compt. rend. trav. lab. Carlsberg, Sér. physiol.* **25,** 241.

Winge, Ö., and Roberts, C. (1954a). *Compt. rend. trav. lab. Carlsberg, Sér. physiol.* **25,** 285.

Winge, Ö., and Roberts, C. (1954b). *Heredity* **8,** 295.

Winge, Ö., and Roberts, C. (1955). *Compt. rend. trav. lab. Carlsberg, Sér. physiol.* **25,** 331.

Winge, Ö., and Roberts, C. (1956). *Nature* **177,** 383.

Winge, Ö., and Roberts, C. (1957). *Compt. rend. trav. lab. Carlsberg, Sér. physiol.* **25,** 419.

Winkler, H. (1930). "Die Konversion der Gene." Gustav Fischer, Jena.

Yamamoto, Y. (1940). *Botan. and Zool. (Tokyo)* **8,** 916.

CHAPTER V

Aspects of the Chemical Composition of Yeast

A. A. EDDY

1. Mineral Constituents

Analysis of the Ash. Controlled combustion of yeast leaves a residue of ash variously reported as comprising from 1.9 to 10% of the initial dry weight of the cells. Early determinations (Czäpek, 1920), showed that, depending on the strain, a given yeast grown in various media might yield a relatively constant or variable amount of ash. While Czäpek favored a value on the low side (about 2%), Jörgensen (1948) quotes 5 to 9% as typical for top and bottom yeasts. Two examples illustrate the kind of behavior encountered; Wiley and associates (1950) found 5.5–9.8% ash in a certain strain of *Torula* grown on a commercial scale in various bulk media, the value for any given culture depending on the amount of phosphate supplied during growth. Similarly, Fulmer *et al.* (1921) reduced the ash content of a yeast from 7.5% to 3.8% by omitting calcium and magnesium from the growth medium. In spite of the variation encountered with any one strain, different yeasts are said to show small but consistent differences in ash content under comparable circumstances of growth (Schönfeld and Hirt, 1911).

The amount (per cent) of various major constituents of yeast ash as

TABLE I

THE MAJOR CONSTITUENTS OF YEAST ASH (*Saccharomyces cerevisiae*) Composition as per cent of yeast ash

P_2O_5	K_2O	Na_2O	MgO	CaO	SiO_2	SO_3	Cl	FeO	References
44.8–59.0	28.0–48.0	0.06–0.7	4.0–8.1	1.0–4.5	0.0–1.6	0.4–6.0	0.03–1.0	0.1–7.3	Joslyn (1941)
50.6	33.4	Trace	6.1	5.5	1.3	0.56		0.5	Czäpek (1920)
54–58	29–31	0.8–1.9	4.0–7.0	1.6–2.5	Trace			0.8–7.3	Béchamps (1952)

TABLE II

TRACE METALS IN YEAST (*Saccharomyces cerevisiae*)
Composition as μg./g. dry weight cells; — indicates that the element was not detected

Yeast	Al	Ba	B	Cr	Co	Cu	Fe	Pb	Mn	Mo	Ni	Sn	V	Zn	References
Baker's A	1000	150	—	—	50			400	70			200		3000	Webb and Fearon (1937)
Baker's B, C, D	1000	150	—	—	50			8	70			—		3000	
Brewer's A	100	200	200	10	—			—	10			—			
Baker's E						20	170							130	Frey (1948)
Brewer's B					5	40	90		5					50	
Brewer's C	3					37	17	2	4	0.1	3	3	0.04		Hudson (1956)
Brewer's D	2					104	17	14	5	0.04	4	>100	0.04		
Brewer's E	1					34	25	100	11	2.7	3	3	0.07		

quoted by various authorities are given in Table I. Corresponding figures for elements usually present in lesser amount are given in Table II, the figures in this case being expressed in micrograms per gram dry weight of whole cells. The figures obtained by Webb and Fearon (1937) and by Hudson (1956) are based on a refined spectrographic technique. The work of Richards and Troutman (1940), although it has been widely quoted, has not been included in Table II because the results were only semi-quantitative and on examination lead one to suspect that they represent not the relative amounts of the elements in the yeast itself but rather the relative intensities of the corresponding spectral lines appearing on the photographic plates.

Certain broad regularities emerge from the data in Tables I and II. The greater part of the ash is seen to consist of potassium phosphate, magnesium being the next element in order of abundance. However, it is interesting to note that there is at least one report of a yeast containing as much sodium as potassium on a molecular basis (Davies et al., 1953). A study by Rubinstein and Burlakowa (1934) illustrates further the variations that occur. Using 2 mg.% and 90 mg.%, respectively, of calcium in a synthetic medium, 37 and 93 mg.% were found in the yeast. Similarly 5 mg.% of sodium in the medium led to 197 mg.% being accumulated in the yeast, while 200 mg.% in the medium gave 314 in the yeast.

A further point concerns the possibility that the small amounts of certain metals normally found in samples of yeast have not actually been taken up by the cells but have merely been retained with traces of liquid medium not removed by washing. This matter is especially important in view of the existence of an outer region of the yeast permeated by ions (see p. 231). Hudson (1956) found that only 0.005 γ/ml. of molybdenum and vanadium and 0.1γ/ml. of manganese were present in the wort in which his yeasts were growing. A simple calculation then shows that each of these elements was in fact concentrated by the yeast and not just entrapped with adhering medium. A similar conclusion is probably justified regarding his other data, and, possibly, the further figures quoted in Table II. It will be noted that in some cases only small amounts of certain metals, such as vanadium and molybdenum are found in the yeast. This suggests that actual requirements for growth are also quite small; thus an uptake of 0.1 μg. of metal/g. dry weight of cells corresponds to about 0.1 μg. of metal/l. of mature culture containing 4–5 g. of wet yeast. Such a small amount is probably less than what would normally remain after purification of a growth medium by precipitation techniques (see Olson and Johnson, 1949), the inference being that the existence of the requirement would go undetected as there would be no need to supplement the medium with the metal in question (see Chapter VII).

Uptake of Metal Ions by Yeast. There are various reports in the literature about the loss as well as about the accumulation of metal ions by yeast, which in part explain why a given yeast may on different occasions vary in composition. Thus yeast cells may lose, or gain, specific cations by a process resembling ionic exchange. For example, Genaud in 1930 (Genevois, 1951) reported that of 10 meq. of cation in a certain sample of yeast, 2.6 meq. (1.4 of K^+ plus 1.2 of Ca^{++}) were excreted by the cells when they were suspended in a solution of a lead salt, 2.7 meq. of lead being taken up instead. The yeast was still partly viable after this treatment and fermented glucose vigorously. During the first minute 60% of the lead eventually to be absorbed appeared to be fixed in the cell wall where it stained black with a solution of sodium sulfide. Further uptake depended on a slow process of diffusion through the region of the cell wall into the cytoplasm and thence to the vacuoles, where appreciable concentrations of lead appeared to collect. Repeated washing with a solution of a lead salt resulted in all the original cation being displaced by lead. Sodium, ammonium, and potassium were likewise able to change places with the cell cations but not so readily as the divalent metals, calcium and lead.

Analogous behavior is encountered when yeast is actually grown in the presence of one or more metal ions. Indeed, with the proper choice of conditions, metals normally present in trace quantities may be extensively absorbed, as Abelson and Aldous (1950) have shown using radioactive nickel and cobalt with a strain of *Torula utilis* (see Perlman and O'Brien, 1954). In one investigation, nearly all the nickel in solution, corresponding to 120 μg./g. of dry weight of the cells was taken up in the presence of 0.2 p.p.m. of magnesium, but only 6 μg./g. when the concentration of magnesium was increased one hundredfold. Cobalt showed a similar behavior; using low concentrations of magnesium and high concentrations of cobalt in the external medium, 60,000 μg. cobalt/g. of dry weight entered the cells, a figure corresponding to 6% of the dry weight. Even when 20 p.p.m. of magnesium was present the cobalt content only fell to 6000 μg./g., an amount at least 100 times greater than that normally encountered (Table II). Although the above authors state that cobalt accumulated largely during active metabolism, an uptake of similar magnitude has been reported (Drews *et al.*, 1952) using a simple aqueous solution of a cobalt salt, so that the mechanism may well involve the exchange reaction described by Genaud, unless it be supposed that the starved yeast cells were in fact able to metabolize their own nutrient reserves.

The question of the mechanism of the antagonism by magnesium is of interest because a hundredfold increase in the concentration of the latter seems to result in the exclusion of about 1 mM. cobalt/g. of dry yeast, whereas the normal content of magnesium (see Table I) is appreciably less, being of the order of 0.1 mM. This suggests that magnesium does not merely displace cobalt from sites normally occupied by magnesium itself but in some way restricts the entry of a much greater quantity of cobalt than would be required to cover these sites, perhaps by modifying the permeability of the cell surface.[1]

The specific effect of magnesium has its counterpart in other observations which show that although the majority of cations of a given kind may exchange with foreign ions, apparently without loss of cell function, a residual fraction are unable to do so, a specific role in cell metabolism in fact being reserved for certain metals such as magnesium, iron, copper, zinc, manganese, and potassium (see Chapter VII). This is clearly brought out in the extensive work on potassium metabolism by yeast (see Conway and Moore, 1954; Scott *et al.*, 1951).

When yeast is allowed to ferment its own reserves of carbohydrate, the amount of potassium in the cells falls to a low level. Addition of a fermentable carbohydrate such as glucose results in a rapid and specific uptake of 0.5–0.8 meq. of potassium/g. of dry wt. of the cells, even in the presence of excess ammonium or sodium ions. The most probable explanation is that anions formed during the breakdown of carbohydrate trap potassium in the cells. Conway and his associates (1941) investigated the possibility of replacing the potassium used in this way by sodium ions or, in other experiments, by ammonium ions. This was achieved by omitting potassium salts and allowing the yeast to ferment glucose in the presence of sodium citrate, with the result that after seven successive periods of fermentation an amount of sodium approximately equivalent to the potassium originally present was taken up, while the potassium itself decreased fiftyfold. Schmidt and Hecht (1944) have also prepared a "sodium" yeast, by depriving the cells of magnesium and adding excess of sodium. In spite of the fact that potassium appeared to be quantitatively replaceable by sodium or ammonium, the substituted strains were found to grow less rapidly than the normal yeast and may in fact have depended on traces of potassium to function at all.

A broad view of the various exchange phenomena already mentioned and of work dealing with the uptake of nickel, sodium, and other metals

---

[1] This suggestion is rendered the more plausible by the fact that ions appear not to enter the cell by free diffusion but rather by a "carrier mechanism" (see p. 233). It may be imagined that in the absence of excess of magnesium the normal carrier of this metal attaches itself to cobalt.

leads to the conclusion that much of the normal complement of cell cations is either (a) associated in the cell, or (b) permitted to enter the cell only in association with anions showing a fairly marked but not exclusive preference for particular cations.[2] On the other hand, the existence of absolute requirements for certain metals indicates that highly specific attachments are also formed, the role of iron in the formation of the heme enzymes belonging to this category.

2. Vitamins

B Group. In the course of the extensive studies during the last thirty years of the chemical composition and structure of the principal vitamins, a detailed literature has grown up about their distribution. Proposals to use yeast as a food, and the search for cheap and plentiful sources of particular vitamins, has led to much detailed study of the factors influencing their synthesis by different yeasts under diverse conditions (van Lanen and Tanner, 1948). Representative figures for the amounts of the various water-soluble vitamins of the B group in yeast are given in Table III.

In general the amounts of inositol and choline encountered greatly exceed those of the other vitamins. Both substances probably form an essential part of the actual cell structure, possibly in the form of lipids. Detailed studies have revealed the complexity of the factors governing the amount of the vitamins in the cells but few general principles have emerged. For instance, Eremothecium ashbyii, a plant pathogen, normally excretes much riboflavin (about 200 μg./ml.), though under the appropriate conditions this is retained, as crystals have been seen to separate in the vacuoles (Guillermond et al., 1935; Raffy, 1937). Maximum production of riboflavin takes place under aerobic conditions (Raffy, 1939). Another plant pathogen Ashbya gossypii is also capable of producing high concentrations of riboflavin under selected conditions, although early investigators failing to discover these believed that the yeast had no special ability in this direction (Guillermond et al., 1935; Schopfer and Guillond, 1945). Candida guillermondii is another species of yeast capable of elaborating as much as 200 μg./ml. riboflavin; in this case, as with other microorganisms producing riboflavin, the maximum yield is produced only in the presence of critical concentrations of iron (e.g., values 0.005–0.01 p.p.m. have been quoted for certain yeasts). The amount of air and iron available are said to influence also the riboflavin content of

---

[2] In the case of metals such as potassium, it seems likely that the selective forces responsible are analogous to those ordering the process of crystallization, in which specific metals frequently participate to the exclusion of others.

TABLE III
VITAMINS IN YEAST (μg./g.)

Yeast	Folic acid	Thiamine	Ribo- flavin	Panto- thenic acid	Niacin	Biotin	p-Amino benzoic acid	Pyri- doxine	Inositol	Choline
Candida arborea	15–19	32	46–69		157–580	0.3				
Endomyces vernalis		15–34								
Hansenula suaveolena	1.7	8.5	54	180	590		16			
Mycotorula lipolytica	3.1	5.3	59		600	118	31			
Odium lactis	6–15	20–29	40–55		195–248					
Saccharomyces carlsbergensis		31								
Saccharomyces ellipsoideus		38								
Saccharomyces cerevisiae	19–35	29–90		118–198	190–585	0.5–1.8	8–95		4320	
Saccharomyces logos		7–30								
Torula utilis	4–31	6–53	26–62	86–180	210–535	1.1–1.9	17–21	35	3500	
Willia anomala	57	10–30								
Zygosaccharomyces sp.		39								
Baker's	15–80	9–40		180–330	200–700		22–175	16–65		2100
Enriched baker's		650–750			29–30					
Brewer's	3	50–360	36–42	100	310–1000		9–102	25–100	2700–5000	4850

strains of the yeast *Saccharomyces cerevisiae* (van Lanen and Tanner, 1948), a constant amount of vitamin being retained by the yeast but a variable amount excreted.

Partial syntheses of vitamins from complex starting materials are also of commercial importance. One such method is based on the discovery that a mixture of the appropriate pyrimidine and thiazole, which in the molecule of the vitamin are condensed as a quarternary thiazolium salt, was able to satisfy a requirement for thiamine itself by *Staphylococcus aureus* (Knight, 1937). In the presence of these substances and certain of their derivatives (see van Lanen and Tanner, 1948) the normal complement of thiamine in baker's yeast (9–40 μg./g.) may increase up to 1000 μg./g. Other kinds of yeasts carry out this reaction, though often less efficiently (van Lanen *et al.*, 1942). An interesting feature of the reaction is that it is stimulated markedly by aeration, a condition which normally tends to reduce the production of thiamine (see Lewis *et al.*, 1944).

Another and perhaps related form of behavior is encountered with yeasts which lack the ability to synthesize their own requirements of vitamins and normally rely therefore on external sources. Chang and Peterson (1949) showed that a strain of *Torula utilis* as well as another of *Candida arborea* neither required biotin to be added to the growth medium in order to proliferate, nor accumulated it in quantity when it was added. A strain of S. *cerevisiae*, on the other hand, accumulated quantities of the order of 100 μg./g. from solutions containing more than 500 μg./ml. and failed to grow maximally when less than about 0.2 μg./ml. was included in the medium. As Ingram has noted (1955), when the cells are unable to supply their own needs the amount of vitamin absorbed may greatly exceed the minimum requirements for growth. A difference in ability to synthesize pantothenate and niacin may also account for the failure, noted by Peterson (1948), of a certain strain of S. *cerevisiae* to accumulate the first vitamin from enriched culture media, in contrast to its ability to accumulate approximately 3000 μg./g. of the second vitamin (see Novelli and Lipmann, 1950). Just as yeasts may show a wide range of abilities to synthesize particular vitamins, the extent to which absorption takes place from the medium, or to which the medium is supplemented by excretion may be expected in general to vary from strain to strain and with the nature of the medium itself (see Lewis *et al.*, 1944).

The complex types of behavior with respect to excretion and accumulation of vitamins are only to be understood in relation to the various forms in which particular vitamins occur intracellularly. There is for instance the combined form of biotin, biocytin, examined by Chang and Peterson (1949). Of the total biotin in the cells of various yeasts, some with and others without the ability to accumulate biotin from the medium, they found that part was readily extracted with hot water while the remainder was firmly bound in the cell, being liberated only after prolonged hydrolysis with acid. Furthermore, the soluble fraction contained both free and combined biotin, on the basis of tests with two strains of lactobacilli which appeared to differ in ability to utilize the combined form. Typical results are illustrated in Table IV for a strain

TABLE IV

DISTRIBUTION OF BIOTIN IN *Torula utilis*[a]

Biotin in growth medium (γ/100 ml.)	Biotin in yeast (μg./g.)			
	Total	Free	Soluble bound	Insoluble bound
0	3.5	0.02	0.3	2.9
8	5.1	0.59	0.8	3.4
32	6.0	1.2	2.3	3.1
64	7.4	1.6	2.6	2.9
128	7.6	1.9	2.0	2.9

[a] Adapted from Chang and Peterson (1949).

of *Torula utilis*. It is at once apparent that in spite of the large increases in the total uptake of biotin in supplemented media, the amount bound in an insoluble form is approximately constant. Soluble bound biotin, biocytin, has been identified as ϵ-N-biotinyl-L-lysine (Wright *et al.*, 1952). The insoluble fraction is probably associated with protein (Chang and Peterson, 1951).

The various familiar coenzymes containing particular vitamins as a part of the molecule are given in Table V. Hydrolysis with acid is one means of releasing the simpler forms of the vitamin. Alkaline conditions are to be avoided, as they tend to destroy vitamins such as thiamine. Autolytic procedures are also used as is treatment with suitable enzymes.

An interesting case which illustrates the kind of behavior encountered when groups of closely related compounds are formed is that of the *folic acid group* of vitamins which Allfrey and King (1950) found to be associated with certain proteins in fractions obtained from yeast hydrolysates by precipitation with neutral salts. The parent substance of the folic acid group, pteroylglutamic acid, stimulates the growth of *Lactobacillus casei, Streptococcus faecalis*, and chicks. A related substance, folinic acid, is identified by its ability to stimulate the growth of a certain strain of

TABLE V

VITAMINS AND DERIVED COENZYMES

Vitamin	Coenzyme complex
Niacin (nicotinic acid)	"Cozymase," Coenzyme I (DPN)
	Coenzyme II (TPN)
Thiamine (aneurin)	Cocarboxylase (thiamine pyrophosphate)
Pantothenic acid	Coenzyme A
Riboflavin	Flavine mononucleotide (FMN)
	Flavine adenine dinucleotide (FAD)
Biotin	Biocytin and similar complexes
Folic acid group	Pteroylglutamic acid, citrovorum factor, etc.
p-Aminobenzoic acid	Folic acid group
Pyridoxine	Pyridoxamine, pyridoxal, and their phosphates

Leuconostoc citrovorum. Both folic acid and folinic acid are principally found in nature in conjugation with several glutamic acid residues, in which form they lack ability to stimulate the microorganisms but retain their potency towards chicks. The active forms are released on treatment with specific enzymes, conjugases, occurring in various animal organs. Pteroylheptaglutamic acid was isolated from yeast by Pfiffner and his associates (1945), while a folinic acid conjugate was obtained in a concentrated but still impure form by Hill and Scott (1952). A related substance is a p-aminobenzoylpolyglutanic acid (Ratner *et al.*, 1944, 1946) containing no pteridine group and 10–11 glutamic acid residues linked in the γ position (Kandel and Kandel, 1955; Bricas and Fromageot, 1953). This important group of substances appears to conform to the general plan illustrated below.

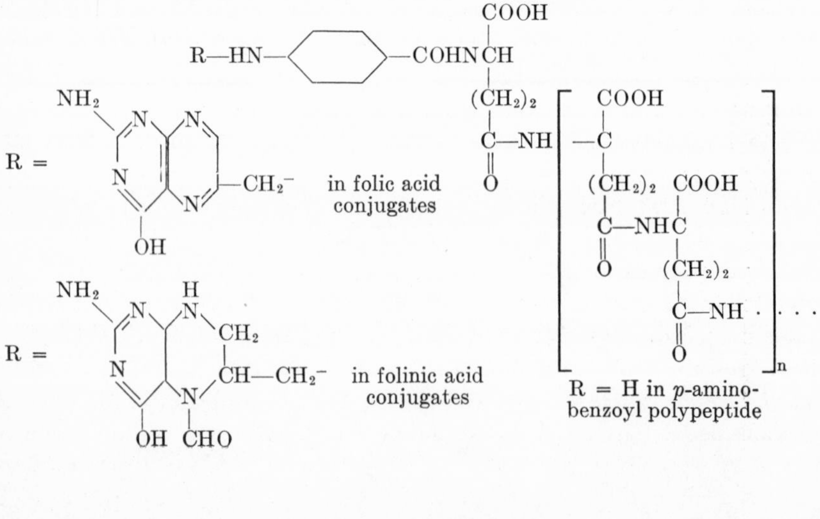

Doctor and Peterson (1955) found that in a number of yeasts grown in the laboratory the folic acid factors accounted for from 31–65% of the combined activity due to folic and folinic acid factors.

Other Vitamins. Yeast contains little or no ascorbic acid (vitamin C) (Boas-Fiscen and Roscoe, 1940) but may absorb it from the medium (quoted by van Lanen and Tanner, 1948). Vitamin B_{12} is likewise deficient (<0.3 γ/g. dry weight) even when excess cobalt, a metal forming part of the molecule, is fed externally (Drews *et al.*, 1952; see Briggs and Daft, 1955).

As regards the fat-soluble vitamins, vitamin A itself is lacking, although related substances may be found in the carotenoid pigments produced by yeasts of the genus *Rhodotorula* (see p. 208). Vitamins E and K are likewise absent. On the other hand, yeast is a good source of ergosterol which is known to produce calciferol, vitamin D_2, on irradiation with ultraviolet light, a substance closely related chemically and physiologically to natural vitamin D_3 in liver oil (see p. 205). Linolenic and linoleic acid, two of the so-called essential fatty acids probably occur in yeast fat (Kleinzeller, 1948). Certain unidentified factors required for animal welfare and insect nutrition may be provided in the form of yeast (Zucker and Zucker, 1950; Johnson, 1955). Recently one such factor vitamin B_T, has been identified as $(CH_3)_3N^+ \cdot CH_2 \cdot CH(OH)CH_2COO^-$ (Carter *et al.*, 1952).

3. Amino Acids

Free Amino Acids. When yeast is extracted in the cold with 10% trichloroacetic acid about 6–27%, typically 15% of the total nitrogen is removed, more than half of which is accounted for as "amino" nitrogen (Roine, 1946; Carter, 1950; Dunn, 1952). Of the remaining undissolved nitrogen the part (64–76% of the total nitrogen) not present as purine or pyrimidine is mostly in the form of protein.

The work of Gale and his associates has shown that the presence of appreciable amounts of readily extractable amino acid in the washed cells is a typical characteristic of gram-positive as opposed to gram-negative microorganisms, the behavior of yeast being no exception to this rule (Gale, 1953). In order to measure the relative amounts of a particular amino acid in the free and combined form, the amount released when the yeast cells are boiled for 15 minutes in water (or extracted with 10% trichloroacetic acid or 70% aqueous ethanol) is compared with the total amount released by complete hydrolysis (Freeland and Gale, 1947).[3] In the case summarized in Table VI, the total free amino acid in the 5 cases examined was found to represent about a third of the whole. This fact

[3] These authors carried out the assays with specific amino acid decarboxylases.

would seem to account for the common experience that certain enzyme activities in well-nourished yeast may develop in the absence of an external supply of nitrogen for growth and furthermore that the cells may even start to divide under these conditions (Stephenson, 1949; Spiegelman *et al.*, 1955). The use of the term free amino acid for the soluble fraction is perhaps open to criticism, even if justifiable by common usage; at least it seems that whatever combinations occur with other constituents inside the cell, they are highly unstable, as the free form of, for example, glutamic acid is not distinguishable from the simple acid itself after extraction (Gale, 1953).

TABLE VI

FREE AND COMBINED AMINO ACIDS OF YEAST[a]

Results expressed as per cent of total cell nitrogen; "free" amino acid is that extracted by solvents such as 70% ethanol

Amino acid	% "Free"	% Combined
Lysine	7.4	7.6
Histidine	1.6	3.3
Tyrosine	0.07	1.4
Glutamic acid	2.3	5.8
Arginine	5.0	7.8

[a] From Freeland and Gale (1947).

Shirley Taylor has shown that the amounts of particular amino acids in the extractable form vary widely with the nature of yeast and the conditions of growth (Taylor, 1947, 1949). For instance, a Dutch top yeast contained about 450 μM of lysine per gram of dry weight after growth in a medium containing casein digest and yeast extract, but only 9 μM when these substances were replaced by ammonium sulfate and various essential growth factors. In contrast, yeast foam, another strain of *S. cerevisiae* contained only 39 μM even when harvested from a rich medium. The age of the cells also was important, decreases of up to 50% occurring during the second day of growth. Cells partially depleted of glutamic acid were found to accumulate it from solution in the absence of other nutrients. The accumulation of lysine however, required that glucose be present, although no detailed studies of the mechanism have been reported as in the case of bacteria (Davies *et al.*, 1953; see Gale, 1953).

Qualitative studies of the free amino acids using chromatographic techniques have also been made by Ljungdahl and Sandegren (1950) and by Miettinen (1951) and a quantitative study by Lindan and Work

(1951). Arginine, lysine, and glutamic acid figure prominently on the chromatograms, together with small amounts of the various other common amino acids. Various peptides have been detected, in some cases containing glutamic acid, glycine and alanine but otherwise uncharacterized. The occurrence of γ-aminobutyric acid, presumably produced by the action of glutamic acid decarboxylase, was demonstrated by Ljungdahl and Sandegren (1950) and earlier by Schales and his associates (1946). The α-aminobutyric acid has also been detected, as well as β-alanine; cystine and methionine are lacking but glutathione occurs (Lindan and Work, 1951). The relationship of the free amino acid "pool" to protein and enzyme synthesis has been extensively studied by the Spiegelman school.

Combined Amino Acids. Although the amino acid content of whole yeast would be expected to vary with the conditions of culture, if only because of the fluctuations in the amounts of free amino acids, Block and Bolling (1943a,b, 1945) reached the conclusion that the composition of "yeast protein"[4] with respect to the essential amino acids was relatively independent of the cultural conditions, a statement which may well be true as a first approximation. However, Lüers and Vaidya (1942) claim to have shown that when a certain yeast was grown in dilute molasses its arginine content, expressed as a fraction of the total nitrogen, decreased from 3.5 to 0.5%, while the histidine content increased from 2.7 to 6.5%. Barton-Wright (1949) has also examined this question, using microbiological assays of seven amino acids. The yeast was grown in seven media: two worts, synthetic medium A + ammonium sulfate, A + ammonium sulfate + asparagine, A + peptone, A + peptone + casein hydrolysate and, finally, A + casein hydrolysate + methionine + phenylalanine + histidine. Whereas addition of methionine was found to increase the amount in whole yeast, addition of histidine and phenylalanine failed to increase the respective cell content. The range of compositions encountered is shown in Table VII and is indeed quite narrow in view of the very different amounts of amino acids supplied by the various media. The amino acids appear in each case to have been incorporated in relatively constant amounts into the various cultures of the yeast, and probably into the yeast proteins themselves, although the additional information required for this calculation is not available. Nevertheless, it may be noted that in each of the seven media used in

---

[4] "Yeast protein" is the hypothetical material equivalent in nitrogen content to the whole cells, its weight being taken as 6.45 × cell nitrogen. In calculations of the food value of yeast the presence of free amino acids and of nucleic acid is often ignored.

this work and, indeed, in Block and Bolling's cultures, ample nutrient was available; wider variations in the conditions of culture, such as are definitely known to modify cell activity (Virtanen *et al.*, 1930), might well have induced changes in composition of the magnitude reported by Lüers (see Nagai, 1954; Chiao and Peterson, 1953[5]).

TABLE VII
RANGE OF VARIATION IN AMINO ACID CONTENT OF A SELECTED YEAST[a]

Amino acid	Amount as % of "yeast protein"
Methionine	1.2–3.5
Phenylalanine	2.9–4.0
Histidine	2.2–3.4
Lysine	6.6–8.7
Leucine	5.6–6.9
Isoleucine	4.6–5.8
Valine	5.1–6.5

[a] A certain strain of *Saccharomyces cerevisiae* was grown in seven different media (see text) and the respective amounts of seven amino acids were measured in each case. (Adapted from Barton Wright, 1949.)

The significance to be attached to these findings must be considered, moreover, in relation to the special problems involved in measuring the amounts of the amino acids in natural materials (see Brand and Edsall, 1947; Tristam, 1949). With such reservations in mind and the relative paucity of data, a detailed assessment of the apparent differences in amino acid content, which have been reported for different kinds of yeast is hardly justifiable, though of great interest (Tables VIII and IX). Nevertheless, that differences do in fact occur, even among related species, seems highly probable on the basis of the figures quoted. Here Freeland and Gale's measurements with yeasts grown in the laboratory in a medium controlled composition are of particular value, as having also been corrected to allow for the free amino acids.[6] Lindan and Work (1951) also found small differences, particularly with respect to arginine, threonine, and phenylalanine, between the "protein" fractions of a brewer's and a baker's yeast. All the amino acids (22 in number; see Desneulle,

[5] These authors attempted to increase the content of methionine above the normal rather low level in order to improve the food value of the yeast, but were unable to alter the amounts relative to other amino acids, despite increasing the absolute levels.

[6] An interesting comparison with various bacteria is made in the original paper, particularly as regards the amount of arginine.

groups, the structure being 1-α-D-glucosido-1-α-D-glucose. Trehalose may amount to 10% of the dry weight of top yeast but bottom yeasts contain appreciably less (Tanret, 1931; Myrbäck, 1949; Stewart *et al.*, 1950). Glycogen too may comprise up to 20% of the dry weight of yeast (Lindegren, 1945).

The structural carbohydrates of brewer's and baker's yeast are a *glucan* and a *mannan*, forming about 10% of the dry weight. Microanalytical procedures for determining the various carbohydrates are described by Trevelyan and Harrison (1952) and by Chung and Nickerson (1954).

Tentative early reports of the presence of a levulan and a methyl-pentosan[12] in *Saccharomyces cerevisiae* have not been confirmed (Oshima, 1902; see Lüers, 1929, for a review). The formation of oligosaccharides containing fructose by the transfructosidase activity of invertase may also be mentioned (Fischer *et al.*, 1951), as well as the formation of oligasaccharides containing galactose during hydrolysis of lactose by *Saccharomyces fragilis* (Aronson, 1952).

There is less detailed information available about the carbohydrates in other yeasts but several interesting facts have come to light. Thus the pathogenic capsulated *Torulopsis* species are known to produce both a polysaccharide resembling *starch* and a *pentosan,* each of which has been studied. On the basis of the iodine test, certain strains of *Rhodotorula glutinis* (and of *Candida*) have also been shown to produce starch, though others fail to do so (Lodder and Kreger-van Rij, 1952). The slimy, gelatinous character of cultures of this yeast and of old cultures of many yeasts which form true mycelia seems to imply the presence of carbohydrates. An observation by Usden and Burrell (1952) is of interest in this connection; they isolated a carbohydrate from *Rhodotorula gracilis* (*glutinis*) which gave no color reaction with iodine and which was hydrolyzed to glucose. This yeast shows other unusual properties: it contains neither the mannan nor the glucan of the type present in the wall of baker's yeast. *Schizosaccharomyces octosporus* also lacks the mannan but contains a little glucan together with another polysaccharide of undetermined structure containing glucose and, possibly, acidic residues (Kreger, 1954). An analogous substance seems to occur in certain *Penicillia* and *Endomyces*. The spores of S. *octosporus* contain starch

[12] A fructan might possibly have originated by bacterial activity as occasional heavy infection was by no means unknown in commercial practice. The presence of a thiomethylpentose is now well established (Weygand, 1950). The possibility that changes may occur during isolation and hydrolysis of a polysaccharide should also be considered. Thus isolation of the yeast carbohydrates may involve heating with strong acids or alkali in the presence of air, conditions which are known to induce complex changes in sugar molecules.

(Lodder and Kreger-van Rij, 1952), a fact possibly of significance in relation to the early opinion that certain strains of this genus lack glycogen (see Fink et al., 1940). The distribution of mannan and glucan and of the acetylglucosamine polymer *chitin* is discussed on p. 238.

A. Polysaccharides of Saccharomyces cerevisiae

Glycogen. The initial step in isolating glycogen from yeast involves rupturing the cell walls, for instance, by prolonged grinding with fine sand or by treatment with a warm solution of sodium hydroxide, procedures which are facilitated by first drying the yeast. Part of the glycogen may thus be obtained in solution, but most remains attached to the residue, from which it may be released by treatment with warm dilute acetic acid or cold dilute hydrochloric acid (Northcote, 1953). Nucleic acid is precipitated from the alkaline solution by acidification with acetic acid and after concentration the glycogen is precipitated with ethanol. It is freed from mannan (yeast gum) by precipitation with Fehling's solution and after dialysis and reprecipitation with alcohol is obtained as a white powder in 1.5–3% yield on the basis of dry weights.

Analysis reveals that traces of phosphorus (about 0.1%) are often retained even by rigorously purified yeast glycogen (see Jeanloz, 1944). They are said to be removed by the appropriate phosphatases. According to Schäffner and Specht (1938) the reverse process, addition of phosphate, takes place in the presence of yeast maceration juice.

The basic unit from which the glycogen molecule is constructed is D-glucose which is formed in about 96% of the theoretical yield on complete hydrolysis with acid. No significant amounts of other reducing sugars are present judged from chromatographic tests (Manners and Khin Maung, 1955a). Several recent studies have been directed towards examining the way in which the glucose residues are linked in the native polysaccharide and they agree in concluding that a close similarity exists between yeast glycogen and various animal glycogens. The resemblance includes a similar ability to bind iodine with formation of a characteristic red-brown coloration. Northcote, using the two standard procedures which involve, respectively, oxidation with periodate (oxidation of free hydroxyl groups at adjacent carbon atoms) and isolation of the terminal tetramethylglucose units from the exhaustively methylated polysaccharide, deduced that on the average one glucose residue in about 11 or 12 was situated at the end of a chain. Furthermore, the preponderance of 2,3,6-trimethylglucose in the hydrolysis products from the methylated polysaccharide indicated that the majority of glucose units were linked in the 1,4 positions as shown in the figure for the units R_1 and R_2:

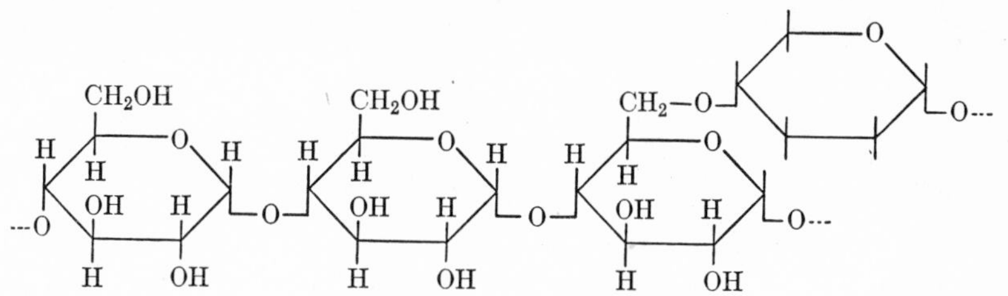

However, the presence of a significant amount of 2,3-dimethylglucose (approximately $\frac{1}{11}$ of the amount of trimethylglucose) showed that some of the residues contained glucosidic links both in the 1,4 and 1,6 positions (e.g., R_3 in the diagram). The glycogen molecule has therefore a branched structure. Peat and his associates drew similar conclusions about the types of linkage from their examination of the di- and trisaccharides liberated during partial acid hydrolysis of the glycogen under conditions where polymerization of simple sugars was shown not to occur (Peat *et al.*, 1955). Thus, identification of maltose as one major product showed that the polysaccharides contained 1,4 glucosidic links with the α configuration. And in corroboration of Northcote's conclusions, the presence of isomaltose with its α-1,6 link and the presence of the trisaccharide panose containing both an α-1,6 and an α-1,4 link was also demonstrated.

While considerations of this kind show that the glycogen molecule is branched, the mode of branching remains an open question (Fig. 1). It might be single as in (I), multiple as in (II), or involve a combination of these two modes (see Manners, 1955; Fig. 1) and, given a multiply branched "tree" structure, there is the further question of the relative lengths of the exterior and interior chains. Here the new techniques using specific enzyme preparations have proved of special value. For instance, the enzyme α-amylase of salivary secretion catalyzes the random hydrolysis of nonterminal α-1,4 linkages (Whelan and Roberts, 1952) and liberates maltose[13] and α-dextrins from yeast glycogen (Manners and Khin Maung, 1955a). An essentially different result is obtained with β-amylase from soya beans, which catalyzes the stepwise hydrolysis of alternate linkages in a chain of α-1,4 linked glucose residues. The reaction starts at the nonreducing end and is finally arrested at a branching point, probably when 2 or 3 glucose residues still remain in the depleted chain.

[13] The process was complicated by the fact that the enzyme preparation was contaminated with a maltotriase so that glucose was also found in the hydrolysate.

The number of molecules of maltose liberated by the action of β-amylase therefore provides a measure of the average exterior chain length, while the difference between the exterior and the over-all chain length determined by chemical methods is taken to be the average length of an interior chain. Application of this procedure to yeast glycogens has shown that whereas the exterior chains contain on the average 8 residues, the interior chains contain 2–4 residues (Manners and Khin Maung, 1955a; Northcote, 1953). Examination of structures I and II shows that a distinction between them may also be made on the basis of the ratio of the number of A chains to B chains, the former being relatively infrequent

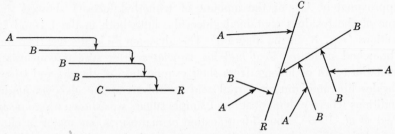

Fig. 1. Two types of branched polysaccharides. The diagram represents two ways of linking unit chains of sugar residues. The arrow indicates a branching point which in yeast glycogen, for instance, involves an α-1,6 linkage, the unit chains containing on the average 12–13 glucose residues in α-1,4 linkage. Three types of unit chains may be distinguished: A's attached to only one other chain; B's which contain one or more points of branching and C's to which other chains are attached and which, furthermore, possess a free terminal reducing group R. *Interior chains* lie between two successive branching points. *Exterior chains* start at the nearest branching point and terminate at the free end of a unit chain. I: single branching; II: multiple branching.

in the laminated structure (I) but approximately as numerous as the B type in the "tree" structure (II). The kind of result to be expected may be inferred from the behavior of an analogous glycogen from rabbit liver.

Using successive treatments with α-amylase and R enzyme[14] Whelan and Roberts (1953) deduced that at least some of the B chains in rabbit glycogen were of the type containing two α-1,6 linkages which is absent from I. Furthermore, the mode of action of yeast isoamylase on yeast glycogen itself has been taken to mean that this has a multiply branched structure (Manners and Khin Maung, 1955b).

[14] Yeast isoamylase hydrolyzes both terminal and nonterminal α-1,6 linkages; R enzyme is the so-called debranching enzyme hydrolyzing nonterminal α-1,6 linkages.

The reported effects of the α- and β-amylases on yeast glycogen both corroborate and extend therefore the chemical findings, although further work is needed to discover the precise manner in which the branches are constructed. In confirmation of the conclusion already outlined, Northcote has also shown that the β-glucosidases, Z-enzyme, and emulsin, which hydrolyze β-glucosidic linkages, are without detectable effect on yeast glycogen, from which he infers that the anomalous β-glucosidic linkages which may possibly occur in other glucosans are probably absent from the yeast polysaccharide.

The molecular weight of yeast glycogen is approximately 2×10^6, so that the molecules consist of about 10^3 unit chains each comprising on the average 12 or 13 linked glucose residues (Northcote, 1953; Manners and Khin Maung, 1955a). Solutions of yeast glycogen resemble other glycogens in being polydisperse (Bell et al., 1948) but the molecules appear to be less symmetrical than, for instance, rabbit glycogen.

The presence of molecules of different sizes probably explains why more than one species of glycogen has been reported to occur in yeast (see Trevelyan and Harrison, 1952; Fales, 1951). Northcote who paid particular attention to this problem, failed to discover any difference between the chemical properties of the glycogen extracted from dried yeast by means of dilute alkali and the material which was subsequently released from the cell debris by treatment with dilute acid. Formerly, the apparent sharp differences in solubility of these two fractions had led to a belief that something more than a mere physical difference was involved, but this conclusion now appears to be incorrect.

Mannan. Another well-defined polysaccharide has been recognized in the residue of partially autolyzed yeast, as well as in extracts prepared by boiling the cells with dilute solutions of sodium hydroxide. Prolonged autolysis liberates mannan in solution but some is destroyed by an enzyme present in yeast. An alternative procedure is to solubilize the mannan with enzymes such as activated papain or diastase (Kraut et al., 1927). Mannan is the primary constituent of the substance known as yeast gum, described by Salkowski (1894a).[15] Fehling's solution precipitates it as a blue copper complex even from dilute solution,[16] and after removal of copper by washing with acid, the mannan is taken up in water and repeatedly precipitated with alcohol, the yield being about 2% of the cells' dry weight (Garzuly-Janke, 1940a; Haworth et al., 1941). The

[15] The various gluco-mannans described from time to time (see Garzuly-Janke, 1940a, for the earlier literature) are probably mixtures of mannan with glucans.

[16] According to Deuel and Neukom (1949) neutral or alkaline copper solutions readily precipitate polysaccharides containing many cis hydroxyl groups.

polysaccharide is obtained finally as a white hygroscopic powder readily soluble in water. Haworth and his associates failed in their attempts to separate either the acetylated or the methylated derivatives into distinct subfractions and concluded that they were dealing with a single molecular species.

Yeast mannan neither reduces Fehling's solution nor does it stain with iodine. Hydrolysis with acid liberates D-mannose in about 95% of the amount expected for a molecule composed solely of mannose units. No other sugars have been found using a chromatographic technique (Trevelyan and Harrison, 1952; Northcote and Horne, 1952); pentoses and uronic acids had earlier been shown to be absent (Haworth et al., 1937).

The osmotic pressure of solutions of mannan indicates values for the particle weight corresponding to between 200 and 400 mannose units ($\sim$50,000).

Less is known about the structure of yeast mannan than of yeast glycogen. The most complete study to date has been made by Haworth and colleagues (1941) who methylated the molecule and isolated equimolecular proportions of 2,3,4,6-tetramethylmannose, 3,4-dimethylmannose and trimethylmannose, respectively, the latter consisting of approximately equimolecular amounts of 3,4,6- and 2,4,6-trimethylmannose, together with 10% 2,3,4,-trimethylmannose. Confirmatory studies have been made by Cifonelli and Smith (1955a). The first group of authors put forward three possible formulae based on various arrangements within a unit structure of 6 D-mannose residues. That two-thirds of the mannose residues contain a free primary hydroxyl group has been confirmed by Lindstedt (1947) using the trityl group as substituent. The general arrangement of the molecule is probably therefore that of a long primary chain bearing at close intervals side chains of one or two mannose residues; the details, however, have still to be elucidated. The main chain is believed to consist of 1,2-glycosidic links, possibly interspersed with 1,3 links. The high value of the dextro rotation may be taken to mean that the configuration at the majority, but not necessarily at all, the links is α (Table XIV) (see, however, Gorin and Perkin (1956) for another interpretation of the structural problem).

A point of special interest is that the mannan from yeast is undoubtedly highly branched, whereas that from ivory nuts is linear in configuration, being essentially a β-1,4 mannosan (Aspinall et al., 1953). The difference in structure is confirmed by the fact that an algal mannase which attacks ivory nut mannan has no action on the yeast mannan (Manners, 1955).

Northcote and Horne, in confirmation of earlier findings by other

TABLE XIV

THE PRINCIPAL POLYSACCHARIDES OF *Saccharomyces cerevisiae*

Property	Glycogen	Glucan	Mannan
Optical activity	+184–198		+89
Optical activity of acetylated polysaccharide		−62 to −72	+62
Inter-residue link			
predominant	α-1,4	β-1,3	α-1,2[a]
secondary	α-1,6	β-1,2	α-1,3
			α-1,6

[a] For details see p. 190.

workers, have shown that mannan is located in the cell wall in close association with proteins, a matter which is treated in greater detail on p. 238. Other reports (e.g., Cifonelli and Smith, 1955a; Sumner and O'Kane, 1948) have dealt with its occurrence in purified preparations of yeast invertase, from which it has now been separated and shown to be identical with the mannan obtained from antolyzed yeast. Previous to this work, the carbohydrate associated with yeast invertase was usually considered to be distinct from yeast mannan on account of the inability of Fehling's solution to precipitate it. However, Cifonelli and Smith give reasons for believing that the true nature of the enzyme mannan is masked by the presence of relatively small amounts of attached protein which has become denatured during purification of the carbohydrate and not only inhibits the precipitation test but also reduces the solubility. Concavalin A, a jack bean protein, precipitates yeast mannan (Cifonelli and Smith, 1955b).

An interesting article by Nickerson and Falcone (1956) describes a mannan-protein complex derived from the isolated cell walls of baker's yeast by mild extraction with alkali. Evidence was obtained suggesting that certain yeasts which habitually form chains of attached cells were relatively deficient with respect to a protein disulfide reductase identified in normal yeast and capable of reducing the above mannan complex, a function which may be involved in cell division. The mannan complex is probably related to certain fractions released from yeast cell walls by enzyme extracts prepared from malt and from papain and which appear to be involved in yeast flocculation (Eddy and Rudin, 1957). A further application of the enzyme studies has consisted in the preparation of protoplasts from yeast (Eddy and Williamson, 1957).

Yeast Glucan. After the glycogen and mannan have been removed from the cell wall residue obtained by boiling yeast with dilute alkali, a grayish white or cream-colored powder remains. Further treatment with hot water and organic solvents gives yeast glucan in yield of about 8% of the dry weight of cells (Hassid et al., 1941; Bell and Northcote, 1950). The glucan was originally termed "yeast cellulose" (see Salkowski, 1894b), although Zechmeister and Tóth (1934, 1936) recognized that it failed to show the characteristic reactions of true cellulose.[17] The latter used another procedure to isolate the cell membrane, first of all killing the whole cells with dilute acetic acid, then digesting them with pepsin and diastase and, finally, dissolving the glucan with boiling 3% sulfuric acid. Bell and Northcote, however, recommend several extractions with warm dilute acetic acid in the final stage, as stronger acids tend to depolymerize the glucan and liberate reducing groups. The best preparations retain traces of nitrogen (about 0.5%), evidently as impurities as they are no longer present in the methylated and acetylated materials.

Yeast glucan lacks reducing power. It fails to give a blue color with iodine and is insoluble in water, dilute acids or alkalis. It is hydrolyzed with difficulty even by moderately concentrated hydrochloric acid, the major and probably only sugar residue produced being D-glucose which has been isolated as its phenylosazone derivative. On the basis of chromatographic tests, it would seem that no other sugars are released during hydrolysis (Bell and Northcote, 1950; Hassid et al., 1941). During this process the specific optical rotation increases progressively, a fact which suggests that the glucose units are in the β configuration in the polymer molecule, but that, subsequently, mutarotation occurs. The large negative specific optical rotation of the acetylated polysaccharide and the small positive value for the methylated polysaccharide confirm this view (see Table XIV).

The action of suitable enzymes on yeast glucan provides further evidence for the predominant occurrence of β linkages. For example, an enzyme system in seaweed extracts and the enzyme emulsin which are both active against β-glucosans, hydrolyze yeast glucan to glucose (Manners, 1955). Furthermore, Barry and Dillon (1943) have shown that oligosaccharides obtained by partial hydrolysis of the molecule with fuming hydrochloric acid are hydrolyzed to glucose by emulsin but not by taka diastase.

The principle product formed by hydrolysis of the exhaustively methylated glucan is 2:4:6-trimethyl-D-glucose (Hassid et al., 1941; Bell and Northcote, 1950). For each 7 moles of the trimethyl sugar, the latter succeeded in isolating also 1 mole of each of 2,3,4,6-tetramethylglucose

[17] They isolated a disaccharide by hydrolysis, containing two glucose residues in 1,3 linkage.

and 4,6-dimethylglucose. These results mean that the commonest linkages are 1,3 linkages (free 2,4,6 positions yielding the corresponding trimethyl sugar). The average length of a chain would appear to be 9 units, because 1 residue in 9 contains a free 3 position (affording the tetramethyl sugar) corresponding to the open end of a chain. In general agreement with this, titration with periodate gave a value of 10 glucose residues for the average chain length.

It may be noted that the 1,3-linked glucosans, lacking free adjacent hydroxyl groups in the majority of glucose residues, show relatively little ability to reduce periodate in comparison with, for example, 1,4-linked glucosans, in which each residue not at a branching point consumes 1 mole of periodate. Indeed, Barry and Dillon on the basis of this evidence alone were led to conclude that a glucosan obtained by extracting yeast with dilute alkali contained a majority of 1,3 linkages. The aldehyde groups arising from treatment with periodate were then oxidized with bromine and an acid isolated as the silver salt. From the composition of the latter, they decided that the average chain length was 28 units. Hassid and his associates failed to isolate a tetramethyl sugar from hydrolysates of the methylated polysaccharide and tentatively assigned a closed ring structure to the native polysaccharide. However, more weight may be attached to Bell and Northcote's evidence for the molecule being highly branched than to the earlier work, especially in view of their improvements in the method of isolation.

The importance of technique is further emphasized by the work of Houwink and Kreger (1953) who studied the x-ray diffraction pattern and appearance in the electron microscope of intact cell walls treated with acid and alkali. On progressive exposure to boiling dilute acid, thin fibrils of material derived from glucan were formed, although the native walls showed little evidence of being similarly organized. The fibrils[18] were found to dissolve in dilute alkali but the glucan, as it occurred in the cells, was for the most part insoluble. A likely explanation is that partial hydrolysis takes place in the presence of acid, with the formation of free reducing groups and an increase in the tendency to dissolve in alkaline solutions. At the same time the broken chains become organized into micelles, thus imparting to the treated wall a degree of crystallinity originally lacking.

Some oxidation may also occur in the presence of hot dilute acid (McAnally and Smedley-Maclean, 1937), the product being acidic and

[18] The authors name this material hydroglucan. It probably corresponds to the material isolated by Hassid et al. (1941) which had the rather low molecular weight of approximately 6500.

slightly soluble in water, in contrast to Bell and Northcote's glucan which was insoluble both in water and alkali. It may be added that Houwink and Kreger also found that a part of the cell wall "glucan" was soluble in hot alkali; the status of this fraction is, however, unknown. Sevag *et al.* (1935) isolated a water-soluble polysaccharide containing glucose from yeast autolyzed in the presence of organic solvents. It colored red-brown with iodine, showed a high positive optical rotation ($\alpha_D = 148$), was hydrolyzed by dilute acid and contained 9% of acetyl groups, 0.3% of phosphorous, and 0.3% of nitrogen. These properties suggest an affinity with glycogen rather than with the β-glucans. There seem to be no adequate grounds for believing that this material originates in the cell wall as Vogel (1949) implies.

B. *Carbohydrates of Encapsulated Torulopsis Species*

Starch. A small group of nonfermenting asporogenous yeasts, principally various *Torulopsis*, produce a capsule which stains an intense blue color with iodine. Besides the starchlike material which is an amylose, at least one other carbohydrate with the properties of a "pentosan" is also present (Mager and Aschner, 1947; Mager, 1947). Indeed, under the appropriate conditions of culture only the latter is formed; on the other hand, there are certain variant strains which produce starch but no capsule or pentosan.

The aymlose was not separated from the culture fluid in a pure form by Mager but was obtained by Hehre and his associates (1949) by precipitating sterilized cultures of the animal pathogen *Torulopsis neoformans* (*Torula histolytica, Cryptococcus neoformans*) in synthetic medium with ethanol at pH 7, extracting the precipitate with hot water at pH 6 and adding amyl alcohol to the hot solution. The substance which crystallized on slow cooling was almost insoluble in water but readily soluble in cold dilute sodium hydroxide solution. It retained traces of minerals and nitrogen. The reducing sugar liberated on hydrolysis was isolated as an osazone with the properties of glucose phenylosazone. The hydrolysate contained less than 1% of pentose or uronic acid and had 91% of the reducing power to be expected for a polysaccharide composed entirely of glucose residues. The high positive values of the optical rotation indicated a preponderance of α links as did (Mager, 1947) the ability of various α- and β-amylase preparations to destroy the potentiality to produce a blue color with iodine.

Hehre and his associates compared various properties of their preparation from yeast with on the one hand corn amylose and on the other hand corn amylopectin, in order to decide whether the glucosan molecules were predominantly linear or branched. The authentic amylose and the yeast polysaccharide, but not the amylopectin, were (a) precipitated by iodine, (b) colored intensely by and readily bound iodine and, (c) extensively (> 86%) converted into maltose by β-amylase. The available evidence indicates therefore that the yeast starch is an unbranched 1,4-glucosan.

Pentosan. Mager (1947) hydrolyzed the polysaccharide precipitated from the culture medium with ethanol and showed that that fraction of it not fermented by baker's yeast was most probably a pentose and, on the basis of the optical rotation and fermentation characteristics towards various bacteria, probably, D-xylose. A sharper separation of the pentose fraction was achieved by growing the *Torulopsis* yeasts in a medium in which the acidity was poised at a value greater than pH 5. Under these conditions starch failed to accumulate and an alcohol-precipitable carbohydrate containing approximately 85% of pentose and 15% of hexose residues was formed.

A further contribution was made by Evans and Mehl (1951) who hydrolyzed the three analogous polysaccharides from three antigenic types of *Torulopsis neoformans* and identified in each preparation xylose, mannose, and galactose, and a substance (presumed to be a uronic acid) with similar, but not identical, mobilities to glucuronic and galacturonic acids on a series of chromatograms developed with four different solvents. If these preparations were indeed homogeneous, it would appear that the capsular polysaccharide is a complex substance. However, the situation is complicated by Stanley's report (1949) of the isolation from cultures of *T. neoformans* of a polysaccharide which contained pentose but failed to give a positive reaction for uronic acids with the Dische reagent.

C. *Glucosamine and Chitin*

Animal chitin is believed to consist of long unbranched molecules containing N-acetyl-D-glucosamine residues bonded in the 1,4-β configuration and various lines of evidence indicate that a material resembling it occurs in the cell walls of certain yeasts. Chitin has also been recognized as a constituent of the mycelia and spores of fungi (particularly the *Phycomyces*) where it serves as a structural component analogous to the cellulose in the walls of higher plants. But whereas the identity of fungal and animal chitin has been rendered highly probable by chemical and physical studies (see van Iterson *et al.*, 1936; Heyn, 1936), information about the properties and structure of the yeast chitin is as yet very scanty.

A major difficulty not yet overcome is that of preparing material in sufficient quantity free from other constituents of the cell wall such as glucan. In place of the conventional methods of organic chemistry special emphasis has had to be placed therefore on certain microchemical tests, more than is perhaps warranted by the nature of the tests themselves. For instance, the color reaction devised by van Wisselingh (1924) and Brunswik (1921) consists essentially in degrading chitin to chitosan by treatment with hot concentrated alkali, and adding successively dilute iodine-potassium iodide solutions and dilute sulfuric acid; if a violet color develops, the presence of chitin is assumed. Brunswik proposed a further test based on the preparation of chitosan sulfate crystals which occur in a characteristic form, show negative birefringence and stain fast with picric acid. The value of these tests would be greater were it known that chitinlike substances built up from other hexosamine residues did not occur in nature.

In their relative insolubility in acid and alkali, animal and fungal chitin resemble plant cellulose and hence in the earlier attempts to isolate chitin from yeast drastic treatments based on preliminary extractions with hot acid and hot alkali were often included. This was despite the fact that alkali was known to degrade the molecule to the mixture of substances called chitosan containing fewer acetyl groups and shorter chains of acetyl glucosamine residues. Schmidt (1936) decolorized the insoluble residue remaining from the treatment with acid and alkali by means of a solution of dilute permanganate, finally obtaining from each of 5 strains of filamentous yeast (2 Odium; 2 Endomycopsis; Eremascus) a substance containing 6–6.5% of nitrogen and 0.3–1.7% of ash in over-all yield of 0.5–5.5% on a dry weight basis. Little residue, and that of lower nitrogen content, was isolated, however, from a strain of Saccharomyces cerevisiae. The difference in yield is in accordance with what has been found subsequently about the relative amount of chitin in these yeasts. The theoretical amount of nitrogen for the pure chitin polymer is 6.9% but such a product is notoriously difficult to obtain from fungi and, apparently, from yeast, where also chitin appears to be intimately associated with other carbohydrates. Schmidt's product gave a positive reaction in the iodine test, though variations in the color formed led him to suspect the value of the test as a diagnostic aid (see Roelofsen and Hoette, 1951). Belief that the residue actually contained chitin is supported by Schmidt's claim to have prepared the pentaacetyl and the tetrabenzoyl derivative of glucosamine after hydrolysis with concentrated hydrochloric acid but unfortunately no details of physical constants were supplied. More specific evidence for the occurrence of glucosamine, probably as an acetyl compound, in the cell wall residue of autolyzed yeast is given by Meisenheimer (1919). There of course remains the possibility that part of the glucosamine was in a form other than chitin, for instance, as a mucopolysaccharide. Schmidt improved the yield of chitin by using a single extraction with cold concentrated hydrochloric acid on the cell wall residue obtained by a short initial period of treatment of the whole cell with dilute acid followed by dilute alkali. He found that crystals separated when the strongly acid extract was diluted and it is likely that these consisted of partially depolymerized chitin (see Clark and Smith, 1936). Yeast glucan is said not to be appreciably dissolved during this modified procedure, which may cause less extensive degradation than processes involving repeated extraction. An essentially similar method was used by Roelofsen and Hoette (1951), who further showed by a chromatographic technique that the substance extracted from a baker's yeast gave rise to a hexosamine on hydrolysis. However, the presence of glucose and traces of mannose was also recorded, so that either purification was incomplete, or the hexosamine originated in a molecule other than chitin. The second possibility is perhaps less likely in view of the identification of chitosan sulfate in the Brunswik test. Yet another method of isolation was employed by Nabel (1939). This entailed heating with glycerol at 300°C., a procedure which is said to dissolve all but the chitin and "cellulose" (glucan) from the cell wall.

This imperfect though suggestive evidence for the existence of chitin in yeasts is nevertheless supported by the results of studies using x-rays (Frey, 1950; Houwink and Kreger, 1953; Kreger, 1954). Frey, in agreement with Schmidt's findings, detected the interference patterns due to chitin in the filamentous yeasts but found none in various other yeasts including *Saccharomyces cerevisiae*. For these experiments he used cell walls disrupted and cleaned with strong alkali, a technique which may well have destroyed the chitin where only traces were initially present. Thus Kreger *et al.* using cell walls which had been broken in a Mickle disintegrator and cleaned with dilute alkali and acid, an appreciably milder treatment, found clear evidence of a diffraction pattern resembling that of crustacean chitin with the yeast *Candida tropicalis* and with baker's yeast. More recently Roelofsen and Hoette have detected chitin in 30 species of yeast belonging to 13 genera by means of the chitosan sulfate test, though earlier tests with the same strains by the latter authors had given negative results in a number of cases. Three strains of *Schizosaccharomyces* which failed to yield chitosan sulfate failed also to show the chitin interference patterns with x-rays (Kreger,

1954). Conversely, the inferred presence of chitin in certain yeasts was confirmed by x-ray tests. An interesting incidental observation was made with the walls of a certain strain of fungus which appeared to contain chitosan but no chitin itself.

6. Lipids

General. When both differences between strains and the variation shown by any one strain of yeast are taken into account, lipids are found to constitute quite a variable proportion of the total cell material and one, moreover, of extreme complexity. In the so-called fat yeasts (*Torulopsis lipofera, Endomyces vernalis, Rhodotorula gracilis* and *Oospora lactis*) lipids may exceed 50% of the dry weight, a fact which has been exploited commercially (see Chapter XI). In such cases it is not surprising that actual droplets of liquid fat should be visible within the cell (Heide, 1939). Brewer's and baker's yeast, however, usually contain less lipid (< 7%), the exact quantity, as in the case of the fat yeasts, varying specifically with the strain and with circumstances of growth. For instance, in the presence of air, lipid may be formed from an external source of carbon such as acetate, ethanol, or glucose, or lacking one of these, from the cells' own reserves of carbohydrate (Smedley-Maclean and Hoffert, 1923; Klein, 1955; Kleinzeller, 1948; see Chapter IX). Examples of differences between strains of related yeasts will be mentioned in connection with particular classes of lipid.

Free acid is present in the lipid fraction and more may be formed when mineral acid is used to hydrolyze the cells prior to extraction with a solvent such as ether. For this reason initial extraction by means of neutral solvents has been recommended (e.g., a mixture of 50 parts of benzene and 20 parts of ethanol, or successive extraction with methanol, ether, and chloroform) but a difficulty arises from the fact that of the total lipid a part which may comprise 1% of the dry weight of cells is usually tenaciously bound in the form of complexes such as the lipoproteins. In order to free this, prolonged treatment with methanol has been used, the lipid subsequently being taken up in ether (Reichert, 1944; see Macheboeuf and Polonovski, 1949). Alternatively, the yeast is first extracted for free lipid and then the bound lipid is released by hydrolysis using, for example, acidified alcohol. Whatever method is employed, the presence of unsaturated acids renders it advisable to exclude air during the extractions if oxidation is to be avoided.

The lipids[19] of yeast may conveniently, if somewhat arbitrarily, be con-

sidered under five headings: (1) triglycerides or fats, (2) glycerophosphatides, (3) cerebrins, which have certain similarities with the natural
sphingolipids, (4) sterols, and (5) the carotenoids and other unsaturated
hydrocarbons. The shortness of this list is probably a measure more of
the difficulties involved in separating and handling this class of substances than of the true complexity of the lipid fraction of yeast. A notable omission, for instance, is of lipids containing inositol of which substance, it may be noted (Table III), the cells contain as much as of
choline.

Triglycerides. The general formula and a specific instance of a triglyceride are:

$$CH_2O \cdot R_1 \qquad CH_2O \cdot Ol \qquad \begin{array}{l} Ol = oleic\ acid \\ Pal = palmitic\ acid \end{array}$$

$$CHO \cdot R_2 \qquad CHO \cdot Pal$$

$$CH_2O \cdot R_3 \qquad CH_2O \cdot Pal$$

General formula α-Oleo-α',β-dipalmitin

The possibilities of structural isomerism in this type of compound are
evident and the natural yeast fat is probably a complex mixture of gly-
cerides, but little detailed information is available on this point. In the
case of the "fat" yeasts, the over-all composition with respect to fatty
acids may be taken as a measure of the composition of the triglyceride
fraction, as this certainly comprises the greater part of the crude fat.
Representative figures are given in Table XV for a number of yeasts. In
all probability the application of modern methods of analysis would
reveal the presence of other acids than are included in Table XV and it
may even be doubted whether a description which includes only alternate members of the series of homologous fatty acids will finally prove
adequate (see Hansen *et al.*, 1953, for a comparable case). However, in
general, the presence of palmitic and oleic acids as the predominant constituents shows that yeast fat and the common animal and plant fats are
rather similar. Kleinzeller (1944) makes the interesting observation that
the actual degree of unsaturation of the fat becomes less as fat accumulates and it seems likely that at the same time the relative proportions of
the different fatty acids may also change.

The ability of yeast to deaminate amino acids suggests that volatile
fatty acids might be found in the raw fat. This may account for observa-

[19] For the difficulties involved in satisfactorily defining the term lipid see the
monograph by Lovern (1955).

tions such as that of Weiss (1931) who isolated what was probably a mixture of two isomers of isovaleric acid.

Glycerophosphatides. These form but a minor fraction of the total lipid in fat yeasts, though a major fraction with brewer's and related yeasts (see Nielsen and Nilsson, 1955). Separation from the crude lipid is usually effected by repeated precipitation with acetone in which the yeast phospholipids are sparingly soluble.

TABLE XV

FATTY ACIDS IN THE "TRIGLYCERIDES" OF YEAST FAT

Yeast	Saturated fatty acids %		Unsaturated fatty acids %	
Rhodotorula gracilis	C_{14}	1.1		
	C_{16} (palmitic)	29.8	C_{16}	1.8
Holmberg (1948)	C_{18} (stearic)	8.8	C_{18} (oleic)	40.1
	$C_{20,22,24}$ (arachidic, etc.)	1.4	(linoleic)	11.2
			(linolenic)	4.8
			C_{20} (arachidonic, etc.)	1.0
Torulopsis lipofera				
strain 1	Total	20	Total	80
strain 2	Total	39	Total	61
Kleinzeller (1948)				
Saccharomyces cerevisiae	$C_{<16}$	Trace		
Newman and Anderson (1933)	C_{16}	30	C_{16}	15
	C_{18}	10	C_{18}	45

Certain general findings about this class of substance may first be mentioned. The parent substance may be regarded as α-glycerophosphoric acid; the corresponding β acid is found, however, after hydrolysis of the phosphatides, owing to the fact that both in alkaline and in acid solution the phosphoric acid radical tends to migrate reversibly between the α and β positions. Current opinion is that there is no reliable evidence that the lipids derived from β-glycerophosphoric acid occur in nature (see Long and Maguire, 1953). In the phospholipids glycerophosphoric acid occurs as esters in which, on the one hand, the two free hydroxyl groups are esterified with long-chain fatty acids and, on the other hand, the phosphate group is esterified with a basic alcohol. In lecithin the latter is choline and in cephalin (kephalin) it is either ethanolamine or serine.

CH$_2$OCOR   CH$_2$OCOR   CH$_2$OCOR
| | |
CHOCOR'   CHOCOR'   CHOCOR'
| OH | OH | OH
| / | / | /
CH$_2$OP=O   CH$_2$OP=O   CH$_2$OP=O
       \   \   \
        OCH$_2$ OCH$_2$ OCH$_2$
        | | |
        CH$_2$ CH$_2$ CHCOOH
        | | |
        N(CH$_3$)$_3$OH   NH$_2$ NH$_2$

Phosphatidylcholine   Phosphatidylethanolamine   Phosphatidylserine
Lecithin   Cephalin

The cephalins are less soluble in alcohol than lecithin, a fact on which their separation may be based, for instance, by precipitating them with alcohol from solution in chloroform.

Alkaline hydrolysis of the phosphatides splits the fatty acid ester linkages and the choline, ethanolamine, or serine ester linkages but not the phosphoric ester linkage in glycerophosphoric acid. Ethanolamine and serine tend to be destroyed, however, in the course of alkaline hydrolysis and they are best estimated after acid hydrolysis, which also hydrolyzes the choline ester linkage and, more slowly, glycerophosphoric acid itself (see Lovern, 1955).

It will be noted that the ratio of amino nitrogen to total nitrogen, or to choline, provides a convenient measure of the proportion of cephalin to lecithin and in fact many investigators have been content to measure this ratio without examining further the nature of the bases involved. But whereas phosphatides containing choline and ethanolamine have long been known, recognition of phosphatidylserine as a constituent of the crude cephalins is a comparatively recent development in lipid chemistry. Isolation of relatively pure lecithin with a *nitrogen:phosphorus* ratio approximating to unity has proved to be a simpler matter than obtaining a corresponding fraction of the cephalin. The work of Newman and Anderson (1933) and of Salisbury and Anderson (1936), as well as that of others, established that ethanolamine formed a major part of the basic material in the cephalin fraction from brewer's yeast, the latter fraction being approximately 20 to 50% of the total phosphatide. On the other hand, in a similar fraction from *Rhodotorula gracilis,* Usden and Burrell (1952) were unable to find ethanolamine in chromatographic tests but only serine, while Dirr and Ruppert (1948) reported that only 75% of the phosphatide nitrogen from a strain of *Torula* consisted of choline and ethanolamine (colamin). Evidently there is a considerable diversity with respect to phosphatide composition among different kinds of yeast and possibly, as has frequently been suggested, other bases besides those already mentioned are also present (see Rewald, 1930; Peck and Hauser, 1940).

The predominant fatty acids in glycerol ester linkage are probably oleic and palmitic acids as in the triglycerides. Salisbury and Anderson and further, Newman and Anderson (1933) who prepared lecithin free from amino nitrogen and cephalin containing all the nitrogen in the amino form, found that the component fatty acids were similar in both cases. Each contained about 14% of saturated fatty acids and 86% of unsaturated acids. The saturated substances consisted of approximately equal amounts of palmitic and stearic acids. The unsaturated acids were reduced catalytically to a mixture of 60% of palmitic and 40% of stearic acids together with a trace of lauric acid and were believed to consist of a mixture of palmitoleic and oleic acids with only very little acid containing more than one double bond per molecule. A relatively high proportion (84%) of unsaturated acid is also reported for *Torula* phosphatide but here linoleic acid was found together with oleic (Dirr and Ruppert, 1948).

It is interesting to note that in the case already mentioned, where about 86% of the acids found in the phosphatides were unsaturated, the triglyceride fraction contained only 60% and, moreover, the relative proportions of the saturated palmitic and stearic acids were also rather different in the two lipid fractions.

The crude phosphatides of each kind probably contain various isomers and homologues corresponding to different pairs of acid radicals. Thus Sedlmayr (1903) appears to have isolated a dipalmitylcholine lecithin. Another such compound, in this case comprising about 60–70% of the total lecithin, has recently been isolated from baker's yeast using a chromatographic technique (Hanahan and Jayko, 1952). It was identified as a dipalmitoleyl-L-α-glycerylphosphorylcholine by catalytic reduction and comparison of the product with authentic synthetic dipalmitol-L-α-lecithin, which together with other phosphatides has recently been synthesized (see Deuel and Alfin-Slater, 1952). In spite of the presence of two double bonds, it proved to be quite stable in contact with air. It appears to be the first substance of this kind containing two unsaturated fatty acid radicals to be isolated from nature.

Cerebrin. Yeast cerebrin (which is not a phosphatide) is characterized by a rather low solubility in ether and has been found to separate spontaneously from ethereal extracts containing ergosterol (Reindel *et al.*, 1940). The cerebrin is hydrolyzed by acid, or more slowly in alkaline solution, with the formation of a long-chain hydroxy acid and a complex base. The experimental difficulties involved in studying such acids are formidable but Reindel and his associates (1940) partly identified it as α-hydroxyhexacosanoic acid. More recently, on the evidence of x-ray diagrams and the melting point, Chibnall, Piper and Williams (1953) have more completely identified the substance as α-hydroxy-n-hexacosanoic acid in admixture with not more than 10% of α-hydroxy-n-tetracosanoic acid. Reindel and his associates considered that the empirical formula of the base was $C_{20}H_{43}O_3N$ and that it was not sphingosine nor methylsphingosine, although cerebrin itself appeared to be structurally analogous to the cerebrosides containing sphingosine. However, this formula has now been modified in the light of work by Carter and his associates (1954) who have identified the basic component in certain plant phosphatides with that occurring in fungal cerebrin. They found that the empirical formula corresponds to a C_{18} compound and is tentatively assigned the structure 1,3,4-trihydroxy-2-amino-octadecane, with the D configuration for the amino group with respect to the terminal carbon atom. Oda (1952) described a similar base in two (possibly three) cerebrins from a *Penicillium* and proposed a similar structure. The name phytosphingosine has been suggested for the base, but whereas the respective basic components of the fungal cerebrins and the yeast cerebrin would seem to be identical, the acids are probably different, being predominantly α,β-dihydroxytetracosanoic acid and α-hydroxytetracosanoic acid in the former case and α-hydroxyhexacosanoic acid in the latter. In the light of the recent evidence about the structure of phytosphingosine, Reindel's formula for yeast *cerebrin* may be revised as follows:

$$CH_3(CH_2)_{13}CH(OH)CH(OH)CHCH_2OH$$
$$NHCCH(OH)(CH_2)_{23}CH_3$$
$$O$$

Sterols. The sterols, it will be recalled, are a group of lipids wholly different in structure from those already mentioned being modelled on the four-ring system of cyclopentanoperhydrophenanthrene. They are neutral substances containing an alcoholic group, crystallizing readily either alone or in intimate mixture with other sterols. For this reason the isolation of particular sterols from natural sources, where several kinds invariably occur in close association, presents a problem of great difficulty. For the same reason information about the distribution of various sterols in different kinds of yeast is relatively scanty, as will be apparent from the fact that in spite of the extensive work carried out during the last three decades on the sterols of one species of yeast,

Saccharomyces cerevisiae, the discovery of a new sterol which is not a minor constitutent of the nonsaponifiable lipid fraction has only recently been announced.

The over-all yield of sterol depends markedly on the nature of the yeast and the medium in which growth has occurred (see Appleton *et al.,* 1955, for a recent study and earlier references). As with the fats, conversion of stored carbohydrate to sterol takes place when cells are aerated in the absence of an external source of carbon (Klein, 1955).

It has been stated that yeasts of the genus *Saccharomyces* commonly produce the greatest yield of sterol (1–9%), though individual strains appear to differ widely in this respect. According to Appleton and his co-workers (1955), members of the family Endomycetaceae yield rather more than 0.5% of sterol, while the Cryptococcaceae produce less (*Rhodotorula gracilis* would seem to be an exception). Indeed, among the latter class there were some yeasts in which no sterol was detected, possibly because an initially low yield was reduced further by losses during isolation, a possibility which may well account for some of the differences reported by different investigators. It is of special interest that the "fat" yeasts contain no more sterol than yeasts which fail to accumulate fat in unusual quantity.

A convenient rapid method of analyzing the sterols is that based on the Liebermann-Burchard color reaction in which a solution of the sterol in chloroform is treated with acetic anhydride and sulfuric acid. After a short delay, a sequence of colors occurs, characteristic of the sterol and to some extent of diagnostic value (see Schoenheimer *et al.,* 1935). Another reaction which has been widely used both to separate and to estimate sterols in extracts from yeast depends on the fact that digitonin (a glycosidic saponin) forms remarkably stable and insoluble equimolecular compounds with certain members of the group. The minor yeast sterol cerevisterol does not precipitate in this way.

An account of the chemistry of the sterols is to be found in the monograph by Fieser and Fieser (1949) and no attempt is made here to describe the complex and subtle investigations by means of which the structures of the yeast sterols have been established.

In brewer's yeast, as in other fungi, the typical sterol is ergosterol. It may be noted, however, that the number of cases in which ergosterol has been actually isolated from other yeasts is rather small. Two examples are provided by Usden and Burrell (1952) and Reichert (1945). It will be recalled that in higher animals the typical sterol is cholesterol, while in several higher plants β-sitosterol commonly occurs. The skeleton formulae are:

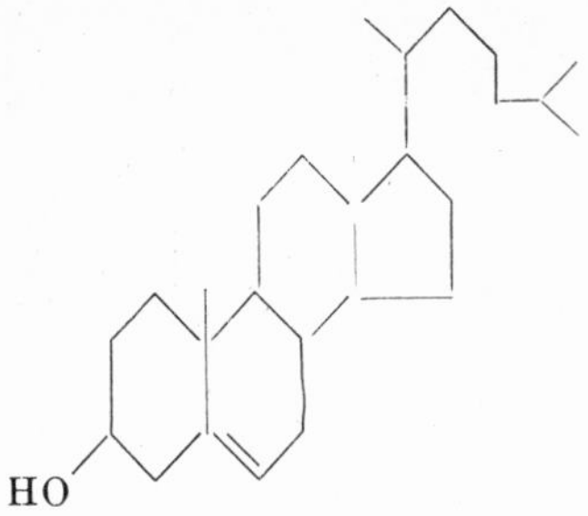

Cholesterol

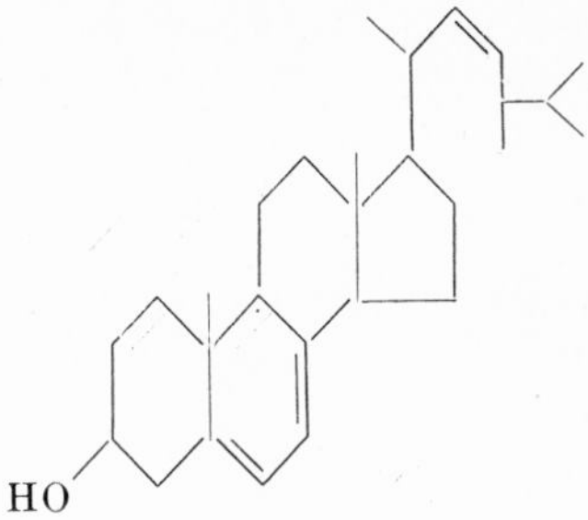

Ergosterol

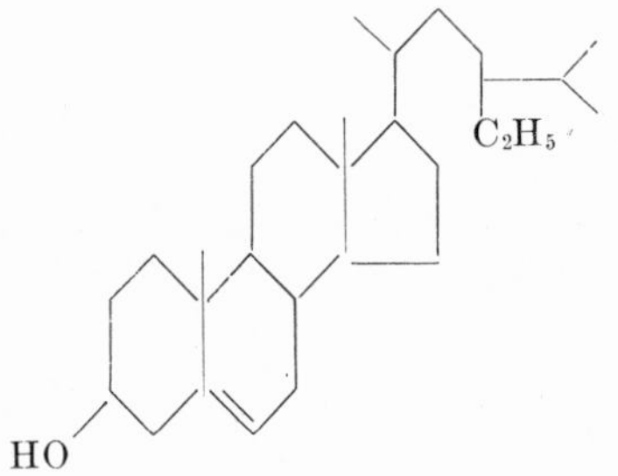

β-Sitosterol

Ergosterol has the important property of being converted into vitamin D_2 (calciferol) on irradiation with ultraviolet light, a substance which even in small doses cures the disease of rickets. Ergosterol is insoluble in water, slightly soluble in alcohol or ether and more readily soluble in benzene and in chloroform. Nevertheless the problem of extracting it quantitatively from the cell, where much of it appears to be closely bound, is only overcome by special treatment of the kind already mentioned on p. 198. That a substance with the specific and elaborate structure of ergosterol should play an important part in the structural organization of the cell material seems likely and it is of interest therefore that various other sterols differing in structural detail have also been isolated from brewer's yeast. Another yeast, *Rhodotorula gracilis*, was reported by Usden and Burrell (1952) to contain two unidentified sterols, differing in properties from the recognized sterols of brewer's yeast.

Of these latter, zymosterol and the new sterol to be discussed later, come next to ergosterol in order of abundance, while various minor sterols have been characterized principally by Wieland and his associates (1942) during investigations of the residues from the industrial production of ergosterol. Probable structures and certain properties are enumerated in

Table XVI. For details, the monograph by Fieser and Fieser (1949) and the other references cited should be consulted.

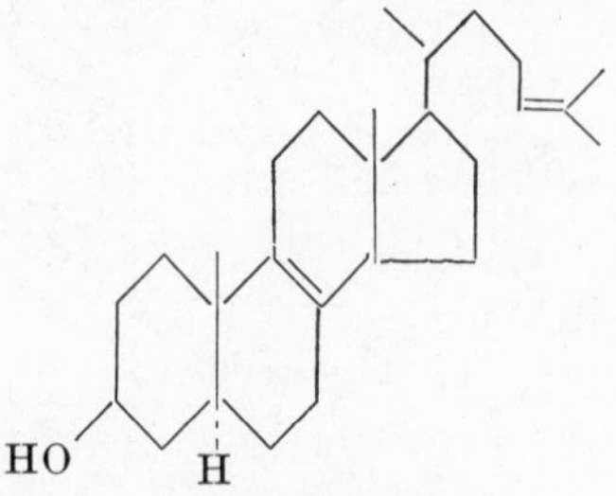

Zymosterol

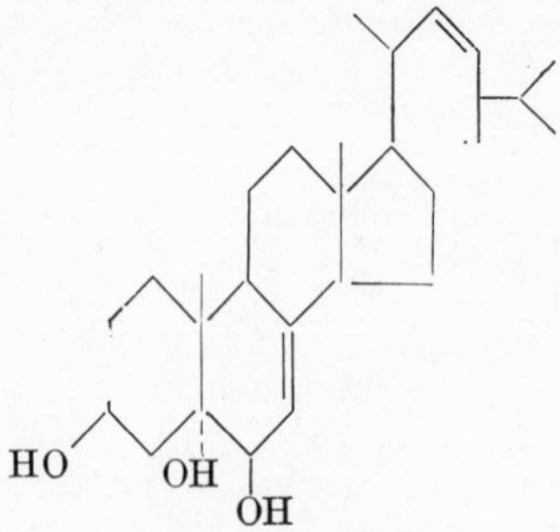

Cerevisterol*

* Alt and Barton (1952).

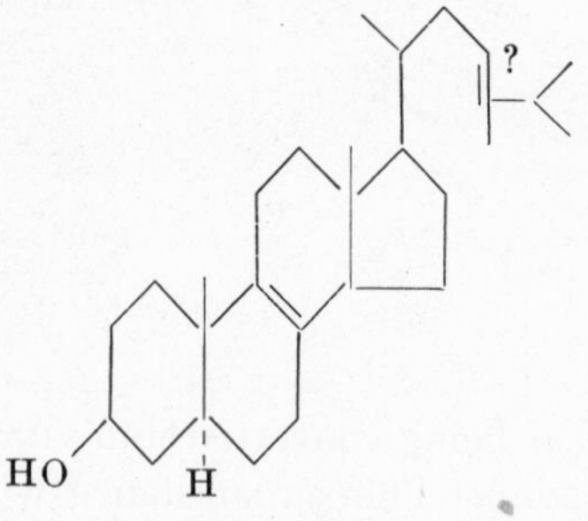

Ascosterol

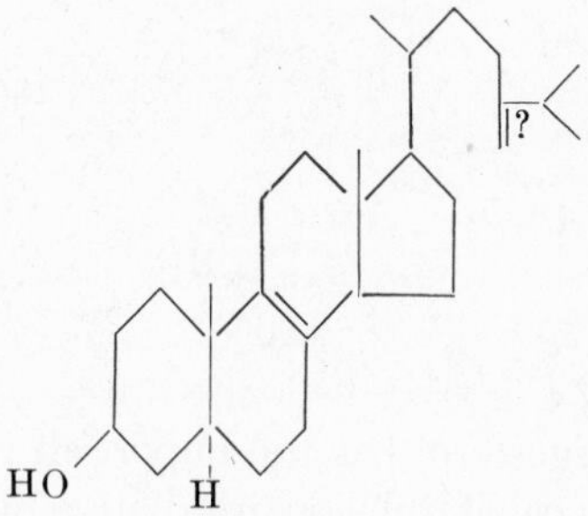

Fecosterol

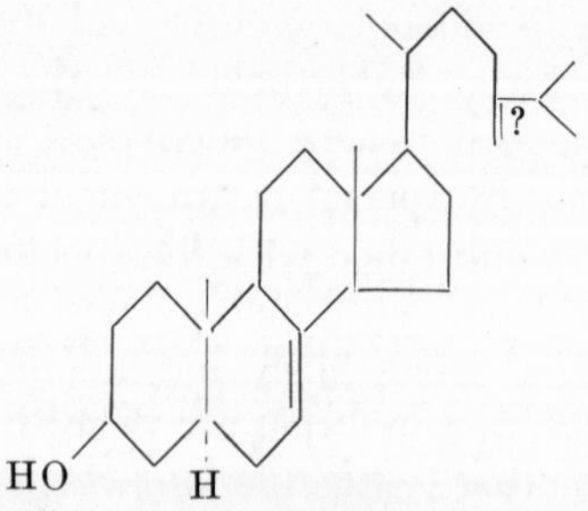

Episterol

The structures of two other sterols *anasterol* and *hyposterol* have not been established. The substance *5-dihydroergosterol* has also been isolated, both independently and in molecular combination with ergosterol as a compound formerly considered to be a distinct sterol, neosterol (Barton, 1945).

A new sterol has recently been discovered in baker's yeast and a vari-

TABLE XVI
STEROLS OF *Saccharomyces cerevisiae*[a]

Sterol	Double bonds	Melting point	$[\alpha]_D$
Ergosterol	3	163–5	−130
Zymosterol	2	109	+49
Tetraethenoid sterol	4	118–120	−78
Ascosterol	2	142	+45
Fecosterol	2	162	+42
Episterol	2	151	+6
Anasterol	2	159	−8
Hyposterol	3	102	+12
Cerevisterol	2	254	−79
5-Dihydroergosterol	2	174	−21
Wieland's sterol	—	144	−34

[a] Representative values (see Fieser and Fieser, 1949) for the physical constants are given as those in the literature vary somewhat; $[\alpha]_D$ values usually in chloroform as solvent.

ety of other (unspecified) yeasts by Breivik and his associates (1954). The nature of the absorption spectra in the ultraviolet and infrared regions suggests that the side chain contains a pair of conjugated double bonds, probably attached to the ergosterol nucleus as shown:

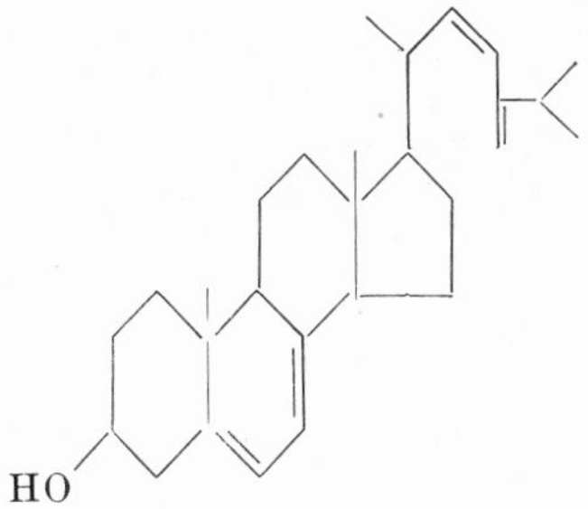

Some evidence was obtained for the presence of a further sterol with a conjugated side chain, which may have been related to zymosterol in the same way as the above compound is to ergosterol. The new sterol is not a minor sterol, being produced under the appropriate though unspecified conditions in as great a yield as ergosterol itself.

Others Components of the Nonsaponifiable Lipids

(1) *Squalene and Cryptosterol.* The unsaturated hydrocarbon *squalene* has repeatedly been identified in yeast lipid. It is conveniently isolated as its hexahydrochloride by leading dry hydrogen chloride into a cold

solution of the lipid in acetone. Squalene, as is suggested by the formula $C_{30}H_{50}$, is a triterpene having structural affinities with the carotenoids.

$$CH_3\underset{\underset{CH_3}{|}}{C}=CHCH_2CH_2\underset{\underset{CH_3}{|}}{C}=CHCH_2CH_2\underset{\underset{CH_3}{|}}{C}=CHCH_2CH_2CH=$$

$$\underset{\underset{CH_3}{|}}{C}CH_2CH_2CH=\underset{\underset{CH_3}{|}}{C}CH_2CH_2CH=\underset{\underset{CH_3}{|}}{C}CH_3$$

Squalene

Its presence is said to account for the relatively high degree of unsaturation of yeast lipid, as shown by the "iodine number."

Klein has made an interesting observation about the particular fraction of the unsaponifiable lipid residue which lacks the ability to react as a sterol in the Liebermann–Burchard reaction and which he termed the "hydrocarbon fraction." Using a certain strain of *Saccharomyces cerevisiae* he found that this hydrocarbon fraction comprised about 80–90% of the total unsaponifiable material when growth had taken place in the absence of air but only 30–35% in its presence (Klein, 1955). Klein's "hydrocarbons" probably include squalene which has been reported to occur in amount equivalent to 16% of the total lipid (Täufel *et al.*, 1936). Another substance of a triterpenoid nature, cryptosterol ($C_{30}H_{50}O$), has also been isolated and partly characterized. Before the correct empirical formula had been obtained, it was included among the sterols proper, since, like them, it is precipitated by digitonin. The molecule contains one double bond which is reduced readily, as well as an inert double bond, a secondary hydroxyl group, and a four-ring system (Wieland and Benend, 1942).

(2) *Carotenoids.* A defining characteristic of yeasts in the genus *Rhodotorula* is their ability to form colored pigments of a carotenoid nature, typically red, orange, and yellow, respectively, in *Rhodotorula rubra, R. bronchialis,* and *R. flora* (see Lodder and Kreger-van Rij, 1952).

Light is said to influence pigment formation (Fink and Zenger, 1934; see Bonner *et al.*, 1946) but a yeast which is typically red after having been grown at 25°C. may grow in a yellow form at 5°C. or in the absence of air (Mackinney, 1952). The nature of the growth medium is also important; for instance, Fromageot and Tchang (1938) found that a particular yeast formed pigment on a gelatin–glycerol medium but not on a gelatin–glucose medium.

In view of the taxanomic importance of the ability to form carotenoid pigments much attention has been paid to the problem of identifying them simply (Lodder and Kreger-van Rij, 1952; Peterson *et al.*, 1954).

According to the latter authors (see, however, Bonner and his co-workers, 1946) alcoholic or aqueous solutions of alkali do not readily extract the pigments from the cells, while hydrochloric acid, unless quite dilute, tends to destroy them and modify the absorption spectra, particularly in the case of the yellow yeasts. However, Peterson, *et al.* (1954) describe a medium yielding cell from which the pigments may be extracted directly with cold acetone. Addition of water and light petroleum then results in most of the pigments separating into the upper (epiphasic) layer. Procedures involving extraction with acetone after preliminary extraction with alcohol and grinding with sand have also been used in preparative work.

Lederer (1934) absorbed the hydrocarbon mixture from the red yeast *Torula rubra* (Rhodotorula rubra) onto an alumina column and eluted a substance identified as *β-carotene* on the basis of its melting point, crystalline form and absorption spectrum. A further neutral pigment, torulene, the structure of which has not been ascertained, was purified and found to be both epiphasic and xanthophyllic. Although a relationship with the pigment rhodoviolascin was proposed by Lederer (1934), Karrer and Rutschmann (1946) who also isolated torulene were able to show that the two pigments were separable by chromatographic means. Lederer also isolated an acidic pigment having some resemblance to astaxanthin, while Karrer and Rutschmann isolated an acidic pigment torularhodin finding it to be accompanied by α-, β-, and possibly γ-carotene, as well as another acidic pigment, perhaps related to the astaxanthin-like substance already mentioned. Torularhodin is sparingly soluble in methanol and light petroleum and colors equally both phases in mixtures of the two solvents. Its behavior towards alkali shows that it contains one carboxyl group, which gives a crystalline monomethyl ester. The presence of a β-ionone ring is assumed on the basis of a pseudo-vitamin A activity weaker than that of β-carotene. With the empirical formula $C_{37}H_{48}O_2$, the structure proposed is:

Torularhodin (12 double bonds; red)

The other pigments identified are:—

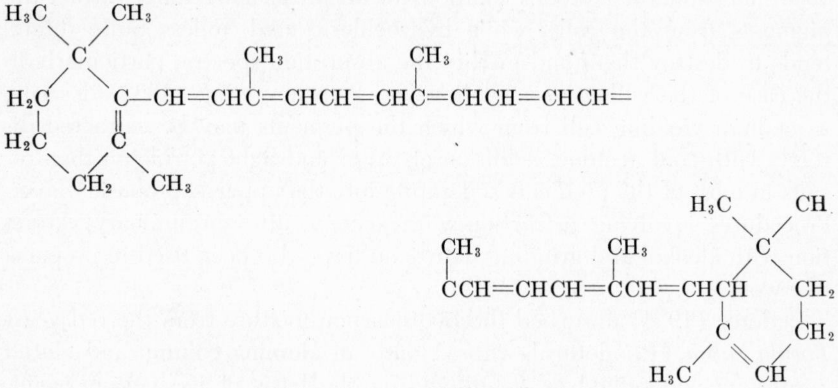

H₃C CH₃ C
H₂C C—CH=CHC=CHCH=CHC=CHCH=CHCH=
H₂C C
CH₂ CH₃

(See structural formula)

α-Carotene (11 double bonds; yellow)

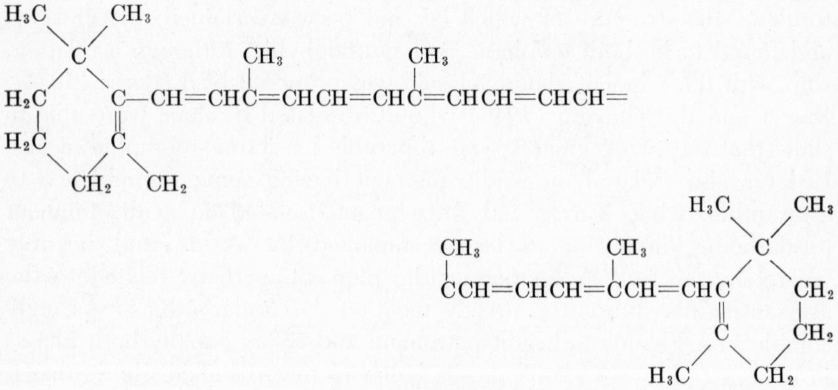

(See structural formula)

β-Carotene (11 double bonds; yellow)

(See structural formula)

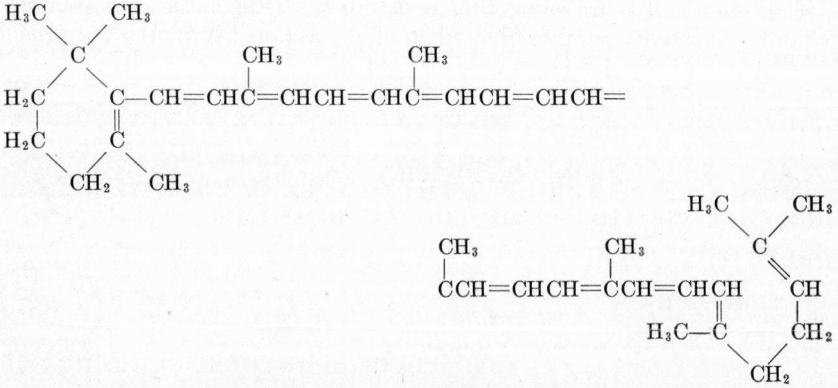

γ-Carotene (12 double bonds; yellow)

Yet another pigment detected in *Rhodotorula rubra* is the substance *neurosporene* first discovered in *Neurospora* and since in tomatoes. It is probably identical with "pigment A" of Bonner and associates (1946), and possibly has the formula $C_{40}H_{58} \pm 2H$ (Haxo, 1949). Traces of ζ-carotene may also occur in certain mutants of this yeast (see Bonner *et al.*, 1946).

Further complexities are revealed in the mixture of pigments from the red yeast *Rhodotorula sanniei*, where eight carotenoids have been distinguished. Of these, seven (of which three occur in traces only) are neutral, while one, probably torularhodin, is acidic and forms the major component [290 mg./100 g. dry weight (Fromageot and Tchang, 1938)]. Torulene (15 mg./100 g. dry weight cells) and γ-carotene were isolated in addition and the presence of β-carotene and the yellow-red lycopene, an open-chain isomer of the carotenes ($C_{40}H_{56}$), were also inferred.

In addition to the colored pigments, appreciable amounts of colorless but strongly fluorescent polyenes are probably present. For instance, phytofluene, for which the formulae $C_{40}H_{64}$ or $C_{40}H_{68}$ have been suggested (Porter and Lincoln, 1950), appears on the basis of spectroscopic evidence to occur in *Rhodotorula rubra*, while in *Rhodotorula glutinis* the presence of polyenes more saturated than lycopene but less saturated than phytofluene has been inferred (Bonner *et al.*, 1946; Tang *et al.*, 1949; Nakayama, 1952).

7. Yeast Nitrogenous Pigments

Introduction. With the exception of certain strains of red and yellow yeasts (notably *Candida* and *Rhodotorula* species) described on pp. 208 and 221, the presence in yeasts of substances with characteristic absorption bonds is only revealed by special methods. For instance, in the infrared region of the spectrum, bands at 9–10 μ are found with *Hansenula* and *Saccharomyces* species and are attributed to the presence of glucans (Simon and Hedrick, 1955). In the ultraviolet and visible regions of the spectrum of an aqueous suspension of yeast cells, the presence of distinctive absorption bonds tends to be obscured by scattering of light at the cell interface, although this is much reduced by using a suspending medium of similar refractive index to the cells themselves (Barer, 1955). Absorption in the ultraviolet region is governed principally by proteins and nucleic acids and in the hands of Caspersson and his associates this property has been made the basis of a method for examining the intracellular distribution of the latter group of substances (Brandt, 1945). In the visible region, however, characteristic absorption bands are due to tetrapyrrole derivatives such as the *iron porphyrin pro-*

teins whose fundamental role in oxidation-reduction reactions is described in Chapter VIII. Another important group of pigments are the flavoproteins (see Chapter VIII) which owe their yellow color to the presence of riboflavin derivatives.

Tetrapyrroles. In the course of his researches into the nature of the porphyrins, Hans Fischer prepared three substances of this kind from yeast (Fischer and Orth, 1937–1940). They were coproporphyrin, protoporphyrin, and hemin, respectively, which were identical with materials derived from human blood.

Ferrous Protoporphyrin IX
(heme)

Ferric Protoporphyrin IX Chloride   Ferrous Coproporphyrin I
(hemin, protohemin)

The structures of the iron complexes are given above; the ring-system is probably planar, with the iron atom placed at the center. In the laboratory, hemin may be prepared from heme by oxidation of the ferrous iron to the ferric state by means of reagents such as ferricyanide.

The amount of hemin in brewer's and baker's yeasts is usually about 5–20 mg./kg. (Fink, 1929). The traces of coproporphyrin which normally occur may be identified spectroscopically but the substance itself is more conveniently isolated from certain strains of *Saccharomyces anamensis*, especially when the yeast has first been allowed to ferment in a sugar solution containing urea, calcium chloride, magnesium chloride, and phosphate buffer. Stich and Eisgruber (1951) have shown that addition of pantothenate to this medium increases the production of coproporphyrin to about 1600 mg./kg. yeast. Riboflavin, on the other hand, diminishes the yield but increases that of hemin to about 120 mg./kg. A further procedure devised by Fischer involves the use of toxic metallic salts of copper or lead to promote formation of coproporphyrin at the expense of hemins. Such observations have led to the belief that formation of coproporphyrin is the result of a pathological condition.

Extensive conjugation of the numerous double bonds in the porphyrin nucleus results in characteristic absorption bonds being displayed in the visible and ultraviolet regions of the spectrum. Advantage is taken of this behavior under various conditions of acidity and in the presence of various reagents in the detection of particular porphyrins. For instance, protoporphyrin in neutral solution shows four absorption bands in the visible region, 500–700 mμ, with a further strong band, the so-called Soret band, in the near ultraviolet at approximately 400 mμ. The following articles review porphyrin chemistry: Granick and Gilder (1947), Theorell (1947, 1951a), and Paul (1951).

In acid solution, however, the above four bands are replaced by two bands in addition to the Soret band, as a result of the formation of a symmetrical resonating structure with one proton per pyrrole ring. A further important characteristic is provided by the fluorescent spectra, light of wavelength 380–430 mμ, for instance, exciting a powerful red fluorescence which in acid solution may reveal the presence of as little as 0.1 γ/ml. of the porphyrin (see Stich and Eisgruber, 1951).

When a divalent metal ion such as iron, copper, manganese, or magnesium is introduced into the porphyrin, symmetrical structures are formed of the kind already depicted, their spectra resembling those of the free porphyrin in acid solution. There are, in general, besides the Soret band two strong bands, the α and β, in the regions 550–600 and 520–540 mμ, respectively.

Although the copper complex of coproporphyrin has been found in yeast (Granick and Gilder, 1947), it is only the iron complexes which appear to play a significant role in cell metabolism. The reason undoubtedly lies in the ability of the latter to become attached to specific proteins which determine whether the porphyrin prosthetic group functions primarily as a carrier of oxygen, as in hemoglobin, as an electron carrier as in cytochrome c, or as a catalyst of reactions involving hydrogen peroxide, as in the peroxidases and catalases. This ability depends on the capacity of ferrous and ferric ions to form octahedral complexes with six coordinate bonds. Thus in ferrous porphyrins, with the four planar coordinated nitrogen atoms, there are two free positions which in the absence of other coordinating groups are occupied by two molecules of water. Similarly, hemin carries a chloride ion and a water molecule, while in the hemochromogens substances such as amines, imidazole compounds, and pyridine participate. A convenient procedure for determining the porphyrin derivatives in yeast is based on this fact, the dried yeast being extracted with cold pyridine and the pyridine hemochromogens estimated spectroscopically.

Both the spectra and oxidation-reduction potential may be modified by complex formation and the more complex modes of coordination are briefly considered here.

(1) *Hemoglobin.* The presence of hemoglobin in yeast is inferred by Keilin who found the absorption band of oxyhemoglobin at 583 mμ in several strains of yeast under conditions of vigorous aeration (Keilin, 1953). In this compound, oxygen occupies the fifth coordination position and it can be replaced by carbon monoxide. The sixth position is presumably attached to the protein, perhaps through the nitrogen atoms of imidazole residues of histidine, as is believed to occur in animal hemoglobin.

(2) *Cytochromes.* The typical absorption bands of the reduced (ferrous) porphyrin complexes (for an account of recent ideas about the mechanism of electron transport see Green and Beinert, 1955) are revealed by inspecting thin layers or dense suspensions of anaerobic yeast cells by means of a suitable spectroscope. As in the case of other tissues the main bonds may be attributed to cytochromes a, b, and c. Yeasts which have been growing under aerobic conditions prior to being reduced for the test—an operation conveniently carried out by addition of hydrosulfite—typically show four or five absorption bands (a, b, c, d etc.), while anaerobic conditions of growth tend to result in the appearance of a two banded spectrum in which band a is missing and b merges with c into a single broad band (Table XVII: Ephrussi and Slonimski, 1950). Further complexities emerge when the cells are frozen in liquid air. This intensifies the α bands and slightly displaces them. A weak band attributed to a cytochrome e may also appear. Cytochrome c has been found to be relatively stable to heat. Thus the bands corresponding to

cytochromes a and b disappear when the cells have been heated to 80°C. for 20 minutes while those of cytochrome c persist. In many cases it has proved possible to obtain either the 2 or 4-banded spectrum at will by controlling the amount of air available during growth. The circumstances of growth are probably more important than the nature of the yeast in determining which type of spectrum appears. In accordance with the interpretations developed by Keilin, the a, b, and c bands represent the α bands of cytochromes a, b, and c, respectively (see Fruton and Simmonds, 1953).

TABLE XVII

TYPICAL ABSORPTION BANDS OF REDUCED CYTOCHROMES IN INTACT YEAST[a]

Band	a	b	c	d
After aerobic growth	603–605	562–564	549–550	510–530
After anaerobic growth	—	540–570		510–535

[a] The table shows the range of wavelengths (mμ) within which the principal bands are to be found. Bands a, b, and c are α-bands of the respective cytochromes, band b sometimes being weak. The corresponding β-bands fall within the region for band d which may be diffuse. After anaerobic growth a two-banded spectrum is usually shown, bands b and c merging into a single band. A further band at 582 mμ has been attributed to hemoglobin, while another weak band at 588–592 mμ has been noted with certain yeasts (from Fink, 1932; Ephrussi and Slonimski, 1950).

An elegant technique developed by Chance consists in measuring by means of a recording spectrophotometer the difference in optical density of the oxidized and reduced forms of the pigments as a function of wavelength. The comparison is made with two cell suspensions maintained under oxidizing and reducing conditions, respectively. Addition of the appropriate metabolites or inhibitors to one suspension is used to bring about changes in the proportion of oxidized and reduced pigments. From the corresponding changes in spectra and a knowledge of the molecular extinction coefficients, the kinetic properties of the various cytochrome components as they function in the cell may be deduced (Keilin, 1953).

Cytochrome "a." Study of the effect of various inhibitors on the intensity of the bands attributed to cytochrome a of yeast and also of heart muscle led Keilin and Hartree (1939) to postulate a more complex structure for the a band than was originally supposed. One component, with a band at 605 mμ, is now designated as cytochrome a and a second component, showing a band at 600 mμ as cytochrome a_3, being distinguished further by an ability to combine with carbon monoxide. As the resultant compound gives an α band at 590 mμ and a Soret band which together coincide with those of the carbon monoxide compound of Warburgs' *Atmungsferment* (see Chapter VIII), it is now believed that cytochrome a_3 and the *Atmungsferment* are the same substance and probably identical, moreover, with cytochrome oxidase or Keilin's indophenol oxidase (Keilin, 1929; Chance, 1953; Yamaguchi *et al.*, 1936).

The a cytochrome system appears to be associated with particulate material and it has not yet proved possible to purify it extensively, although active extracts have been prepared (Smith, 1954). Evidence concerning the nature of the porphyrin prosthetic groups has been derived, however, from spectroscopic studies. Thus Keilin and Hartree (1939), following Warburg and Negelein (1932), drew attention to the similar spectroscopic properties of the hemin of a certain invertebrate, *Spirographis*, and those of the a_3 and a components of yeast and heart tissue. The *Spirographis* hemin has proved to be 1,3,5,8-tetramethyl-2-formyl-4-vinylporphyrin-6,7-dipropionic acid. Further comparison with the cytochrome oxidase pigments of heart muscle has led to the structure 1,5,8-trimethyl-3-formyl-2,4-divinylporphyrin-6,7-dipropionic acid being proposed for the latter (Rawlinson and Hale, 1949), from which it would now seem that the yeast pigment, too, may in fact differ from *Spirographis* hemin.

Assuming that *Atmungsferment* protein carries a single porphyrin group, Warburg (1946) has calculated that the molecular weight of the enzyme is 75,000.

Cytochrome b. On the basis of their spectrographic studies, Keilin and Hartree considered that the b component of yeast was derived from iron protoporphyrin. This has now been amply confirmed by examining crystalline, electrophoretically homogeneous cytochrome b_2, a heme substance previously found in purified extracts of lactic dehydrogenase (Appleby and Morton, 1954; see Yakushiji and Mori, 1937). The absorption spectrum of the pyridine hemochromogen, separated by denaturation of the enzyme and addition of pyridine, was found to be identical with that from pure hemin. Two points of special interest are that cytochrome b_2 is the first cytochrome to have been actually crystallized and, secondly, that the enzyme appears to consist of a single protein with two prosthetic groups, namely, the heme and flavine mononucleotide. A solution of it is brown in the oxidized form and pink on reduction.

An extract of cytochrome b_2 with an even greater specific activity than the crystals already mentioned was obtained by Boeri and his associates (1955, 1956) from 100 g. of baker's yeast as 10 ml. of 10^{-5} M cytochrome

b_2 solution. Dried yeast was autolyzed for 5 hours, extracted with buffer, and the cytochrome adsorbed onto calcium phosphate gel. It was eluted with aqueous ammonium sulfate, then precipitated twice with this substance at a neutral pH and once at pH 8. Calculation showed that it would require 230,000 g. of the resultant protein to contain one mole of flavine mononucleotide and one of the heme residue, and that this quantity would include 8 g. atom of iron not bound as heme nor removed by dialysis with a chelating agent. The enzyme would seem therefore to be a ferroflavoprotein.

L($+$)-Lactic acid acts specifically as hydrogen donor, both prosthetic groups being rapidly reduced. The reduction probably affects first the flavine group which in turn reduces the heme. Evidence was presented for the occurrence of the reverse reaction, using pyruvic acid and the reduced nucleotide under anaerobic conditions. Using ferricytochrome c as electron acceptor, approximately 9000 molecules were reduced per minute per flavine group of the cytochrome b_2 preparation. Methylene blue, ferricyanide, and certain quinones were also reduced by the enzyme in the presence of lactic acid. The enzyme differs from lactic dehydrogenase of animal origin in not being activated by diphosphopyridine nucleotide.

Cytochrome c. Cytochrome c of yeast was one of the first cytochromes to be studied but later workers have preferred to use animal tissues as a more convenient source with the result that little recent attention has been given to separating it from yeast. A procedure based on the techniques developed by Keilin and Theorell is briefly mentioned by Boeri *et al.* (1955). Keilin (1930) devised a method for partially separating the thermostable cytochrome from other yeast proteins, the plasmolyzed cells being treated with hot water and then allowed to autolyze in aqueous suspension containing bisulfite. The liquid which was now colored pink with reduced cytochrome c was supplemented with calcium chloride and treated with sulfur dioxide which precipitated the bulk of the foreign proteins but left the cytochrome c in solution. The cytochrome was then oxidized by shaking with air, in which form it was slowly precipitated by sulfur dioxide (see Hill and Keilin, 1930).

Treatment of the crude cytochrome with sulfur dioxide and hydrochloric acid liberated porphyrin c. In view of the alleged similarity between the cytochromes of yeast and of heart muscle, porphyrin c may be assumed to be identical with the substance prepared since then by analogous methods from highly purified animal cytochrome c. In this a cysteine molecule is linked as a thioether to each of the side chains at the 2 and 4 positions of the porphyrin nucleus, the mode of attachment of the prosthetic group to the apoprotein according to Theorell being as follows (Paul, 1951):

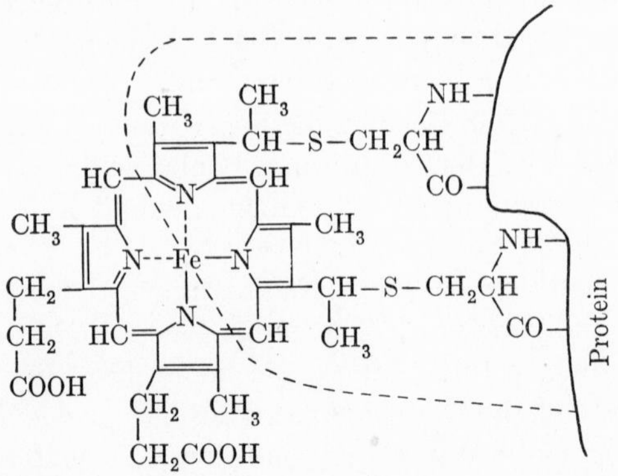

Cytochrome c fails to combine with oxygen or carbon monoxide, the iron atom being fully coordinated in the structure postulated.

A method of preparing crystalline cytochrome c from yeast has been reported by Hiroshi Matsubara *et al.* (1957). The yeast enzyme is said to contain two N-terminal residues from threonine and arginine, respectively, whilst corresponding preparations from heart muscle are believed to contain one N-terminal residue.

TABLE XVIII

CONCENTRATION OF HEME ENZYMES IN DISRUPTED CELL SUSPENSIONS[a]
AND IN WHOLE YEAST CELLS[b]

Enzyme	Enzyme concentration	
	Extract (μM)	Yeast (g./kg. dry wt. cells)
Cytochrome oxidase	0.92	—
Cytochrome c peroxidase	2.7	4
Catalase	0.08	0.2

[a] Cells broken mechanically with glass beads.
[b] Adapted from Smith (1954).

(3) *Other Heme Enzymes.* Yeast exhibits weak catalase activity and contains a powerful peroxidase specifically oxidizing ferrocytochrome c in the presence of hydrogen peroxide (see Table XVIII). Brown (1953) succeeded in concentrating the catalase of a baker's yeast 1000-fold,

giving a product which was about 20% pure but which was too unstable to be fractionated further. The reduced pyridine hemochromogen derived from the prosthetic group resembled that from protoporphyrin. The properties of the enzyme were consistent with its being a catalase containing four porphyrin groups per molecule and similar to various animal catalases.

The peroxidase has been extensively purified, though not crystallized, the most active preparations representing a purification of 500–1000-fold (Abrams *et al.*, 1942). The enzyme activity was found to be proportional to the extent of absorption in the Soret band and to the hemin content (maximum, 0.75%). Although the presence of a porphyrin derivative was demonstrated, the position of the nuclear substituents was not ascertained. Study of the spectral changes occurring in the presence of hydrogen peroxide—the brown solution becomes red with the formation of the complex between the enzyme and the substrate—indicated that the molecular weight was not greater than 60,000, with one heme group per enzyme molecule.

Flavine Complexes. The classical researches stemming from the work of Warburg and Christian on the nature of the yellow ferment (*the old yellow enzyme*) in the system catalyzing oxidation of glucose-6-phosphate by oxygen or methylene blue illustrate the behavior of the flavoproteins (for a review see Theorell, 1951b). The yellow prosthetic group becomes detached from the protein carrier when an acidified solution of the enzyme is dialyzed or precipitated with ammonium sulfate, the colorless protein lacking the enzyme activity of the yellow protein complex. Once the separated protein has been dialyzed against water, it may be recombined with the flavine moiety with restoration of the catalytic activity. This experiment, it will be recalled, constituted the first demonstration of the reversible cleavage of an enzyme into apoprotein and prosthetic group.

The yellow enzyme has been isolated from the maceration juice of a bottom yeast by a procedure involving precipitation with lead acetate, acetone, and methanol, followed by electrophoresis at pH 4.2–4.5 and fractional precipitation with ammonium sulfate (Theorell, 1935, 1937).

The prosthetic group is flavine mononucleotide, there being 1 mole per mole of enzyme. The molecular weight of the enzyme is 75,000–80,000 and the isoelectric point at pH 5.2.

The apoprotein has been found to combine with flavine adenine dinucleotide giving an enzyme with 70% of the activity of the old yellow enzyme.

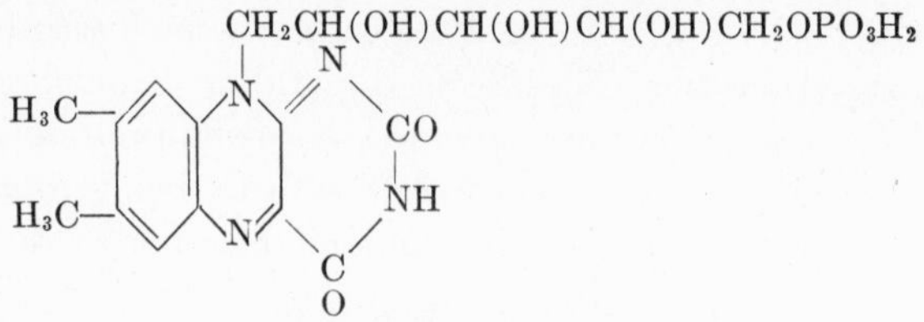

$$CH_2CH(OH)CH(OH)CH(OH)CH_2OPO_3H_2$$

Flavine Mononucleotide

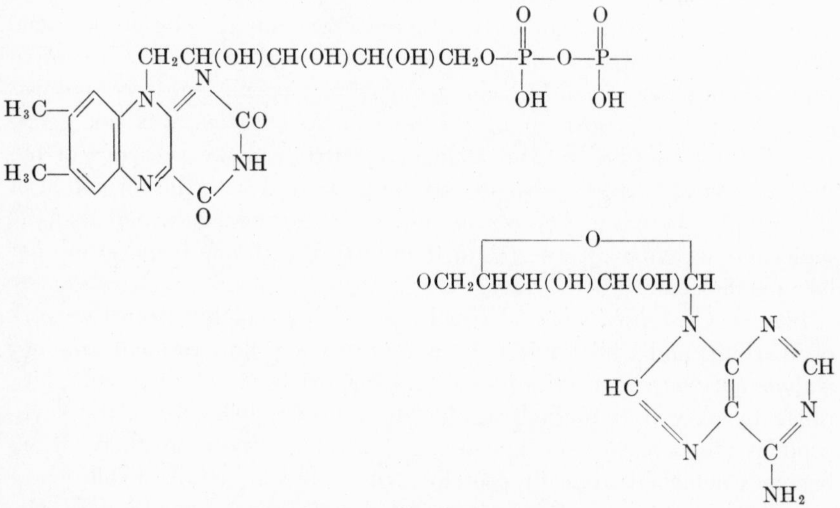

$$CH_2CH(OH)CH(OH)CH(OH)CH_2O—P—O—P—$$

$$O—$$

$$OCH_2CHCH(OH)CH(OH)CH$$

Flavine Adenine Dinucleotide

The absorption spectrum of the flavine in the greenish yellow mononucleotide is slightly displaced to a longer wavelength when the compound is combined as the yellow enzyme. The standard redox potential increases from —0.18 volt to —0.06 volt and this has been taken to mean that not only is the phosphoric acid group of the nucleotide linked to the protein but so also is the isoalloxazine ring. A change of particular interest concerns the loss of the characteristic ability of the free flavine to fluoresce, when it combines with the protein. Combination is so rapid that the mononucleotide can be titrated against the protein, addition of a slight excess of the nucleotide at once restoring the fluorescence.

The hydrogen donor for the enzyme is reduced triphosphopyridine nucleotide (TPNH). The reduced nucleotide is frequently referred to as dihydrotriphosphopyridine nucleotide although the reduction actually involves addition of one hydrogen ion and two electrons. Oxygen, methylene blue, or cytochrome c can act as hydrogen acceptors.

An important property of the isoalloxazine ring system is its capacity to undergo reversible oxidation and reduction; addition of the pair of electrons apparently occurs in two steps with formation of a semi-quinonoid intermediate. Although this has been demonstrated explicitly only with the detached flavine prosthetic groups, a similar process probably occurs during oxidation and reduction of the enzyme.

The *new yellow enzyme* of Haas (1938) contains flavine adenine dinucleotide (FAD) as prosthetic group which cannot be substituted by flavine mononucleotide (FMN). The protein component differs, therefore, from that of the old yellow enzyme. The natural function of both enzymes and of *diaphorase* (prosthetic group probably FAD; hydrogen donor TPNH, DPNH), of *cytochrome* c *reductase* (prosthetic group FMN; hydrogen donor TPNH), and of *fumaric dehydrogenase* (prosthetic group FAD; hydrogen donors unknown) is discussed in Chapter VIII. *Lactic acid dehydrogenase* (prosthetic groups FMN and iron protoporphyrin; hydrogen donor lactic acid) is discussed under the heading of cytochrome b_2.

Miscellaneous Pigments. Folic acid and its glutamyl derivatives are discussed on p. 221. Their intense yellow color originates in the pterin nucleus (2-amino-4-oxypteridine), though the normal content in the cell is too small for the color to be seen.

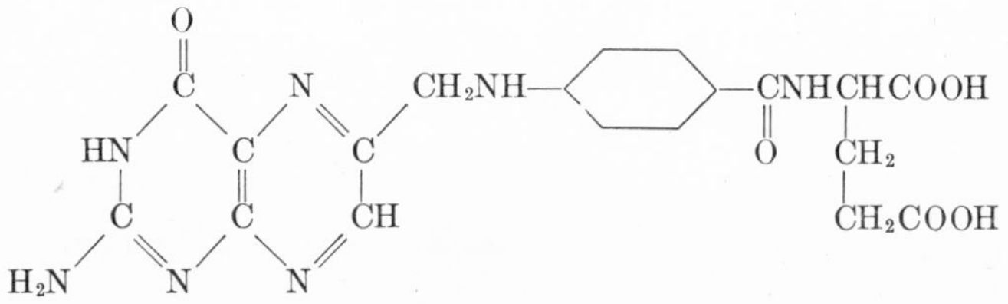

Pteroylglutamic Acid

Pulcherrimin. The red color of *Candida pulcherrima* is due to an iron derivative produced in yields of up to 30 mg. per gram of dry weight of cells. The pigment is insoluble in the common organic solvents but dissolves in concentrated sulfuric acid from which it can be recovered on dilution. Alkaline conditions eventually destroy it but acidification after removal of ferric hydroxide yields a dibasic acid pulcherriminic acid whose ferric salt is the pigment itself. Hydrolysis of the acid with hydrochloric acid yields leucine. Pulcherrimin was originally formulated as a piperazine derivative (Kluyver *et al.*, 1953) but a recent study by Cook and Slater (1956) indicates that it is in fact a pyrazine derivative $C_{12}H_{20}O_4N_2$. The new evidence shows that the pigment may be regarded as the ferric salt of the compound shown below, a substance structurally analogous to the antibiotic aspergillic acid.

OH
|
Isobutyl   N   O

HO   N   Isobutyl
|
O

Pulcherriminic Acid

Several other yeast species appear to produce a pigment closely related to pulcherrimin, including strains of *Saccharomyces cerevisiae* growing in media deficient in biotin (Kluyver *et al.*, 1953; van der Walt, 1952).

8. Proteins and Enzymes

General. Prior to the development of enzyme chemistry, various proteins had been isolated from yeast which were probably complex mixtures including partially denatured material. For instance, an albumin (Lüers and Schuster, 1923) and a phosphoprotein resembling casein (Lüers and Nowak, 1924) were obtained. Chief interest is attached, however, to those proteins which have been isolated in the form of relatively pure enzymes catalyzing specific reactions. In such cases, changes in the value of the specific activity of the preparations provides an additional measure of the progress of purification, which may subsequently be related to properties such as solubility, rate of diffusion in electrical and gravitational fields and immunological behavior. Mention may be made of the various crystalline proteins which have been isolated and subsequently found to consist of relatively pure enzymes; an example is provided by the yeast protein No. 2 of Kunitz, subsequently shown to be the glyceraldehyde phosphate dehydrogenase which will be discussed later. At the same time, it must be emphasized that, ability to crystallize has proved a less satisfactory criterion of purity in the field of complex macromolecules than in conventional organic chemistry.

An account of the methods used to separate proteins would lie outside the scope of the present essay. Details will be found in the articles by Taylor (1953) and in "Methods in Enzymology" (Colowick and Kaplan, 1955). The problems involved in extracting enzymes from microorganisms are discussed by Hugo (1954), while shorter reviews are those of Zittle (1953) and of Schwimmer and Pardee (1953).

An essential preliminary is an examination of the conditions under which extracts of particular enzymes may be obtained from a yeast.

Buchner's method of pressing the internal juice from the cells has been largely superseded by more convenient procedures based on (1) Lebedew's and Ivanov's observations that, from suitably dried yeast, water extracts mixtures causing alcohol fermentation and (2) the use of mechanical abrasives. According to Neuberg and Lustig (1942) Ivanov's contribution has been largely overlooked, the methods usually being ascribed to Lebedew. For instance, thin layers of yeast may be dried in air (e.g. 2–3 days at room temperature), or in a vacuum, processes which render the cell wall permeable to substances of low molecular weight, as well as allowing changes of an autolytic nature to occur. Alternative procedures entail drying the yeast with acetone at 20°C., or plasmolyzing it with reagents such as sodium chloride, ammonium phosphate, chloroform, or toluene. The dried yeast is subsequently extracted with water or buffer solution for several hours at 25–37°C. complex autolytic changes being initiated and rendering soluble the loosely bound enzymes such as hexokinase. Initially an enzyme such as invertase, however, would mostly be retained by the cell debris, being liberated only after a further period of antolytic digestion, preferably carried out in the presence of toluene in order to suppress infection. The precise value of the acidity may markedly influence the course of autolysis. A given enzyme may become available in solution only during a critical period, as the yeast tends to dissolve completely on prolonged autolysis, with breakdown of the proteins into substances of lower molecular weight. Particular amino acids have in fact been prepared by this method (Meisenheimer, 1921).

Attention is drawn to the following particular aspects of yeast enzymes, which illustrate special problems as well as general methods:

(1) The use of n-butanol to separate lactic dehydrogenase from particulate lipid material (Appleby and Morton, 1954).

(2) Fractional autolysis in the preparation of invertase (Willstätter et al., 1925; Willstätter, 1926) and of proteolytic enzymes (Grassmann and Dyckerhoff, 1928).

(3) Preparation of a phosphatase involving prolonged antolysis (Hommerberg, 1935).

(4) Differences between yeasts as regards ease of extraction of particular enzymes such as lactic dehydrogenase (Bach et al., 1946) and a polypeptidase (Johnson, 1941); analogous problems arise in the preparation of active fermentation enzymes from top yeasts (Neuberg and Lustig, 1942; Meyerhof, 1945) as opposed to bottom yeasts.

(5) The stabilizing effect of certain substrates on their enzymes; e.g. glucose on hexokinase, lactic acid on lactic dehydrogenase.

(6) The possibility of developing alternative fractionation procedures, for instance, in the case of crystalline hexokinase, as discussed by Bailey and Webb (1948).

(7) The possibility that the cell contains more than one species of enzyme catalyzing a particular reaction (glyceraldehyde phosphate dehydrogenase; Krebs, 1953). This possibility is of special interest when evidence is available about the genetic structure of the cell and when hybrids of known genetic composition can be prepared and their enzymes compared. The genetic basis of maltose fermentation has been examined by Winge and Roberts (1955) but the maltases have yet to be characterized (see Phillips, 1956).

A further matter concerns the amounts of various enzymes in yeast. Whereas those participating in the main glycolytic sequence may individually constitute more than about 0.1% of the total yeast protein (e.g. carboxylase, 2.5%, Green *et al.*, 1941; hexokinase, 0.3%, Kunitz and McDonald, 1946; glyceraldehyde phosphate dehydrogenase, 20%, Krebs *et al.*, 1953) others are certainly present only in much smaller amount. McIlwain (1946, 1947) has shown that the observed rates of transformation of various coenzyme and vitamin derivatives in bacteria and yeast are of the order of 1 millimicromole ($m\mu M$)/mg. of dry wt. of cells/hour, or a few molecules per cell per second, while substrates such as glucose are handled at rates of the order of 1 micromole (μM)/mg. of dry wt. of cells/hour. He infers that in each cell the actual number of enzyme molecules synthesizing coenzymes and the like is also quite small and approaching unity. The net amount of such enzymes would therefore be of the order of $10^{-6}\%$ of the yeast protein, on the assumption of a molecular weight of 10^5 and a cell weight of 2×10^{-11} g.

The various enzyme activities displayed by intact cells may vary in a complex and specific manner with the conditions of growth and composition of the medium (see Davies, 1956, for the cases of lactase and of invertase). Direct extraction of disrupted cells without further fractionation may give solutions several times more active than the original yeast. The reason for this has yet to be established, though various suggestions have been made (Davies, 1956).

The Properties of Representative Enzymes. Although the enzymes isolated in a purified condition have all proved to be proteins, it seems unlikely that enzyme activity is the exclusive property of this class of substance (see Binkley, 1954), especially in view of the wider meaning which is now attached to the word enzyme, for instance in discussions of the possible relationship between protein and nucleic acid synthesis where both components may fulfill an enzymic role.

It will be convenient to consider the properties of three enzymes, namely, hexokinase, glyceraldehyde phosphate dehydrogenase, and ethanol dehydrogenase, as illustrating the behavior of this class of substance. Certain properties of cytochrome peroxidase, lactic dehydrogenase, and of certain flavin enzymes have already been discussed.

Yeast Hexokinase. The enzyme as crystallized from baker's yeast (Kunitz and McDonald, 1946; Bailey and Webb, 1948) is a protein of the albumin type to which the former authors assigned the following elementary composition, the figures in each case representing per cent of dry weight; C,52.2; H,7.1; N,15.6; P,0.1; S,0.9; ash 0.4. The molecular weight is 96,600. The isoelectric point is at pH 4.5–4.8, the optimum enzyme activity at pH 8–9, though preparations are most stable at pH 5. The enzyme appears homogeneous in the ultracentrifuge, on electrophoresis, and in regard to its solubility behavior.

The crystalline enzyme catalyzes the phosphorylation of D-glucose, D-fructose, D-mannose, and D-glucosamine according to the reaction:

$$\text{ATP} + \text{hexose} \rightarrow \text{hexose-6-phosphate} + \text{ADP}$$
$$\text{ATP} = \text{adenosine triphosphate}; \text{ADP} = \text{adenosine diphosphate}$$

D-galactose, D-lactose, D-xylose, L-arabinose, L-rhamnose, sucrose, and maltose fail to react.

The turnover number is about 13,000 molecules per molecule enzyme per minute at pH 7.5 and 30°C. The enzyme is activated by magnesium but appears to contain no special prosthetic group. Dilute solutions tend to lose their activity, a change which may be retarded by addition of various proteins including insulin.

Yeast Glyceraldehyde Phosphate Dehydrogenase. The original method of Warburg and Christian (1939) for the isolation of crystalline triosephosphate dehydrogenase involved precipitation of proteins with nucleic acid at acidities in the range pH 4.75–4.50 and subsequent removal of the nucleic acid with protamine. Further work has shown that whereas the crystalline enzyme is only obtained from a fraction precipitated in the above range, noncrystalline material of similar specific activity may be obtained at lower acidities (Krebs, 1953; Krebs *et al.*, 1953). Different fractions obtained in this way appear to have closely similar molecular weights on the basis of their behavior in the ultracentrifuge although they differ in electrophoretic mobility. The solubility curves of certain fractions also indicates that they are heterogeneous. It has yet to be established, however, whether this means that the enzyme naturally exists as a family of related molecular species, or whether the differences are only apparent in that they arise during purification, or by association of the enzyme with impurities. A discussion of this problem in relation to enzymes from various sources including yeast is given by Colvin, Smith, and Cook (1954). The reaction catalyzed is:

Glyceraldehyde-3-phosphate + DPN^+ + phosphate $\rightleftharpoons$
$$1,3 \text{ diphosphoglycerate} + DPNH + H^+$$

Maximal activity is achieved only in the presence of cysteine at pH 8.3–8.5 and the availability of the highly purified enzyme has stimulated research into the mechanism of this reaction. Of special interest is the fact that the enzyme preparations show a weak reversible activity (0.01% of that towards glyceraldehyde phosphate) towards various other aldehydes including acetaldehyde, which is oxidized to acetyl phosphate, DPN and phosphate (or arsenate) participating (Harting and Velick, 1954). This reaction is in all probability due to the triosephosphate dehydrogenase itself rather than to an enzymic impurity. Transfer of the acetyl groups of acetyl phosphate to various acceptors such as inorganic phosphate, arsenate, and the thiol groups of coenzyme A and glutathione is also catalyzed.

These findings have been interpreted in terms of a model postulating formation of an acyl-enzyme intermediate which subsequently reacts with phosphate:

(a) $\quad\quad RCHO + enzyme\ (DPN)_2 \rightleftharpoons acyl\text{-}enzyme \overset{\displaystyle DPNH}{\underset{\displaystyle DPN}{\diagup\diagdown}} + H^+$

(b) $\quad\quad acyl\text{-}enzyme \diagup \diagdown + phosphate \rightleftharpoons acyl\ phosphate + enzyme \diagup \diagdown$

The mode of binding of DPN by the glyceraldehyde phosphate dehydrogenase has been examined. Although the enzyme as isolated contains no attached DPN, added nucleotide is strongly bound to the extent of 2 moles per mole of enzyme, with the appearance of a characteristic absorption band at 340 mμ. The reduced nucleotide (DPNH) behaves similarly. DPN is released, however, in the presence of certain derivatives of phenyl mercuric chloride which are known to form mercaptides with thiol groups, two equivalents of inhibitor being bound per mole of enzyme. These may be displaced and enzyme activity restored by addition of cysteine. This and other lines of evidence indicate that thiol groups play an integral role in binding the coenzyme. It is of interest in this connection that Krimsky and Racker (1952) found glutathione to be firmly bound in preparations of the dehydrogenase from muscle. A comparison between the enzyme from rabbit muscle with that from yeast, which as already noted may represent only a selected fraction of the natural material, has revealed both a general similarity between them and certain differences (Table XIX). The differences include variations

TABLE XIX
YEAST AND RABBIT GLYCERALDEHYDE-3-PHOSPHATE DEHYDROGENASES[a]

Property	Yeast enzyme	Rabbit enzyme
Amino acid end group	2 valine	2 valine
Molecular weight	120,000	118,000
Essential thiol groups	2	3
DPN binding (moles/mole enzyme)	2	2 or 3[b]
Antigenicity in chicks	+	−
Stability at 26°C. at pH 5 in solution	Stable	Unstable
DPN in crystals	Absent	2 moles

[a] Adapted from Velick and Udenfriend (1953); see also Krebs and Najjar (1948).
[b] After treatment with charcoal.

in amino acid composition. For comparison, values for a crystalline pyrophosphatase isolated from yeast are also included in Table XX.

Yeast Ethanol Dehydrogenase. Ethanol dehydrogenase has been crystallized both from brewer's and from baker's yeast (Negelein and Wolff, 1937; Hayes and Velick, 1954).

The reaction catalyzed by the enzyme is:

$$RCH_2OH + DPN^+ \rightleftharpoons RCHO + DPNH + H^+$$

Ethyl alcohol and various other alcohols are oxidized. The specific co-enzyme is diphosphopyridine nucleotide but another enzyme associated with triphosphopyridine nucleotide may also exist in yeast (Racker, 1955). The enzyme contains thiol groups essential for its activity. Like triosephosphate dehydrogenase, it is inhibited by iodoacetate, against which the substrate provides protection.

A maximum of 4 molecules of DPN (or DPNH) are bound per enzyme molecule; the molecular weight is 150,000 and the turnover number at pH 7.9 and 26°C. is 27,000. Corresponding figures for a horse liver alcohol dehydrogenase are 2 molecules DPN, a molecular weight of 73,000, and turnover number of about 2500. Furthermore, the relative values of the absorption coefficients at 280 mμ indicate that the yeast enzyme contains a greater proportion of aromatic amino acid.

A study of the mechanism of reduction of DPN in the above system by means of deuterolabeling has shown that the enzyme is stereospecific

TABLE XX

COMPARISON OF THE AMINO ACIDS[a] OF THREE ENZYMES[b]

Amino acid	Yeast pyrophosphatase	Yeast triosephosphate dehydrogenase	Rabbit triosephosphate dehydrogenase
Alanine	6.4	7.3	7.1
Arginine	3.2	6.0	5.2
Aspartic acid	14.2	9.9	10.6
Glutamic acid	10.2	4.3	5.7
Glycine	3.7	4.9	5.9
Histidine	2.6	3.5	5.0
Isoleucine	10.3	—	—
Leucine	7.5	—	—
Lysine	12.5	10.7	9.7
Methionine	1.6	2.8	2.7
Phenylalanine	7.1	4.9	5.8
Proline	7.4	3.8	3.4
Hydroxyproline	—	0.00	0.00
Serine	3.7	4.7	4.4
Threonine	5.9	6.0	5.2
Tryptophan	3.6	2.2	2.1
Tyrosine	6.5	5.2	4.6
Valine	5.0	10.3	9.2

[a] Expressed as grams of amino acid/100 g. protein.

[b] Data from Hausmann (1952) and Velick and Udenfriend (1953).

for both ethanol and DPN, only one of the H atoms at the 4 position in the pyridine ring of DPNH being involved (Fischer *et al.*, 1953).

Activity of the enzyme appears to depend on the presence of zinc, about 1 mole per binding site, constituting about 0.17% of dry weight, being required (Vallee and Hoch, 1955).

9. Water in Yeast

External and Internal Water. It has long been recognized that even centrifuged yeast retains water in the spaces between the cells. On the assumption that these are spherical and not deformed by pressure, the interspace corresponding to close-packing of spheres may be calculated to be about 26% of the total volume. For yeasts of irregular form, or those with a tendency to produce chains of cells, the figure would naturally be lower. The volume of liquid in the interspace may be measured by adding a small volume of a solution of a substance of high molecular weight which is thus diluted externally without penetrating the cells; hemoglobin, inulin, gelatin, and peptone have each been used for this purpose and give values of 22–24% with centrifuged yeast, in agreement with theory (see Just, 1940). Lower values are found when the yeast has first been dried on a Buchner filter or pressed, but the final 0.5% of external water resists removal (Conway and Downey, 1950a). The remaining water in the cell is conveniently determined from the loss of weight on drying. It constitutes, typically, about 65% of commercial pressed yeast (White, 1954).

White (1954) reports that the relative amount of water in a certain strain of baker's yeast was a function of the conditions of growth. For instance, the yeast contained, respectively, 76.2 and 66.2% water after growth at 20 and 43°C. The amount of nutrient available to the growing yeast also affected the water content, though here small changes in the shape and size of the cells and consequently in the amount of external water may account for the small differences observed. However, whatever the explanation, the fact is of significance to yeast manufacturers (see Chapter X). That wide variations occur in the weight of the individual cell is also of interest in this connection. Thus Seliber and Katznelson (1929) found the number of cells in a gram of centrifuged yeast dried at the pump to vary between 3×10^9 and 20×10^9, the exact value in any given case depending on the nature of the sugar and nitrogenous constituents used in the growth medium.

The Effect of Osmotic Pressure on Water Content. The effect of changing the osmotic pressure in the surrounding medium on the water content of yeast has often been examined, especially with a view to measuring the osmotic pressure of the cells. Whereas addition of substances that rapidly penetrate the body of the cell would hardly be expected to affect the distribution of water between it and the environment, substances that failed to penetrate would, according to the familiar principles of osmosis, tend to reduce the amount of internal water. In the case of the yeast cell, gain and loss of water is partly accommodated by a change in the over-all size of the elastic cell wall. Only in solutions of high osmotic pressure does plasmolysis occur, whereby the contents of the cell shrink away from the wall. Owing to the elastic nature of the wall, observation of the minimum external osmotic pressure necessary to induce plasmolysis is not therefore a suitable means of measuring the osmotic pressure of the cell contents. In a typical case the average volume of the cells of a certain strain of yeast was found to decrease from $430\mu^3$ to $160\mu^3$ when the concentration of sodium chloride was increased from 0.1 M to 1.0 M (Drabble, Drabble and Scott, 1907). As Harman and Kitiyakara (1955) have pointed out, however, reversible swelling may occur with gels lacking a superficial membrane. Such behavior is not therefore a unique property of osmotic systems. Besides demonstrating the flexibility of the cell envelope this experiment suggests too that the sodium chloride had failed to penetrate to the inner regions of the cell, a conclusion which has been amply confirmed by other investigators (see Conway and Downey, 1950b; Hevesey and Nielsen, 1941; Malm, 1947).

Measurement of the change in weight occurring when a given number of yeast cells are suspended in solutions of sodium chloride of various concentrations provides a convenient way of measuring their osmotic pressure, which may be assumed to be equivalent to that of a solution of sodium chloride causing no net loss or gain of water by the yeast. Seliber and Katznelson (1927, 1929) showed in this way that during a half-hour period, by which time equilibrium had been reached, water was taken up to the extent of 22% of the initial weight when the cells were placed in distilled water and lost to the extent of 21% in 6% sodium chloride solution. From their data it may be calculated that the weight of the cells would have remained consant in 0.4–0.5 N solution of sodium chloride, presumably the osmotic equivalent of the yeast. From other evidence obtained by the same authors, it appears that when the yeast was grown in the presence of 1% sugar solution it was in osmotic equilibrium with a concentration of sodium chloride <0.04 N, while using 10% sugar the corresponding figure was >0.17 N. Using a similar technique, Malm (1947) found a value of 0.10 M sodium chloride solution applicable to another yeast. The figures quoted are estimated from the experimental observations without using the original author's method of calculations which gives widely divergent values for the osmotic pressure when all the readings are taken into account. It is perhaps only to be expected that the osmotic pressure of yeast would be a function of the conditions of growth, as the mechanical properties of the cell wall may then be expected to vary and in turn influence the effective osmotic pressure of the cells, the latter pressure being equivalent to the difference between the osmotic pressure of the cell contents and the confining mechanical pressure exerted by the elastic envelope. Changes in medium may of course also influence the accumulation of diffusible soluble substances in the cell juice. The behavior of osmophilic yeasts is perhaps dependent on this property. For such reasons, it seems unlikely that the low values for the osmotic pressure of about 0.03 N saline reported by White (1949) are applicable to all yeasts, although they may commonly be found with yeasts grown by the so-called incremental method in very dilute nutrient.

White (1954) describes an ingenious method of determining whether a given salt solution causes water to be taken up or removed from the cells. It makes use of the fact that over a certain range, changes in the amount of external liquid exert a marked effect on the viscosity of pastes of cells in water. Yet another method is to follow the changes in concentration of an external solute, such as sodium chloride, resulting from dilution by water withdrawn from the cells (Malm, 1947). For this purpose the water in the outer region must be taken into account (see below) and Malm fails to make this correction so that his values of the osmotic pressure are presumably too high.

Permeability of the Outer Region of the Cell Wall. A further and related class of phenomena is concerned with the relative ability of various substances to penetrate the yeast cell wall.

The method of measuring the external water (about 22–24% total volume) in centrifuged yeast, with the aid of substances such as peptone, has already been mentioned. When arabinose, galactose, or lactose were used instead, allowance being made for water abstracted from the cells, a value for the interspace of 33–34% of the total volume was obtained (Conway and Downey, 1950b). It is interesting to note that analogous, though less convincing, results were described earlier by Wieringa (1930). The outer region, apparently readily accessible to lactose but not to peptone, may be identified as the space occupied by the thick cell wall. Its reality is confirmed by the fact that sodium chloride, potassium chloride, and glyceric, succinic, and various other acids also penetrate rapidly to a region of equal volume, presumably the same as that defined by using lactose. On the other hand, succinate ions only penetrate it with difficulty. Another group of compounds, including formic, acetic, propionic, and butyric acids, but not their derivatives containing amino or hydroxyl groups, freely penetrate the whole intracellular liquid and not merely into the outer space identified with the region of the cell wall.

Permeability of the Inner Region. Conway's experiments lead to a clear distinction between the outer region of the cell in which the wall lies and the true internal environment. The ability of certain acids to penetrate the inner barrier impermeable to lactose has already been noted and the question now arises what other substances also possess this ability. It will already be apparent from Conway's findings with sodium chloride that the inner barrier is probably the site of the semipermeable membrane on which depends the osmotic behavior of the yeast cell discussed in a previous section. Sobotka and his associates (1936) noted, without apparently appreciating the significance, the fact that lactose rapidly entered a tenth part of the total cell volume. They showed that in 5 minutes glucose, xylose, and maltose were taken up by the cells in amounts approximately 80, 60, and 30%, respectively, of what would have been absorbed had the sugars dissolved freely in all the water that was present. As no appreciable amount of the glucose had fermented, and as the xylose absorbed diffused out freely in the expected amount when the cells were placed in distilled water, it would seem that at least these two sugars were able to penetrate the inner osmotic barrier. A remark by Drabble *et al.* (1907) is perhaps relevant in this connection; they state that sugars such as glucose and fructose are well known not to exert a permanent osmotic effect on yeast, implying that diffusion into the cell takes place generally readily. However, Conway's experiments of short duration (½ hour) provide no evidence that glucose penetrated the whole cell and the detailed work of Ørskov (1945) also shows that penetration is slow with certain yeasts. The discrepancy may be due to the fact that different yeasts were used by the various investigators, or that the measurements were made under slightly different conditions; Ørskov, for instance, has shown that permeability is a function of the acidity of the medium.

Ørskov's studies were based on an examination of the changes in cell volume occurring when a foreign substance was added to the yeast suspension. Using glycerol, for example, a rapid contraction took place within 2–3 minutes as a result of the correspondingly rapid movement of water from the cells, after which the volume remained approximately constant. In contrast, using glycol, urea, or various other substances, the initial sharp contraction was soon compensated by a change in the opposite sense. Ørskov devised a technique for studying the volume changes which was based on measurements of the optical density of the cell suspension; alternatively, he measured the volume directly in the hematocrit. As the substances passed through into the cell fluid, a slow return to the original volume occurred, on the basis of which permeability constants were calculated using various equations derived from Fick's law of diffusion. Yet another class of substances, including alcohol and urethan, entered the cell at least as rapidly as water itself, so that estimates of the rate referred to a process involving simultaneous movement both of water and the substance in question. A selection of the results obtained which represent rather the order of magnitude than an exact value of the rates of diffusion into the cell are given in Table XXI.

Various attempts have been made, both with yeasts and with other organisms, to interpret data of this kind in terms of a comprehensive theory of permeability. The work of Overton and subsequently of Collander showed in a general way that the substances penetrating most readily into plant cells were those dissolving readily in lipids, of which it was therefore assumed that the natural membranes were composed. As a measure of the solubility, an oil–water or ether–water partition coefficient has often been used and Ørskov in fact attributed the particularly rapid penetration of ethanol, methanol, propanol, urethan, and antipyrine in his experiments to their tendency to dissolve in lipids.

TABLE XXI

PERMEABILITY OF YEAST TO VARIOUS SUBSTANCES[a,b]

Substance	Relative rate of penetration	Approximate partition coefficient (ether/water) $\times 10^5$	Molecular volume
Formamide	6.6	100	10.6
Acetamide	1.2	200	14.9
Glycol	0.05	600	14.4
Urea	0.01	40	13.7
Glycine	0.001	—	16.4
Malonamide	0.0004	25	22 9
Dimethylurea	2.4	400	23.4
Xylose	0.015	4	31.4
Arabinose	0.0008	5	31.4
Antipyrine	0.53	7000	56.1

[a] Measurements at pH $\simeq$ 4.5.
[b] Adapted from Ørskov (1945).

Another approach has been to regard the process as one of diffusion through pores, in which case the size of the molecule as expressed in the molecular volume would be expected to be a critical factor. It will be seen in Table XXI that there is indeed a general tendency for the larger molecules to permeate more slowly, with certain notable exceptions such as dimethylurea which may, however, enter rapidly rather in virtue of a tendency to dissolve in lipid. Yet another factor of a specific nature appears to be involved, since particular sugars such as glucose and galactose, or the two optical isomers of arabinose, differ in ability to penetrate rather more than would be expected on the basis of their respective solubilities and molecular size.

Permeability in Relation to Metabolism. It is probable, though few detailed studies have been made with yeast, that the semi-permeable membrane restricting entry of sodium chloride is not freely penetrated by other ions such as those of sulfate, phosphate, magnesium, or potassium (see Spiegelman and Kamen, 1947; Rothstein and Meier, 1949; and Hevesey *et al.*, 1937, for the case of phosphate). A novel example is provided by the acid benzimidazole ion (Slonimski, 1956). Fluoride appears to enter as hydrogen fluoride (Malm, 1947). Mitchell (1954) has recently demonstrated that in *Micrococcus pyogenes* phosphate outside the cell may exchange with that inside and vice versa, in such a way that no net movement of ions takes place. The results of the experiments with yeast are probably not incompatible with a mechanism of this kind, merely showing that movement of phosphate is restricted. A similar deduction has been made from studies of the electrical conductance of yeast cells (Fricke, 1953). The question then arises how these substances, and others such as the amino acids which Conway found not to permeate the resting cell, become available during metabolism. A likely explanation, which has also been favored in connection with similar problems presented by other organisms (see Overstreet and Jacobson, 1952), is that entry occurs in association with specific carrier substances themselves participating in metabolism. For instance, the rapid uptake of potassium ions occurring during fermentation by yeast (Pulver and Verzár, 1940) has been supposed to involve an inward movement of a carrier anion across the osmotic barrier, the anion being involved in oxidation-reduction processes while potassium is temporarily attached to it. A strong but not exclusive preference for potassium is indicated by the fact that in its absence magnesium or sodium ions appear to participate instead, but are readily displaced even by low concentrations of potassium (Conway, 1955; Conway and Brady, 1950). Nevertheless, from starving cells of *Saccharomyces cerevisiae* or *S. fragilis* during accumulation of lysine, the net movement of potassium is in the outward direction (Davies *et al.*, 1953). The explanation would seem to depend on the general principle that the movement of a positive ion into the cell necessarily involves either the simultaneous excretion of another positive ion or assimilation of a negative ion, as the following example illustrates. Succinate ion (or succinic acid) was shown by Conway not to be absorbed from the external medium into the inner cell of baker's yeast, but to be excreted rapidly from this region in the form of succinic acid during fermentation of glucose in the absence of potassium. In the presence of potassium, however, succinate ion was retained by the cells, while hydrogen ions were excreted and potassium ions absorbed. Alternatively, provided the cells were vigorously aerated, bicarbonate ions, approximately equivalent in amount to the potassium absorbed, accumulated in place of succinate. Further examples of exchange between ions are described on p. 160. Holzer (1953) and Windisch *et al.* (1956) have recently discussed the relationship between uptake of phosphate and its stimulation by metabolism.

The Hydrogen Ion Concentration of the Aqueous Phase. That hydrogen ions fail to diffuse freely across the cell boundaries is shown by the ability of yeast to maintain the intracellular liquid at an approximately constant acidity in spite of variations outside. Gottschalk determined the value for the internal liquid directly from the pH value of the liquid obtained by freezing the cells either in liquid air or in solid carbon dioxide and alcohol, and then rupturing them by thawing. Values of 5.9–6.0 were found in agreement with Conway's value of approximately 5.8 obtained by a similar technique and confirmed by calculations based on the distribution of acetic and carbonic acid between the internal liquid and the external medium at various acidities (Gottschalk 1943, 1947). In addition to being isolated from direct contact with the external medium, the internal liquid is found to possess an appreciable buffering power. Gottschalk showed that 1 ml. of 0.045 N sulfuric acid solution scarcely affected the acidity of 50 g. of liquid yeast, while 5 ml. only brought it to pH 5.6.

Conway detected an increase of the order of 0.29–0.70 units in the value of the internal pH during fermentation of glucose, the outer region of the cell wall meanwhile increasing markedly in acidity (pH <4.2), as was inferred from the distribution of free succinic acid between it and the medium. Although the acidity of the outer, in contrast to the inner, region seems to be largely controlled by that of the environment, certain ions, notably those of potassium, are believed to exert an indirect buffering action by competing with and displacing hydrogen ions from essential negative groups situated in the outer region of the cell surface and thus stimulating fermentation (Rothstein and Demis, 1953). This conception is clearly related to Conway's concept of potassium ions exchanging with hydrogen ions during the excretion of acid. An analogous buffering action was described earlier in the case of a bacterium of the coliform group (Eddy and Hinshelwood, 1951).

10. Complex Subcellular Units

Mitochondria and Other Particulate Fractions. The presence of particulate elements in the yeast cytoplasm has long been recognized by direct microscopic examination of both stained and unstained cells (see Chapter IV). According to a recent cytological study by Yotsuyanagi (1955) at least two kinds of particles are involved apart from inclusions of fat and glycogen which have been noted by various observers and volutin granules, probably consisting of polyphosphates (Lindegren, 1947). The first group are visible as highly refractile granules and stain with dilute alcoholic solutions of Sudan III. The second are identified as mitochondria stainable by Altmann's technique as well as by Janus green B. They are probably equivalent to the spheroidal particles 0.2–0.3 μ in diameter isolated from baker's yeast by Linnane and Still (1955) using

Nossal's (1954) ultra-rapid mechanical disintegrator or, alternatively, grinding with fine carborundum to rupture the cell wall. The particulate system extracted by cold buffered sucrose solution was freed from cell debris and then separated in the centrifuge at 25,000 × g. It was found to oxidize various substrates involved in the citric acid cycle, consuming oxygen in the process. This notable achievement represents the first isolation of respiring mitochondria from a microorganism. Nossal (1954) made a detailed study of the various enzyme activities displayed by an analogous particulate fraction which, however, lacked the ability to consume oxygen. Prolonging the period of disintegration resulted in a loss of enzymes from the particles into the supernatant liquid (Table XXII).

TABLE XXII

ENZYME ACTIVITIES ASSOCIATED WITH A PARTICULATE FRACTION[a]

Enzyme system	Activities of particles isolated after		
	10 sec.	30 sec.	90 sec.
Dehydrogenase ($Q_{M,B}$, units of activity)			
Blank	<0.5	<0.5	<0.5
Succinate[b]	21	16	10
Citrate[b]	7	3	1
Ethanol	49	16	9
Lactate[c]	9	8	4
L-Malate	27	15	9
L-Glutamate[c]	5	2	0.5
Arbitrary units of activity			
Fumarase	130	39	7
Aconitase	16	8	3

[a] Baker's yeast was disintegrated by shaking with glass beads at 5600 rev./min. for periods up to 90 sec. Enzyme activities associated with a particulate fraction sedimenting at 3800 × g were demonstrated but tended to diminish as disintegration proceeded. $Q_{M,B}$ = μl. of methylene blue decolorized/mg. dry wt./hr. (From Nossal, 1954.)

[b] Activities tended to be destroyed on further disintegration.

[c] Activities initially predominated in the supernatant rather than the particles.

Those isolated from yeast exposed only for 10 seconds constituted about 15% of the dry weight of the cell.

Particulate material containing cytochromes a and b but little cytochrome c was also isolated by Chantrenne. They were only visible, however, in the ultramicroscope and probably represented wholly, or in part, a degraded fraction of the mitochondria. Analysis of a similar preparation indicated that it was essentially a lipoprotein containing lipid (24%) and phosphorus (1.3%), a third of the latter being in the form of ribonucleic acid; most of the bound inositol (approximately 1% dry weight) is contained in the granules (Nyman and Chargaff, 1949; Ridgway, 1954). These figures represent averages, no account having been taken of the possible differences in composition of different granules. Critical evidence for the presence in the yeast cytoplasm of small particles analogous to the microsome fraction (~0.1 μ diameter) of animal cells is lacking.

The Region of the Cell Surface. Isolated references to components of the cell wall and to certain aspects of its structure in relation to permeability have already been made and it remains now to consider these together. Decisive experiments are due to Northcote and Horne (1952), to Kreger (1954), and to Roelofsen and Hoette (1951) who in each case worked with cell walls isolated by mechanical disintegration in a Mickle vibrator (see Schumacher, 1928; Meisenheimer, 1919, for methods based on autolysis, or extraction with acid and alkali).

The primary carbohydrate constituents of the cell wall of baker's yeast (and probably of other strains of Saccharomyces cerevisiae) are yeast glucan (~30%) and yeast mannan (~30%) (Northcote and Horne, 1952; Roelofsen, 1953; see Chung and Nickerson, 1954; Trevelyan and Harrison, 1952). Northcote and Horne found evidence of the glucan and mannan, the latter in association with protein, being placed in distinct layers, which can be revealed as such particularly when the lipids of the wall are extracted. Although equal amounts of mannan and glucan have been reported by several investigators, the proportion may vary with the conditions of growth (Chung and Nickerson, 1954). Glycogen, which frequently has been found to accompany mannan and glucan in wall preparations obtained by dissolution of whole cells by means of strong alkali, is probably not a constituent of the cell wall proper. Thus Northcote and Horne isolated it from mechanically disintegrated yeast in the form of a particulate fraction quite distinct from the wall residues.

Among the nitrogenous constituents of the cell wall, which contains about 1% of nitrogen, the presence of proteins has been demonstrated (Nickerson and Falcone, 1956). Small amounts of glucosamine and of chitin, from which the former may be derived are believed to occur in certain yeasts (see p. 195). Further information about a variety of yeasts is summarized in Table XXIII where it will be noted that considerable diversity exists with respect to composition.

The wall of baker's yeast is said to contain approximately 8.5% of lipid which consists mainly of neutral fat (Northcote and Horne, 1952; see Hurst, 1952).

TABLE XXIII
COMPONENTS OF ISOLATED CELL WALLS OF YEASTS OF VARIOUS GENERA[a]

Genus	Mannan	Chitin	Yeast glucan
Candida	+	+	+
Endomyces	−	+	+
Endomycopsis	+	+	+
Nadsonia	−	+	+
Rhodotorula	−	+	−
Saccharomyces	+	+	+
Schizosaccharomyces	−	−	+

[a] Chitin was detected by its x-ray diffraction pattern and by the chitosan test; yeast glucan by x-rays; mannan by precipitation with Fehling's solution. Presence (+) or absence (−) is indicated rather than actual proportions which appear to vary among the yeasts (from Kreger, 1954; see p. 189 and Garzuly-Janke, 1940b, and Roelofsen and Hoette, 1951).

The possibility that certain enzymes occur in the cell wall, or at least in an outer region of the cell, has been suggested by various authors. For instance, yeast invertase even after careful fractionation is usually found to be contaminated by mannan, with which it would appear therefore to be intimately associated, presumably in the cell wall.[20] In support of this conclusion, Wilkes and Palmer (1932) found that the ability of living yeast to hydrolyze sucrose was influenced by the acidity of the medium and by other variables such as temperature and substrate concentration, in a similar manner to an isolated preparation of the enzyme. They inferred that invertase was located in an outer region of the cell accessible to external acid rather than within the cell where the acidity is maintained at a relatively constant value. Demis and associates (1954) reached the same conclusion from a study of the effect of uranyl ions on the invertase activity of intact cells. Similar suggestions have been made about trehalase and lactase (Myrbäck and Vasseur, 1943) despite difficulties of interpretation (see Davies, 1956).

The converse argument has also been used regarding, for instance, fermentation of glucose and maltose, which as carried out by the intact cell proves to be relatively insensitive to changes in acidity but, nevertheless, markedly sensitive once the surface membrane has been ruptured by drying. At least two possibilities then arise, on the assumption that the inherent properties of the enzyme are not modified by the drying process. Either the relevant enzymes are located within the osmotic barrier excluding hydrogen ions, or they are outside it, perhaps on the

[20] The writer has directly demonstrated the invertase activity of isolated cell walls.

surface of the cytoplasmic membrane, where they are protected, however, by some other buffering mechanism, the protection failing when the organization of the surface is destroyed by drying. An actual example is provided by the evidence cited on p. 235, which indicates that at least one step in the utilization of glucose by yeast takes place peripherally and is partially protected against hydrogen ions by potassium.

Certain phosphatases hydrolyzing, for instance, adenosine triphosphate and glucose phosphate, labeled in each case with radioactive phosphorus, liberate phosphate ions into the surrounding medium without exchange occurring with intracellular phosphate ions. It may be inferred that these phosphatases are situated in the region of the cell wall, at the surface of the plasma membrane or beyond it (Rothstein and Meier, 1949). Sevag and his associates (1954), have reported experiments with α-glycerophosphatase which seem to prove the point in a different way. They showed that the anti-enzyme serum, which may be assumed to have access only to the surface of the yeast inhibited the activity of the enzyme *in vivo*. In contrast, similar experiments with anti-hexokinase and anti-carboxylase showed that these two enzymes were not superficially placed. However, they might lie in the outer region of the wall in Conway's sense, for this is inaccessible to molecules such as peptone and probably therefore to antibodies. On the other hand, possible grounds for doubt are provided by the ability of certain yeasts to excrete enzymes which presumably traverse these outer regions.

The presence of phosphate groups in the outer region has been deduced on the basis of a study of the effect of uranyl ions on glucose fermentation (see Rosenburg and Wilbrandt, 1952). Independent evidence is provided by the regular presence of a small but significant amount of phosphorus in the wall constituent termed yeast glucan. It may be significant that the amount of phosphate encountered, were it uniformly distributed, would contribute an electric charge of the same order of magnitude as is observed, namely about 1 negative charge per 10,000 $Å^2$ of yeast surface.

The ability of various substances of low molecular weight to penetrate the outer region of the wall suggests that this latter possesses a relatively open porous structure, the pores being small enough to exclude larger molecules of gelatin, inulin, and peptone.

There are various properties of brewer's and baker's yeast which suggest in a general way that the extreme outermost surface possesses an organized structure, but little is known about the details of the mechanisms involved. For instance, spontaneously flocculent yeasts, the cells of which tend to adhere, are found to be dispersed by specific sugars in a manner indicating that particular sugars are adsorbed on the surface at relatively specific sites which would otherwise be free to bind complementary structures carried by adjacent cells (Eddy, 1956).

Further aspects of cell structure in relation to wall structure are dealt with in Chapter IV (see Bartholemew and Levin, 1955).

References

Abelson, P. H., and Aldous, E. (1950). *J. Bacteriol.* **60**, 401.

Abrams, R., Altschul, A. M., and Mognes, T. R. (1942). *J. Biol. Chem.* **142**, 303.

Allfrey, V. G., and King, C. G. (1950). *J. Biol. Chem.* **182**, 367.

Alt, G. H., and Barton, D. H. R. (1952). *Chemistry & Industry* **45**, 1103.

Appleby, C. A., and Morton, R. K. (1954). *Nature* **173**, 749.

Appleton, G. S., Kieber, R. J., and Payne, W. J. (1955). *Appl. Microbiol.* **3**, 249.

Aronson, M. (1952). *Arch. Biochem. and Biophys.* **39**, 370.

Aspinall, G. O., Hirst, E. L., Percival, E. G., and Williamson, I. R. (1953). *J. Chem. Soc.* **1953**, 3184.

Austrian, R. (1952). *Bacteriol. Revs.* **16**, 31.

Bach, S. J., Dixon, M., and Zerfas, L. G. (1946). *Biochem. J.* (*London*) **40**, 229.

Bailey, K., and Webb, E. C. (1948). *Biochem. J.* (*London*) **42**, 61.

Barer, R. (1955). *Science* **121**, 709.

Barry, V. C., and Dillon, T. (1943). *Proc. Roy. Irish Acad. B* **49**, 177.

Bartholomew, J. W., and Levin, R. (1955). *J. Gen. Microbiol.* **12**, 473.

Barton, D. H. R. (1945). *J. Chem. Soc.* **1945**, 813.

Barton-Wright, E. C. (1949). *European Brewery Conv. Proc.* **1**, 19.

Béchamps (1952). Quoted by Haehn, H. (1952). "Biochemie der Gärungen," p. 99. Walter De Gruyter and Co., Berlin.

Bell, D. J., Gutfreund, H., Cecil, R., and Ogston, A. G. (1948). *Biochem. J.* (*London*) **42**, 405.

Bell, D. J., and Northcote, D. H. (1950). *J. Chem. Soc.* **1950**, 1945.

Bendich, A. (1955). "The Nucleic Acids" (E. Chargaff and J. N. Davidson, eds.), Vol. I, p. 81. Academic Press, New York.

Binkley, F. (1954). *Proc. Roy. Soc.* **B142**, 170.

Block, R. J., and Bolling, D. (1943a). *Arch. Biochem.* **3**, 217.

Block, R. J., and Bolling, D. (1943b). *Arch. Biochem.* **6**, 277.

Block, R. J., and Bolling, D. (1945). *Arch. Biochem.* **7**, 313.

Boas-Fiscen, M. A., and Roscoe, M. H. (1940). *Nutrition Abstr. & Revs.* **9**, 795.

Boeri, E., Cutolo, E., Luzzati, M., and Tosi, L. (1955). *Arch. Biochem. and Biophys.* **56**, 487.

Boeri, E., and Tosi, L. (1956). *Arch. Biochem. and Biophys.* **60**, 463.

Bolomey, P. (1939). *Ann. fermentations* **5**, 221.

Bonner, J., Sandoval, A., Tang, Y. W., and Zechmeister, L. (1946). *Arch. Biochem. and Biophys.* **10**, 113.

Bourdet, A., and Mandel, P. (1953). *Compt. rend.* **237**, 530.

Brand, E., and Edsall, J. T. (1947). *Ann. Rev. Biochem.* **16**, 223.

Brandt, K. (1945). *Acta Physiol. Scand.* **10 Suppl.** 30, 93.

Breivik, H., Owades, J. L., and Light, R. F. (1954). *J. Org. Chem.* **19**, 1734.

Bricas, E., and Fromageot, C. (1953). *Advances in Protein Chem.* **8, 1.**

Briggs, M., and Daft, F. S. (1955). *Ann. Rev. Biochem.* **24**, 389.

Brown, D. M., and Todd, A. R. (1955a). "The Nucleic Acids" (E. Chargaff and J. N. Davidson, eds.), Vol. I, p. 409. Academic Press, New York.

Brown, D. M., and Todd, A. R. (1955b). *Ann. Rev. Biochem.* **24**, 311.

Brown, G. L. (1953). *Acta Chem. Scand.* **7**, 435.

Brunswik, H. (1921). *Biochem. Z.* **113**, 111.

Caldwell, P. C., and Hinshelwood, C. N. (1950). *J. Chem. Soc.* **1950**, 3156.

Cabib, E., and Leloir, L. F. (1954). *J. Biol. Chem.* **206**, 779.

Cantoni, G. L. (1952). *J. Am. Chem. Soc.* **74**, 2942.

Carter, H. E. (1950). "Yeasts in Feeding," p. 5. Garrard Press, London.

Carter, H. E., Bhattacharyya, P. K., Weidman, K. R., and Fraenkel, G. (1952). *Arch. Biochem. and Biophys.* **38**, 405.

Carter, H. E., Celmer, W. D., Lands, W. E., Mueller, K., and Tomizawa, H. H. (1954). *J. Biol. Chem.* **206**, 613.

Caspersson, T., and Brandt, K. (1941). *Protoplasma* **35**, 507.

Cavalieri, L. F., Kerr, S. E., and Angelos, A. (1951). *J. Am. Chem. Soc.* **73**, 2567.

Chance, B. (1953). *J. Biol. Chem.* **202**, 383–416.

Chang, W., and Peterson, W. H. (1949). *J. Bacteriol.* **58**, 33.

Chang, W., and Peterson, W. H. (1951). *J. Biol. Chem.* **193**, 587.

Chantrenne, H. (1953). "The Nature of Virus Multiplication" *2nd Symp. Soc. Gen. Microbiol.* Cambridge Univ. Press, London and New York.

Chargaff, E. (1951). *Federation Proc.* **10**, 645.

Chargaff, E. (1955). "The Nucleic Acids" (E. Chargaff and J. N. Davidson, eds.), Vol. I, p. 370, Academic Press, New York.

Chargaff, E. (1956). *Nature* **178**, 682.

Chargaff, E., and Davidson, J. N. eds. (1955). "The Nucleic Acids," Vol. I. Academic Press, New York.

Chargaff, E., and Zamenhof, S. (1948). *J. Biol. Chem.* **173**, 327.

Chargaff, E., Zamenhof, S., Brawerman, G., and Kevin, L. (1950). *J. Am. Chem. Soc.* **72**, 3825.

Chayen, R., Chayen, S., and Roberts, E. R. (1955). *Biochim. et Biophys. Acta* **16**, 117.

Chiao, J. S., and Peterson, W. H. (1953). *J. Agr. Food. Chem.* **1**, 1005.

Chibnall, A. C., Piper, S. H., and Williams, E. F. (1953). *Biochem. J. (London)* **55**, 711.

Chung, C. W., and Nickerson, W. J. (1954). *J. Biol. Chem.* **208**, 395.

Cifonelli, J. A., and Smith, F. (1955a). *J. Am. Chem. Soc.* **77**, 5682.

Cifonelli, J. A., and Smith, F. (1955b). *Anal. Chem.* **27**, 1639.

Clark, G. L., and Smith, A. F. (1936). *J. Phys. Chem.* **40**, 863.

Cohen, S. S. (1945). *J. Biol. Chem.* **158**, 255.

Cohn, W. E., and Volkin, E. (1952). *Arch. Biochem. and Biophys.* **35**, 465.

Colowick, S. P., and Kaplan, N. O. eds. (1955). "Methods in Enzymology," Vol. I. Academic Press, New York.

Colvin, J. R., Smith, D. B., and Cook, W. H. (1954). *Chem. Rev.* **54**, 687.

Conway, E. J. (1955). *Intern. Rev. Cytol.* **4**, 377.

Conway, E. J., and Brady, T. G. (1950). *Biochem. J. (London)* **47**, 360.

Conway, E. J., and Downey, M. (1950a). *Biochem. J. (London)* **47**, 347.

Conway, E. J., and Downey, M. (1950b). *Biochem. J. (London)* **47**, 355.

Conway, E. J., and Moore, D. T. (1954). *Biochem. J. (London)* **57**, 523.

Conway, E. J., O'Brien, M. F., and Boyle, P. J. (1941). *Nature* **148**, 662.

Cook, A. H., and Slater, C. A. (1956). *J. Chem. Soc.* pp. 4130, 4133.

Crampton, C. F., Lipshitz, R., and Chargaff, E. (1954). *J. Biol. Chem.* **211**, 125.

Crestfield, A. M., and Allen, F. W. (1956). *J. Biol. Chem.* **219**, 103.

Crestfield, A. M., Smith, K. C., and Allen, F. W. (1955). *J. Biol. Chem.* **216**, 185.

Czäpek, F. (1920). "Biochemie Der Pflanzen." Zweiter Band. Fischer, Jena.

Davies, A. (1956). *J. Gen. Microbiol.* **14**, 425.

Davies, R., Folkes, J. P., Gale, E. F., and Bigger, L. C. (1953). *Biochem. J.* (*London*) **54**, 430.

Demis, D. J., Rothstein, A., and Meier, R. (1954). *Arch. Biochem. and Biophys.* **48**, 55.

Desneulle, P. (1953). *Advances in Enzymol.* **14**, 261.

Deuel, H. J., Jr., and Alfin-Slater, R. (1952). *Ann. Rev. Biochem.* **21**, 159.

Deuel, H., and Neukom, H. (1949). *Makromol. Chem.* **4**, 97. Quoted by Whistler, R. L., and Smart, C. L. (1953). In "Polysaccharide Chemistry," p. 46. Academic Press, New York.

DiCarlo, F. J., and Schultz, A. S. (1948). *Arch. Biochem.* **17**, 293.

Diemar, W., and Fresenus, W. F. (1948). *Chem. Zentr.* **II**, 753.

Dirr, K., and Ruppert, A. (1948). *Biochem. Z.* **31**, 163.

Doctor, V. M., and Peterson, W. H. (1955). *Appl. Microbiol.* **3**, 29.

Drabble, E., Drabble, H., and Scott, D. G. (1907). *Biochem. J.* (*London*) **2**, 211.

Drews, B., Just, F., Olbrich, H., and Vogl, J. (1952). *Brauerei Wissenschaftl. Beil.* **4**, **5**, 99.

Dunn, C. G. (1952). *Wallerstein Lab. Communs.* **15**, 61.

Ebel, J. (1952). *Bull. soc. chim. biol.* **34**, 330.

Eddy, A. A. (1956). *J. Inst. Brewing* **62**, 320.

Eddy, A. A., and Rudin, A. D. (1957). *Proc. Soc. Gen. Microbiol.* April Meeting.

Eddy, A. A., and Williamson, D. (1957). *Nature* in press.

Eddy, A. A., and Hinshelwood, C. N. (1951). *Proc. Roy. Soc. B.* **138**, 228.

Elson, D., and Chargaff, E. (1954). *Nature* **173**, 1954.

Ephrussi, B., and Slonimski, P. P. (1950). *Biochim. et Biophys. Acta* **6**, 256.

Evans, E. E., and Mehl, J. W. (1951). *Science* **114**, 10.

Fales, F. W. (1951). *J. Biol. Chem.* **193**, 113.

Felix, K., and Pendl, I. (1948). *Hoppe-Seyler's Z. physiol. Chem.* **283**, 128.

Fieser, L. F., and Fieser, M. (1949). "Natural Products related to Phenanthrene." 3rd ed. Reinhold, New York.

Fink, H. (1929). *Biochem. Z.* **211**, 73.

Fink, H. (1932). *Hoppe-Seyler's Z. physiol. Chem.* **210**, 197.

Fink, H., Silbereisen, K., and Hoepfner, J. (1940). *Wochschr. Brau.* **57**, 105 (1941). *J. Inst. Brewing* **40**.

Fink, H., and Zenger, E. (1934). *Wochschr. Brau.* **51**, 129.

Fischer, H., and Orth, H. (1937–40). "Die Chemie des Pyrrols," Vol. II. Akademische Verlagsgesellschaft, M.B.H. Leipzig.

Fisher, H. F., Conn, E. E., Vennesland, B., and Westheimer, F. H. (1953). *J. Biol. Chem.* **202**, 687.

Fischer, E. H., Kohtés, L., and Fellig, J. (1951). *Helv. Chim. Acta* **34**, 1132.

Fletcher, W. E., Gulland, J. M., and Jordan, D. O. (1944). *J. Chem. Soc.* **1944**, 33.

Franklin, R. F., and Gosling, R. G. (1953). *Nature* **172**, 156.

Freeland, J. C., and Gale, E. F. (1947). *Biochem. J.* (*London*) **41**, 135.

Frey, C. N. (1948). Quoted by Peterson (1950) in "Yeasts in Feeding." Garrard Press, London.

Frey, R. (1950). *Ber. schweiz. botan. Ges.* **60**, 199.

Fricke, H. (1953). *Nature* **172**, 731.

Fromageot, C., and Tchang, J. C. (1938). *Arch. Mickrobiol.* **9**, 434.

Fruton, J. S., and Simmonds, S. (1953). "General Biochemistry," p. 64. Wiley, New York.

Fulmer, E. I., Nelson, V. E., and Sherwood, F. F. (1921). *J. Am. Chem. Soc.* **43**, 191.

Furberg, S. (1952). *Acta. Chem. Scand.* **6**, 634.

Gakuzo Tamura, Toshinao Tsunoda, Jiro Kirimura, and Shigeru Miyazawa (1952). *J. Agr. Chem. Soc. Japan* **29**, 480. See also *Chem. Abstr.* (1954) **48**, 14109g.

Gale, E. F. (1953). *Advances in Protein Chem.* **8**, 285.

Garzuly-Janke, R. (1940a). *J. prakt. Chem.* **156**, 45.

Garzuly-Janke, R. (1940b). *Zentr. Bakteriol. Parasitenk.* **102**, 361.

Genevois, L. (1951). *Rev. fermentations et inds. aliment.* **6**, 88.

Gorin, P. A. J., and Perkin, A. S. (1956). *Can. J. Chem.* **34**, 1796.

Gottschalk, A. (1943). *Australian J. Exptl. Biol. Med. Sci.* **21**, 133.

Gottschalk, A. (1947). *Biochem. J.* (*London*) **41**, 276.

Granick, S., and Gilder, H. (1947). *Advances in Enzymol.* **7**, 320.

Grassmann, W., and Dyckerhoff, H. Quoted by Willstätter, R. (1928). "Untersuchungen über Enzyme." Julius Springer, Berlin.

Green, D. E., and Beinert, H. (1955). *Ann. Rev. Biochem.* **24**, 1.

Green, D. E., Herbert, D., and Subramanyan, V. (1941). *J. Biol. Chem.* **138**, 327.

Gulland, J. M. (1947). *Cold Spring Habor Symposia Quant. Biol.* **12**, 95.

Gulland, J. M., Jordan, D. O., and Taylor, H. F. W. (1947). *J. Chem. Soc.* **1947**, 1131.

Guillermond, A., Fontaine, M., and Raffy, A. (1935). *Compt. rend.* **201**, 1077.

Haas, E. (1938). *Biochem. Z.* **298**, 378.

Hanahan, J., and Jayko, M. E. (1952). *J. Am. Chem. Soc.* **74**, 507.

Hansen, R. P., Shortland, F. B., and Cooke, N. J. (1953). *Biochem. J.* (*London*) **53**, 374.

Harman, J. W., and Kitiyakara, A. (1955). *Exptl. Cell Research* **8**, 411.

Harting, J., and Velick, S. F. (1954). *J. Biol. Chem.* **207**, 857, 867.

Hassid, W. Z., Joslyn, M. A., and McCready, R. M. (1941). *J. Am. Chem. Soc.* **63**, 295.

Hausmann, W. (1952). *J. Am. Chem. Soc.* **74**, 3181.

Haworth, W. N., Hirst, E. L., and Isherwood, F. A. (1937). *J. Chem. Soc.* **1937**, 784.

Haworth, W. N., Heath, R. L., and Peat, S. (1941). *J. Chem. Soc.* **1941**, 833.

Haxo, F. (1949). *Arch. Biochem.* **20**, 400.

Hayes, Jr., J. E., and Velick, S. F. (1954). *J. Biol. Chem.* **207**, 225.

Hehre, E. J., Carlson, A. S., and Hamilton, D. M. (1949). *J. Biol. Chem.* **177**, 289.

Heide, S. (1939). *Arch. Mikrobiol.* **10**, 135.

Hevesey, G., Linderstrøm-Lang, K., and Nielsen, N. (1937). *Nature* **140**, 726.

Hevesey, G., and Nielsen, N. (1941). *Acta Physiol. Scand.* **1**, 354.

Heyn, A. N. J. (1936). *Proc. Acad. Sci. Amsterdam.* **39**, 132.

Hill, C. H., and Scott, M. L. (1952). *J. Biol. Chem.* **196**, 189.

Hill, R., and Keilin, D. (1930). *Proc. Roy. Soc. B.* **107**, 286.

Holmberg, J. (1948). *Svensk. Kem. Tidskr.* **60**, 14.

Holzer, H. (1953). *Biochem. Z.* **324**, 144.

Hommerberg, C. (1935). *Svensk. Kem. Tidskr.* **47**, 63.

Hopkins, F. G. (1918). *Ann. Rep. on Prog. Chem. Soc. London* **15**, 157.

Houwink, A. L., and Kreger, D. R. (1953). *Antonie van Leeuwenhoek J. Microbiol. Serol.* **19**, 1.

Hudson, J. (1956). Private communication.

Hugo, W. B. (1954). *J. Bacteriol.* **18**, 87.

Hurst, H. (1952). *J. Exptl. Biol.* **29**, 30.

Ingram, M. (1955). "Biology of Yeasts," p. 21. Pitman, London.

Jeanloz, R. (1944). *Helv. Chim. Acta* **27**, 1501.

Jeener, R., and Brachet, J. (1944). *Enzymologia* **2**, 222.

Johnson, B. C. (1955). *Ann. Rev. Biochem.* **24**, 419.

Johnson, M. J. (1941). *J. Biol. Chem.* **137**, 575.

Jordan, D. O. (1955). "The Nucleic Acids" (E. Chargaff and J. N. Davidson, eds.), Vol. 2, p. 410. Academic Press, New York.

Jörgensen, A. (1948). "Micro-Organisms and Fermentation." Griffin, London.

Joslyn, M. A. (1941). *Wallerstein Labs. Communs.* **11**, 49.

Just, F. (1939). *Biochem. Z.* **303**, 239.

Just, F. (1940). *Biochem. Z.* **306**, 33.

Kagan, B., and Stadnichenko, M. (1938). See *Chem. Abstr.* (1940) **34**, 1347[5].

Kandel, I., and Kandel, M. (1955). *Experientia* **11**, 95.

Karrer, P., and Rutschmann, J. (1946). *Helv. Chim. Acta* **29**, 355.

Katchman, B. J., and O'Fetty, O. (1955). *J. Bacteriol.* **69**, 607.

Keilin, D. (1929). *Proc. Roy. Soc. B.* **104**, 206.

Keilin, D. (1930). *Proc. Roy. Soc. B.* **106**, 418.

Keilin, D. (1953). *Nature* **172**, 390.

Keilin, D., and Hartree, E. F. (1939). *Proc. Roy. Soc. B.* **127**, 167.

Khouvine, Y., and DeRobichon-Szulmajster, H. (1951). *Bull. soc. chim. biol.* **33**, 1508.

Klein, H. P. (1955). *J. Bacteriol.* **69**, 620.

Kleinzeller, A. (1944). *Biochem. J. (London)* **38**, 480.

Kleinzeller, A. (1948). *Advances in Enzymol.* **8**, 299.

Kluyver, A. J., van der Walt, J. P., van Triet, A. J. (1953). *Proc. Nat. Acad. Sci. U.S.* **39**, 583.

Knight, B. C. J. G. (1937). *Biochem. J. (London)* **31**, 966.

Kornberg, S. R. (1956). *J. Biol. Chem.* **218**, 23.

Kraut, H., Eichhorn, F., and Rubenbauer, H. (1927). *Ber. deut. chem. Ger.* **60B**, 1644.

Krebs, E. G. (1953). *J. Biol. Chem.* **200**, 417.

Krebs, E. G., and Najjar, V. A. (1948). *J. Exptl. Med.* **88**, 569.

Krebs, E. G., Rafter, G. W., and McBroom Junge J. (1953). *J. Biol. Chem.* **200**, 479.

Kreger, D. R. (1954). *Biochim. et Biophys. Acta* **13**, 1.

Krimsky, I., and Racker, E. (1952). *J. Biol. Chem.* **198**, 751.

Kunitz, M., and McDonald, M. R. (1946). *J. Gen. Physiol.* **29**, 393.

Lederer, E. (1934). *Compt. rend. soc. biol.* **117**, 1083.

Lee, W. A., and Peacocke, A. R. (1951). *J. Chem. Soc.* **1951**, 3361.

Levene, P. A., and Bass, L. W. (1931). "The Nucleic Acids." Chemical Catalog Co., New York.

Levene, P. A., and Simms, H. S. (1925). *J. Biol. Chem.* **65**, 519.

Levene, P. A., and Simms, H. S. (1926). *J. Biol. Chem.* **70**, 327.

Lewis, J. C., Stubbs, J. J., and Noble, W. M. (1944). *Arch. Biochem.* **4**, 389.

Linnane, A. W., and Still, J. L. (1955). *Arch. Biochem. and Biophys.* **59**, 383.

Lindan, O., and Work, E. (1951). *Biochem. J. (London)* **48**, 337.

Lindegren, C. C. (1945). *Arch. Biochem.* **8**, 119.

Lindegren, C. C. (1947). *Nature* **159**, 63.

Lindstedt, G. (1947). *Arkiv Kemi, Mineral. Geol.* **A20**, 13; cited in *Chem. Abstr.* **41**, 1209.

Ljungdahl, L., and Sandegren, E. (1950). *Acta Chem. Scand.* **4**, 1150.

Lodder, J., and Kreger-van Rij, N. J. W. (1952). "The Yeasts. A Taxonomic Study." North Holland Publ., Amsterdam.

Long, C., and Maguire, M. F. (1953). *Biochem. J. (London)* **54**, 612.

Lovern, J. A. (1955). "The Chemistry of the Lipids." Methuen, London.

Lucy, J. A., and Butler, J. A. Y. (1954). *Nature* **174**, 32.

Lüers, H. (1929). "Chemie des Brauwesens," Berlin; quoted by Brandt, K. (1942). *Protoplasma* **36**, 77.

Lüers, H., and Nowak, G. (1924). *Biochem. Z.* **154**, 304.

Lüers, H., and Schuster, K. (1923). *Kolloid-Z.* **32**, 334.

Lüers, H., and Vaidya M. (1942). *Z. Spiritusind.* **59**, 377; quoted in Neuberg, C. (1946). *Ann. Rev. Biochem.* **15**, 444.

Macheboeuf, M., and Polonovski, J. (1949). *Bull. soc. chim. biol.* **31**, 125.

Mackinney, G. (1952). *Ann. Rev. Biochem.* **21**, 481.

McAnally, R. A., and Smedley-MacLean, I. (1937). *Biochem. J. (London)* **31**, 72.

McIlwain, H. (1946). *Nature* **158**, 898.

McIlwain, H. (1947). *Advances in Enzymol.* **7**, 409.

Magasanik, B. (1955). "The Nucleic Acids," Vol. I, p. 373. Academic Press, New York.

Mager, J. (1947). *Biochem. J. (London)* **41**, 603.

Mager, J., and Aschner, M. (1947). *J. Bacteriol.* **53**, 283.

Mallette, M. F., and Lamanna, C. (1953). *Arch. Biochem. and Biophys.* **47**, 174.

Malm, M. (1947). *Arkiv Kemi, Mineral. Geol.* **25A**, 187.

Malmgren, B., and Hedén, C. G. (1948). *Acta Pathol. Microbiol. Scand.* **24**, 496.

Manners, D. J. (1955). *Quart. Revs. London* **9**, 73.

Manners, D. J., and Khin Maung (1955a). *J. Chem. Soc.* **1955**, 867.

Manners, D. J., and Khin Maung (1955b). *Chemistry and Industry* **1955**, 950.

Marshak, A., and Vogel, H. J. (1951). *J. Biol. Chem.* **189**, 597.

Matsubara, H., Hagihara, B., Horio, T., and Okunuki, K. (1957). *Nature* **179**, 251.

Mazia, D. (1954). *Proc. Nat. Acad. Sci. U.S.* **40**, 521.

Mečir, R. (1947). *Chem. Listy.* **41**, 41.

Meisenheimer, J. (1919). *Hoppe-Seyler's Z. physiol. Chem.* **104**, 229.

Meisenheimer, J. (1921). *Hoppe-Seyler's Z. physiol. Chem.* **114**, 205.

Meyerhof, O. (1945). *J. Biol. Chem.* **157**, 105.

Miettinen, J. K. (1951). *Acta. Chem. Scand.* **5**, 962.

Mitchell, P. (1954). *J. Gen. Microbiol.* **11**, 73.

Mitchell, P., and Moyle, J. (1950). *Nature* **166**, 218.

Mojonnier, M. L., Hedrick, L. R., and Porter, T. (1955). *J. Nutrition* **57**, 579.

Myrbäck, K., and Vasseur, E. (1943). *Hoppe-Seyler's Z. physiol. Chem.* **277**, 171.

Myrbäck, K. (1949). *Ergeb. Enzymforsch.* **10**, 185.

Nabel, K. (1939). *Arch. Mikrobiol.* **10**, 515.

Nagai, S. (1954). Abstracted in *Chemical Abstracts* **48**, 10103. [*J. Inst. Polytech. Osaka City Univ. Ser. D* (1953) **4**, 35.]

Nakayama, T. (1952). Private communication quoted by Mackinnney, G. (1952). *Ann. Rev. Biochem.* **21**, 473.

Negelein, E., and Wolff, W. J. (1937). *Biochem. Z.* **293**, 351.

Nielsen, N., and Nillson, N. G. (1953). *Acta Chem. Scand.* **7**, 1064, 984.

Neuberg, C., and Lustig, H. (1942). *Arch. Biochem.* **1**, 191.

Newman, M. S., and Anderson, R. J. (1933). *J. Biol. Chem.* **102**, 219.

Nickerson, W. J., and Falcone, G. (1956). *Science* **124**, 722.

Northcote, D. H. (1953). *Biochem. J.* **53**, 348.

Northcote, D. H., and Horne, R. W. (1952). *Biochem. J.* **51**, 232.

Nossal, P. M. (1954). *Biochem. J.* **57**, 62.

Novelli, G. D., and Lipmann, F. (1950). *J. Biol. Chem.* **182**, 213.

Nyman, M. A., and Chargaff, E. (1949). *J. Biol. Chem.* **180**, 741.

Oda, Takeshi (1952). *J. Pharm. Soc. Japan* **72**, 136, 142. Astracted in *Chem. Abstr.* (1952) **46**, 6192.

Ogur, M., Minckler, S., Lindegren, G., and Lindegren, C. C. (1952). *Arch. Biochem. and Biophys.* **40**, 175.

Olson, B. H., and Johnson, M. J. (1949). *J. Bacteriol.* **57**, 235.

Ørskov, S. L. (1945). *Acta Pathol. Microbiol. Scand.* **22**, 523.

Oshima, 1902. *Hoppe-Seyler's Z. physiol. Chem.* **36**, 42.

Overstreet, R., and Jacobson, L. (1952). *Ann. Rev. Plant. Physiol.* **3**, 189.

Paul, K. G. (1951). "The Enzymes" (J. B. Summer and K. Myrbäck, eds.), Vol. II, part I, p. 357. Academic Press, New York.

Peat, S., Whelan, W. J., and Edwards, T. E. (1955). *J. Chem. Soc.* **1955**, 355.

Peck, R. L., and Hauser, C. R. (1940). *J. Biol. Chem.* **134**, 403.

Perlman, D., and O'Brien, E. (1954). *J. Bacteriol.* **68**, 167.

Peterson, W. J. (1948). "Yeasts in Feeding," p. 26. Garrard Press, London (1950).

Peterson, W. J., Bell, T. A., Etchells, J. L., and Smart, W. W. G., Jr. (1954). *J. Bacteriol.* **67**, 708.

Pfiffner, J. J., Calkins, D. G., O'Dell, B. L., Bloom, E. S., Brown, R. A., Campbell, C. J., and Bird, O. D. (1945). *Science* **102**, 228.

Phillips, A. (1956). *J. Inst. Brewing*, in preparation.

Porter, J. W., and Lincoln, R. E. (1950). *Arch. Biochem.* **27**, 390.

Pulver, R., and Verzár, F. (1940). *Helv. Chim. Acta* **23**, 1087.

Racker, E. (1955). *In* "Methods in Enzymology" (S. P. Colowick and N. O. Kaplan, eds.), Vol. 1, p. 500. Academic Press, New York.

Raffy, A. (1939). *Compt. rend.* **209**, 900.

Raffy, A. (1937). *Compt. rend. soc. biol.* **126**, 875.

Ratner, S., Blanchard, M., Coburn, A. F., and Green, D. E. (1944). *J. Biol. Chem.* **155**, 689.

Ratner, S., Blanchard, M., Coburn, A. F., and Green, D. E. (1946). *J. Biol. Chem.* **164**, 691.

Rawlinson, W. A., and Hale, J. H. (1949). *Biochem. J.* (*London*) **45**, 247.

Reichert, R. (1945). *Helv. Chim. Acta* **28**, 484.

Reichert, R. (1944). *Helv. Chim. Acta* **27**, 961.

Reindel, F., Weickmann, A., Picard, S., Luber, K., and Turula, P. (1940). *Ann. Chem. Justus Liebigs* **544**, 116.

Rewald, B. (1930). *Biochem. Z.* **218**, 481.

Richards, O. W., and Troutman, M. C. (1940). *J. Bacteriol.* **39**, 739.

Ridgway, G. J. (1954). *Dissertation Abstr.* **14**, 752.

Roelofsen, P. A. (1953). *Biochim. et Biophys. Acta* **10**, 477.

Roelofsen, P. A., and Hoette, I. (1951). *Antonie van Leeuwenhoek. J. Microbiol. Serol.* **17**, 297.

Roine, P. (1946). *Suomen Kemistilehti* **B19**, 37.

Rosenburg, T., and Wilbrandt, W. (1952). *Intern. Rev. Cytol.* **1**, 73.

Rothstein, A., and Demis, C. (1953). *Arch. Biochem. and Biophys.* **44**, 18.

Rothstein, A., and Meier, R. (1949). *J. Cellular. Comp. Physiol.* **34**, 97.

Rowen, J. W., and Norman, A. (1954). *Arch. Biochem. and Biophys.* **51**, 524.

Rubinstein, D. L., and Burlakowa, H. (1934). *Biochem. Z.* **270**, 324.

Salisbury, L. F., and Anderson, R. J. (1936). *J. Biol. Chem.* **112**, 541.

Salkowski, E. (1894a). *Ber. deut. chem. Ges.* **27**, 497.

Salkowski, E. (1894b). *Ber. deut. chem. Ges.* **27**, 3325.

Schäffner, A., and Specht, H. (1938). *Hoppe-Seyler's Z. physiol. Chem.* **251**, 144.

Schales, A., Mims, V., and Schales, S. S. (1946). *Federation Proc.* **5**, 152.

Schmidt, G. L., and Hecht, L. (1944). *J. Biol. Chem.* **178**, 733.

Schmidt, M. (1936). *Arch. Mikrobiol.* **7**, 241.

Schoenheimer, R., Dam, H., and Gottenberg, von K. (1935). *J. Biol. Chem.* **110**, 659.

Schönfeld, F., and Hirt, W. (1911). *Wochschr. Brau.* **28**, 436.

Schopfer, W. H., and Guillond, M. (1945). *Experientia* **1**, 332.

Schumacher, J. (1928). *Centr. Bakteriol. Parasitenk. Abt. I*, **108**, 193.

Schwimmer, S., and Pardee, A. B. (1953). *Advances in Enzymol.* **14**, 375.

Scott, G. T., Jacobson, M. A., and Rice, M. E. (1951). *Arch. Biochem.* **30**, 282.

Scott, J. F. (1948). *Biochim. et Biophys. Acta* **2**, 1.

Sedlmayr (1903). *Z. ges. Brauw.* **26**, 381–392.

Seliber, G., and Katznelson, R. (1929). *Protoplasma* **7**, 204.

Seliber, G., and Katznelson, R. (1927). *Compt. rend. soc. biol.* **97**, 449.

Sevag, M. G., Cattaneo, C., and Maiweg, L. (1935). *Ann. Chem. Justus Liebigs* **519**, 111.

Sevag, M. G., Newcomb, M. D., and Miller, R. E. (1954). *J. Immunol.* **72**, 1.

Simon, S., and Hedrick, L. R. (1955). *J. Bacteriol.* **69**, 4.

Slonimiski, P. P. (1956). *Exptl. Cell Research.* **10**, 160.

Smedley-Maclean, I., and Hoffert, D. (1923). *Biochem. J.* (*London*) **10**, 135.

Smith, Lucille (1954). *Arch. Biochem. and Biophys.* **50**, 285, 299, 315.

Sobotka, H., Holzmann, H., and Reiner, M. (1936). *Biochem. J.* (*London*) **30**, 333.

Spiegelman, S., Halvorsen, H. O., and Ben-Ishai, R. (1955). *In* "Amino Acid Metabolism" (W. McElroy and B. Glass, eds.), p. 124. Johns Hopkins, Baltimore.

Spiegelman, S., and Kamen, M. D. (1947). *Cold Spring Harbor Symposia Quant. Biol.* **12**, 211.

Stanley, N. F. (1949). *Australian J. Exptl. Biol. Med. Sci.* **27**, 409.

Stephenson, M. (1949). "Bacterial Metabolism," 3rd ed., p. 296. Longmans, New York.

Stewart, L. C., Nelson, K. R., and Hudson, C. S. (1950). *J. Am. Chem. Soc.* **72**, 2059.

Stich, W., and Eisgruber, H. (1951). *Hoppe-Seyler's Z. physiol. Chem.* **287**, 19.

Stokes, J. L., and Gunness, M. (1946). *J. Bacteriol.* **52**, 195.

Sumner, J. B., and O'Kane, D. J. (1948). *Enzymologia* **12**, 251.

Tang, Y. W., Bonner, J., and Zechmeister, L. (1949). *Arch. Biochem.* **21**, 455.

Tanret, G. (1931). *Compt. rend.* **192**, 1056.

Täufel, K., Thaler, H., and Schreyegg, H. (1936). *Fettchem. Umschau.* 43, 26; see also *Chem. Abstr.* (1936) 30, 4534.

Taylor, Shirley, K. (1947). *J. Gen. Microbiol.* 1, 86.

Taylor, Shirley, K. (1949). *J. Gen. Microbiol.* 3, 211.

Taylor, J. F. (1953). *In* "The Proteins" (H. Neurath and K. Bailey, eds.), Vol. I, Part A, p. 1. Academic Press, New York.

Theorell, H. (1947). *Advances in Enzymol.* 7, 265.

Theorell, H. (1935). *Biochem. Z.* 278, 263.

Theorell, H. (1937). *Biochem. Z.* 290, 293.

Theorell, H. (1951a). *In* "The Enzymes" (J. B. Sumner and K. Myrbäck, eds.), p. 397, Vol. II, part I. Academic Press, New York.

Theorell, H. (1951b). *In* "The Enzymes" (J. B. Sumner and K. Myrbäck, eds.), p. 335, Vol. II, part I. Academic Press, New York.

Trevelyan, W. E., and Harrison, J. S. (1952). *Biochem. J. (London)* 50, 298.

Tristam, G. R. (1949). *Advances in Protein Chem.* 5, 83.

Usden, U. R., and Burrell, R. C. (1952). *Arch. Biochem. and Biophys.* 36, 172.

Vallee, B. L., and Hoch, F. L. (1955). *J. Am. Chem. Soc.* 77, 822, 1392.

Vandendriessche, L. (1951). *Compt. rend. trav. lab. Carlsberg Sér. Chim.* 27, 341.

van der Walt, J. P. (1952). Ph.D. Thesis, p. 95. Technical High School, Delft.

van Iterson, G., Meyer, K. H., and Lotmar, W. (1936). *Rec. trav. chim.* 55, 61.

Van Lanen, J. M., and Tanner, F. W. (1948). *Vitamins and Hormones* 6, 164.

Van Lanen, J. M., Broquist, H. P., Johnson, M. J., Baldwin, I. L., and Peterson, W. H. (1942). *Ind. Eng. Chem.* 34, 1244.

van Wisselingh, I. (1924). Die Zellenmembran, "Handbuch der Pflanzen Anatomie," Vol. 3, p. 170. G. Borntraeger, Leipzig.

Velick, S. F., and Udenfriend, S. (1953). *J. Biol. Chem.* 203, 575.

Virtanen, A. I., Karström, H., and Turpeinen, O. (1930). *Hoppe-Seyler's Z. physiol. Chem.* 187, 7.

Vischer, E., and Chargaff, E. (1948). *J. Biol. Chem.* 176, 703.

Vischer, E., Zamenhof, S., and Chargaff, E. (1949). *J. Biol. Chem.* 177, 429.

Volkin, E., and Carter, C. E. (1951). *J. Am. Chem. Soc.* 73, 1516.

Volkin, E., and Cohn, W. E. (1953). *J. Biol. Chem.* 203, 319.

Vogel, H. (1949). "Die Bierhefe und ihre Verwertung," Wepf, Basel.

von Euler, H., and Hahn L. (1948). *Arkiv Kemi Mineral Geol.* 25A, 11, 1.

Warburg, O. (1946). *Naturwiss.* 33, 93.

Warburg, O., and Christian, W. (1933). *Biochem. Z.* 257, 492.

Warburg, O., and Christian, W. (1939). *Biochem. Z.* 303, 40.

Warburg, O., and Negelein, E. (1932). *Biochem. Z.* 244, 239.

Watson, J. D., and Crick, F. H. (1953). *Nature* 171, 737.

Webb, D. A., and Fearon, W. R. (1937). *Sci. Proc. Roy. Dublin. Soc.* 21, 487.

Weiss, G. (1931). *Biochem. Z.* 243, 269.

Weygand, F. (1950). *Chem. Ber.* 83, 269.

Whelan, W. J., and Roberts, P. J. R. (1952). *Nature* 170, 748.

Whelan, W. J., and Roberts, P. J. R. (1953). *J. Chem. Soc.* 1953, 1298.

White, J. (1949). *Intern. Congr. Biochem. Abstr. of Communs. 1st Congr. Cambridge, Engl.* p. 554.

White, J. (1954). "Yeast Technology," Wiley, New York.

Wiley, A. J., Dubey, G. A., Lueck, B. F., and Hughes, L. P. (1950). *Ind. Eng. Chem.* 42, 1830.

Wiame, J. M. (1949). *J. Biol. Chem.* **178**, 919.

Wieland, H., and Benend, W. (1942). *Hoppe-Seyler's Z. physiol. Chem.* **274**, 215.

Wieringa, K. T. (1930). *Protoplasma* **8**, 522.

Wilkes, B. G., and Palmer, E. T. (1932). *J. Gen. Physiol.* **16**, 233.

Wilkins, M. H. F., Stokes, A. R., and Wilson, H. R. (1953). *Nature* **181**, 738.

Willstätter, R. (1926). *Naturwiss.* **14**, 937.

Willstätter, R., Schneider, K., and Bamann, E. (1925). *Hoppe-Seyler's Z. physiol. Chem.* **147**, 248.

Windisch, F., Nordheim, W., and Heumann, W. (1956). *Hoppe-Seyler's Z. physiol. Chem.* **303**, 153.

Winge, Ö., and Roberts, C. (1955). *Compt. rend. trav. lab. Carlsberg, Sér. physiol.* **25**, 331.

Work, E., and Dewey, D. L. (1953). *J. Gen. Microbiol.* **9**, 394.

Wright, L. D., Cresson, E. L., Skeggs, H. R., Peck, R. L., Wolf, D. E., Wood, T. R., Valiant, J., and Folkers, K. (1952). *Science* **114**, 635.

Yakushiji, E., and Mori, T. (1937). *Acta Phytochim. Japan* **10**, 113.

Yamaguchi, S., Tamiya, H., and Ogura Y. (1936). *Acta Phytochim. Japan* **9**, 103.

Yotsuyanagi, Y. (1935). *Nature* **176**, 1208.

Zamenhof, S., and Chargaff, E. (1950). *J. Biol. Chem.* **187**, 1.

Zamenhof, S. (1956). *Progr. Biophys. and Biophys. Chem.* **6**, 86.

Zechmeister, L., and Tóth, G. (1934). *Biochem. Z.* **270**, 309.

Zechmeister, L., and Tóth, G. (1936). *Biochem. Z.* **284**, 133.

Zittle, C. A. (1953). *Advances in Enzymol.* **14**, 319.

Zucker, T. F., and Zucker, L. M. (1950). *Vitamins and Hormones* **8**, 30.

CHAPTER VI

Yeast Growth

E. O. Morris

1. Introduction

Yeasts are living entities and as such they require food to maintain them in a healthy state so that reproduction of their kind can continue; this food must include sources of carbon, nitrogen, sulfur, and certain minerals and many yeasts also require certain nutrilites. Complex undefined media such as extracts of malt or certain fruit juices are generally able to satisfy these demands. However, it is at times necessary to use defined synthetic media that can be guaranteed to have the same composition from time to time. In order to prepare such media it is necessary to determine what chemically defined compounds are potential sources of yeast food. As is to be expected, certain of these utilizable substances are more acceptable in this respect than are others and, further, it is known that antagonistic effects sometimes result from growing yeasts in the presence of a mixture of compounds even though the individual components of the mixture are beneficial to the organism. Variations in the physical conditions of the culture that are able to influence growth include changes of temperature, pH, and aeration. In order to assess these various factors it is necessary to be able both to measure changes in the yeast population and also to understand the simpler kinetics of growth. The object of this account is to consider such factors together with cultural characteristics of yeasts and the factors that influence sporulation, pseudomycelium formation, and the preservation of yeast cultures.

2. Kinetics of Growth

In order to determine accurately changes in the growth rate of yeasts grown under various cultural conditions, it is essential to have a knowledge of the techniques employed to assess the number of cells present at any time while bearing in mind the limitations of these methods. The most important of these techniques are described and discussed here.

A. Methods for Determining Cell Numbers

(1) *Total Cell Counts.* The method that requires the least equipment consists in counting the total number of cells in a known volume of liquid. For this purpose the yeast is thoroughly dispersed in the culture medium, diluted to a convenient cell density, and a small volume of this suspension is transferred to a hemocytometer chamber. The total number of cells in a known volume, as revealed by microscopical examination, is determined. When a "Thoma" type chamber is used the following formulae can be employed:

$$\text{Total number of cells/ml.} = \frac{\text{No. of cells counted} \times 4 \times 10^6 \times \text{dilution}}{\text{No. of small squares examined}}$$

As cultures mature, many yeasts have a tendency to aggregate in clusters and these prevent uniform dispersion of the cells in the counting chamber. In this connection Eddy (1955a) has shown that aggregates of yeast cells can often be dispersed by maltose, and in practice it has been found that diluting yeast specimens with a 20% solution of maltose generally ensures a uniformly dispersed preparation. Little work has been done to determine the precision of various counting techniques when applied to yeasts, but for bacteria, Topley and Wilson (1948a) state that a variation of not more than ±10% should be attainable provided care is taken during the preparation of the specimen.

Turbidimetric methods for estimating the total number of cells are frequently employed, such techniques depending upon measuring the amount of light scattered or absorbed by the cells. Generally a calibration curve is prepared by plotting the amount of light absorbed or scattered by suspensions of known cell density against the number of cells present, a typical calibration curve being shown in Fig. 1. By reference to such a curve the number of cells in any culture grown in a similar medium can be estimated by determining the amount of light absorbed. The method is undoubtedly rapid and useful but it should be remembered that its accuracy is dependent upon the assumption that all the cells of different cultures at different stages of growth are of the same size, shape, and opacity and further, that the amount of light absorbed by the suspending fluids is constant; this latter point is particularly important when the culture media are colored. Turbidimetric methods are useless for dealing with flocculent yeasts and in such instances dispersion of the flocs

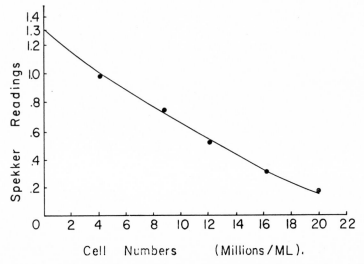

Fig. 1. A typical calibration curve showing the relationship between the number of cells in a synthetic medium and the amount of light passing through the culture as measured by a Spekker photoelectric apparatus.

by maltose has been found to be extremely useful. Liese (1926), Strausz (1930), and Skar (1934) have considered the factors involved in the use of these techniques for the enumeration of bacteria.

Estimates of either the dry weight of yeast cells or of the total cell nitrogen have also been employed to assay the total number of cells. Such estimates are reliable when once it has been established that the average cell weight or cell nitrogen is constant throughout the course of growth. This need not always be so, as will be seen from Plate IA,B which illustrate the large cells commonly found during late lag phase and the variation in cell size during the decline phase. When marked variation in cell size is known to occur, it is advisable to prepare calibra-

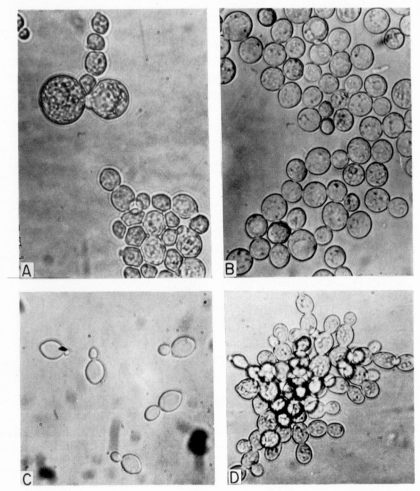

PLATE I. A: Large cells in a culture of *Saccharomyces cerevisiae* often observed during the late lag phase.

B: Variation in the size of the cells in a 9-day-old culture of *Saccharomyces cerevisiae*.

C: Cells from a strain of *Saccharomyces cerevisiae* in which the daughter cells separate from the mother cells at maturity. Liquid cultures 18 hours old.

D: Cells from a strain of *Saccharomyces cerevisiae* in which the daughter cells do not separate from the mother cells. Liquid cultures 18 hours old.

tion curves applicable to individual stages of the growth cycle. An important factor which is often overlooked is that cell weights vary according to the salt concentration of the medium in which the yeasts are grown (Seliber and Katznelson, 1927, 1929).

(2) *Viable Cell Counts.* When estimates of cell numbers are based upon total cell counts it is obviously hazardous to assume that all the cells in the original inoculum are viable. This is not necessarily so, particularly if the inoculum is taken from an old culture in which case the total number of cells will mostly far exceed the number of viable ones. Consequently, a more informative picture of the changes in any yeast culture can best be obtained from a consideration of both the number of viable cells and the total number of cells.

A technique commonly used to estimate the number of living cells in a culture is the dilution plating method. In practice, several consecutive known dilutions of the culture are made and one unit of each of these is mixed with a nutrient agar or gelatin medium in a petri dish or roll tube. After a suitable period of incubation the number of colonies developing is taken as a measure of the number of viable cells. The majority of publications dealing with the precision of this technique have been confined to studies of bacteria (see Wilson *et al.,* 1935; Jennison and Wadsworth, 1940). This method when applied to yeasts has severe limitations, because reliable estimates cannot be made when the yeast cells are flocculent, when chains of cells are present, or when the cells are actively budding; it is clear that under such conditions each colony cannot be regarded as originating from a single cell.

A staining technique described by Townsend and Lindegren (1953) is probably more reliable and a comparison of the results obtained by the use of these two techniques is shown in Table I. It will be seen that the methods compare favorably when the cultures have few budding cells or chains of cells, but that in other cases the plating method gives results that are consistently and markedly lower than those obtained by the alternative method.

The respective merits of various staining techniques for the demonstration of dead cells in a culture of yeast has been recently investigated by Ketterer (1956) and it appears that both methylene blue and acridine orange, at a concentration of about 1:10,000, exhibit slight toxic effects but these are sufficiently small so as to fall well within the experimental errors inherent in such techniques, provided that the counts are made within a reasonably short time after the cells have been exposed to the dyes. A comparison between cell counts made by staining and culturing techniques show that there is close agreement when the cells are culti-

TABLE I

A COMPARISON OF THE NUMBER OF VIABLE YEAST CELLS DETERMINED BOTH BY A
DILUTION PLATING TECHNIQUE AND BY A METHYLENE BLUE STAINING METHOD

Age and morphology of culture (*Saccharomyces cerevisiae*)	% Viable cells	
	Plating method	Staining method
48-hour-old culture; cells dispersed, few buds observed[a]	93.0	96.0
18-hour-old culture; cells dispersed but a large number of buds observed	60.2	100.0
48-hour-old culture; cells occasionally in chain formation	79.4	91.2
18-hour-old culture; young budding cells and some chain formation	51.7	99.8

[a] Each bud is counted as an individual cell in the staining technique.

vated under normal conditions; however, poor agreement is obtained when the cells have been exposed to toxic agents.

B. *Growth Curves*

The kinetics of yeast growth can best be illustrated by the simple case where a small number of cells are seeded into a relatively large volume of fully nutrient medium under conditions near to the optimum as regards temperature, pH, aeration, and agitation. In such a case the following phases of growth can be recognized: lag phase, exponential growth phase, stationary phase, and phase of decline. A diagrammatic representation of a typical curve is shown in Fig. 2, while Table II illustrates the behavior of a representative strain of *Saccharomyces cerevisiae*.

(1) *Lag Phase*. This phase is generally considered to be that period preceding the stage of exponential growth. The duration and pattern of the lag is markedly influenced by the strain of yeast being investigated, the age of the cells before transfer, and the composition of both the medium in which the yeast has been previously kept and of that to which the cells are transferred. In general, the lag phase is of short duration when the cells of the parent culture are actively growing and when the composition of both the old and new media are similar.

Immediately after the yeast is transferred to a fresh medium the number of living cells may commonly decrease and this phenomenon is often marked when the yeast is grown in the presence of slightly inhibitory substances (Ingram, 1955a). When yeasts, which are actively growing in a medium to which fresh nutrients are added incrementally (incremental yeasts), are transferred to molasses there is an initial loss of viability and a loss in weight of the entire cell population. However, when actively growing cells which have not been grown incrementally are transferred, no such pronounced loss of viability or weight occurs,

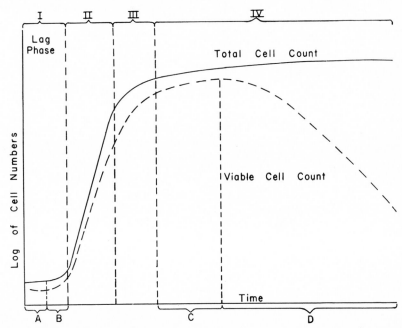

FIG. 2. Diagrammatic representation of yeast growth curves showing the various phases of growth and the difference between the total cell counts and the viable cell counts.

I. Lag phase.
II. Exponential growth phase.
III. Period of negative acceleration.
IV. Apparent stationary phase.

A. Period of adaptation.
B. Period of recovery.
C. Real stationary phase.
D. Phase of decline.

particularly when the carbohydrate concentration of the original medium approximates that of the fresh one (see Table III) (White and Munns, 1953b). These latter investigations also revealed that the smaller the inoculum the more rapid is the period of recovery. This statement appears to be contrary to the views of Richards (1932a) who observed that the smaller the inoculum the longer was the lag phase but it is doubtful if the cultural conditions employed by the different workers are comparable.

The lag phase is sometimes considered in two parts: (a) a period of adaptation during which the cells are becoming used to their new surroundings and in which a fall in the percentage viable cells may be noted; and (b) a period of recovery when cell division starts to occur at

TABLE II

A COMPARISON OF TOTAL CELL COUNTS AND VIABLE CELL COUNTS SHOWING THE REGULAR INCREASE AND DECREASE IN THE NUMBER OF LIVING CELLS AND THE PROGRESSIVE INCREASE IN THE NUMBER OF DEAD CELLS

Time (hours)	Total number of cells per ml.	Viable cells per ml.	% Viable cells	Total number of dead cells per ml.
0	5.2×10^3	4.0×10^3	76.9	1.2×10^3
0.5	5.0×10^3	4.2×10^3	84.0	0.8×10^3
1.0	4.8×10^3	4.0×10^3	83.3	0.8×10^3
1.5	5.6×10^3	4.4×10^3	78.6	1.2×10^3
2.0	7.2×10^3	5.8×10^3	80.6	1.4×10^3
2.5	7.6×10^3	5.2×10^3	68.4	1.4×10^3
3.0	8.0×10^3	6.5×10^3	81.3	1.5×10^3
3.5	1.0×10^4	8.1×10^3	81.0	1.9×10^3
4.0	1.04×10^4	8.5×10^3	81.7	1.9×10^3
4.5	1.12×10^4	9.1×10^3	81.3	2.1×10^3
5.0	1.22×10^4	1.0×10^4	82.0	2.2×10^3
5.5	1.44×10^4	1.19×10^4	82.6	2.5×10^3
6.0	1.56×10^4	1.31×10^4	84.0	2.5×10^3
6.5	1.58×10^4	1.33×10^4	84.2	2.5×10^3
7.0	1.72×10^4	1.46×10^4	84.9	2.6×10^3
7.5	2.52×10^4	2.18×10^4	86.5	3.4×10^3
24.0	1.73×10^7	1.70×10^7	98.3	3.0×10^5
25.5	1.79×10^7	1.76×10^7	98.3	3.0×10^5
27.0	1.77×10^7	1.73×10^7	97.7	4.0×10^5
50.0	2.37×10^7	2.34×10^7	98.7	3.0×10^5
74.0	2.41×10^7	2.35×10^7	97.5	6.0×10^5
98.0	2.99×10^7	2.90×10^7	97.0	9.0×10^5
146.0	1.10×10^8	1.05×10^8	96.2	5.0×10^6
170.0	1.10×10^8	1.05×10^8	96.4	5.0×10^6
194.0	1.12×10^8	1.01×10^8	90.3	1.1×10^7
218.0	1.13×10^8	9.22×10^7	81.7	2.1×10^7
232.0	1.13×10^8	8.17×10^7	72.3	3.1×10^7

an increasing rate. Early in the period of recovery certain yeasts produce a considerable number of large cells (Plate IA). The significance of these cells is not known, but it may be postulated that although the cells have recovered their ability to reproduce cellular material they have not yet developed the power to divide and the following evidence favors this view. When such large cells are removed from the culture by micro-manipulation, it is found that their progeny are normal in size and have the same general characters as the parent culture.

Various mathematical considerations have been applied to the precise computation of the duration of the lag phase in the case for bacteria (see Lodge and Hinshelwood, 1943; Monod, 1949; Squire and Hartsell,

TABLE III

DIFFERENCE IN GROWTH RATES OF YEASTS FED "INCREMENTALLY AND "NONINCREMENTALLY"[a]

Time from commencement of experiment (hour)	% Increase in yield of "incremental" yeasts	% Increase in yield of "nonincremental" yeasts
0.5	−8.2	0.92
1.0	−4.5	22.2
2.0	1.7	51.5
3.0	12.1	90.4
4.0	42.2	141.1
5.0	93.1	—
5.5	114.2	—
6.0	137.5	—

[a] From the data of White and Munns (1953a).

1955; and Finn, 1955) and these may be usefully translated to the study of yeasts. For an estimate of the duration of the lag phase to have any real value, the culture must exhibit a short recovery period and a well-defined exponential phase of growth.

In the simple case illustrated in Fig. 3, where x_0 = number of cells initially present and x_1 = number of cells present after time T, if the number of cells were to increase exponentially from the beginning of the test, the population would increase from x_0 to x_1 in a lesser time T_1. It will be seen that the points $ABCD$ mark out a parallelogram such that $AB = CD$ and that $T - T_1 = L$ (lag period).

T can be measured and T_1 calculated from the expression

$$K = \frac{2.303 \times \log_{10} \frac{x_n}{x}}{T_1}$$

where K is the modulus of exponential growth (see below).

Studies of the lag phase have been made by McIlwain et al. (1939)

and Lwoff and Monod (1947) in order to investigate metabolites produced by bacteria during growth.

This approach has been used in the study of adaptive changes when
yeast cells are transferred from one environment to another and here

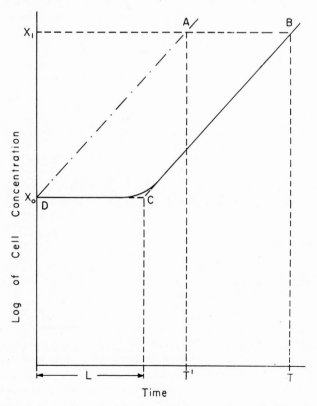

Fɪɢ. 3. Illustration of the principles involved in a simple method for the computation of the duration of the lag phase.

the work of Lodge and Hinshelwood (1939) and Morel (1941) may
be cited.

(2) *Exponential Growth Phase.* The lag period is followed by a phase
during which the number of cells increases exponentially, that is to say
each cell divides at a constant interval. In the ideal case, an individual
yeast cell will divide by budding, or less frequently by fission, in time *g*
and the resulting two cells will again divide in a further time *g* and so
on. White (1954) has aptly remarked that this form of progression is
similar to the Compound Interest Law.

$$A_0 = P_0 e^{\frac{rt}{100}}$$

By substituting symbols such that x = the initial number of cells and x_n = the number of cells present after time T_1, the following relation results

$$x_n = x e^{KT_1}$$

in which K = the modulus of growth. By transposition,

$$K = \frac{\log_e \frac{x_n}{x}}{T_1} \text{ or } \frac{2.303 \times \log_{10} \frac{x_n}{x}}{T_1}$$

This equation can incidentally be employed to determine the weight of yeast which will be produced in a given time by substituting weights of the yeast crops for cell numbers. The mean generation time—the average time taken for each cell to reproduce itself—can also be established from this relation. For instance, suppose the growth modulus $(K) = 0.3$, then the time required for each cell to produce a new cell, that is when $x_n/x = 2$, is given by the expression

$$0.3 = \frac{2.303 \times \log_{10} 2}{T_1},$$

from which $T = 2.31$ units of time.

It is often observed that not all the cells divide or survive even during the period of maximum growth. This fact is clearly indicated in Table II from which it is apparent that although the percentage of viable cells increases so also does the number of dead cells; however, the surviving cells will still increase by a geometrical progression. In such cases the ratio of viable to total cells (V/t) increases at each cell division until a value approximating $p - 1$ is attained where p = the generation index, a constant for each culture (Topley and Wilson, 1948b). If both the total and viable cell numbers are determined on two occasions during the exponential phases, the value of p can be established from the following equation:

$$p - 1 = \frac{V_2 - V_1}{t_2 - t_1}$$

In fact a more precise estimate of the generation time may be obtained by substituting the value of p for the number 2 in the simple illustration above.

The estimation of the mean generation time of yeast cells may in certain cases amount only to an approximation because, firstly, not all the cells will produce only one daughter cell while, secondly, it is commonly observed that some cells produce two or more buds at the same time. Little is known about the rate of growth of such cells but it may be that cells can only reproduce new cellular material at a given rate so that those producing more than one bud at a time will grow at a proportionally slower rate than those that produce only one. In that event the two factors will oppose each other and the resultant effect will be less serious than might otherwise be the case.

The duration of the exponential phase is controlled to a large extent by the composition and physical state of the medium, and the number of cells per unit volume. Generally the composition of media is so chosen that there is an excess of nutrients present so that many generations of cells can take place before the medium becomes depleted of nutrients. When preparing media it is, however, important to remember that, as the exponential phase progresses, the nutrients are eventually being utilized very rapidly following the enormous increase in cell numbers. Consequently damage to the cells, as a result of the accumulation of metabolic end products, may occur. The culture should also be continuously agitated to prevent localized "staling" of the medium and to encourage a free exchange of gases between the medium and the outside atmosphere. Media which are well buffered favor the duration of the exponential phase by protecting the cells against changes of pH that would otherwise occur due to the accumulation of certain acidic end products. The size of the inoculum does not influence the rate of growth during the exponential phase, but small inocula result in a prolonged phase of active growth which continues until the total cell population reaches that attained in cultures derived from a large inoculum (Clark, 1922; Richards, 1932a). This is probably only another way of expressing the observations of Rahn et al. (1951) who found that, no matter what size of inoculum be used, growth is inhibited when the concentration of end products attains a critical value (see Table IV). It is pertinent to add that all determinations of growth rates should be performed under conditions that permit the rigid control of temperature, because variation of this factor is generally reflected in substantial change in growth rate.

(3) *Stationary Phase.* After a time, depending upon the strain of yeast under examination and the environmental conditions, the period of exponential growth comes to an end. Total cell counts show that the rate of growth first slows down until eventually the number of cells in the culture may remain almost constant over a considerable period of time, i.e., there is apparently a stationary phase. A consideration of the viable cell counts on the other hand reveals a different sequence of events. As

TABLE IV

AMOUNTS OF ALCOHOL PRODUCED DURING THE GROWTH OF YEAST CULTURES DERIVED FROM DIFFERENT SIZED INOCULA[a]

Size of inoculum (g.)	0.02	0.04	0.08	0.16	0.31	0.62	1.25	2.5	5.0	10.0	20.0
Total amount of alcohol produced (%)											
Experiment I	11.75	—	11.80	11.75	12.45	—	—	12.6	13.35	13.35	—
Experiment II	—	12.35	12.0	11.95	12.90	13.10	13.02	13.2	13.75	13.90	10.35

[a] From the data of Rahn et al. (1951).

the culture nears the end of the period of deceleration the rate at which cells die approaches that at which new cells are formed and for a comparatively short time there is a state of equilibrium between the two conditions so that this may be regarded as a "real" stationary phase.

Undoubtedly there are many factors concerned in this reduced rate of reproduction, but it is certain that in the majority of cases they are associated with either the depletion of nutrients or the accumulation of toxic end products.

The effect that the depletion of any particular nutrient of the medium will have upon the rate of growth is dependent on the function of that nutrient in cell metabolism. For instance, exhaustion of the carbon source results necessarily in a rapid decrease in the growth rate; on the other hand, depletion of certain nutrilites from the medium will cause a fairly rapid decrease in the growth rate if the cells have an absolute requirement for these substances, but only a less marked retardation when the cells have a partial requirement as when the yeast can synthesize the nutrilite, albeit slowly. On occasion the rate of growth will return to near maximal for a short period of time if fresh medium be added in a concentrated form so as not to alter appreciably the volume of the medium; in such cases the decline in growth rate is obviously brought about by exhaustion of the medium. Other cultures may not show precisely this response, although if the medium be appreciably diluted at the same time as the fresh nutrients are added, renewed vigor is sometimes noted indicating that toxic end products have been at least partly responsible for the reduced rate of growth.

(4) *Decline Phase.* Eventually the number of cells that die exceeds the number of new cells produced and then the culture is said to enter the decline phase. The rapidity at which this phase proceeds is governed by those same conditions which affect the duration of the exponential phase. Actually the total number of cells commonly slowly increases even during this phase. On occasion it may be observed that sporadic increases occur, moreover, in the number of viable cells, a possible explanation being that during this period autolysis occurs resulting in the liberation of nutrients which can be reutilized by the viable cells.

Finally, many of the cells which survive for a long period in the decline phase enter a different stage in their life cycle in that they may form either "durable cells" or ascospores.

Liquid Cultures. The foregoing account indicates that, under ideal conditions for growth, vegetative reproduction conforms to a regular and orderly pattern. However, it must not be assumed that (a) all fluid cultures are morphologically similar, (b) the environment in a liquid medium is homogeneous, at least under conditions frequently employed in the laboratory, or (c) the yeast population need necessarily retain its characteristics in subsequent cultures. The reasons why these assumptions cannot be made are rather complex but will probably be more readily appreciated from the following considerations.

Two fundamental facts concerning the reproduction of yeast cells in liquid medium under carefully controlled conditions (Lindegren and Haddad, 1954) relate firstly, to the fact that a mother cell usually attains its maximum volume before a bud is produced and secondly, to the obser-vation that the time taken for successive generations to be reproduced by two individual cells of the same age is of the same order. These principles almost certainly apply in the early exponential stage of the growth of most yeast cultures, although the morphology of the cells in various cultures may differ considerably, not only between widely differ-ent genera or species, but also between strains of the same species (Townsend and Lindegren, 1955). In this latter connection certain strains of *Saccharomyces cerevisiae* during the initial stages of growth produce buds which, as soon as they mature, separate away from the mother cells before either the mother or daughter cells produce further buds (Plate IC). Other strains of this species reproduce in a somewhat different manner, the daughter cell remaining in close contact with the mother cell and both of these cells producing buds which also remain attached to their parent cells, this process being repeated until eventually small complex, stellate colonies are formed (Plate ID). In this latter case, the production of such micro-colonies continues throughout the growth of the culture and they can often be seen with the unaided eye (Morris and Hough, 1956). It is emphasized that this process of small branched colony formation should not be mistaken for the phenomenon of flocculation which occurs as the cultures age. Between the two ex-tremes of dispersed cells and branched colonies, intermediate types are commonly encountered and not infrequently during early growth short chains of cells are observed.

If the temperature and composition of the medium are near the opti-mum, reproduction during the early stages of growth will be rapid and uniform throughout the medium. However, a very different state of affairs soon prevails in cultures which are not aerated or agitated. Generally, the first disturbing influence is the development of anaerobic or micro-aerobic conditions in the deepest parts of the medium, due to the rate of uptake of oxygen by the cells being greater than that at which oxygen can diffuse into this region. As growth continues, the conditions become still less favorable until truly aerobic conditions exist in only a relatively thin layer at the surface of the medium. Consequently, the growth of those yeasts which are essentially aerobes can only continue satisfactorily in this region and this is particularly true when cultures are maintained at a constant temperature in an incubator when mixture of the medium by convexion currents is less prompt. Under such conditions many yeasts form pellicles. The characteristics of these pellicles are often used as an aid in the identification of yeasts (see Chapter I), but whereas the extreme cases are easily recognized, the description of intermediate forms may be difficult and subjective. The three main types of pellicle formation are: (a) thick membranous pellicles which are composed almost entirely of pseudomycelia; (b) a thin, lusterless, wrinkled type which often develops very soon after active growth has commenced; and (c) a very thin, even film that usually starts as a ring around the junction of the surface of the medium and the tube.

It is commonly observed that not all of the yeast cells are to be found in the pellicle, some remaining dispersed throughout the medium and others settling to the bottom of the cultures as a deposit. The relative amounts of yeast in each location is dependent upon the age of the culture, the composition of the medium, and the strain of yeast (see Table V).

In almost every case, a liquid culture of yeast will, sooner or later, form a more or less dense ring of cells at the interface of the surface of the medium and the culture vessel; in some cases the culture will actually creep up the side of the container for a considerable distance. In these regions the conditions for growth are far from ideal as the supply of nutrients is restricted and the conditions favor the accumulation of metabolic end products. Furthermore, since an abundant supply of oxygen is available, it is not surprising that spores are commonly found in this location.

It is clear that localized environmental conditions are set up in static liquid cultures and these are important from the point of view of laboratory experiments and of those industrial processes which involve the cultivation of yeasts. In the laboratory, it is generally assumed that when a new culture is started, it will have the same characteristics as the parental strain, but when the conditions for growth are such as those mentioned above, this cannot be guaranteed. Firstly, if sporulation can occur there is obviously a chance that segregation of characters may take place. Secondly, in old cultures where pellicle formation and perhaps deposition of cells has occurred there is a considerable risk that the depletion of nutrients or an accumulation of toxic end products may result in a heterogeneous population by the preferential killing of cells

TABLE V

VARIATIONS IN THE APPEARANCE OF LIQUID CULTURES WITH RESPECT TO NATURE OF THE MEDIUM, THE AGE OF THE CULTURE, AND THE TYPE OF YEAST

Yeast	Malt extract-yeast extract-peptone-glucose broth		Hopped malt wort	
	24 hours	72 hours	24 hours	72 hours
Pichia membranaefaciens	Thin pellicle; few cells in suspension; no deposit	Well-formed wrinkled pellicle; very few cells in suspension; slight deposit	Thin film; very few cells in suspension; slight deposit	Well-formed wrinkled pellicle; very few cells in suspension; slight deposit
Saccharomyces cerevisiae var. *ellipsoideus*	No obvious film; all cells in suspension	Slight ring around tube; many cells in suspension; moderate deposit	Loose foamy head formed; many cells in suspension; no deposit	Foamy head formed; many cells in suspension; moderate deposit
Saccharomyces cerevisiae	No obvious film; most cells in suspension; slight deposit	Slight ring round tube; moderate number of cells in suspension; heavy deposit	Dense yeast head formed; moderate number of cells in suspension; slight deposit	Dense head formed, beginning to drop to the bottom of the culture; few cells in suspension; very heavy deposit

to such an extent that when fresh cultures are started selection has already taken place. Apart from this last-mentioned type selection, another mechanism is encountered which is well demonstrated by strains of *Saccharomyces cerevisiae* which are commonly used for brewing in Great Britain. In this connection, experience has shown that such yeasts comprise various strains which differ, among other characters, in their tendency to aggregate in the form of flocs so that they either form a yeast head at the surface of the medium or a deposit of cells at the bottom of the container. Clearly, if the culture has reached the stage at which flocculation occurs, the balance of the various types of yeast in a new culture will depend to a large extent upon the location in the parental culture from which the inoculum is taken. Inocula taken from the head and the deposit will contain more of the flocculent type of cell than an inoculum from the center of the tube where the cells are still in suspension and presumably mostly nonflocculent. It would thus appear that variation between different subcultures of the same yeast is less likely to occur when the parental cultures are, firstly, continually agitated or aerated throughout growth, thus preventing the setting up of localized conditions, secondly, not kept long enough for excessive staling of the medium to occur and, thirdly, thoroughly shaken immediately before new cultures are made so as to increase the chance of transferring a representative sample of the population.

Although not a common occurrence, certain yeasts develop a mucilaginous form of growth in liquid cultures. A characteristic of such cultures is that, when rapidly swirled, the cells rise from the bottom of the vessel in an intact viscous column, the supernatant culture fluid remaining relatively free from cells. In an extreme case it may be very difficult indeed to disperse the cells throughout the medium. This type of growth is most commonly found in cultures of certain species of *Rhodotorula*, *Cryptococcus*, and *Sporobolomyces*.

Comparatively few yeasts produce any appreciable amount of pigment and those that do so almost exclusively exhibit red or yellow pigments although the various coloring matters may be chemically unrelated. The various species of the genus *Rhodotorula* are by definition all pigmented, the color varying from a pale to deep salmon pink. The pigment, which is carotenoid, does not diffuse into the medium, and its intensity is often enhanced in cultures which have been aerated. Another pigmented yeast that is fairly commonly encountered is *Candida pulcherrima* which usually develops a deep red coloration. It has been shown that the development of color by this yeast is dependent upon the presence of iron in the medium and further that if the concentration of iron is relatively small the pigment may diffuse into the medium. Another type of pigmentation in yeast is usually associated with certain nutritional abnormalities. For example, Lindegren (1949) describing a mutant strain of the colorless *S. cerevisiae* which was pink in color found that production of the pigment was dependent upon the presence of methionine.

Solid Media. When an inoculum containing comparatively few cells is placed on the surface of a nutrient medium solidified with agar or gelatin, the cells multiply to form a colony. Formerly, the shape of such colonies was considered to be of value as an aid in the classification of yeasts, because it was believed that particular types of colony formations were fairly specific. Gross differences in the morphology of colonies are still useful, for example, in detecting yeast contamination; in this connection Plate IIA shows the striking differences between colonies of *Oospora lactis, Saccharomyces cerevisiae,* and *Rhodotorula glutinis* all of which were of the same age and on the same medium. More recently, however, the use of this characteristic for taxonomic purposes has fallen somewhat into disfavor, because in certain cases the differences between various species, or even genera, are less distinct than those between certain strains of the same species, and, indeed, important use has now been made of the fact that different strains of the same species often produce characteristic colonies. For instance, it has been found that various cultures of S. *cerevisiae,* each derived from a single cell can often be distinguished when they are grown on a solid medium under carefully controlled conditions (see Plate IIB,C,D) (Hall 1954a,b), and further that differences in colonial formations are frequently associated with differences in other characters (Hough and Morris, 1957).

The character of the colony is not only dependent upon the yeast and upon the nutrient composition of the medium, but also varies with the nature of the supporting matrix. Thus, in this latter respect gelatin gives better differentiated colonies than does agar, which in turn is better than silica-gel. Those colonies grown upon such media as malt wort-gelatin, solidified cornsteep medium, or solid media containing infusions of fruit or vegetables are usually better differentiated than those grown on media comprising, for example, malt extract, yeast extract, peptone, glucose and agar or gelatin. Why this is so is difficult to understand, because a medium containing the latter components is still an excellent medium for yeast growth (Wickerham, 1951). Again, the patterns of colonies grown on purely synthetic media are often ill-defined. Even differences in the method of preparing the medium may at times influence the degree of colonial differentiation so that poorly defined colonies may form on a malt wort-gelatin which has been subjected to rather more heating than

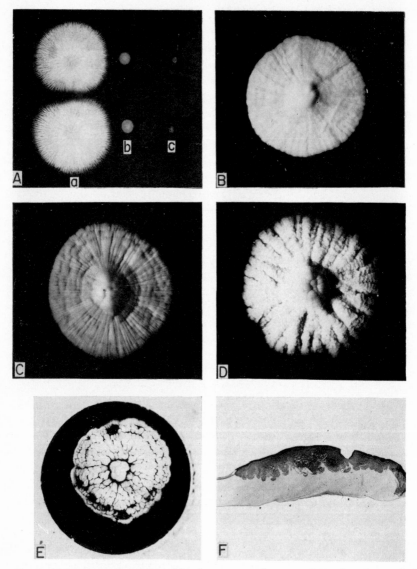

PLATE II. A: Twenty-one-day-old cultures on malt wort gelatin showing marked differences in colonial characteristics of (1) *Oospora lactis*, (2) *Saccharomyces cerevisiae*, and (3) *Rhodotorula glutinis*.

B, C, and D: Giant colonies of different strains of *Saccharomyces cerevisiae* grown on malt wort gelatin. Cultures 28 days old.

E: Giant colony of *Saccharomyces cerevisiae* after the surface growth has been washed away. All the growth shown in this photograph is firmly in the medium.

F: Transverse section through a giant colony showing the extent of the penetration of the yeast into the medium.

is necessary to dissolve the gelatin and sterilize the medium. Further the age of the culture and the temperature at which they have been kept are also important factors; actually, well-differentiated colonies of *Saccharomyces cerevisiae* are usually obtained when the cultures are grown at 15–18°C. for 3–6 weeks on malt wort-gelatin.

These morphological characters can be extremely complex and consequently are difficult to describe, critical comparisons of various yeasts

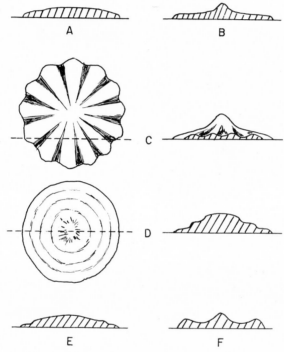

FIG. 4. Component features of the contours of giant colonies.

grown at different times being best made by means of photographic records. When verbal description has to be made, it is important to note whether the surface of the colony is matt or shiny, as well as to describe the contours. In its simplest form a colony is more or less free from convolutions and is flatly convex, or more commonly flatly convex with a central dome (Fig. 4A,B). In the more complex colonies radial (Fig. 4C) or concentric convolutions (Fig. 4D) may be prominent and further the rim of the colony may be thin (Fig. 4E) or resemble a tire on a wheel (Fig. 4F) and apparently almost any combination of these contours may present itself at the same time. In extreme cases the colonies may exhibit very irregular formations and such colonies are often referred to as "rugose."

The regularity with which a pure strain of yeast, when grown under rigidly controlled conditions, is able to reproduce essentially the same colonial formations suggests that this feature is an expression of growth characteristics which are specific for a particular strain. Very little is known about such factors except that (a) those colonies producing an appreciable amount of pseudomycelia give rise to the rougher type of colony with a matt surface, (b) haploid colonies are generally rougher and more complex than their related diploid strains, and (c) the evidence of Subramaniam (1945) suggests that colonies of yeasts which are reported to be tetraploid are simpler than those of the parent diploids.

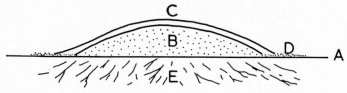

Fig. 5. Giant colony of yeast on agar medium (from Lindegren and Hamilton, 1944).

A. Agar medium.
B. Apparently healthy cells.
C. Zone of autolyzed cells containing asci.
D. Thin spreading edge of colony.
E. Pseudomycelia penetrating into the agar.

The micro-structure of yeast colonies has received very little attention except for the report of Lindegren and Hamilton (1944) who examined sections of yeast colonies grown on an agar medium. It is unfortunate that, from the time this work was reported until the present day, other authorities have implied that the features originally described are common to all yeasts on any medium. Recently Morris and Hough (1956) have studied the micro-anatomy of various strains of *Saccharomyces cerevisiae* which had been grown on malt wort-gelatin. Certain differences between these two reports may possibly be attributed to the use of a different matrix and to the fact that different yeast cultures were examined.

The yeasts grown on agar generally spread slowly over the surface of the medium while thin threads of pseudomycelium penetrate deeply into the agar (see Fig. 5), the picture on malt wort-gelatin differing markedly. In this respect the lower part of the agar colony becomes deeply embedded in the gelatin forming at the same time papillate protrusions in the medium (see Fig. 6 and Plate IIF). When sections of the various colonies are examined under high magnification, it is seen that those colonies having a rough contour show elongated cells which in extreme cases approach pseudomycelial forms (Plate IIIA,B) whereas, on the other hand, the smooth colonies are composed, almost exclusively, of round to oval cells that penetrate into the medium on a broad front and show little tendency for individual cells to penetrate deep into the matrix (see Plate IIIC). Another difference between colonies grown on agar and on gelatin is that on the former a thin layer of cells extends in advance of the dense edge of the colony for a considerable distance over the surface of the agar, whereas on gelatin no such layer is noted. In

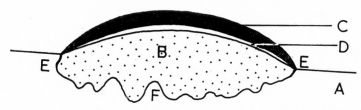

Fig. 6. Giant colony of *Saccharomyces cerevisiae* on malt wort gelatin (from Morris and Hough, 1956).

   A. Gelatine medium.

   B. Apparently healthy cells.

   C. Zone of resting cells probably containing asci.

   D. Zone of autolyzed cells.

   E. No thin surface film. Advanced edge of colony may be in gelatine.

   F. Lower portion of colony embedded in gelatine. Pseudomycelium may or may not be present.

fact it is commonly observed that the most extensive growth occurs immediately below the surface of the gelatin (see Plate IIIE). It is interesting to note that from the time that the colonies on gelatin are about seven days old, the upper portion of the colony can be washed away but a regular pattern of yeast cells remains embedded in the gelatin and these cannot be removed by gentle abrasion (see Plate IIE). In the case of colonies the cells of which are predominantly rounded, it is difficult to believe that these protrusions into gelatin medium result entirely from a "mechanical" process. Consequently it seems reasonable to postulate that intact cells liberate a limited amount of proteinase resulting in a very localized liquefaction of the gelatin around each cell, thus permitting the cells to sink into the gelatin. In this connection, it is known that yeast autolysates contain proteinase, but it is generally believed that when proteolysis is active, autolysis of the cells occur. If it be accepted

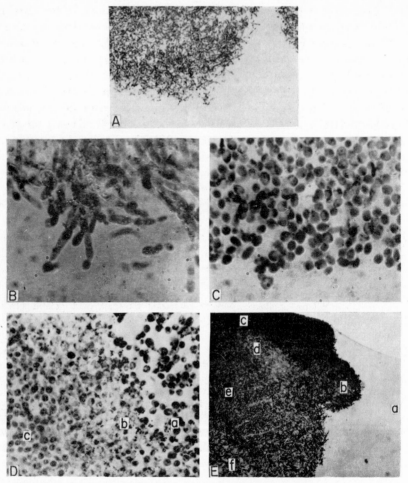

PLATE III. A: Low-power photomicrograph of a section through a giant colony showing the lobate type of penetration with pseudomycelium-like cells projecting into the medium. Yeast as in Plate ID.

B: High-power photomicrograph of the same section.

C: High-power photomicrograph of section through giant colony Yeast as in Plate IC.

D: High-power photomicrograph of section through giant colony showing (a) uppermost layer of cells containing densely stained material; these are probably resting cells, (b) well-demarcated layer of autolyzed cells, and (c) healthy cells in the main body of the colony.

E: Low-power photomicrograph of section through the edge of a giant colony. (a) Gelatin medium, (b) most advanced edge of colony which may be in the gelatin immediately below the surface, (c) outer layer of resting cells, (d) layer of auto-lyzed cells, (e) central zone composed mainly of roun cells, and (f) deepest layer of cells composed of pseudomycelium-like cells.

that living yeast cells break down the gelatin, it may offer an explanation as to how food becomes available to the deeper regions of the colony where, even after three to four weeks growth, a surprisingly large number of budding cells can be observed. In this respect such proteolysis would result in the liberation of amino acids and other assimilable nitrogenous material which could reach the deeper regions of the colony by diffusion, cell-wall transfer, or translocation. It is nevertheless difficult to understand how the cells in the deeper zone of the colonies can tolerate the high concentrations of end products which must inevitably occur unless (a) the cells can utilize such end products, or (b) these substances can diffuse away from the cells by the same mechanisms as the nutrients reach these zones. The photographic records presented by Lindegren and Hamilton (1944) reveal, under their experimental conditions and using their strain of yeast, a very distinct and relatively thick outer layer of autolyzed cells; in this region spores are readily identified. On the other hand, all the colonies of *Saccharomyces cerevisiae* grown on wort-gelatin (Morris and Hough, 1956) present a totally different picture where the outer cells are composed almost entirely of well-formed cells having thick walls and containing large deposits of material which are stained intensely by methylene blue and which appears to consist of typical resting cells. None of the strains examined readily produced spores on any medium, but very occasionally what appeared to be spores were noted among the resting cells. A thin, but definite zone of autolyzed cells can be seen situated immediately below this layer of resting cells but above the main mass of apparently healthy ones (see Plate IIID). The presence of autolyzed cells in this region is not surprising, because the environmental conditions prevailing in this region are those generally associated with yeast autolysis, namely a compact mass of cells depleted of nutrition under relatively anaerobic conditions.

3. Sources of Carbon

Fruit juices and other plant infusions or decoctions have been used for centuries for the production of alcoholic beverages and some of the earliest microbiological studies revealed that these products were the result of the action of yeasts upon the relatively simple carbohydrates contained in such substrates. Investigation has established that two processes are involved in these metabolic activities, the first being concerned with the breakdown of much of the sugars to alcohol and carbon dioxide and the second with growth or the incorporation of some of the carbon of the sugars into the cell substance itself.

A large volume of work has been devoted to establishing an understanding of the former process, but relatively few studies have been made to determine the range of organic compounds which can serve as sources of carbon for yeast growth. Such work as has been done has usually been directed towards the use of various test compounds for taxonomic purposes. In this connection two of the most important tools employed in the classical studies of Lodder and Kreger-van Rij (1952) (see Chapter I) depend upon the varying ability of yeasts to ferment or utilize a few common sugars; for this purpose, the most generally used carbohydrates

TABLE VI

A COMPARISON OF THE ABILITY TO FERMENT AND TO ASSIMILATE
DIFFERENT CARBOHYDRATES AS REVEALED BY VARIOUS YEASTS[a]

Yeast	Carbohydrate fermented					Carbohydrate assimilated				
	Glucose	Galactose	Sucrose	Maltose	Lactose	Glucose	Galactose	Sucrose	Maltose	Lactose
Debaromyces vini	−	−	−	−	−	+	+	+	+	−
Candida lipolytica	−	−	−	−	−	+	−	−	−	−
Candida pulcherrima	+	±	−	−	−	+	±	+	+	−
Cryptococcus laurentii	−	−	−	−	−	+	±	+	+	+
Hansenula anomala	+	±	±	+	−	+	−	±	+	−
Kloeckera africana	+	−	−	−	−	+	−	±	+	−
Saccharomyces cerevisiae	+	+	+	+	−	+	−	+	+	−
Torulopsis ernobii	+	−	−	−	−	+	+	+	+	−
Torulopsis sphaerica	+	+	−	+	+	+	+	+	+	+

[a] − = No reaction; + = positive reaction; ± = weak or variable reaction.

are glucose, fructose, galactose, sucrose, maltose, lactose, melibiose, and raffinose. The examples set out in Table VI show that the ability of yeast to assimilate any particular carbohydrates does not necessarily imply that the latter can be fermented.

It is often observed during fermentation experiments that the actual yield of carbon dioxide is appreciably less than the theoretical and this discrepancy has been thought to be due, under certain experimental conditions, to the carbon dioxide being assimilated. Conclusive proof of this has been made possible by isotopic carbon studies, and in this connection it has been shown that growing cells can obtain as much as 5% of their carbon requirements by assimiliating carbon dioxide (Liener and Buchanan, 1951). There is also evidence that, besides being directly assimilated, the gas may have other functions in the cell metabolism, as is instanced by the fact that succinic acid is only produced from glucose in its presence (Kleinzeller, 1948).

Undoubtedly the most comprehensive study of the utilization of a large number of organic compounds as possible sources of carbon was that of Wickerham and Burton (1948) whose findings concerning the more common compounds may be summarized as follows:

(a) Those compounds not utilized by any yeast include cyclohexane, cyclohexanol, maleic acid, kojic acid, ethylene glycol, methanol, and acetone.

(b) Those used by a few yeasts include malonic, laevulinic, and ascorbic acids.

(c) Many yeasts can utilize fumaric, malic, or glutamic acids.

(d) Those used by many yeasts and considered to be of special value for taxonomic studies include xylose, arabinose, adonitol, dulcitol, mannitol, sorbitol, citric acid, succinic acid, lactic acid, cellibiose, melezitose, salicin, and salts of gluconic acid. To this group, of course, can be added the more common hexoses, disaccharides, and trisaccharides normally used for taxonomic purposes.

(e) Those compounds used by the majority of yeast and not therefore of great taxonomic value include ethanol, pyruvic acid, and glycerol.

The few investigations designed to extend the range of carbon compounds used by the Dutch workers for the classification of yeasts, indicate that valuable information may be provided only when more comprehensive studies have been made both with regard to providing a standard technique and to understanding how different strains of the same species react in such tests. An example of the use of a large number of carbon compounds in a taxonomic study is shown in Table VII.

Certain of the glucogenic group of amino acids can also serve as a source of nitrogen (Sperber, 1945; Ehrensvärd et al., 1947; Schultz et al., 1949) and in this respect glutamic acid, proline, alanine, asparagine, aspartic acid, and arginine are the most active. These compounds are more readily assimilated when traces of glucose are present as starters. Table VIII clearly indicates the effects of a glucose starter in the assimilation of carbon from amino acids.

While it is frequently the case that yeasts may not at first be able to utilize particular carbon sources, or at the best grow only slowly in their presence, certain yeasts can be trained to utilize particular compounds by being repeatedly subcultured in media containing the compounds compounds in low concentration, subsequent transfers being made to under investigation. Generally, the initial media should contain the test

TABLE VII

CARBOHYDRATES AND CARBOHYDRATE DERIVATIVES ASSIMILATION SPECTRA OF TWELVE YEASTS[a,b]

Yeast	Aesculin	Arabinose	Cellibiose	Citric acid	Dextrin	Ethanol	d-Erythritol	Galactose	Glycerol	Inulin	Lactic acid	Lactose	Maltose	Mannitol	Melezitose	Raffinose	Rhamnose	Salicin	Sorbitol	Sorbose	Succinic acid	Sucrose	Starch	Trehalose	Xylose	α-Methyl-d-glucoside	Potassium-d-gluconate	5-Ketogluconic acid
Candida guilliermondii	+	+	+	+	V	+	−	+	+	+	+	−	+	+	+	+	−	+	V	+	+	+	−	+	+	+	+	+
Candida kruseii	−	−	−	+	−	+	−	−	+	−	+	−	−	−	−	−	−	−	−	−	+	+	−	−	+	−	+	−
Candida mycoderma	−	−	−	−	−	+	−	−	+	−	+	−	−	−	−	−	−	−	−	−	+	−	−	−	V	−	−	−
Hansenula anomala	+	−	+	+	+	+	+	+	+	+	+	−	+	+	+	V	−	+	+	−	+	+	+	+	+	+	+	−
Kloeckera apiculata	−	−	+	−	−	−	−	−	−	−	−	−	−	−	−	−	−	+	−	−	−	V	−	−	−	−	+	−
Pichia membranaefaciens	−	−	−	−	−	+	−	−	+	−	+	−	−	−	−	−	−	−	−	−	+	−	−	+	V	−	−	−
Rhodotorula mucilaginosa	+	+	+	+	−	+	−	+	+	+	+	−	+	V	+	+	+	+	+	+	+	+	−	−	+	−	+	−
Saccharomyces carlsbergensis	−	−	−	−	−	+	−	+	+	+	+	−	+	V	+	+	−	−	V	−	V	+	−	−	V	+	V	−
Saccharomyces cerevisiae	−	−	−	−	−	+	−	+	+	+	+	−	+	V	V	+	−	−	V	−	V	+	−	−	−	+	−	−
Saccharomyces willianus (festianans)	−	−	−	−	−	+	−	+	+	+	+	−	+	+	+	+	−	−	+	+	+	+	−	−	−	+	−	−
Torulopsis famata	+	+	+	+	−	+	+	+	+	+	+	−	+	+	+	+	−	+	+	+	+	+	−	+	+	+	−	+
Torulopsis stellata	−	+	−	−	−	−	−	−	+	+	+	−	−	+	+	−	−	−	−	+	−	+	−	+	−	−	−	−

[a] V = Variable, some strains growing, others not growing; − = no reaction; + = positive reaction.

[b] From Wiles (1953).

TABLE VIII

THE EFFECT OF TRACES OF GLUCOSE ON THE CARBON ASSIMILATION OF INDIVIDUAL AMINO ACIDS BY YEASTS[a,b]

| Yeast | | | | | | | | | | |
Classification according to Schultz et al. (1949)	Classification according to Lodder and Kreger-van Rij (1952)	Glucose (mg.)	Glutamic acid	Proline	Alanine	Asparagine	Aspartic acid	Serine	Glycine	Arginine
Saccharomyces cerevisiae	Saccharomyces cerevisiae	10	?	+	−	−	−	−	−	−
		0	−	−	−	−	−	−	−	−
Torulopsis cremoris	Candida pseudotropicalis	10	+	+	?	−	−	−	−	−
		0	+	−	?	−	−	−	−	−
Zygosaccharomyces marxianus	Saccharomyces marxianus	10	++	++	+	−	−	−	−	−
		0	+	−	−	−	−	−	−	−
Candida pseudotropicalis	Candida pseudotropicalis	10	++	++	++	?	+	+	−	−
		0	+	+	−	−	−	−	−	−
Saccharomyces pastorianus	Saccharomyces pastorianus	10	++	++	++	++	++	++	+	++
		0	++	+	+	+	++	+	−	++
Torulopsis pulcherrima	Candida pulcherrima	10	++	++	+	++	++	+	−	−
		0	+	+	+	+	+	−	−	−
Torulopsis utilis	Candida utilis	10	++	++	++	++	++	++	+	?
		0	++	++	++	?	?	?	?	−
Candida guilliermondii	Candida guilliermondii	10	++	++	++	++	++	++	++	++
		0	++	+	+	+	++	−	−	?

[a] − = No response; ? = doubtful response; + = definite utilization; ++ = good utilization.

[b] From Schultz et al. (1949).

media containing progressively increasing amounts. The following examples of the training of yeasts to assimilate various carbon sources may be quoted. Active growth of Saccharomyces cerevisiae may occur in media containing acids involved in the Krebs cycle only after the yeast has been trained for several generations (Kilkenny and Hinshelwood, 1951); after the yeasts become adapted to such substrates, acetic acid, citric acid, fumaric acid, lactic acid, malic acid, oxalacetic acid, pyruvic acid, and succinic acid can be more or less readily assimilated. Different species of the same genus may respond differently to training, so that, for example, *Rhodotorula glutinis* but not *R. gracilis* can be trained to utilize xylose (Nielson and Nilsson, 1950). Recently certain compounds isolated from seaweed have been found to act as a source of carbon for a number of yeasts after a period of training; these compounds include fucoidin, fucose, laminarin, and sodium alginate (Morris, 1955) (see Table IX).

TABLE IX

UTILIZATION BY VARIOUS YEASTS OF COMPOUNDS
ISOLATED FROM SEAWEED[a]

Yeast	Test compound			
	Fucoidin	Fucose	Laminarin	Sodium alginate
Candida kruseii	+	+	+	+
Candida solani	+	+	+	−
Nadsonia fulvescens	+	+	+	+
Hansenula anomala	+	−	−	+
Kloeckera antillarum	+	−	−	−
Pichia membranaefaciens	+	+	+	+
Hansenula saturnus	+	−	+	+
Oospora lactis	+	+	+	+

[a] From Morris (1955).

The ability of certain yeasts to split the β-glucosides aesculin and arbutin has been used for taxonomic purposes (Lodder and Kreger-van Rij, 1952, 1954), the yeast presumably using the glucose portion as a carbon source (Veibel, 1950). Later studies, however, indicate that care should be taken in the interpretation of such tests, because two factors appear to be involved, firstly the method of determining whether the compound has been utilized, and secondly the medium upon which yeasts have been grown prior to carrying out the test. When colorimetric tests were used to detect the breakdown of aesculin by yeasts which had been grown in nutrient medium, many more yeasts were found to possess this property than had hitherto been supposed although only about half of these can split this β-glucoside after growth in a synthetic medium

(Barnett and Swain, 1956). It is also probable that many more yeasts can split arbutin than had previously been thought possible (Barnett, 1956).

Further work by Barnett *et al.* (1956) has shown that certain strains of *Kloeckera* have the ability, albeit in some case slight, to hydrolyze arbutin; such findings are of course contrary to the accepted belief. The hydrolytic activity of these yeasts is much more readily demonstrated in media having high nutrient values, for example when the yeast water medium, as used in taxonomic studies, is replaced by Wickerham's "MYGP" medium. The enhancement of glucosidase activity in nutrient-rich medium may well account for the observation that baker's yeast can hydrolyze arbutin whereas stock laboratory cultures of *Saccharomyces cerevisiae* will not do so. The position regarding the hydrolysis of aesculin is less clear, since it appears that in nutrient-rich media nearly all yeasts can hydrolyze this glucoside to some extent. Despite these findings it is apparent that certain generalizations can be made, namely, that all strains of *Hansenula* show pronounced β- glucosidase activity, whereas such activity is absent or weak in cultures of *Pichia*.

Other factors must also be considered when deciding to what extent particular compounds can be used as sources of carbon. For instance, ethanol and pyruvate can be built into the cell substance more readily if a simple utilizable carbohydrate be also present while, further, both inulin and lactic acid are more completely assimilated when the cultures are violently aerated (White and Munns, 1954).

4. Sources of Nitrogen

An extracellular supply of nitrogenous material is essential for the continued production of new protoplasm and yeasts generally derive this element from such relatively simple substances as ammonium salts, nitrates, amino acids, and amides although there is evidence that dipeptides or even higher peptides may also be assimilated.

Until recently it has been a common belief that yeasts are unable to "fix" atmospheric nitrogen, but evidence is now available that certain strains of *Rhodotorula* and at least one strain of *Saccharomyces* have this property. When such yeasts are grown in a medium free of nitrogen, but in an atmosphere containing isotopic nitrogen, oxygen, and argon, the isotope can be detected in the cell substance (Metcalfe and Chayen, 1954; Roberts and Wilson, 1954). These facts are, however, mainly of academic interest, because the amount of growth obtained by such procedures is very meager when compared with that obtainable from a fully nutrient medium.

Ammonium salts such as the phosphate, sulfate, and nitrate have been incorporated in many synthetic media as the sole source of nitrogen and the majority of yeasts will then grow provided that other requirements such as carbon, nutrilites, and mineral salts are satisfied. In this connection there is evidence that, in a well-balanced medium, ammonium salts will support at least as much growth as any other single source of nitrogen.

Not all yeasts are able to utilize other sources of inorganic nitrogen and in fact the ability to use nitrates is regarded as a diagnostic feature. Thus in general most of the species comprising the genera *Saccharomyces, Pichia, Hanseniaspora,* and *Debaryomyces* fail to assimilate nitrate, unlike all species of *Hansenula.* Nickerson (1944) suggested that the demonstration of nitrite in a nitrate medium by means of the sulfanilic acid–α-naphthylamine test was sufficient proof that nitrate had been utilized but Lodder and Kreger-van Rij (1952) disagree. Auxanographic tests (see also Chapter I) are usually employed to determine whether a yeast can or cannot grow when nitrate is the sole source of nitrogen, but it is worth noting that Wickerham (1946) has shown that these tests may only be reliable when the medium contains a full complement of essential nutrilites.

In natural media the most common sources of nitrogen which are easily assimiliated by yeasts are the amino acids, and in recent years, the response of yeasts to individual members of this group has been investigated. In this connection it is essential to bear in mind that the defined basal medium in experiments designed to determine the ability of yeasts to use various nitrogen sources should be as complete as possible not only in so far as carbon source and nutrilites are concerned, but also with respect to its mineral content. In this latter respect it is now known that amino acids will not be assimilated by *Saccharomyces cerevisiae* unless magnesium ions are present though this factor may be less important in more complex media because certain amides, when present in concentrations of about 2.5% of the total nitrogen, can replace the need for magnesium (Sheffner and Grabow, 1953). Thorne (1941), who studied the response of *S. cerevisiae* to various amino acids, showed that under the conditions of his tests aspartic acid and asparagine were better sources of nitrogen than was ammonia, and that glutamic acid was at least as active as the latter. Alanine, α-aminobutyric acid, valine, leucine, isoleucine, serine, ornithine, arginine, phenylalanine, tyrosine, and proline were found to have about two-thirds of the activity of ammonia, and tryptophan was only slightly active, whereas glycine, lysine, and cysteine were scarcely used at all.

The work of Massart and Horens (1953) indicates that various amino acids, as well as acting as building substances, may be associated with the respiratory function of the cells. Thus yeasts suspended in a solution containing a small amount of glucose showed an increased uptake of oxygen immediately after the addition of ammonium salts, alanine, or glutamic acid following which nitrogenous material is itself assimilated. The addition of cysteine to the glucose–yeast mixture resulted in the inhibition of respiration and in this connection it is interesting to recall that Thorne had shown that this amino acid is not readily utilized.

Thorne (1944, 1946a,b) tested various amino acids in different combinations, and in general it was found that paired amino acids increased the yield by approximately 10% of that obtained with the individual reagents. However, certain anomalies were noted. For example, ammonium phosphate and glycine when paired showed a marked increase in yield, but glycine alone was scarcely used, while tyrosine and glycine were shown to antagonize one another. When the amino acids were combined three at a time, the response was increased by a further 8%. The dipeptides leucylglycine, glycylglycine, alanylglycine, leucyltyrosine, and glutylglutamic acid were found to have only about 90% of the activity of the individual amino acids and tripeptides were even less active (Damlé and Thorne, 1949).

A study of the uptake by S. cerevisiae of the various amino acids in malt wort (Barton-Wright and Thorne, 1949) revealed that about 90% of the initial concentration of each of fourteen different amino acids is removed (see Table X), although a preferential assimilation was noted. In this respect arginine is by far the greatest single contributor accounting for approximately 35.0% of the total nitrogen assimilated, followed by lysine which accounts for about 10%. This latter observation is of interest because it may be recalled that S. cerevisiae is unable to grow when lysine is the sole source of nitrogen, a fact which will be later referred to at greater length. Returning now to uptake of amino acids from wort, it was found that only relatively small proportions of the total amounts of proline and cysteine are utilized. The results illustrated in Table X indicate that the small contribution made by methionine to the total assimilated nitrogen is due to limited amounts of this amino acid in the wort and not to an inability of the yeast to utilize it.

By testing a large number of yeasts in the presence of many different amino acids, Schultz and Pomper (1948) generally confirmed the findings of Thorne regarding the assimilation of individual substances, but noted that various yeasts responded differently to particular compounds. This work suggested that the ability of yeasts to utilize various sources of nitrogen may be important in the classification of yeasts, provided that a suitable technique can be developed. In this connection Barnett and

TABLE X

ASSIMILATION BY *Saccharomyces cerevisiae* OF AMINO ACIDS FROM MALT WORT[a]

	Valine	Leucine	Isoleucine	Serine	Threonine	Aspartic acid	Glutamic acid	Methionine	Cystine	Lysine	Arginine	Proline	Phenylalanine	Tyrosine	Histidine	Tryptophan
Percentage of the initial amino acid concentration utilized after 96 hr.	93	93	91	82	90	92	83	100	63	85	94	14	94	93	85	99
Contribution of each amino acid to the total amount of amino acids utilized	7.9	7.0	4.3	3.7	5.0	3.2	5.2	1.3	0.5	9.9	35.0	3.8	2.8	2.8	4.9	2.8

[a] From data of Barton-Wright and Thorne (1949).

Ingram (1955) have studied various factors which are concerned in the development of such a test.

Walters and Thiselton (1953) have used the selective utilization of amino acids by yeasts as a means of exposing contamination of brewing yeast by other yeasts. It was found that the majority of yeasts are able to grow in media in which lysine is the sole source of nitrogen, but that most *Saccharomyces* are unable to do so; consequently, if an industrial culture of *Saccharomyces* be inoculated into a lysine medium, only yeasts other than *Saccharomyces* will grow. More recently, Morris and Eddy (1956) have shown that this test can be used quantitatively.

The accumulated knowledge of the various sources of carbon and nitrogen which can support yeast growth might suggest that synthetic media can be prepared which will stimulate growth to the same extent as the complex undefined media. However, many additional factors have to be taken into account and the following examples will serve to illustrate this point. It has already been noted that certain amino acids which do not support growth when used alone can nevertheless stimulate growth in the presence of another nitrogen source. Such stimulatory effects can be very complex as is abundantly clear from the work of McVeigh and Bracken (1955) who studied the growth requirements of *Schizosaccharomyces pombe*. This yeast has an absolute requirement for the nutrilites pantothenic acid, biotin, and inositol, but growth was still stimulated by the addition of pyridoxine and aneurin or adenine and uracil. Further, this yeast will grow in media containing ammonium sulfate or asparagine as the sole source of nitrogen but an increased yield is obtained when glutamic acid and aspartic acid are included in the medium, and a still further stimulation of growth results from the addition of vitamin-free casein hydrolysate. It has been mentioned earlier that antagonistic effects also may result from growing yeast in certain mixtures of amino acids and Miller and Harrison (1950) reported yet another inhibitory phenomenon. These workers found that uracil at concentrations as low as 1.5×10^{-5} M will inhibit the growth of *Saccharomyces cerevisiae*, but the presence of arginine in the medium will reverse this effect which appears to be specific.

5. Nutrilite Requirements

As early as 1901, it was established by Wildiers that, in general, yeasts fail to grow on a synthetic medium comprising what might have been thought to be suitable sources of nitrogen, carbon, and mineral salts, but that growth could be induced when extracts of yeasts or the supernatant fluid from old yeast cultures were added to the basically simple medium. It was concluded that these ill-defined materials contained a specific substance essential for the growth of yeast, and this unknown factor was called "bios." Little interest was paid to this observation for two decades, after which its importance became apparent as investigations revealed that the "bios" factor was in fact a complex of substances, some of which are essential not only for the growth of yeasts and other microorganisms but also for the well being of higher animals. At least six of the component factors of "bios" are known to be important for the growth of yeast, these nutrilites being aneurin (thiamine), biotin, inositol, nicotinic acid (niacin) or nicotinamide, pantothenic acid and pyridoxine. *p*-Aminobenzoic acid also has been shown to be a nutrilite essential for the growth of certain strains of *Saccharomyces cerevisiae*. The structure of these substances together with those of related compounds, the function of which will be discussed later, are set out in Fig. 7.

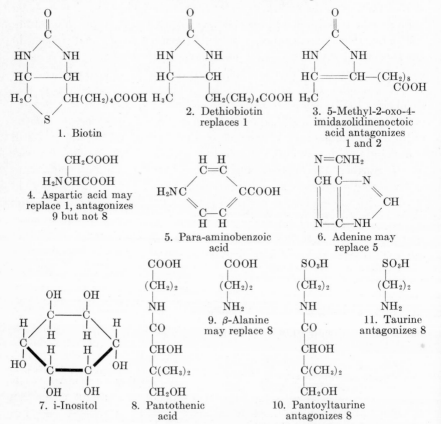

FIG. 7. The chemical structure of yeast nutrilites and of related compounds by which they may be antagonized or partially or completely replaced.

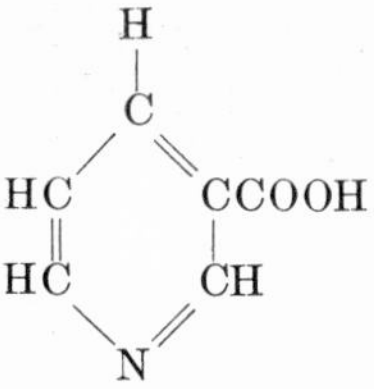

12. Nicotinic Acid

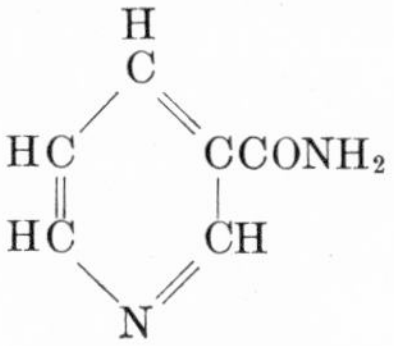

13. Nicotinamide interchangeable with 12; both are precursors of 14

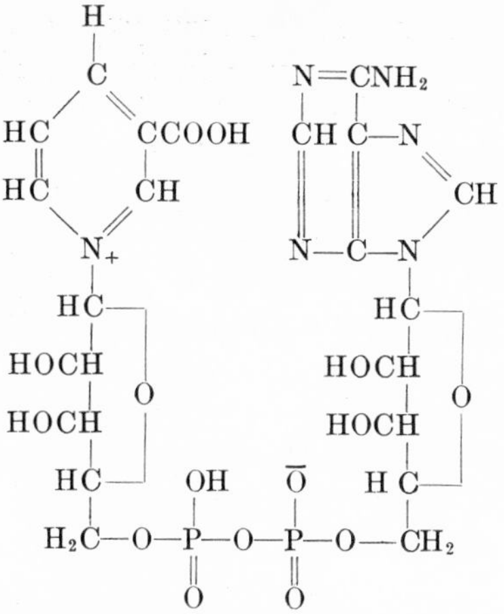

14. Coenzyme 1

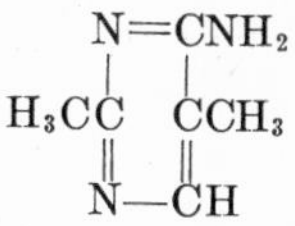

15. Pyrimidine may replace 17

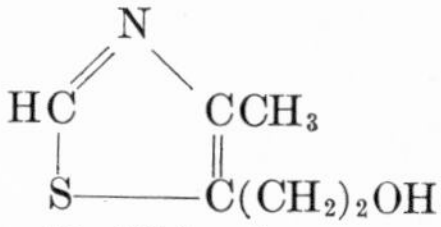

16. Thiazole may replace 17

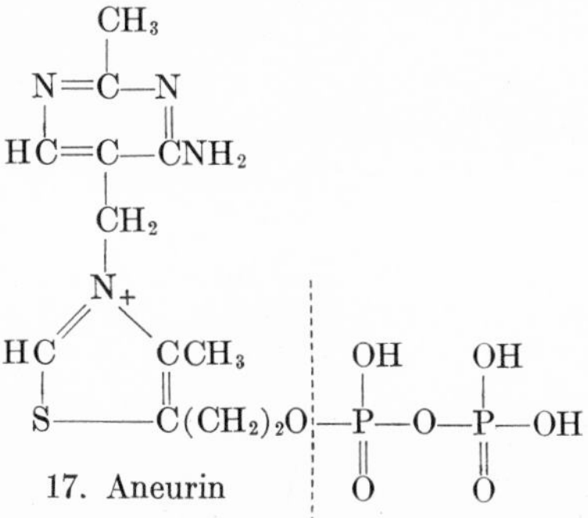

17. Aneurin

18. Cocarboxylase

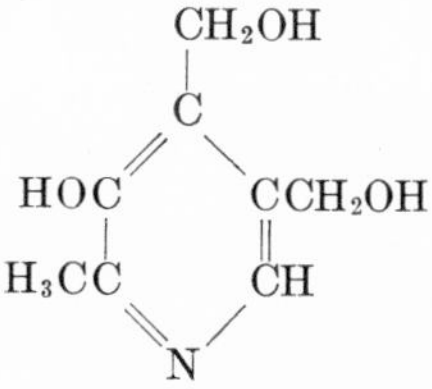

19. Pyridoxine

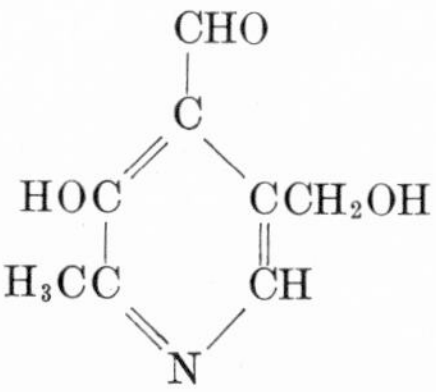

20. Pyridoxal

Interchangeable, precursors of 21

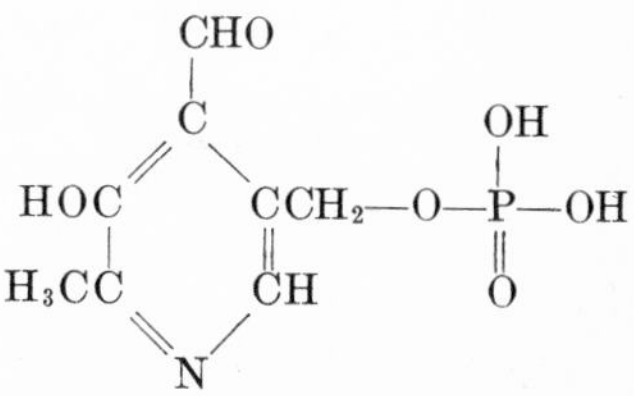

21. Pyridoxal-5-phosphate probable structure of amino acid codecarboxylase

FIG. 7. (*Continued*).

These nutrilites are active in astonishingly small concentrations; for example, a yeast which fails to grow in the absence of particular nutrilites may give high yields when the nutrilite concentrations are of the order of $1:10^{-5}$ to 10^{-9}. Generally it is found that biotin is the most active, maximum response being attained by concentrations as low as $1:10^{-6}$ to 10^{-9}, the optimum amount depending to some extent upon the particular yeast examined. By comparison, inositol is much less active, its stimulating effects being only one-tenth to one-five hundredth of that of biotin. This vast difference in optimal concentrations between inositol and the other nutrilites suggests that its function in the yeast cell may be of a different character from that of biotin, aneurin, pyridoxine, pantothenic acid, and nicotinamide. It is known that biotin is associated with nitrogen metabolism and that pyridoxine, aneurin, and nicotinic acid are precursors of the coenzymes of transaminase, decarboxylase, and of coenzyme I, respectively. Inositol is believed to be built into the cell structure, possibly being associated with cell division since Smith (1951) observed that clumps of unseparated cells can be seen in cultures grown in an inositol-deficient medium.

The main effect of growing yeasts in media containing less than the optimal amounts of essential nutrilites is that as soon as the available nutrilites have been taken up by the cells, the rate of both growth and fermentation are markedly decreased; further, in certain cases the number of cells producing spores is also reduced. A deficiency of pantothenate is known to reduce the keeping qualities of yeast when stored in the form of pressed yeast-cake (White and Munns, 1953a). Again, it has been shown recently that valuable information can be obtained concerning certain metabolic processes in the cell by growing yeasts in a medium deficient in particular nutrilites. For instance, certain strains of *Saccharomyces cerevisiae*, when grown in a medium deficient in pyridoxine, accumulate anthranilic acid and indole, a fact which has led to a greater understanding of the tryptophan–indole cycle (Eddy and Kirsop, 1955; Eddy, 1955b).

Before discussing the particular nutrilite requirements of yeasts it will be useful to outline the principle of the technique employed to establish them. A basal medium is prepared comprising a simple source of nitrogen, a utilizable carbohydrate, and a mineral salt mixture. The yeast is inoculated into the basal medium, into the basal medium provided with in addition a full complement of nutrilites, and into a series of media identical with the last except that each is in turn deficient in a particular nutrilite. The amounts of growth obtained in the various deficient media are compared with that in the complete medium, lack of growth in a deficient medium indicating a requirement of the yeast for the particular nutrilite omitted. This technique has been extensively investigated and standardized (Schultz and Atkin, 1947), but recent workers have realized that, for certain purposes, the system of interpretation as suggested in the earlier studies is too rigid and, consequently, more flexible systems have been proposed (Wiles, 1953; Kirsop, 1955). The types of response theoretically feasible and a typical set of results interpretated according

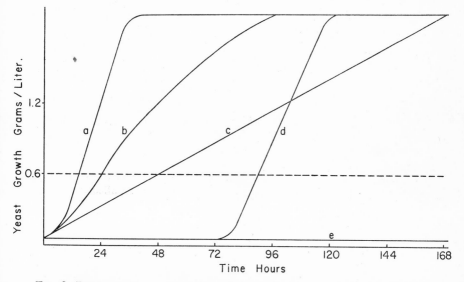

FIG. 8. Diagrammatic representation of the various types of response by yeasts grown in synthetic medium deficient in a single nutrilite.
a. No requirement.
b and c. Partial requirement designated by an arabic numeral.
d. Partial requirement (adaptation) designated by an arabic numeral in parentheses.
e. Absolute requirement designated by a roman numeral.

to the system proposed by Kirsop are shown in Figs. 8 and 9. Despite the variations in the criteria used by different workers to interpret their results, these tests afford valuable information in several fields of study. Possibly the two most extensive uses of the technique are firstly, the recognition of different strains of the same species of yeasts which might otherwise be difficult to differentiate and secondly, by making use of modifications of the test, the assay of nutrilites. A few examples of the work reported in the literature will serve to illustrate the general trend of these studies.

Burkholder *et al.* (1944) examined a large number of yeasts and typical

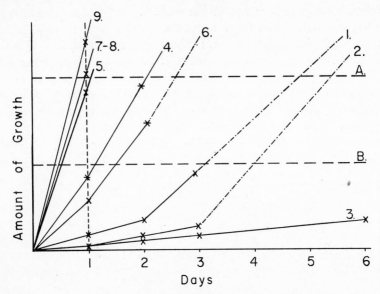

Fig. 9. A typical series of growth curves shown by a strain of *Saccharomyces cerevisiae* when grown in synthetic media, each deficient in a particular nutrilite.

Media deficient in	Type of requirement
1 Inositol	Adaptive
2 Pantothenate	Adaptive
3 Biotin	Absolute
4 Aneurin	Partial
5 Pyridoxine	None
6 Aneurin and pyridoxine	Partial
7 Nicotinic acid	None
8 Para-aminobenzoic acid	None
9 Complete medium	

A. Amount of growth to be attained in complete medium between 24 and 40 hours.

B. Yeast exceeding this amount of growth in the same time as A signifies independence of nutrilite. ·—·—·—· Maximum growth reached between two readings.

results may be illustrated by the behavior of 100 cultures representing 25 species from 8 genera. Biotin was required by 78 cultures, aneurin by 33, pantothenate by 30, inositol by 15, and nicotinic acid and pyridoxine by 13. Of the species of which several cultures were examined *Hansenula anomala* (24 cultures) had no requirement for any one nutrilite, *Candida guilliermondii* var. *membranaefaciens* (29 cultures) all required biotin while *Saccharomyces delbruckii* was found to be dependent upon both biotin and pantothenate. It is interesting to note that close agreement was observed between the nutrilite requirements of these yeasts and their morphological and biochemical characters. Lochhead and Landerkin (1942) reported similar agreement between these characteristics in a group of yeasts designated, according to their criteria of classification as *Zygosaccharomyces* species. However, it must be added that no such agreement is observed when these yeasts are classified according to the criteria of Lodder and Kreger-van Rij (1952) who do not recognize this genus (see Table XI). This example cannot, of course, be taken to indi-

TABLE XI

THE RELATIONSHIP BETWEEN NUTRILITE REQUIREMENTS[a] AND CLASSIFICATION OF VARIOUS YEASTS

Classification according to Lockhead and Landerkin (1942)	Requirement for pantothenate	Classification according to Lodder and Kreger-van Rij (1952)
Zygosaccharomyces variabilis	None	*Saccharomyces rouxii*
Zygosaccharomyces nadsonii		
Zygosaccharomyces felsineus		*Saccharomyces rouxii* var. *polymorphus*
Zygosaccharomyces rugosus	Partial	*Saccharomyces rouxii*
Zygosaccharomyces barkeri		*Saccharomyces rouxii* var. *polymorphus*
Zygosaccharomyces amoeboideus		
Zygosaccharomyces richteri		*Saccharomyces mellis*
Zygosaccharomyces acidifaciens		*Saccharomyces acidifaciens*
Zygosaccharomyces japonicus	Absolute	*Saccharomyces rouxii*
Zygosaccharomyces nectarophilus	Inositol also required	*Saccharomyces mellis*

[a] All need biotin.

cate that the Dutch system of classification is less discriminating than other proposed systems, for in fact it is surprising that the former workers found such close agreement between the nutrilite requirements of yeasts and a conventional system of classification. Indeed, many workers studying different cultures of the same yeast of undoubted specific rank, have reported differences in the nutrilite requirement of the various strains. This is illustrated by the finding that, of 53 lager yeasts (*Saccharomyces carlsbergensis*), 14 required biotin, 23 biotin and pantothenate, 4 biotin and inositol, and 12 required all the 3 nutrilites (Atkin *et al.*, 1949). The same authors also found that 5 strains of *Saccharomyces cerevisiae* required aneurin and pyridoxine as well as biotin, inositol, and pantothenate, whereas other strains of S. *cerevisiae* have been found to have an absolute requirement for p-aminobenzoic (Rainbow, 1948). Further, appreciable variation in the nutrilite requirements of strains of *Schizosaccharomyces pombe* was observed by Ahmad *et al.* (1954) who distinguished 5 groups according to their need for pantothenate, riboflavin, aneurin, nicotinic acid, inositol, biotin, and pyridoxine.

An interesting observation relating the nutrilite requirements of yeasts to a biochemical characteristic was reported by Rugosa (1943) who claimed that all nonlactose-fermenting yeasts are independent of nicotinic acid. This statement was later limited by Schultz and Atkin (1947) to the enunciation that all lactose-fermenting yeasts need this nutrilite.

The use of yeasts as tools for the assay of vitamins and nutrilites is possible because, when such accessory factors are present in quantities less than that required for optimal growth, there is a relationship between the amount of growth and their concentration. For instance, Jackson and Kilkenny (1951) observed that the response of a particular strain of yeast to aneurin was directly proportional to the amount of this nutrilite when present at concentrations below 10^{-8} M and incidentally they estimated that each cell division required 4.5×10^4 molecules of aneurin. Again, the growth of a strain of *S. carlsbergensis* was believed to be proportional to the concentration of inositol in the medium (Smith, 1951), and further Saburo Fukui (1955) showed that the growth of a "Sake" yeast, a strain of *S. cerevisiae*, was proportional to the concentration of pantothenate below 2×10^{-8} when the inoculum was between 4×10^3 and 12×10^4 cells per milliter of medium.

A perusal of the literature concerning the many investigations into the response of yeasts to nutrilites reveals the need to specify exactly the conditions under which such tests are carried out, for it is apparent that variation in nutrilite requirement occurs under different environmental conditions. In some cases the difference may only be quantitative but in certain cases even qualitative differences have been noted. Further, various interactions have been recorded between the yeast, the type of basal medium used, and particular combination of nutrilites studied. It would appear that, wherever possible, yeast isolates should be maintained in a medium the nutrilite content of which approximates to that of the natural medium from which the yeast was originally isolated. This factor is important, because there is evidence that certain yeasts may adapt themselves to grow in a medium deficient in a nutrilite for which they previously have had a requirement. Thus Leonian and Lilly (1942a) trained a particular yeast to be independent of external sources of biotin, aneurin, pyridoxine, nicotinic acid, and p-aminobenzoic acid all of which were originally required for growth. Furthermore these changes were

fected relatively quickly, for the ability to grow in the absence of each
nutrilite was developed in only 4–7 transfers in a deficient medium. It is
essential that the size of inoculum used in nutrilite requirement tests be
accurately controlled, because a large inoculum, even of washed cells,
may liberate into the medium sufficient nutrilities to support an appreci-
ble amount of growth; for example, in a representative case, an inocu-
um equivalent to 0.01 mg. of dried yeast failed to grow in a basal
medium devoid of added nutrilites, whereas, when the inoculum was
increased to 0.2 mg., moderate growth ensued although the lag phase
was markedly prolonged (Leonian and Lilly, 1942b). Interaction between nutrilites may also occur and a further complication arises when
yeasts are able to synthesize nutrilities from precursors present in the
medium; such interactions can best be illustrated by the following
examples. Pyridoxine and aneurin antagonize each other to such an extent that the growth of a yeast having a requirement for either of them
one may be partially or completely inhibited when both nutrilites are
present (Williams et al., 1940; Schultz and Atkin, 1947) and a similar
relationship exists between aneurin and inositol (Williams et al., 1940).
The response of various strains of Saccharomyces cerevisiae to aneurin
may differ markedly, some strains being stimulated while on the other
and different strains may be inhibited (Lochhead and Landerkin,
1941). The majority of nutrilites may be replaced by other compounds
whose structure is incorporated in, or closely resembles, that of the
nutrilite itself (see Fig. 7). Generally, the activities of the substitutes are
much less than that of the corresponding nutrilites, and, moreover, vari-
us yeasts may react differently in their response to these alternative
sources. For instance, strains of Trichosporon cutaneum and Torulopsis
abida are unable to utilize either the pyrimidine or thiazole moieties of
aneurin when the appropriate substances are tested independently, but
growth occurs when the two moieties are present simultaneously as presumably the yeasts are able to link the two nuclei together. By contrast,
a strain of Rhodotorula mucilagenosa grew in the presence of either
moiety alone (Miller and Aschner, 1952), whereas another strain of
Rhodotorula failed to grow when the thiazole moiety alone was present,
although the pyrimidine moiety supported growth up to $\frac{1}{5}$th that obtained
with the complete nutrilite (Rainbow, 1951). In the case of pantothenate,
the vitamin can be partially replaced by β-alanine, a substance not found
in the free state in nature (Lockhead and Landerkin, 1942) and in this
connection leucine enhances the response to the latter substance (Miller,
1936). In a few cases the relationship between a substance which is able
partially to replace a nutrilite and the nutrilite itself is not always so

apparent as those cited above; for example, p-aminobenzoic acid can
replaced by adenine when methionine and to a lesser extent histidine a
also present and biotin can be replaced to some extent by aspartic ac

Not all structurally related compounds can replace the correspondi
nutrilites, and many of the analogues are frankly antagonistic. Such ar
logues presumably act in a manner somewhat similar to the well-kno
phenomenon of competitive inhibition as shown by sulfonamides wi
respect to p-aminobenzoic acid. A number of analogues of biotin ha
been tested (Ju-Hwo Chu, 1948) and of these D-dethiobiotin has 100%
the activity of biotin, DL-dethiobiotin 53%, 5-methyl-2-oxo-4-imidazolidir
butyric acid and 2-oxo-4-imidazolidine valeric acid are only slightly acti
while, 5-isopropyl-5-methyl-2-oxo-4-imidazolidine propionic acid is ina
tive and homodethiobiotin and 5-methyl-2-oxo-4-imidazolidinenonoic ac
have actual antibiotic effects. It has been shown that β-alanine can som
times replace pantothenate and it is interesting to note that the stim
latory effects of these individual compounds can be specifically inhibit
by different substances. Thus whereas aspartic acid inhibits the effe
of β-alanine but has no interaction with pantothenate (Atkin et c
1944), taurine and pantoyltaurine inhibit the growth response to pant
thenate but not to β-alanine (Sarett and Cheldelin, 1945). The nature
the assimilable nitrogen can also influence the response of certain yea
to particular nutrilites, e.g., when the ammonium salts in a medium a
replaced by urea, a yeast may require more biotin and less pantothena
for optimal growth (Schultz et al., 1940) although when amino aci
replace ammonia in synthetic media the growth response to biotin is i
creased (Thorne, 1949). Not only are amino acids able to influence t
response of yeasts to nutrilites, but there is evidence that the converse
also true; for example, Krishnaswamy and Giri (1954) studied a strain
S. cerevisiae which was unable to utilize glutamic acid to any great exte
unless biotin was present. This type of reaction appears to be speci
as the same authors examined a strain of Rhodotorula glutinis which w
able to utilize glutamic acid in the absence of biotin.

Challinor and Rose (1954) reported that certain strains of Sacchar
myces cerevisiae excrete nicotinic acid into the medium when grown
media deficient in biotin. It is now known that not all strains of tl
yeast behave similarly (Rose and Nickerson, 1956) and the vario
strains can be divided into three groups: (a) those which excrete appr
ciable amounts of nicotinic acid in biotin-deficient medium; (b) tho
which show no gross excretion of nicotinic acid, the presence of whi
can only be demonstrated when the estimates are based on a unit weig
of yeast; and (c) those which liberate nicotinic acid when grown in t

presence of biotin but which show a reduction in the amount of the former as the concentration of the latter is lowered. Moat and Emmons (1954) showed that aspartic acid was able, at least partially, to replace biotin for growth. Since it is now known that aspartic acid does not prevent the excretion of nicotinic acid in biotin-deficient media, it is suggested that biotin has more than one role in the metabolism of yeast.

A further example of a change in the physiology of yeasts due to growth in media deficient in nutrilites is revealed by the fact that the lipid content of the cells is increased from 1.6 to 24.5%, based on dry weight, when the cells are grown in medium deficient in nicotinic acid Challinor and Daniels, 1954).

Besides their function as growth stimulators, nutrilites play an important role in the production of spores. In this connection it has been shown that a yeast requiring biotin and pantothenate for growth is able to produce spores on a sporulation medium devoid of these nutrilites. Nevertheless, when pantothenate is present the percentage of cells producing spores is appreciably increased, whereas no such increase is observed when biotin is added (Tremaine and Miller, 1954). The composition of the resporulation medium significantly influences the number of asci produced but more biotin is required to produce maximum sporulation than is needed for maximum growth. Furthermore, the presence of other nutrilites, for which the yeast has no apparent requirement for growth, may result in an increase in the number of spores formed or may influence the number of spores present in the asci. An illustration is provided by a presporulation medium deficient in inositol which does not impair growth, but sometimes results in a decrease in the number of four-spore asci formed.

Recently attention has been turned to studies concerned with the effects of vitamin K in the physiology of cells and a few workers have studied more particularly the behavior of yeasts in the presence of vitamins K_3 and K_5. Hinz and Harris (1954) showed that vitamin K_3 at concentrations below 60 μg./ml. stimulates the uptake of oxygen, but that at higher concentrations marked inhibition occurs; this vitamin inhibits the evolution of carbon dioxide. The composition of the medium may well be important in this respect for Kitamikado and Ishibashi (1955) showed that the stimulatory effects can be demonstrated in media containing fructose, glucose, galactose, or pyruvate but not in a medium containing sucrose. The action of K_5 appears to be the converse of K_3 because oxygen uptake is inhibited at all concentrations, whereas carbon dioxide evolution is slightly stimulated at concentrations below 15 μg./ml. In extracts of yeast, a factor has been demonstrated which behaves in

a manner reminiscent of a nutrilite but which has not been identified with
any of the common ones (Rich and Stern, 1956): it has the unique ability
of reversing the toxic effect of quaternary ammonium compounds. No
growth occurs when yeasts, which have been exposed to inhibitory con
centrations of quaternary ammonium compounds, are transferred to nu
trient media free from the toxic substance, but growth takes place afte
the addition of extract of yeast to the medium containing the inhibitor
substance. In this latter connection the experimental evidence appears to
rule out the possibility that the reversal effect is due to the inactivatio
of the quaternary compound by direct combination with a substance con
tained in the yeast extract. It has been suggested that the active fac
tor replaces a deficiency in a nutrilite brought about by the blocking, b
the quaternary compound, of a metabolic route; alternatively the facto
may enable the yeast to circumvent the blockage by opening up a
alternative pathway. The ability of this substance to restore norma
growth conditions also indicates that the suggested mode of action o
quaternary ammonium compounds, due to seepage of amino acids fror
the cells into the surrounding medium (Gale and Taylor, 1946), ma
not be entirely satisfactory.

6. Mineral Requirements

The role played by mineral salts in the growth of yeasts is extreme
difficult to ascertain because of the technical problems encountered i
ensuring that the basal media are entirely free of the elements unde
examination. Consequently it is not surprising that little precise in
formation is available concerning this fundamentally important and inte
esting topic. Certain elements have been shown to be essential for growt
when they are present in small amounts whereas others, while not absc
lutely necessary, can nevertheless exhibit stimulatory effects; furthe
many elements are inhibitory at concentrations only slightly in excess o
that required for optimal growth. As limited as our knowledge is of th
part played by the elements in the growth of yeast, it does none the le
suggest a reason why defined synthetic media in general do not suppo
growth to the same extent as do such undefined media as malt wort o
corn-steep liquor. Most of the synthetic media contain relatively few el
ments and even supposing that the requirements for nitrogen, carbo
and vitamins are satisfied, it is almost certain that the media are un
balanced so far as trace metals are concerned, particularly if salts of
high degree of purity are used. A large number of defined synthet
media have been devised but most of these are based on the formul
described by Fulmer et al. (1921), Devereux and Tanner (1927), an

elling-Dekker (1931). They generally contain almost exclusively the
llowing salts: potassium dihydrogen phosphate, dipotassium hydrogen
10sphate, disodium hydrogen phosphate, calcium salts as the chloride,
Irbonate and/or nitrate, magnesium sulfate, and the chlorides of sodium
1d potassium. Ingram (1955b) remarked that it is surprising that such
edia are able to support as much growth as they do, since they only
ntain relatively small amounts of sulfur. It is clear that the few ele-
ents that are contained in media of this type must include those that
e absolutely essential for growth; however, that they do not contain
1e optimal requirement of all elements, at least for certain yeasts, can be
ferred from the relatively small total populations that such media can
pport. Further, it has been observed on occasion that continued sub-
lture in synthetic media eventually leads to a progressive reduction in
past crop, such observations suggesting that the media are deficient in at
ast one unknown factor, which may be a trace element.

Phosphorus is essential for the growth of yeast, and among other func-
ons this element plays an important part in the mechanism of carbo-
ydrate metabolism, being concerned with the adenosine phosphate-
lenosine diphosphate reaction, a reaction which is discussed more fully
sewhere.

The effect of the different halogens varies considerably, but chlorine
ppears to be essential for growth and is readily available in most media.
dine, either as elemental iodine, or as the iodides of potassium, sodium,
calcium, stimulates growth at concentrations between 1 p.p.m. to 10
p.m. (Greaves et al., 1928). It is not known for certain whether bromine
absolutely essential, but Gruber-Oberfeuchtner (1953) reports that
owth is stimulated by extremely small concentrations and that media
ntaining bromides at a concentration of 0.5 N are quite toxic. The in-
bitory action of fluoride upon the carbohydrate metabolism of yeasts
of course well known, although it appears that its inhibitory effects
ay vary considerably according to the strain of yeast and the composi-
on of the medium used.

Sodium does not appear to be necessary for growth, unlike potassium.
he function of the latter is not fully understood, but it is known that it
taken up early in the growth of young cultures and that at least a
rtion of it is released later into the medium (Atkin and Gray, 1947).
is associated with the respiratory functions of yeast cells, but certain
asts have been studied in which ammonium ions can replace those of
tassium without either respiration or fermentation being affected.

Calcium does not appear to be essential for growth of yeast cells,
though it has been established that the amount of yeast ash is reduced

by approximately one-half when the medium in which the cells hav
been grown is devoid of calcium. There is, however, insufficient eviden
to indicate whether yeasts grown in a calcium-deficient medium a
actually independent of calcium or whether the cells grow by virtue
the calcium that they have previously accumulated from a calcium-ric
medium. Complete independence from the metal can only be regarde
as established after yeasts have been repeatedly subcultured in a calciun
free medium over a prolonged period of time. Many workers have show
that certain amounts of calcium definitely increase the amount of yea
growth, but opinions differ as to the concentrations required to suppo
maximum growth. Fulmer *et al.* (1921) report that the amount
growth is progressively stimulated as the concentration of calcium i
creases from 1000 p.p.m. to 6000 p.p.m. after which no further increa:
occurs; on the other hand Richards (1925) claims that the optimum co
centration of calcium, as the sulfate, is of the order of 140 p.p.m. ar
that inhibitory effects are exhibited above this amount. It is interestir
to note that many waters used for the production of media contain a
amount in excess of this latter figure. The evidence of Kondrat'ev
(1940) indicates that the function of calcium in cell metabolism is cor
plex for not only does its presence in media increase the total yeast cro
but it also stimulates sporulation and the production of intracellular f
and metachromatin. Lasnitzki and Szorenzi (1934) showed that calciu
can be replaced to a large extent by magnesium. It is not then surprisir
that the role of magnesium in yeast growth has been found by mar
workers to be similar to that of calcium, despite the earlier belief
Devereux and Tanner (1927) that magnesium is essential for growt
Fulmer *et al.* (1921) noted a double reaction when magnesium was su
plied as the sulfate, for it was found that concentrations up to 200 p.p.r
were inhibitory, whereas between 200 and 400 p.p.m. growth was stim
lated, no further enhancement being observed from 400 to 1000 p.p.r
There can be no doubt that magnesium is essential for the production
high yields of yeasts and it is known that it is associated with metabolis
both of carbohydrates through the activation of enzymes concerned wi
the transfer of phosphate and of nitrogenous compounds. Deficiency
magnesium in synthetic media reduces the response of certain strains
Saccharomyces cerevisiae to "bios" factors, a fact that has been useful
employed by Lesk *et al.* (1938) to differentiate strains of this species.

Interest in the effects of copper on yeast growth is understandable, b
cause a considerable proportion of the fermentation vessels used in i
dustry are made of this metal. The general concensus of opinion is tha
although it is not essential, low concentrations of copper enhance growt

eat differences of opinion being expressed, however, as to what con-
tutes the optimal amount. Thus Elvehjem (1931) claims that 0.1 p.p.m.
mulates growth and White and Munns (1951) found that under cer-
in conditions inhibitory effects begin to appear at concentrations as low
0.175 p.p.m. and that growth is completely inhibited at 1.0 p.p.m.
owever McHargue and Calfee (1931) believed the optimum concentra-
n to be 7.5 p.p.m. and Hanson and Baldwin (1941) quote the optimum
nge as high as 35–40 p.p.m. These latter workers noted that, under nor-
al conditions, the presence of copper increased the total yeast crop, but
olonged the lag phase, although, if the oxidation-reduction potential
above "normal" the lag phase is reduced by the presence of 16 p.p.m.
copper. Olsen and Johnson (1949) claimed that S. cerevisiae grown in
nthetic media require $12–15 \times 10^{-9}$ parts of copper. That yeast can
tain copper may be inferred from the fact that Richards and Troutman
940) were able to demonstrate, by the use of spectrographic tech-
ques, the presence of copper in yeast ash of cells grown in medium
void of this metal.

There is ample evidence that a small amount of iron can appreciably
hance the yield of yeast; recently it has been established that its
esence is essential for full catalase and cytochrome activity. As is the
se with other metals the amount necessary to support maximum growth
s been differently reported by various workers, the range being from
025–0.15 p.p.m. The results of Olson and Johnson (1949) probably ex-
ain these discrepancies, for they established that various strains of the
me species have different optimal requirements and, furthermore, that
e type of response may vary with the species or genus. Thus whereas
cerevisiae shows a logarithmic response, Torulopsis utilis responds
ctilinearly. Apart from its effect upon growth, iron at 400 p.p.m. retards
e autolysis of certain yeasts and Malkov (1950) attributes this to the
ility of the metal to inactivate yeast proteinases. White and Munns
1951) found that relatively large doses of approximately 500 p.p.m. had
ght inhibitory effects.

Zinc is capable of stimulating growth at concentrations varying from
2 p.p.m. to 200 p.p.m. and McHargue and Calfee (1931) claimed that
little as 10 p.p.m. stimulates the production of carbon dioxide. Con-
ntrations between 300–500 p.p.m. partially inhibit growth.

There is no evidence that lanthanum is either necessary or can even
imulate growth, but Richards and Troutman (1940) inferred that it can
accumulated by yeast from the medium. This opinion has been sub-
antiated by Bowen and Robinson (1951) who showed that isotopic
nthanum was preferentially adsorbed by yeast cells from an equilib-

rium mixture of lanthanum and barium. Toxicity tests have reveale
only slight inhibition at concentrations of the order of 500 p.p.m.

Manganese can be accumulated by the cells from the growth mediu
Amounts of the order of 10 p.p.m. stimulate growth and only slight to
effects are noted at concentrations as high as 500 p.p.m. This metal
believed to be associated with the activation of arginase.

Generally chromium is believed to be toxic, growth being partially i
hibited by 140–260 p.p.m. and totally inhibited at 1000 p.p.m. This met
has been detected in yeast ash, and Hebert (1907) claims that minu
amounts stimulate growth.

The function of thallium appears to differ from that of the metals me
tioned above, for whereas the other metals are found in yeasts grown
media to which no special metals have been added, thallium does n
appear in these circumstances. However, Richards (1932b) claims th
the presence of 1 p.p.m. increases the yeast crop by as much as 80% a
this is probably effected by the ability of the metal to block partially t
fermentation cycle as is indicated by the uptake of carbohydrates bei
reduced in its presence. Growth is inhibited by approximately 5% wh
the concentration of thallium is of the order of 400 p.p.m. (White a
Munns, 1951).

The behavior of rubidium is somewhat like that of thallium, that
yeasts do not appear to accumulate or bind the metal in the cell, b
nevertheless growth is stimulated when the concentration in the mediu
is approximately 500 p.p.m. In other living cells rubidium can eith
partially or completely replace potassium but Richards and Troutm
(1940) claim that such an interchange of these metals does not occur
the yeast cell.

The effect of vanadium upon yeast is controversial for whereas Wh
and Munns (1951) found this metal partially inhibited growth at 3 p.p.
and completely inhibited it at 200 p.p.m., Sampath (1944) claimed th
the pentoxide inhibited sporulation at 1000 p.p.m., but that 2000 p.p.
stimulates this process. The latter worker also noted that this metal ga
rise to elongated cells, but that normal growth was resumed when t
yeast was transferred to vanadium-free media.

Spectrographic analyses have shown that the following metals a
absent from cells which have not been deliberately grown in their pre
ence: caesium, germanium, osmium, mercury, cadmium, palladium, ta
talum, and molybdenum. Similar analyses carried out under identi
conditions reveal the presence of barium, gold, lead, silver, and silic
The presence of silver is particularly surprising since White and Mun
have shown that concentrations of as little as 0.4 p.p.m. in the medi

completely inhibit growth. (See Table XII for the toxicity of various metals towards yeasts as investigated by White and Munns.)

It is apparent from the above data that even when various workers are in agreement regarding the general effects of different metals on the growth of yeasts, they frequently disagree on the concentration required to excite particular phenomena. At least four factors may contribute to these differences. Firstly, a reliable comparison of the results obtained

TABLE XII

TOXICITY OF VARIOUS ELEMENTS TOWARDS YEASTS[a]

Category	Elements	Parts per million for 50% inhibition of growth	Parts per million for complete inhibition of growth
Very poisonous	Cd, Os, Hg, Pd	0.125–2.7	1.0–10.0
Moderately poisonous	Li, B, Ni, As, Te, Be	55–285	115–400
Slightly poisonous	Se	400	500–600
Very slightly poisonous	Pb, Al, W, Mo	Ca. 500	—
Nonpoisonous at 500 p.p.m.	Sb, St, Ba, U, Th, Rb, Cs, Ti, Zr		

[a] From the data of White and Munns (1951).

by different workers is often impossible, because it is known that various strains respond differently and at times it is not possible to identify accurately the strain employed in a particular investigation; sometimes, indeed, the only information supplied is that a "yeast" has been used as the test organism. Secondly, the medium in which the yeast is grown markedly influences the results obtained, as when White and Munns (1951) found that, in a synthetic medium, copper at concentrations as low as 1 p.p.m. completely inhibited the growth of a strain of *Saccharomyces cerevisiae*, but that when the carbohydrate in the synthetic medium was replaced by its equivalent amount of molasses, 5 p.p.m. of copper did not materially reduce the amount of yeast growth and that, further, when the same yeast was grown in malt wort no apparent inhibition occurred even when the concentration of copper was as high as 30 p.p.m. Morgan *et al.* (1951) established that the lethal effects of cobalt in a synthetic medium can be eliminated by growing the yeast in the presence of L-histidine and in this connection the molar ratio for the reversal of cobalt toxicity was 25 moles of histidine to 1 mole of cobalt. A further example of reversal of the toxic effects due to metals has been

TABLE XIII

THE UTILIZATION OF ORGANIC SULFUR COMPOUNDS BY VARIOUS YEASTS[a]

Group	Source of organic sulfur used	Yeasts, according to Schultz and McManus (1950)	Yeasts according to Lodder and Kreger-van Rij (1952)
A	Glutathione, methionine, and cysteine	*Brettanomyces bruxellensis*	*Brettanomyces bruxellensis*
		Candida guilliermondii	*Candida guilliermondii*
		Hansenula anomala	*Hansenula anomala*
		Hansenula lambica	*Hansenula anomala* var. *cifferii*
		Saccharomyces acerissacchari	*Hansenula anomala*
		Saccharomyces bailii	
		Saccharomyces behrensianus	*Saccharomyces bailii*
			Saccharomyces rouxii var. *polymorphus*
		Saccharomyces pastorianus	*Saccharomyces pastorianus*
		Willia anomala	*Hansenula anomala*
B	Glutathione and methionine	*Torulopsis utilis*	*Torulopsis utilis*
		Candida pseudotropicalis	*Candida pseudotropicalis*
		Saccharomyces fragilis	*Saccharomyces fragilis*
		Zygosaccharomyces lactis	*Saccharomyces lactis*
		Zygosaccharomyces marxianus	*Saccharomyces marianus*
C	As for B but growth incomplete in methionine	*Saccharomyces cerevisiae*	*Saccharomyces cerevisiae*
		Saccharomyces chodati	*Saccharomyces steineri*
		Saccharomyces anomalus	*Hansenula anomala*
		Saccharomyces logos	*Saccharomyces logos*
		Saccharomyces tokyo	*Saccharomyces cerevisiae* var. *ellipsoideus*
		Saccharomyces tubiformis	*Saccharomyces willianus*
		Saccharomyces carlsbergensis	*Saccharomyces carlsbergensis*
D	Methionine and cysteine	*Zygosaccharomyces mongolicus*	*Saccharomyces delbrueckii* var. *mongolicus*
E	Methionine, growth slow	*Saccharomyces cerevisiae*	*Saccharomyces cerevisiae*

[a] From the data of Schultz and McManus (1950).

demonstrated by Fels and Cheldeton (1949) who found that the inhibitory effects of selenium are reversed when methionine is added to the medium. Thirdly, interaction between metals is now known to occur; thus whereas McHargue and Calfie (1931) found the stimulatory effects of optimum concentrations of copper, manganese, and zinc to be additive,

White and Munns observed that a few parts per million of zinc reduced the toxic effects of cadmium. Finally, it has been shown that yeasts can acquire a resistance against the toxic effects of certain metals. For instance, a strain of S. *cerevisiae* which grew poorly in the presence of cobalt nitrate at 100 p.p.m. and not at all at 200 p.p.m. was trained by Perlman and O'Brien (1954) to tolerate 1000 p.p.m. and to grow well in the presence of 750 p.p.m. Many workers have reported increased tolerance of yeasts to the effects of copper, McHargue for example training a strain of S. *cerevisiae* to acquire a sevenfold resistance. Minagawa (1955) made a remarkable observation when he showed that not only can a yeast be trained to tolerate relatively high concentrations of copper, but that extracts of the resistant strains are able to confer resistance on nonresistant ones, and that the active principle was located in the ribonucleic acid fraction of the extract. A recent example of the toxic effect of a metal ion being directly related to the nature of the medium in which the yeast is grown is revealed by the fact that in organic media, such as malt wort, chromium (0.125 mg. per ml.) has no effect, whereas in a simple defined medium such a concentration of the metal inhibits totally the growth of the organism. It is interesting to note that a fourfold increase in the tolerance of the yeast to the metal, even in synthetic media, can be developed by repeatedly subculturing the yeast in the presence of chromium salts (Hartelius, 1956).

In general, all yeasts can obtain the sulfur necessary for growth from inorganic sulfates such as those of sodium or ammonium and certain yeasts can even use hydrogen sulfide in low concentrations (Sugata and Koch, 1926). Methionine, glutathione, and to a lesser extent cysteine are the most common sources of organic sulfur. Schultz and McManus (1950) investigated the ability of a large number of yeasts to utilize these, the principle results being set out in Table XIII.

7. Effects of Physical Conditions upon Growth

Early studies revealed that yeasts grow more vigorously in aerated cultures than they do in non-aerated ones and further that the yield of cells is increased by agitation. The effects of varying these two factors were not comprehensively investigated until the large-scale industrial production of yeast was undertaken. Recent studies have been mainly concerned with the effects of varying the rate of aeration and the amount of agitation in relation to other specific conditions and, as a result, certain generalizations have emerged.

Under strictly anaerobic conditions the rate of growth is at a minimum, reproduction being limited to 4–5 generations, while the coefficient of fermentation, that is the amount of sugar fermented by a unit amount of yeast, is at its maximum (White and Munns, 1951). Even the presence of quite small amounts of oxygen results in very substantial increases in the yeast crops, so much so that only relatively small subsequent increases in the amount of growth result from very large further increases in the amount of available oxygen. The ability of progressively increasing amounts of oxygen to stimulate increasing growth of yeasts can continue in fact only within certain limits, for example maximum growth of certain strains of *Saccharomyces cerevisiae* cannot occur when the amount of available oxygen is less than 1.6 g. per unit gram of sugar utilized (White and Munns, 1951), whereas, decreasing yields of yeast are obtained when the amount of available oxygen exceeds 1 mM per liter of medium per minute (Olson and Johnson, 1949).

The stimulatory effects of vigorous aeration depend not only on maintaining an adequate supply of oxygen, but also on removing carbon dioxide which has slight but definite inhibitory properties. Further the cells are kept in suspension and in motion so that they are continually brought into contact with fresh medium and localized staling of the medium is avoided. Although the effects of rapid aeration of the cultures must inevitably involve a certain amount of agitation, and conversely rapid agitation must lead to better aeration unless carried out in an inert gas, the two effects can be to some extent independent of one another. In this connection the observations of Singh *et al.* (1948) are of interest. These authors examined strains of *Saccharomyces cerevisiae, Torulopsis utilis,* and *Candida arborea* which had the same fermentation rates independent of both aeration and agitation, although the relationship of the yeast crop with respect to the amount of sugar utilized was dependent upon the amount of aeration and/or agitation. Thus, the yield of *S. cerevisiae* was greatest in vigorously aerated cultures, but was independent of the degree of mechanical agitation; the crops of *T. utilis* were increased by rapid agitation but were independent of the rate of aeration, while the amount of growth of *C. arborea* was dependent both upon the rate of aeration and the amount of agitation.

Little precise information is available concerning the effects upon growth rates of yeasts brought about by changes of temperature and pH. There is evidence that optimal conditions, with respect to these two conditions, may vary somewhat with the strain of yeast being studied. Generally most yeasts grow reasonably well over a temperature range of from 15 to 30°C., the optimal value usually lying much nearer to the upper limiting temperature than the lower one. For instance, it is known that *S. cerevisiae* will grow to some extent at 10°C., and that the optimal temperature is usually about 28°C., but rapid decline in growth occurs when the temperature rises above 30°C. (Richards, 1934). Using another strain of yeast under different cultural conditions, White (1953) found that the amount of growth increased with increasing temperature up to 36°C., but that at 40°C. the amount of growth was only equal to that obtained at temperatures between 20.0–24.5°C. Yeasts are extremely sensitive to exposure to temperatures between 53–60°C., but the cultures do not behave as homogeneous mixtures, for example, in a culture of S. cerevisiae, originally containing 5×10^5 viable cells, only 164 cells were alive after 4 minutes exposure at 55°C., but a further 6 minutes was required to reduce the count to 24 viable cells (White, 1953). The reason why some cells are sensitive and others resistant to heat in this temperature range is not known but even the resistant cells appear to be injured by such temperatures, because on transfer to a new medium at normal temperatures the lag phase of the heat-trained cells is much more prolonged than that of the parent culture. Use has been made of the different thermal death values of various yeasts to detect contamination of brewing yeasts (Webb, 1956) in those cases where the infecting strain has a greater resistance to heat than the pitching yeast.

Slightly acid conditions favor the growth of yeasts, but varying the pH value of media over a relatively wide range does not appear to influence greatly the growth of yeasts in nutrient-rich media. Usually the range over which most active growth occurs is between pH 4.0 and 6.0. Yeasts are, however, surprisingly acid-resistant and many strains are able to tolerate, if not grow in, media in which the pH is as low as 2.5.

8. Factors Influencing Production of Spores

Many yeasts are able to exist both in the haploid and diploid phases; however, spores must be produced before passage from the diploid vegetative phase to the haploid vegetative phase becomes possible. The ability to produce spores is also of fundamental importance, not only for taxonomic purposes, but because genetical analyses have shown that reduction division occurs during spore formation (see Chapter III, Section 3). Consequently the ability of yeasts to sporulate makes possible the controlled hybridization of new strains and, further, leads to a better understanding of the biochemistry of parental strains. Obviously, it is often desirable to be able to induce sporulation more or less at will, but this is not always feasible, because many yeasts tend to lose their ability to form spores after prolonged cultivation in artificial media.

Many fungi other than yeasts are known to maintain their ability to produce spores when they are kept in dry soil cultures. Hartelius and

Ditlevsen (1956) have applied this technique to the preservation of yeast cultures and, of the cultures examined, 50% showed a marked increase in the actual number of asci produced or an increase in the number of asci containing three or four spores. The preliminary experiments indicate that much of the improvement is probably due to selection occurring during storage.

In the past, it has been thought that sporulation was induced by conditions such as near-starvation which were unfavorable to the yeast, but such circumstances might clearly lead to the yeast dying without producing spores. It seems more probable that there is a balance between two sets of conditions, one set favoring vegetative reproduction and the other sporulation and that a change in the environment may favor one phase of the life cycle to the detriment of the other.

It now appears to be reasonably well established that yeasts sporulate more readily when growth in a nutrient-rich medium is followed by a transfer to an environment containing little or no nutrient. Nevertheless, the wide range of presporulation media, devised by many workers, indicates a lack of precise knowledge concerning the essential nutrients and the following examples of the diverse nature of these media may be quoted. Mrak et al. (1942) used a medium containing cucumber, potato, beet, and carrot, while Lindegren and Lindegren (1944) devised a medium containing among other things fruit juices, vegetable extracts, dried yeast, and glycerine. A blend of extracts from eight different vegetables and from pressed yeast has been used by Wickerham et al. (1946), whereas Etchells and Jones (1946) even used liver medium.

The effects of various nitrogenous compounds in synthetic presporulation media does not appear to have been investigated in detail since Ochmann (1932) found that miscellaneous species of Saccharomyces respond differently in media containing various sources of nitrogen. For instance, S. validus spored readily in a medium containing nitrates, but not in one containing glutamic acid as the sole source of nitrogen, whereas the converse was true in the case of S. cerevisiae. On the other hand, S. pastorianus produced a high proportion of sporulating cells in both these media, but most spores were produced in the presence of peptone, a medium which was not suitable for the sporulation of either of the other two species.

One of the most commonly used techniques is to transfer the cells, after growth in a presporulation medium, to gypsum or cement blocks, washed agar, silica-gel, moist filter paper, or moist porcelain. Unfortunately, these techniques are not infallible as is evident from the large number of special sporulation media which are frequently employed.

Among the most common of the ill-defined media are potato, carrot, or cucumber slopes and carrot infusion medium (McKelvey's medium), while of the semi-defined media may be mentioned that of Gorodkowa containing a meat extract and a little added glucose, and Kleyn's medium the essential constituents of which are sodium acetate, glucose and tryptone. Very simple defined media have also been successfully used; in this connection Stantial (1935) and Adams (1950) reported the value of glucose–sodium acetate media, and Kirsop (1954) employed individual solutions of sodium acetate and of utilizable carbohydrates. Even with such an array of media available, repeated "backwards and forwards" transfer from presporulation medium to sporulation medium is frequently necessary before many yeasts can be induced to sporulate. Experience with a large number of yeasts has shown that there is a tendency for certain of these organisms to sporulate more readily on specific media; for example *Hansenula* and *Pichia* often produce spores readily on carrot slopes or McKelvey's medium, while *Debaryomyces* seem suited to Gorodkowa's medium and *S. cerevisiae* to media containing sodium acetate.

Wide differences of opinion have been expressed concerning the optimal physical conditions required to stimulate spore formation. Extracellular moisture has been considered to be unnecessary by Todd and Hermann (1936) and Windisch (1938) and, indeed, Stovall and Bulotz (1932a,b) described a technique which entails growing the yeast on malt agar and then allowing the medium to dehydrate; subsequently the medium is rehydrated, the cells removed and examined for the presence of spores. Hansen (1883) believed moisture to be important but not essential and Kleyn (1954) claimed that water above certain amounts was detrimental to spore formation. However, both Stantial (1935) and Kirsop (1954) have successfully induced a high proportion of cells to form spores in liquid cultures which have been aerated by shaking and it is probable that those investigators who have found the presence of moisture to be detrimental have in fact been dealing not with moisture effects as such, but with the effects of partial anaerobiosis brought about by the moist conditions prevailing in the test medium. That the partial anaerobiosis brought about by fermentation is detrimental to spore formation has been shown by Adams and Miller (1954) who demonstrated that oxygen stimulates sporulation but that the presence of carbon dioxide (40%) results in almost complete inhibition of the process while a 50% concentration of carbon dioxide is totally suppressive.

The optimum pH values for sporulation which have been reported are so different that it is difficult to draw any precise conclusions except that various yeasts have widely different requirements in this respect. Welten (1914a,b) and Baltatu (1939) found that the yeasts investigated by them spored more actively under acid conditions, whereas Oehlkers (1923) and Kufferath (1929) believed that alkaline conditions were the most favorable. Stantial (1935) quotes pH 8.0 as the optimal value and more recently Kleyn (1954) reported that strains of *Saccharomyces cerevisiae* produced spores over a pH range of 6.8 to 8.7 and that the optimum varied between 8.1 to 8.6 according to the buffer system employed. In contrast, Kirsop (1954) also working with *S. cerevisiae* quotes the optimal range as being between 6.4 and 6.8.

Even less information is available concerning the effects of temperature on sporulation and, certainly, *S. cerevisiae* in the form of pressed yeast cakes has been shown to sporulate in an ice chest (Maneval, 1924). More precise information has been presented by Adams and Miller (1954) who demonstrated that spores may form over a range of temperature varying from 3 to 34°C., the optimal value varying between 24 to 27.5°C. according to the strain being studied.

The effect of light upon the formation of spores by yeasts has received little attention despite the fact that it is well known that light can markedly influence the sporulation process in the case of certain molds and other fungi. In this connection it has become apparent recently that various strains of "bottom" yeasts respond differently (Oppenoorth, 1956). For example, one strain which was able only to produce 2% of asci in the dark was stimulated to produce 45.5% by exposing the culture to light for 16 hours per day; a second strain behaved conversely, the number of asci being reduced from 42.9% in the dark to 10.5% in the light; yet a third strain produced only 2.8% and 3.4% in the dark and in the light respectively. It is also interesting to note that replacement of the distilled water used to moisten the gypsum block, by a 1% solution of glucose resulted in an over-all increase in the number of asci but not in the proportion of cells developing asci. On the other hand replacement of distilled water by 0.5% acetate solution had no significant effect.

Many of the earlier studies concerning the value of carbohydrates in sporulation media must now be regarded as being of only historical interest because, as Kirsop (1954) has so aptly indicated, some of the carbohydrates that were supposed to influence sporulation are not even assimilated by the yeast examined. Errors may possibly have arisen through the use of unwashed cells, in which case the carry-over of traces of carbohydrates with the inoculum may have influenced the results. However, there is now evidence that the sporulation response is markedly influenced by the concentration of utilizable carbohydrates present in the medium. Kleyn (1954), using a glucose–acetate medium, found that the glucose was important so far as growth is concerned, but that only the acetate was responsible for sporulation. This is contrary to the experience of other investigators, for example, Saito (1916) and Wagner (1928), who claimed that glucose stimulates sporulation. In this connection more precise information has been presented by Kirsop 1954) who showed that, at critical concentrations, any carbohydrate that is utilized by the yeast can stimulate sporulation provided the medium is buffered to a suitable pH value. For example, a strain of S. *cerevisiae* produced as many spores in the presence of glucose (0.1%) at pH 6.2 as did the same yeast in the presence of an equivalent amount of sodium acetate. Apparently this salt is more valuable for routine purposes than is glucose, simply because the acetate also acts as buffer covering the critical pH range required for sporulation.

Recently, the respective merits of buffered solutions of glucose and of acetate as sporulation media has been reinvestigated (Miller and Halpern, 1956). Under the experimental conditions employed, it was found that glucose (0.1%) induced 38% of the cells to form spores and that an increase in the concentration of glucose to 0.33% resulted in reduction of the number of asci formed to 5%, whereas 56% of the cells developed asci when the concentration of acetate was 0.33% and that further increase in the amount of acetate did not appreciably inhibit the degree of sporulation. When mixtures of up to 0.1% of glucose and 0.33% of acetate were used, inhibition of sporulation failed to occur though this was the case when the glucose was increased to 0.3%. In this instance the use of buffered solutions reduces the possibility that inhibitory effects are due to changes in the pH value of the medium, as indicated by Kirsop (1954). Differences in another respect were also apparent, for Kirsop (1954) finds that a short exposure of the cells to the sporulation medium is sufficient to induce maximum sporulation, even when the cells are then transferred to distilled water, whereas while agreeing with respect to acetate, Miller and Halpern (1956) claim that the inhibitory effect of glucose-acetate media or of high concentrations of glucose are reduced by such a procedure. The possibility that these differences are merely an expression of those inherent in different strains of yeasts cannot be overlooked, because various strains of *Saccharomyces cerevisiae* respond differently to both glucose or acetate (Kirsop, 1956).

The cation of the acetate molecule, however, is also important, for, while the sodium and potassium salts are of the same order of activity, the former stimulates the formation of more four-spored asci. The magnesium salt has only about 80% of the activity of the potassium compound and both the barium and ammonium salts are comparatively inactive in this respect. Lactate, alone of the other Krebs cycle intermediates, was found to have any influence on sporulation (Kleyn, 1954).

A particularly interesting observation has been reported by Kirsop (1954) concerning the relationship of the cell concentration to the degree of sporulation. In this respect when washed yeast cells are suspended in distilled water which has been buffered to the critical pH value with a nonutilizable buffer, the number of cells producing spores is proportional to the number of cells per unit volume of the suspending fluid. Progressive reduction of the cell concentration increases the percentage of cells sporulating to a maximum beyond which further dilution leads to a rapid diminution of the level of sporulation.

It has been suggested that yeast autolysates can stimulate sporulation (Maneval, 1944; Lindegren and Hamilton, 1944), and that *Aspergillus niger* liberates into the medium a substance that stimulates the sporulation of "*Zygosaccharomyces*" as do autolysates of the yeast itself (Nickerson and Thiamann, 1941). In this connection it has been found that the stimulating effects of the *Aspergillus* extracts can be reproduced by riboflavin and sodium glutarate, although the concentrations of these substances in the fungal extract were unsufficient to account for its stimulatory properties (Nickerson and Thiamann, 1943). More recently Kirsop (1956) has shown that cell-free extracts from living yeast cells and from acetone-dried yeast preparations are extremely active, producing many more spores than did any of the other conventional techniques tested. Crude extracts in dilutions as low as 2–3 p.p.m. stimulate spore formation. The precise nature of the active factor is not known but, among other things, it is not retained by either acidic or basic ion exchange resins, is dialyzable, and is soluble in water and ethanol, but not in benzene, chloroform, or ether. No vitamin so far tested has been able to reproduce the activity of the crude extract.

9. Factors Influencing Production of Pseudomycelia

The cells of yeasts grown under favorable conditions are predominantly spherical, ovoid, apiculate, or ogive in shape but, under certain conditions, many yeasts are able to develop elongated cell formations known as pseudomycelia. The ability to produce this type of cell formation is used as a taxonomic criterion in the case of the nonascosporogenous group. Because of this, it is important that the description of the pseudomycelium should be defined and the definition of Lodder (1934) is worthy of note: "*True mycelia arise either as separate, long, thread-like cells that eventually branch, or as septate, branched filaments in which*

single limbs are separated by cross-walls in the filament. By pseudomycelium I understand septate, frequently branched filaments, in which
the long cells are formed one from another by budding." The name implies that a pseudomycelium closely resemble a true mycelium, but it is
common experience that many difficulties of interpreting observations
are encountered at the other end of the scale. In particular, it is often
difficult to decide just when elongation of the cell's major axis ceases to
be regarded as mere elongation and constitutes formation of a pseudomycelium and this is especially so in the case of yeasts which normally
develop in chains.

The examination of a large number of cultures maintained in the
British National Collection of Yeast Cultures has shown that there is
often a marked difference in the ability to produce a pseudomycelium
in different cultures of the same species. Furthermore yeasts, for which
the production of a pseudomycelium is not described as a characteristic
feature, may produce a rudimentary pseudomycelium at least as pronounced as that developed by certain cultures of yeast for which this
characteristic is a diagnostic feature. It would thus appear that the ability
to produce a pseudomycelium is a useful, but not necessarily a specific,
taxonomic character. The ability of certain strains of a species to produce
a pseudomycelium may, however, be a useful tool to separate these different strains. In this connection, Hough (1956) has found that under
specific conditions some strains of Saccharomyces cerevisiae can produce
a rudimentary pseudomycelium, whereas other strains fail to do so.

When cultures in the pseudomycelial phase are transferred to nutrient-
rich media, the cells usually revert to the yeast phase of reproduction and
this has suggested to many workers that the development of a pseudomycelium is associated with unfavorable cultural conditions.

Elongated cells and true pseudomycelia have been observed in cultures
which have been grown at temperatures appreciably below the optimum (Hansen, 1886; Levine and Ordal, 1946). Filamentous forms
are also frequently observed in old cultures, behavior which is regarded
as being due to staling of the medium and in this connection fusel oils
and higher alcohols are believed to be at least in part responsible for the
development of this phase of growth (Segal, 1938a,b). This opinion is
supported by the observations of Levan (1947) who showed that the
degree of pseudomycelium developed in media containing various alcohols is proportional to the number of carbon atoms in the alcohol; for
example, methanol and ethanol are very much less active than "pentonal"
and "octanol." Several other workers have reported that pseudomycelia
develop much more readily in media that are relatively poor sources of

nutrients and this is probably why corn meal-agar is so efficient a medium for this purpose. Another factor known to favor the development of filamentous forms is anaerobiosis and, for this reason, these forms of growth are more commonly found in liquid media than they are in the surface growth on the usual agar or gelatin cultures (Talice, 1930). This factor is used to stimulate the production of pseudomycelium on a solid medium; such a medium, either in a petri dish or on a microscope slide is inoculated with the test yeast, a portion of the inoculum then being covered with a cover slip. It is then observed that the portion of the culture beneath the cover glass produces a pseudomycelium more readily than the other part of the culture (Benham, 1931; Wickerham and Rettger, 1939a,b,c; Diddens and Lodder, 1942; Rivalier and Seydal 1932). The nature of the culture medium in which the yeast has been previously grown is also believed to influence the ability to develop a pseudomycelium. This phenomenon was clearly demonstrated by Connell and Skinner (1953) who showed that certain nonascosporogenous yeasts failed to develop a pseudomycelium when tested on corn meal-agar or beef peptone-gelatin stabs. However, after these yeasts had been maintained on a modified Sabouraud medium for 2–3 years and then transferred back to two test media, it was found that the yeast produced an abundance of filamentous forms, and that, further, the ability to do so was not lost in subsequent transfers to a number of different test substrates.

The most probable explanation for the development of this type of growth is that the cells retain their ability to produce new cellular material, but the mechanism controlling cell division becomes impaired Evidence for this hypothesis can be deduced from the following data (1) Yeasts of the genus *Candida*, characterized by their ability to produce pseudomycelium when grown in a synthetic medium containing glucose as the carbon source, reproduce entirely in the normal yeast phase; however, when the glucose is replaced by starch, glycogen, or dextrin a reduction in the amount of growth is observed and pseudomycelium production is extensive (Nickerson and Mankowski, 1953) (2) Mutant strains of *Candida albicans*, which exist entirely in the filamentous form under normal conditions, are able to accumulate and reduce tetrazolium dyes, whereas the parental strain, in the yeast phase accumulates but fails to reduce the dyes. However, when the parental strain is stimulated to produce pseudomycelium, these cells behave like the mutant. (3) The rates of growth and endogenous respiration, the nutrient requirement, and the polysaccharide content of the mutant and the parental culture are of the same order. It would then appear that, lthough synthesis of cellular material proceeds at the same rate in both he yeast phase and filamentous phase, it is the process of cell division which is disrupted; the reaction to the dyes indicates that the disrupting actor acts through, or is associated with, an alteration of the oxidation-eduction potential of the cell. (Nickerson, 1954).

Apart from the development of pseudomycelium both under natural onditions and in routine laboratory practice, it can be stimulated by pecific substances. Camphor, a substance commonly used to induce nutations in microorganisms, has been found to stimulate the develop-nent of filamentous forms in yeasts (Bauch, 1941, 1943a,b). Likewise, ublethal doses of penicillin induce the production of a high proportion of pseudomycelium, and it is interesting to note that this antibiotic is nown to interfere with cell division in bacteria. Of various salts, those f cobalt, and to a lesser extent those of boron, are known to stimulate his form of growth (Nickerson and van-Rij, 1949).

Sulfydryl compounds inhibit or reverse the formation of pseudomy-elium and even mutant yeasts which are normally filamentous can be nade to revert to the yeast phase when grown in the presence of cysteine. t has been established that this latter substance is a more active inhibi-or than is glutathione which in turn is more active than sodium thiogly-ollate (Nickerson and van-Rij, 1949; Nickerson, 1951).

Earlier it was mentioned that many yeasts aggregate to form flocs as he liquid cultures age and de Hemptinne (1949) suggested that the de-elopment of a pseudomycelium may provide nuclei around which in-lividual cells may aggregate so causing flocculation to occur. The exami-ation of a large number of top fermentation brewing yeasts has failed o substantiate this claim. In this connection, when yeasts which have locculated are removed from the wort medium and then suspended in naltose, the flocs are dispersed and no pseudomycelium is observed. Further, if these cells are washed and returned to their original medium, locculation of the cells again occurs.

10. Preservation of Yeast Cultures

The many factors controlling the growth of yeasts in their vegetative phase have been discussed above and, provided these conditions are atisfied, new cultures can be propagated simply by transferring a small quantity of the culture to fresh medium. It is not, however, always con-venient to maintain yeast cultures by continually subculturing at frequent intervals, especially when a large number of strains are being handled. In this connection the problem of storing yeasts for future reference was realized very early in the study of microorganisms, and even up to the present time yeasts are still stored by the same, or only slightly modified techniques devised by the pioneer workers early in the present century. Probably the oldest satisfactory method is to grow the yeast on a solid medium and, after active growth has ceased, to keep the culture at 1 to 18°C., in reasonably air-tight containers in order to prevent undue evaporation; cultures stored in such a manner have been found to be viable after keeping many years.

As early as 1909, Will reported that the majority of yeast cultures which he had preserved in a 10% sucrose solution, were viable when examined after 8 years. However, after this lapse of time the yeasts appeared to be degenerate and their activity was slow even after repeated subculture. This latter technique was also studied by Meisser (1911) who found that the cultures remained viable over a long period of time when they were kept at various temperatures up to 20°C. The technique is still in use although in the hands of some workers the results have proved somewhat less satisfactory, a result which can possibly be explained on the basis that the present-day commercial preparations of sugar are almost certainly purer than were those used by the original workers. It is interesting to note that a large number of the yeasts which have been stored in sucrose are able to either ferment or utilize this source of carbon. Consequently Owen (1949) advocates the preservation of yeast in 10% lactose, a carbohydrate rarely used by yeasts and further suggests that in the event of the yeast being able to ferment lactose some other nonutilizable carbohydrate should be substituted.

The principle of storing cultures under liquid paraffin was proposed by Lumiere and Chevrotier (1914) but was neglected until the last two decades. The recent renewed interest in this technique is due to its obvious advantages, namely that (a) no particular preliminary treatment of the culture is necessary, (b) no special apparatus or sealing device is necessary, (c) the culture can be transplanted at any time and the stock culture still maintained, and (d) there is no evidence of gross changes occurring in the stock culture. This technique has been quite widely applied for the maintenance of cultures of bacteria and molds, but comparatively few reports are available concerning yeasts. However, those of Schulz (1951), Azello et al. (1951), and Stibbens and Robbins (1949) indicate that the method is worthy of further investigation, particularly since the methods used by various workers all differ in detail. In general it would appear that satisfactory preservation can be attained if the following conditions be observed: (a) the cultures should be grown under environmental conditions as near to the optimal as practicable;

b) the paraffin should be good quality; (c) the cultures should not be stored at temperatures above 18–20°C.; (d) the paraffin should cover the culture to a depth of ½ inch; and (e) new cultures should be made into medium of the same composition as that of the stock culture.

A system which has proved satisfactory is that employed for the maintenance of the British National Collection of Yeast Cultures. The yeasts are grown in a liquid medium comprising malt extract, yeast extract, peptone, and glucose (Wickerham, 1951); after the period of active growth has passed, generally 48 hours at 25°C., the culture is tightly sealed in a screw-capped bottle and stored at between 1 to 4°C. The maximum period that such cultures may be kept has not been ascertained, but many cultures will certainly survive unaltered for 1 year. It is believed that the advantage of storage under such conditions is that fewer spores develop than is the case when the cultures are stored on a solid medium at room temperature and consequently, there is less likelihood of the cultures altering due to segregation of characters.

Freeze-drying (lyophilizing) techniques are now being extensively used for the preservation of bacteria and molds, but unfortunately it is once again noticeable that comparatively few reports are available of the application of this technique to the preservation of yeast cultures. Wickerham and Andreason (1942) preserved cultures both by the freeze-drying method and at the same time in stab cultures, and of the 384 cultures tested 93.8% of freeze-dried cultures and 96.4% of the stab cultures were alive after 6 months, while after 12 months 95.1% of the freeze-dried cultures were alive, whereas only 80% of stab cultures had survived. Atkin et al. (1949) found that, when freeze-dried cultures were "revitalized" after drying, up to 99.8% of the cells failed to survive. Furthermore, changes of the nutrilite requirements were observed in approximately 50% of the cultures. In general these workers observed that the tendency was for the stored yeasts to become more exacting, that is to require more nutrilites for growth. More recently Kirsop (1955) has also observed changes in "bios" requirement of freeze-dried yeasts but her studies showed that the change was towards less exacting requirements, that is the yeast no longer required nutrilites which previously were necessary for optimal growth. She also found that different yeasts vary in their sensitivity to freeze-drying procedures and furthermore that although the initial fall in the number of viable cells was high, very little further change occurred after nine months (see Table XIV). Evidence that other changes may result as a consequence of lyophilization has been presented by Subramaniam and Prahlada Rao (1951) who noted changes in the giant colony characters of a yeast which had been subjected to freeze-drying and believed such changes to be of a mutagenic nature. Many of the discrepancies noted in the different reports concerned with freeze-dried cultures may be due to vastly different technical procedures

TABLE XIV

AVERAGE PERCENTAGE VIABILITY OF YEASTS IN FREEZE-DRIED CULTURES[a]

Yeasts	No. of strains examined	% Viability	
		2 days after treatment	9 months after treatment
Saccharomyces	47	5.1	4.7
Saccharomyces cerevisiae	29	4.6	4.3
Saccharomyces carlsbergensis	8	8.1	5.6
Other *Saccharomyces* spp.	10	4.2	5.1
Debaromyces	4	42.5	26.5
Endomycopsis	2	3.0	0.8
Pichia	4	7.8	3.6
Hansenula	4	7.3	9.3
Schizosaccharomyces	1	27.3	10.6
Torulopsis	4	16.2	23.7
Cryptococcus	2	3.4	1.6
Candida	6	10.6	11.7
Rhodotorula	4	10.1	11.9
Kloeckera	4	8.5	6.1
Brettanomyces	1	0.03	0.0
	83	Average viability of all strains	
		8.6	7.6

[a] From Kirsop (1956).

employed. These problems are mentioned at some length in "Discussion on the Maintenance of Culture by Freeze-drying" (1954),[1] but in general it appears that (a) the cultures to be freeze-dried should be young and actively growing, (b) the incorporation of glucose in the suspending fluid is advantageous, (c) the drying process should be as rapid as possible, (d) desiccation should be carried out at low temperatures, and (e) the dried culture should be stored in an inert gas or vacuum in the dark at temperatures near 0°C.

[1] H. M. Stationery Office, London.

References

Adams, A. M. (1950). *Can. J. Research* **F28**, 413.

Adams, A. M., and Miller, J. J. (1954). *Can. J. Botany* **32**, 320.

Ahmad, M., Chaudhury, A. R., and Ahmad, K. U. (1954). *Mycologia* **46**, 708.

Atkin, L., and Gray, P. P. (1947). *Arch. Biochem.* **15**, 305.

Atkin, L., Williams, W. L., Schultz, A. S., and Frey, C. N. (1944). *Ind. Eng. Chem. Anal. Ed.* **16**, 67.

Atkin, L. A., Moses, W., and Gray, P. P. (1949). *J. Bacteriol.* **57**, 575.

Azello, L., Grant, V. Q., and Gulzke, M. A. (1951). *Arch. Dermatol. and Syphilol.* **63**, 747.

Baltatu, G. H. (1939). *Zentr. Bakteriol. Parasitenk. Abt. I* **101**, 196.

Barnett, J. A. (1956). Personal communication.

Barnett, J. A., and Ingram, M. (1955). *J. Appl. Bacteriol.* **18**, 131.

Barnett, J. A., and Swain, T. (1956). *Nature* **177**, 133.

Barnett, J. A., and Ingram, M., and Swain, T. (1956). *J. Gen. Microbiol.* **15**, 529.

Barton-Wright, E. C., and Thorne, R. S. W. (1949). *J. Inst. Brewing* **55**, 383.

Bauch, R. (1941). *Naturwissenschaften* **29**, 503.

Bauch, R. (1943a). *Ber. deut. botan. Ges.* **60**, 42.

Bauch, R. (1943b). *Arch. Microbiol.* **13**, 352.

Benham, R. W. (1931). *J. Infectious Diseases* **49**, 183.

Bowen, V. T., and Robinson, A. C. (1951). *Nature* **167**, 1032.

Burkholder, P. R., McVeigh, I., and Moyer, D. (1944). *J. Bacteriol.* **48**, 385.

Challinor, S. W., and Daniels, N. W. R. (1954). *Nature* **176**, 1267.

Challinor, S. W., and Rose, A. H. (1954). *Nature* **174**, 877.

Clark, N. A. (1922). *J. Phys. Chem.* **26**, 42.

Connell, G. H., and Skinner, C. E. (1953). *Mycopathol. et Mycol. Appl.* **6**, 65.

Damlé, W. R., and Thorne, R. S. W. (1949). *J. Inst. Brewing* **55**, 13.

Devereux, E. D., and Tanner, F. W. (1927). *J. Bacteriol.* **14**, 317.

Diddens, H. A., and Lodder, J. (1942). "Die Hefesammlang Des Centraal-Bureau Voor Schimmelcultures." II Teil., Die Anaskosporogenen Hefen, Tweite Halfte, N.V. Noord-Hollandsche Uitgevers Maatschappij, Amsterdam.

Eddy, A. A. (1955a). *J. Inst. Brewing* **61**, 307.

Eddy, A. A. (1955b). *J. Gen. Microbiol.* **13**, xiii.

Eddy, A. A., and Kirsop, B. (1955). *J. Inst. Brewing* **61**, 382.

Ehrensvärd, G. C. H., Sperber, E., Saluste, E., Reio, L., and Stjernholm, R. (1947). *J. Biol. Chem.* **169**, 759.

Elvehjem, C. A. (1931). *J. Biol. Chem.* **90**, 111.

Etchells, J. L., and Jones, I. D. (1946). *Am. J. Public Health* **36**, 1112.

Fels, G., and Cheldeton, V. H. (1949). *Arch. Biochem.* **22**, 402.

Finn, R. K. (1955). *J. Bacteriol.* **70**, 352.

Fukui, Saburo (1955). *J. Fermentation Technol. (Japan)* **33**, 1.

Fulmer, E. I., Nelson, V. E., and Sherwood, F. F. (1921). *J. Amer. Chem. Soc.* **43**, 191.

Gale, E. F., and Taylor, E. S. (1946). *Nature* **157**, 549.

Greaves, J. E., Zobell, C. E., and Greaves, J. D. (1928). *J. Bacteriol.* **16**, 409.

Gruber-Oberfeuchtner, J. (1953). *Mitt. Vers. Anst. Gärungsgeer.* **I**, 68.

Hall, J. F. (1954a). *J. Inst. Brewing* **60**, 482.

Hall, J. F. (1954b). *J. Inst. Brewing* **60**, 486.

Hansen, E. C. (1883). *Compt. rend. trav. lab. Carlsberg* **2**, 13.

Hansen, E. C. (1886). *Medd. Carlsberg Lab.* **I**, 168.

Hanson, A. M., and Baldwin, I. L. (1941). *J. Bacteriol.* **41**, 94.

Hartelius, V. (1956). *Compt. rend. trav. lab. Carlsberg, Sér. physiol.* **25**, 382.

Hartelius, V., and Ditlevsen, E. (1956). *Compt. rend. trav. lab. Carlsberg, Sér. physiol.* **25**, 369.

Hebert, A. (1907). *Bull. soc. chim. France* **I**, 1026.

de Hemptinne, Y. (1949). *Fermentatio, No. 4* 1949, 58.

Hinz, C. F., and Harris, J. O. (1954). *Arch. Biochem. and Biophys.* **48**, 261.

Hough, J. S. (1956). Personal communication.

Hough, J. S., and Morris, E. O. (1957). *J. Inst. Brewing.* In press.

Ingram, M. (1955a). "Introduction to the Biology of Yeasts," p. 169. Pitman, London.

Ingram, M. (1955b). "Introduction to the Biology of Yeasts," p. 157. Pitman, London.

Jackson, S., and Kilkenny, B. C. (1951). *J. Chem. Soc.* **2**, 1561.

Jennison, M. W., and Wadsworth, G. P. (1940). *J. Bacteriol.* **39**, 389.

Ju-Hwo Chu, E. (1948). *Chemistry & Industry, No. 8* 1948, 115.

Ketterer, H. (1956). *Brauwissenschaft*, **14**, 59.

Kilkenny, B. C., and Hinshelwood, C. N. (1951). *Proc. Roy. Soc.* **B 138**, 375.

Kirsop, B. H. (1955). *J. Inst. Brewing* **61**, 466.

Kirsop, B. H. (1954). *J. Inst. Brewing* **60**, 393.

Kirsop, B. H. (1956). Ph.D. Thesis. "Studies of Sporulation in the Genus Saccharomyces," Univ. of London.

Kitamikado, M., and Ishibashi, M. (1955). *J. Soc. Brewing (Japan)* **50**, 165.

Kleinzeller, A. (1948). *Advances in Enzymol.* **8**, 299.

Kleyn, J. G. (1954). *Wallerstein Labs. Communs.* **17**, 91.

Kondrat'eva, T. M. (1940). *Mikrobiologiya* **9**, 114.

Krishnaswamy, P. R., and Giri, K. V. (1954). *J. Sci. Ind. Research (India)* **B13**, 110.

Kufferath, H. (1929). *Ann. Soc. Zymol.* **1**, 214.

Lasnitski, A., and Szorenzi, F. (1943). *Biochem. J.* **28**, 1678.

Leonian, L. H., and Lilly, V. G. (1942a). *Am. J. Botany* **29**, 439.

Leonian, L. H., and Lilly, V. G. (1942b). *Science* **95**, 658.

Lesh, J. B., Underkoler, L. A., and Fulmer, E. I. (1938). *J. Amer. Chem. Soc.* **60**, 2505.

Levan, A. (1947). *Hereditas* **33**, 456.

Levine, S., and Ordal, Z. J. (1946). *J. Bacteriol.* **52**, 687.

Liener, I. E., and Buchanan, D. L. (1951). *J. Bacteriol.* **61**, 527.

Liese, W. (1926). *Z. Hyg. Infektionskrankh.* **105**, 483.

Lindegren, C. C. (1949). "The Yeast Cell, Its Genetics and Cytology," p. 151. Educational Publ., St. Louis.

Lindegren, C. C., and Haddad, S. A. (1954). *Genetica* **28**, 45.

Lindegren, C. C., and Hamilton, E. (1944). *Botan. Gaz.* **105**, 316.

Lindegren, C. C., and Lindegren, G. (1944). *Botan. Gaz.* **105**, 304.

Lochhead, A. G., and Landerkin, G. B. (1941). *J. Bacteriol.* **42**, 18.

Lochhead, A. G., and Landerkin, G. B. (1942). *J. Bacteriol.* **44**, 343.

Lodder, J. (1934). "Die Anascosporogenen Hefen." (Erste Hälfte) N.V. Noord-Hollandsche Uitgevers, Maatschappij, Amsterdam.

Lodder, J., and Kreger-van Rij, N. J. W. (1952). "The Yeasts, a Taxonomic Study," North Holland Publ. Co., Amsterdam.

Lodder, J., and Kreger-van Rij, N. J. W. (1954). *Lab. Practice* 3, 483.

Lodge, R. M., and Hinshelwood, C. N. (1939). *J. Chem. Soc.* 11, 1692.

Lodge, R. M., and Hinshelwood, C. N. (1943). *J. Chem. Soc.* 1, 213.

Lumiere, A., and Chevrotier, J. (1914). *Compt. rend.* 158, 1820.

Lwoff, A., and Monod, J. (1947). *Ann. inst. Pasteur* 73, 323.

Malkov, A. M. (1950). *Doklady Akad. Nauk. S.S.S.R.* 72, 85; (1950). *Chem. Abstr.* 44, 10039.

Maneval, W. E. (1924). *Botan. Gaz.* 78, 122.

Massart, L., and Horens, J. (1953). *Enzymologia* 15, 359.

McHargue, J. S., and Calfee, R. K. (1931). *Plant Physiol.* 6, 559.

McIlwain, H., Fildes, P., Gladstone, G. P., and Knight, B. C. J. G. (1939). *Biochem. J.* 33, 223.

McVeigh, I., and Bracken, E. (1955). *Mycologia* 47, 13.

Meissner, R. (1911). *Ber. württem b. Wein b. Vers. Anst.* 7, 21.

Metcalfe, G., and Chayen, S. (1954). *Nature* 174, 841.

Miller, E. J., and Harrison, J. S. (1950). *Nature* 166, 1035.

Miller, G., and Aschner, M. (1952). *J. Gen. Microbiol.* 6, 361.

Miller, J. J., and Halpern, C. (1956). *Can. J. Microbiol.* 2, 519.

Miller, W. L. (1936). *Trans. Roy. Soc. Can. III* 33, 99.

Minagawa, T. (1955). *Biochim. et Biophys. Acta* 16, 539.

Moat, A. G., and Emmons, E. K. (1954). *J. Bacteriol.* 68, 687.

Monod, J. (1949). *Ann. Rev. Microbiol.* 3, 375.

Morel, M. (1941). *Ann. inst. Pasteur* 67, 449.

Morgan, J. F., Morton, H. J., and Parker, R. C. (1951). *Growth* 15, 11.

Morris, E. O. (1955). *J. Sci. Food Agr.* 6, 316.

Morris, E. O., and Eddy, A. A. (1956). *J. Inst. Brewing* 62, 466.

Morris, E. O., and Hough, J. S. (1956). *J. Inst. Brewing* 62, 34.

Mrak, E. M., Phaff, H. J., and Douglas, H. C. (1942). *Science* 96, 432.

Nickerson, W. J. (1944). *Mycologia* 36, 224.

Nickerson, W. J. (1951). *Trans. N.Y. Acad. Sci.* 13, 140.

Nickerson, W. J. (1954). *J. Gen. Physiol.* 37, 483.

Nickerson, W. J., and Mankowski, Z. T. (1953). *Am. J. Botany* 40, 584.

Nickerson, W. J., and Thiamann, K. V. (1941). *Am. J. Botany* 28, 617.

Nickerson, W. J., and Thiamann, K. V. (1943). *Am. J. Botany* 30, 94.

Nickerson, W. J., and Kreger-van Rij, N. J. W. (1949). *Biochim. et Biophys. Acta* 3, 461.

Nielsen, N., and Nilsson, N. G. (1950). *Arch. Biochem.* 25, 316.

Ochmann, W. (1932). *Zeutr. Bakteriol. Parasitank. Abt. I* 86, 458.

Oehlkers, F. (1923). *Ber. deut. botan. Ges.* 41, 31.

Olson, B. H., and Johnson, M. J. (1949). *J. Bacteriol.* 57, 235.

Oppenoorth, W. F. F. (1956). *Nature* 178, 992.

Owen, W. L. (1949). U.S. Patent, 2,624,692.

Perlman, D., and O'Brien, E. (1954). *J. Bacteriol.* 68, 167.

Rahn, O., Iske, B., and Zemgalis, R. (1951). *Growth* 15, 267.

Rainbow, C. (1948). *Nature* 162, 572.

Rainbow, C. (1951). *Nature* 167, 558.

Rich, M. A., and Stern, A. M. (1956). *Can. J. Microbiol.* 2, 453.

Richards, O. W. (1925). *J. Am. Chem. Soc.* 47, 1671.

Richards, O. W. (1932a). *Arch. Protistenk.* 78, 263.

Richards, O. W. (1932b). *J. Biol. Chem.* 96, 405.

Richards, O. W. (1934). *Cold Spring Harbor Symposia Quant. Biol.* 2, 157.

Richards, O. W., and Troutman, M. C. (1940). *J. Bacteriol.* 39, 739.

Rivalier, E., and Seydel, S. (1932). *Ann. parasitol. humaine et comparée* 10, 442.

Roberts, E. R., and Wilson, T. G. G. (1954). *Nature* 174, 795.

Rose, A. H., and Nickerson, W. J. (1956). *J. Bacteriol.* 72, 324.

Rugosa, M. (1943). *J. Bacteriol.* 46, 435.

Saito, K. (1916). *J. Coll. Sci. Imp. Univ. Tokyo* 39, 1.

Sampath, S. (1944). *Current Sci. (India)* 13, 47.

Sarett, H. P., and Cheldelin, V. H. (1945). *J. Bacteriol.* 49, 31.

Schultz, A. S., and Atkin, L. (1947). *Arch. Biochem.* 14, 369.

Schultz, A. S., Atkin, L., and Frey, C. N. (1940). *J. Bacteriol.* 40, 339.

Schultz, A. S., and McManus, D. K. (1950). *Arch. Biochem.* 25, 401.

Schultz, A. S., McManus, D. K., and Pomper, S. (1949). *Arch. Biochem.* 22, 412.

Schultz, A. S., and Pomper, S. (1948). *Arch. Biochem.* 19, 184.

Schulz, K. L. (1951). *Brauwissenschaft, No. 10* 1951, 161.

Segal, R. B. (1938a). *Mikrobiologiya* 7, 93.

Segal, R. B. (1938b). *Mikrobiologiya* 8, 466.

Seliber, G., and Katznelson, R. (1927). *Compt. rend. soc. biol.* 97, 449.

Seliber, G., and Katznelson, R. (1929). *Protoplasma* 7, 204.

Sheffner, A. L., and Grabow, J. (1953). *J. Bacteriol.* 66, 192.

Singh, K., Agarwal, R. N., and Peterson, W. H. (1948). *Arch. Biochem.* 18, 181.

Skar, O. (1934). *Z. Infektionskrankh. parasit. Krankh. u. Hyg. Hanstiere* 46, 110.

Smith, R. H. (1951). *J. Gen. Microbiol.* 5, 772.

Sperber, E. (1945). *Arkiv. Kemi. Mineral. Geol.* A21, 1.

Squire, R. M., and Hartsell, S. E. (1955). *J. Bacteriol.* 69, 226.

Stantial, H. (1935). *Trans. Roy. Soc. Can. III* 29, 175.

Stelling-Dekker, N. M. (1931). "Die Hefesammlung Des Central-Bureau voor Schimmelcultures," Teil I, Die Sporogenen Hefen, Noord Hollandsche Uitgevers Maatschappij, Amsterdam.

Stibbens, M. E., and Robbins, W. J. (1949). *Mycologia* 41, 632.

Stovall, W. K., and Bulotz, A. (1932a). *J. Infectious Diseases* 50, 73.

Stovall, W. K., and Bulotz, A. (1932b). *Am. J. Public Health* 22, 493.

Strausz, W. (1930). *Zentr. Bakteriol. Parasitenk. Abt.* 115, 225.

Subramaniam, M. K. (1945). *Current Sci. (India)* 14, 234.

Subramaniam, M. K., and Prahlado Rao, L. S. (1951). *Experientia* 7, 98.

Sugata, H., and Koch, F. C. (1926). *Plant Physiol.* 1, 337.

Talice, R. V. (1930). *Ann. parasitol. humaine et comparée* 8, 394.

Thorne, R. S. W. (1941). *J. Inst. Brewing* 47, 255.

Thorne, R. S. W. (1944). *J. Inst. Brewing* 50, 186.

Thorne, R. S. W. (1946a). *J. Inst. Brewing* 52, 5.

Thorne, R. S. W. (1946b). *J. Inst. Brewing* 52, 15.

Thorne, R. S. W. (1949). *J. Inst. Brewing* 55, 18.

Todd, R. L., and Herrmann, W. W. (1936). *J. Bacteriol.* 32, 89.

Topley, W. W. C., and Wilson, G. S. (1948a). "Principles of Bacteriology and Immunology," Vol. I, p. 81. Arnold, London.

Topley, W. W. C., and Wilson, G. S. (1948b). "Principles of Bacteriology and Immunology," Vol. I, p. 89. Arnold, London.

Townsend, G. F., and Lindegren, C. C. (1953). *Cytologia* (*Tokyo*) **18**, 183.

Townsend, G. F., and Lindegren, C. C. (1954). *J. Bacteriol.* **67**, 481.

Tremaine, J. H., and Miller, J. J. (1954). *Botan. Gaz.* **115**, 311.

Veibel S. (1950). *In* "The Enzymes" (J. B. Sumner and K. Myrbäck, eds.), Vol. I, p. 583. Academic Press, New York.

Wagner, E. (1928). *Zentr. Bakteriol. Parasitenk Abt. II* **75**, 4.

Walters, L. S., and Thiselton, M. R. (1953). *J. Inst. Brewing* **56**, 401.

Webb, J. I.; cited by Eddy, A. A. (1956). *Brewers Guardian* **85** (No. 3), 3.

Welten, H. (1914–1915a). *Mikrokosmos* **8**, 3.

Welten, H. (1914–1915b). *Mikrokosmos*, **8**, 14.

White, J. (1953). *J. Inst. Brewing* **59**, 470.

White, J. (1954). "Yeast Technology," p. 32. Chapman & Hall, London.

White, J., and Munns, D. J. (1951). *J. Inst. Brewing* **58**, 175.

White, J., and Munns, D. J. (1953a). *Am. Brewer* **86**, 29.

White, J., and Munns, D. J. (1953b). *J. Inst. Brewing* **59**, 405.

White, J., and Munns, D. J. (1954). *Am. Brewer* **87**, 35.

Wickerham, L. J. (1946). *J. Bacteriol.* **52**, 293.

Wickerham, L. J. (1951). *U.S. Dept. Agric. Tech. Bull.* No. 1029.

Wickerham, L. J., and Andreasen, A. A. (1942). *Wallerstein Labs. Communs.* **5**, 165.

Wickerham, L. J., and Burton, K. A. (1948). *J. Bacteriol.* **56**, 363.

Wickerham, L. J., Flickinger, M. H., and Burton, K. M. (1946). *J. Bacteriol.* **52**, 611.

Wickerham, L. J., and Rettger, L. F. (1939a). *J. Trop. Med. Hyg.* **42**, 174.

Wickerham, L. J., and Rettger, L. F. (1939b). *J. Trop. Med. Hyg.* **42**, 187.

Wickerham, L. J., and Rettger, L. F. (1939c). *J. Trop. Med. Hyg.* **42**, 204.

Wildier, E. (1901). *Cellule* **18**, 313.

Wiles, A. E. (1953). *J. Inst. Brewing* **59**, 265.

Will, H. (1909). *Zentr. Bakteriol. Parasitank. Abt. I* **24**, 405.

Williams, R. J., Eakin, R. E., and Snell, E. E. (1940). *J. Amer. Chem. Soc.* **62**, 1204.

Wilson, G. S., Wright, R. S., Hendrey, C. B., Cowell, M. P., and Maiser, I. (1935). *Spec. Rep. Ser. med. Res. Coun.*, London, No. 26.

Windisch, S. (1938). *Arch. Mikrobiol.* **9**, 551.

CHAPTER VII

Fermentation and Respiration[1]

F. F. NORD[2] AND S. WEISS

1. Introduction

It took more than 100 years of research by numerous investigators to unravel the sequence of enzymic reactions involved in the fermentation of carbohydrates by yeast to alcohol and carbon dioxide. The pathway to the final destination has been fraught with difficulties, frustrations, and many scientific arguments which naturally led to the proposal of various hypotheses. From this conglomeration, there has gradually emerged a clarified picture which integrates both past and present data into a coherent whole. It should be kept in mind, however, that even the latest concepts may have to be reinterpreted and extended as additional evidence arises.

Many varied approaches to the problem were attempted to gain an insight into the detailed mechanism of yeast fermentation. The type of

[1] The following abbreviations will be used: Embden-Meyerhof-Parnas: EMP; adenosine triphosphate: ATP; diphosphopyridine nucleotide: DPN; reduced diphosphopyridine nucleotide: DPNH; uridine diphosphate glucose: UDPG; uridine diphosphate galactose: UDPGa; uridine-triphosphate: UTP; hexose monophosphate pathway: HMP; triphosphopyridine nucleotide: TPN; coenzyme A: CoA.
[2] Contribution No. 331. Dedicated to the memory of Carl Neuberg (1877–1956).

experiments employed depended on the era and the state of biochemical knowledge at that time. For example, the earliest workers were mainly interested in the quantitative aspects of yeast fermentation. Thus, the basic chemical equation expressing the changes that occurred during the dissimilation of carbohydrate was first put forward by Gay-Lussac in 1815:

$$C_6H_{12}O_6 \rightarrow 2C_2H_5OH + 2CO_2$$

The next stage began in 1897 when the Buchners and M. Hahn prepared the first yeast juice and showed that fermentation without intact yeast cells was possible. This discovery made the application of modern enzymological techniques to yeast juices feasible so that individual enzyme systems could be purified, isolated, and studied. As a consequence of these *in vitro* investigations, a series of enzymic reactions representing the dissimilation of sugar to alcohol was proposed, in which the participation of phosphorus was considered as indispensable. So great was the emphasis placed on this phase sequence, that it soon appeared to be the *sole* pathway for carbohydrate breakdown in yeast (see Meyerhof, 1948).

However, even during this particular experimental era, strong arguments were advanced against such a claim (see Nord, 1940). For example, the question arose whether such a series of reactions obtained from cell-free extracts or artificial enzyme systems constituted a mirror image of the exact steps occurring within the living cell. Furthermore, did it represent the only metabolic pathway which the microorganism could efficiently utilize for catabolic purposes, or were there other metabolic routes by which dissimilation of the same substrate could occur? These controversial questions remained unsettled, even though disturbing reports by a small band of hardy investigators appeared regularly on the scientific horizon, indicative of multiple or even different dissimilatory pathways in microorganisms. Strangely enough, their objections were overruled in favor of the then existing unilateral concept with the consequence that this one-pathway contention became the prevailing mode of thinking.

That these investigators were correct in their viewpoint for the existence of multiple and even nonphosphorylating pathways in microorganisms is amply justified by recent experiments. For with the advent of radioactive tracer techniques, it has been possible to delve more easily into the complex reaction mechanics of living organisms with the result that today the existence of alternate pathways is a generally accepted fact. Moreover, it is now solidly established that the Embden-Parnasleyerhof route is not an exclusive universal process, since, for example, ertain microorganisms can ferment glucose by a nonphosphorylating athway, while others cleave the carbohydrate molecule in a manner ifferent from the normal glycolysis.

2. Concept of the Phase Sequence of Alcoholic Fermentation

The fermentation of carbohydrates by yeast is an anaerobic process hich leads to the formation of ethanol, an incompletely degraded end roduct. That this optional anaerobic mode of life is not the most efficient ne for the organism is demonstrated by the following equations which ompare the amount of calories liberated under varying degrees of oxiation:

1)
Anaerobic Oxidation
$$C_6H_{12}O_6 \rightarrow 2C_2H_5OH + 2CO_2 + 22 \text{ kg. cal.}$$
2)
Partial Aerobic Oxidation
$$2C_6H_{12}O_6 + 9O_2 \rightarrow 6(COOH)_2 + 6H_2O + 473 \text{ kg. cal.}$$
3)
Complete Aerobic Oxidation
$$C_6H_{12}O_6 \rightarrow 6CO_2 + 6H_2O + 673 \text{ kg. cal.}$$

Hence, under anaerobic conditions, yeast must ferment more sugar han is necessary under other conditions to yield the required energy to ive. In practice, the actual fermentation process is more complex than quation (1) would imply, for the final products (ethanol and carbon lioxide) account for only 95% of the glucose utilized. Pasteur (1872) btained glycerol (3%) and succinic acid (0.6%) as normal constituents f yeast fermentation and other investigators have also detected traces of cetaldehyde, acetic acid, lactic acid, and fusel oil.

It should be remembered that there is a similarity between glycolysis n muscle and anaerobic fermentation in yeast with the result that information derived from one source has in many instances been applied to he other.

The series of enzymic reactions representing the fermentation of arbohydrate by yeast as it is generally considered today is outlined at he top of page 326.

For the sake of clarity, each reaction in the above phase sequence will be discussed separately.

(1) *Glycogen* ⇆ *Glucose-1-phosphate* (Cremer-Cori ester)

Cremer in 1899 was the first to observe the synthesis of glycogen in yeast extracts containing 10% or more of fermentable sugars. Further work (Parnas and Baranowski, 1935; Parnas, 1937) showed that glycogen was phosphorylated to a hexose-6-phosphate, but this latter product was

EMBDEN-PARNAS-MEYERHOF SCHEME

Glycogen

H_3PO_4 $\uparrow\downarrow$ phosphorylase

Glucose-1-phosphate (Cremer-Cori ester)

hexokinase $\uparrow\downarrow$ phosphoglucomutase

Glucose $\rightleftharpoons$ Glucose-6-phosphate (Robison ester)

phosphatase $\uparrow\downarrow$

phosphohexoisomerase

hexokinase

Fructose $\rightleftharpoons$ Fructose-6-phosphate (Neuberg ester)

phosphatase $\uparrow\downarrow$ phosphohexokinase

Fructose-1,6-diphosphate (Harden-Young ester)

$\uparrow\downarrow$ aldolase

Dihydroxyacetone $\rightleftharpoons$ 3-D-Glyceraldehyde phosphate
phosphate   isomerase   (Fischer-Baer ester)

$\uparrow\downarrow$ phosphoglyceraldehyde dehydrogenase $PO_4^=$

1,3-Diphosphoglyceric acid

$\uparrow\downarrow$ ADP

3-D-Phosphoglyceric acid

$\uparrow\downarrow$ phosphoglyceromutase

2-Phosphoglyceric acid

$\uparrow\downarrow$ enolase

DPN·H

Lactic acid $\rightleftharpoons$ Pyruvic acid $\rightleftharpoons$ 2-Phosphoenol pyruvic acid

$\downarrow$ carboxylase

Acetaldehyde + CO_2

$\updownarrow$ DPNH

Ethanol

later identified (Ostern et al., 1936) as a mixture of glucose-6-phosphate and fructose-6-phosphate (the so-called Embden ester). That another phospho-sugar, glucose-1-phosphate, existed prior to the formation of glucose-6-phosphate was proven in experiments using dialyzed muscle extracts and glycogen (Cori et al., 1937, 1938a). While this reaction is reversible in yeast extracts (Schäffner and Specht, 1938; Kiessling, 1939) a catalytic amount of glycogen is necessary for the synthesis of the polysaccharide (Cori and Cori, 1939). The equilibrium constant of this reaction is dependent on the pH (Cori and Cori, 1940; Hanes, 1940a), but at all times it is in favor of the synthesis of glycogen. Although phosphorylases are present in yeast, glycogen itself cannot act as the sole carbon source in vivo, since the cells are unable to excrete the necessary amylases to dissimilate the oligosaccharide into simpler fragments.

(2) Glucose-1-phosphate $\rightleftharpoons$ Glucose-6-phosphate

phosphoglucomutase

The enzyme phosphoglucomutase is found in yeast and many tissues (Cori et al., 1938a) and has been crystallized from rabbit muscle (Najjar

948). Earlier studies indicated that the above reaction is reversible Sutherland et al., 1941; Colowick and Sutherland, 1942), requiring the presence of either magnesium, manganese or cobalt ions to proceed (Cori t al., 1938b). However, the exact mechanism explaining the transfer of he phosphate group from the 1 to the 6 position of glucose has only ecently been elucidated.

The first inkling came with the discovery that α-1,6-glucose diphosphate functions as a coenzyme in the over-all reaction (Leloir et al., 1948; Caputto et al., 1948; Cardini et al., 1949). These results were substantiated in radioactive experiments using P^{32} and C^{14} (Sutherland and associates, 1949a) and further isotopic studies with P^{32} furnished additional basic information concerning the mechanics of this reaction (Jagannathan and Luck, 1949). These workers observed an exchange between a labeled phosphate group in the enzyme and glucose-1-phosphate. The experiments of Najjar and Pullman (1954) finally settled the question of not only how the phosphate group is transferred but also how α-1,6-diphosphate participates in this reaction. They found that two forms of phosphoglucomutase are concerned: (a) a phosphoenzyme and (b) a dephosphoenzyme. In the first instance, the phosphate group can be transferred to either glucose-1-phosphate or glucose-6-phosphate, yielding in either case, glucose-1,6-diphosphate. The latter then can react with the dephospho-enzyme, giving glucose-6-phosphate and the phospho-enzyme again glucose-1-phosphate can also arise by this reaction). These results can be represented as follows:

1)   Glucose-1-phosphate + phospho-enzyme $\rightleftharpoons$ Glucose-1,6-diphosphate
                                                      + dephospho-enzyme
2)   Glucose-1,6-diphosphate + dephospho-enzyme $\rightleftharpoons$ Glucose-6-phosphate
                                                      + phospho-enzyme

By combining these reactions, the over-all result is:

Glucose-1-phosphate $\rightleftharpoons$ Glucose-6-phosphate

This enzyme is not specific for glucose-1-phosphate or glucose-6-phosphate, as it will catalyze in a similar manner the transfer of phosphate groups from mannose-1-phosphate to mannose-6-phosphate (Leloir, 1951b) and ribose-1-phosphate to ribose-5-phosphate (Guarino and Sable, 1954; Klenow, 1953). Moreover, recent studies (Klenow and Emberland, 1955) suggest that glucose-1,6-diphosphate, in the presence of phosphoglucomutase, may act as a source of additional phosphate groups for some phospho-sugars.

(3) *Glucose-6-phosphate* $\underset{\text{phosphohexoseisomerase}}{\rightleftharpoons}$ *Fructose-6-phosphate*

Lohmann (1933) studied this enzymic reaction and showed that a equilibrium, the mixture consisted of 70% of glucose-6-phosphate an 30% of fructose-6-phosphate. Even though the enzyme is apparentl widely distributed (Hanes, 1940a,b; Somers and Cosby, 1945) little i known concerning the mechanism of this isomerization *in vivo*.

These two phosphohexoses can also arise by another enzymic path way in yeast, namely, via the direct phosphorylation of glucose and fruc tose by adenosine triphosphate (ATP), magnesium ions, and the er zyme hexokinase (Berger *et al.*, 1946). For example:

(1) $$\text{Glucose} + \text{ATP} \xrightarrow[\text{hexokinase}]{\text{Mg}^{++}} \text{Glucose-6-phosphate} + \text{ADP}$$

(2) $$\text{Fructose} + \text{ATP} \xrightarrow[\text{hexokinase}]{\text{Mg}^{++}} \text{Fructose-6-phosphate} + \text{ADP}$$

Apparently only the furanose form of fructose can yield the phos phohexose (Gottschalk, 1943; Hopkins and Horwood, 1950). This en zyme has been crystallized from yeast (Berger *et al.*, 1946; Kunitz an McDonald, 1946; Bailey and Webb, 1948) and although the equilibriun for this reaction is far to the right, recent experiments with glucose-C^1 and C^{14} labeled glucose-6-phosphate indicate that it is reversible to a limited extent (Gamble and Najjar, 1954, 1955). Hexokinase will als catalyze the phosphorylation of other sugars such as mannose (Berge *et al.*, 1946), glucosamine (Brown, 1951), and 2-deoxy-D-glucos (Cramer and Woodward, 1952).

(4) $$\textit{Fructose-6-phosphate} + \text{ATP} \underset{phosphofructokinase}{\overset{Mg^{++}}{\rightleftharpoons}} \textit{Fructose-1,6-diphosphate}$$

Fructose-6-phosphate, formed either directly from fructose or from glucose-6-phosphate, is converted in the presence of ATP, magnesiun ions, and the enzyme phosphofructokinase (Taylor, 1951) to fructose-1,6 diphosphate (Ostern *et al.*, 1936; von Euler and Adler, 1935; Lutwak Mann and Mann, 1935). ATP is not specific in the above reaction fo Ling and Lardy (1954) found that uridine triphosphate and inosin triphosphate can also serve as phosphate donors. It has not been con clusively demonstrated whether complete reversibility between th mono- and diphosphofructose exists.

(5) $$\textit{Fructose 1,6-diphosphate}$$
$$\big\updownarrow \textit{aldolase}$$
$$\text{D-3-\textit{Phosphoglyceraldehyde}} \underset{isomerase}{\rightleftharpoons} \textit{Dihydroxyacetone phosphate}$$

Meyerhof and Lohmann (1934) found that the enzyme aldolase catalyzed the cleavage of fructose-1,6-diphosphate into two moles of a phosphotriose identified as dihydroxyacetone phosphate. However, it was later shown (Meyerhof et al., 1936) that not one but two trioses, dihydroxyacetone phosphate and 3-phosphoglyceraldehyde are formed simultaneously. These compounds in the presence of another enzyme, isomerase, come to equilibrium with each other at which time there is present about 95% of the ketone and 5% of the aldehyde (Meyerhof and Kiessling, 1935a, and Meyerhof and Junowicz-Kocholaty, 1942).

The reaction catalyzed by aldolase is reversible (Meyerhof et al., 1936) and the purified enzyme has been obtained from many sources such as yeast (Warburg and Christian, 1943; Warburg, 1948), rat (Warburg and Christian, 1943), rabbit (Taylor et al., 1948), bacteria (Bard and Gunsalus, 1950) and peas (Stumpf, 1948). Apparently the isolated aldolases are not identical since the enzymes from yeast and bacteria are inhibited by metal binders while those from peas and muscle are not. The reduced enzymic activities of the yeast and bacterial aldolases can be restored by the addition of certain divalent ions such as copper, cobalt, iron, or zinc.

It should be briefly mentioned here that these two cleavage products of fructose-1,6-diphosphate (dihydroxyacetone phosphate and 3-phosphoglyceraldehyde), in addition to being the intermediates in the dissimilation of hexose to ethanol, have assumed another important role by the recent discoveries of their pivotal positions in the hexose monophosphate pathway for the oxidation of glucose. These reactions will be discussed later under aerobic oxidation by yeast.

Even though the equilibrium is so far in favor of the dihydroxyacetone phosphate (e.g., 95% present at equilibrium), further dissimilation occurs via the 3-phosphoglyceraldehyde since the ultimate end product is 3-phosphoglyceric acid.

The initial experiments of Needham and Pillai (1937) on muscle extracts, followed by other studies (Meyerhof et al., 1937, 1938a,b; Green et al., 1937) on yeast and muscle, provided the necessary information to explain the oxidation of 3-phosphoglyceraldehyde, summarized in the equation:

$$\text{3-D-Phosphoglyceraldehyde} + PO_4^= + DPN^+ + ADP \rightleftharpoons \text{3-D-Phosphoglyceric}$$
$$\text{acid} + DPNH + ATP$$

However, later work (Negelein and Brömel, 1939a; Warburg and Christian, 1939a,b) showed that this oxidation takes place in two distinct steps. In the first phase, 3-D-phosphoglyceraldehyde is oxidized to 1,3-

diphosphoglyceric acid in the presence of the enzyme, 3-D-phospho glyceraldehyde dehydrogenase, inorganic phosphate, and DPN:

3-D-Phosphoglyceraldehyde $+$ DPN$^+$ $+$ PO$_4^=$ $\rightleftharpoons$ 1,3-Diphosphoglyceric
$$\text{acid} + \text{DPNH} + \text{H}$$

The above equation depicts both a phosphorylation and an oxidation Initially it was thought (Negelein and Brömel, 1939a,b; Warburg and Christian, 1939a,b) that the addition of phosphate to the aldehyde oc curred first to yield 1,3-diphosphoglyceraldehyde, but later evidenc (Drabkin and Meyerhof, 1945; Meyerhof and Oesper, 1947) indicatec that the latter compound did not exist during the oxidation. Recent ex periments by many investigators have shown that the oxidation of th aldehyde precedes phosphorylation.

This alternative mechanism is based on the intermediate formatio of a thiol ester. Krimsky and Racker (1952) found that glutathion was a firmly bound group of the 3-phosphoglyceraldehyde dehydrogenas molecule and by applying previous findings of the glyoxalase enzym system (Racker, 1951) to the oxidation of 3-phosphoglyceraldehyde, the proposed the following series of reactions (Krimsky and Racker, 1952 1955):

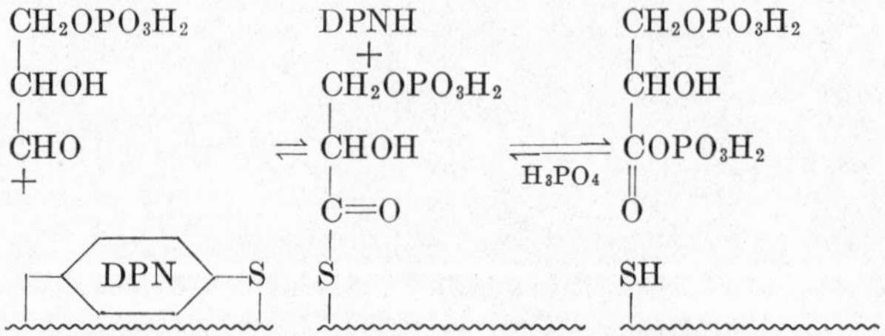

$$
\begin{array}{lll}
\text{CH}_2\text{OPO}_3\text{H}_2 & \text{DPNH} & \text{CH}_2\text{OPO}_3\text{H}_2 \\
| & + & | \\
\text{CHOH} & \text{CH}_2\text{OPO}_3\text{H}_2 & \text{CHOH} \\
| & | & | \\
\text{CHO} & \rightleftharpoons \text{CHOH} & \xrightarrow[\text{H}_3\text{PO}_4]{} \text{COPO}_3\text{H}_2 \\
+ & | & \| \\
 & \text{C}=\text{O} & \text{O} \\
\end{array}
$$

I (DPN-Enzyme)   II (Acyl-Enzyme)   III (SH-Enzyme)

Detailed studies (Velick and Hayes, 1953; Segal and Boyer, 1953 Hartung and Chance, 1953; Oesper, 1954) on the properties of thi enzyme and the functions of phosphate, DPN, and SH groups in thi reaction have supported this view. That this is indeed the correc mechanism was recently demonstrated (Krimsky and Racker, 1955) by the isolation of the acyl-enzyme II depicted above as a stable enzyme-substrate compound when either 1,3-diphosphoglyceric acid or acety phosphate react with the enzyme (III). Moreover, these intermediate could be reduced in the presence of DPNH to the correspondin aldehyde.

The enzymic oxidation of an aldehyde to the corresponding acid a illustrated is more complex than the above equations would imply. Fo

xample, following studies of this particular transformation of 3-phos-
hoglyceraldehyde to 1,3-diphosphoglyceric acid, Segal and Boyer
1953) have depicted in the following series of reactions just how this
ould occur:

$$R = CH_2OPO_3H_2$$
$$|$$
$$CHOH$$

) $RCHO + HS\text{-enzyme-}DPN^+ \rightleftharpoons RCHOH\text{-}S\text{-enzyme-}DPN^+$

) $RCHOH\text{-}S\text{-enzyme-}DPN^+ \rightleftharpoons RCO\text{-}S\text{-enzyme-}DPNH + H^+$

) $RCO\text{-}S\text{-enzyme-}DPNH + DPN^+ \rightleftharpoons RCO\text{-}S\text{-enzyme-}DPN^+ + DPNH$

) $RCO\text{-}S\text{-enzyme-}DPN^+ + H_3PO_4 \rightleftharpoons RCOOPO_3H_2 + HS\text{-enzyme-}DPN^+$

By addition the resultant reaction may be represented as follows:

$$RCHO + DPN^+ + H_3PO_4 \rightleftharpoons RCOOPO_3H_2 + DPNH + H^+$$

The enzyme glyceraldehyde-3-phosphate dehydrogenase from both
abbit muscle (Cori et al., 1948) and yeast (Warburg and Christian,
939a,b; Krebs et al., 1952) has been crystallized. Enzymically the
reparations function similarly but physically they differ in that the
abbit material has DPN as an integral part of the molecule unlike the
east enzyme. The enzyme is not specific in its action, for various un-
hosphorylated aldehydes can also be oxidized by this enzyme but at a
lower rate (Warburg and Christian, 1939a,b; Krimsky and Racker,
952; Bücher, 1947).

The 1,3-diphosphoglyceric acid then reacts with ADP to give 3-phos-
hoglyceric acid and ATP as follows:

1,3-Diphosphoglyceric acid + ADP $\rightleftharpoons$ 3-D-Phosphoglyceric acid + ATP

he enzyme concerned has been crystallized from Lebedew juice by
Bücher (1947) and this reaction thus provides a means for the regen-
ration of ATP in yeast.

It was observed (Embden et al., 1933) that when 3-phosphoglyceric
cid is treated with muscle extracts, pyruvate and phosphoric acid were
ormed. Later Lohmann and Meyerhof (1934) isolated as an inter-
1ediate product of this reaction 2-phosphoenolpyruvic acid. Since the
ormation of this compound occurred by the elimination of water and the
hifting of the phosphate group from the three to the two position, yet
1nother intermediate between 3-phosphoglyceric acid and 2-phospho-
nolpyruvic acid was postulated. This contention was correct, for 2-phos-
hoglyceric acid was isolated from yeast extracts (Meyerhof and
Kiessling, 1935b) and the fuller series of reactions from 3-phospho-
lyceric acid to pyruvate can therefore be depicted as follows:

$$
\begin{array}{cccc}
\text{COOH} & \text{COOH} & \text{COOH} & \text{COOH} \\
| & | \quad -\text{H}_2\text{O} & | \quad\quad \text{ADP} & | \\
\text{CHOH} & \text{CHOPO}_3\text{H}_2 \rightleftharpoons & \text{COPO}_3\text{H}_2 \rightleftharpoons & \text{C}{=}\text{O} \\
| & | & \| & | \\
\text{CH}_2\text{OPO}_3\text{H}_2 & \text{CH}_2\text{OH} & \text{CH}_2 & \text{CH}_3 \\
\text{3-Phospho-} & \text{2-Phospho-} & \text{2-Phospho-} & \text{Pyruvic} \\
\text{glyceric acid} & \text{glyceric acid} & \text{enolpyruvic} & \text{acid} \\
& & \text{acid} &
\end{array}
$$

The conversion of 3-phosphoglyceric acid to 2-phosphoglyceric aci as illustrated above, is catalyzed by the enzyme phosphoglyceromuta. (Meyerhof and Kiessling, 1935b; Meyerhof and Schulz, 1938; Warbu and Christian, 1942). It has been shown (Sutherland *et al.*, 1949b) th 2,3-diphosphoglyceric acid can accelerate this reaction and they pr posed that this compound functions as a coenzyme in the followi manner:

$$
\begin{array}{ccccc}
\text{COOH} & & \text{COOH} & & \text{COOH} \\
| & & | & & | \\
\text{CHOPO}_3\text{H}_2 & \text{COOH} & \text{CHOPO}_3\text{H}_2 & \text{COOH} \\
| & + \;\; | & \rightleftharpoons \;\; | & + \;\; | \\
\text{CH}_2\text{OPO}_3\text{H}_2 & \text{CHOH} & \text{CH}_2\text{OH} & \text{CHOPO}_3\text{H}_2 \\
& | & & | \\
& \text{CH}_2\text{OPO}_3\text{H}_2 & & \text{CH}_2\text{OPO}_3\text{H}_2 \\
\text{2,3-Diphospho-} & \text{3-Phospho-} & \text{2-Phospho-} & \text{2,3-Diphospho-} \\
\text{glyceric acid} & \text{glyceric acid} & \text{glyceric acid} & \text{glyceric acid}
\end{array}
$$

The further postulation by these workers that 2,3-diphosphoglyceric ac functions in a manner analogous to that of glucose 1,6-diphosphate the conversion of glucose-1-phosphate to glucose-6-phosphate, has y to be demonstrated with the purified enzyme.

It has been common knowledge for many years that sodium fluori inhibits yeast fermentation. Further investigations (Lohmann and Meye hof, 1934; Meyerhof and Kiessling, 1935b; Meyerhof and Schulz, 193 revealed that fluoride ions act on the enzyme enolase since under the conditions 2-phosphoglyceric acid accumulates. The site where t fluoride ions react in this enzymic system was clarified by the isolatic of the crystalline enolase (Warburg and Christian, 1942). Enolase r quires magnesium ions to catalyze the formation of 2-phosphoeno pyruvate from 2-phosphoglycerate (Warburg and Christian, 1942; Utt and Werkman, 1942a,b; Massart and Dufait, 1942). When fluoride io and inorganic phosphate are present, the magnesium ions form an i soluble fluorophosphate complex, resulting in a deficiency of this divale ion and hence an inhibition of the enzymic reaction. Manganese io can replace those of magnesium (Utter and Werkman, 1942a,b), but this case, no inhibition of enolase by fluoride ions occur as no insolub metal fluorophosphate complex is formed.

The final step in this series, the conversion of 2-phosphoenolpyruv acid to pyruvic acid is catalyzed by the enzyme phosphoenol trans-phosphorylase.

$$\begin{array}{cc} \text{COOH} & \text{COOH} \\ | & | \\ \text{COPO}_3\text{H}_2 + \text{ADP} \rightleftharpoons \text{C}{=}\text{O} + \text{ATP} \\ \| & | \\ \text{CH}_2 & \text{CH}_3 \end{array}$$

The above reaction has been studied in both muscle (Parnas *et al.*, 1934; Parnas, 1936) and yeast (Lutwak-Mann and Mann, 1935) and shown to be a reversible process in the presence of potassium or magnesium ions.

The pyruvic acid formed is decarboxylated to acetaldehyde and carbon dioxide in the simultaneous presence of magnesium ions and the enzyme carboxylase:

$$\text{CH}_3\text{COCOOH} \xrightarrow[\text{carboxylase}]{\text{Mg}^{++}} \text{CH}_3\text{CHO} + \text{CO}_2$$

This is the only irreversible step in the entire process. Neubauer (1910) first proposed this keto acid as the *in vivo* source of acetaldehyde in yeast fermentation. This suggestion was confirmed (Neuberg and Karczag, 1911) by the demonstration that pyruvate was indeed the direct precurser of acetaldehyde. Later studies on this enzymic system revealed that a coenzyme, identified as thiamine diphosphate was an essential constituent for this reaction to proceed. The magnesium ions on the other hand, can be replaced by other divalent ions, although the reaction rate decreases under these conditions (Green *et al.*, 1940, 1941).

The acetaldehyde is then reduced by DPNH to ethanol:

$$\text{CH}_3\text{CHO} + \text{DPNH} + \text{H}^+ \rightleftharpoons \text{CH}_3\text{CH}_2\text{OH} + \text{DPN}^+$$

The enzyme effecting this reduction was first purified by Negelein and Wulff (1937) and it can be obtained in a highly active state from Baker's yeast (Racker, 1955). Information concerning the mechanism of this reaction comes from the finding of zinc as an integral part of the enzyme molecule (Vallee and Hoch, 1955), four zinc atoms being present per mole of enzyme. Metal binders or compounds such as 1,10-phenanthroline which can combine with zinc inhibit the enzyme and the authors further suggest that other enzymatic systems in which DPN participates will also be found to depend on zinc. This last reaction thus provides the means for the oxidation of DPNH under anaerobic conditions.

A review of the above reactions indicates that, *in vivo*, a means is provided for the regeneration of ATP and DPN utilized during the dissimilation of the substrate so that these substances can function catalytically during the fermentation. For example, if the starting sugar is glucose, two moles of ATP are used in the synthesis of glucose-6-phosphate and fructose 1,6-diphosphate. On the other hand, one mole is formed during the oxidation of 3-phosphoglyceraldehyde to 3-phosphoglyceric acid and another during the formation of pyruvate from 2-phosphoenolpyruvic acid; DPN is reduced during the oxidation of 3-phosphoglyceraldehyde to 1,3-diphosphoglycerate and it is reoxidized when acetaldehyde is reduced to alcohol.

The series of reactions just recorded has received additional confirmation from isotopic tracer studies (Koshland and Westheimer, 1949, 1950). D-Glucose-1-C^{14} was fermented by yeast to ethanol which had practically all of its radioactivity in the methyl group. This is the predicted position, if the glucose molecule is dissimilated according to the scheme just presented in which C_1 of glucose becomes the methyl group of pyruvic acid which in turn, after decarboxylation and reduction, forms the methyl group of ethanol.

3. Fermentation of Miscellaneous Hexoses and Disaccharides

In addition to attacking glucose and fructose, yeast can also ferment other monosaccharides. In these cases however, consideration must be given not only to the stereochemical configuration of the particular hexose employed (Gottschalk, 1947; Kluyver and Custers, 1940) but also whether it is necessary to adapt the yeast so that it can utilize the sugar. Various aspects of this topic are discussed elsewhere in this volume (see for example, Chapters I, V, and VI), but from the present viewpoint the fermentation of the hexoses, mannose and galactose, has attracted the interest of many investigators.

(a) *Mannose.* It has long been known (Slator, 1908; Harden and Young, 1909) that mannose behaves similarly to glucose with regard to fermentation. Young (1909) observed that glucose, fructose, or mannose gave the same hexose diphosphate when incubated with inorganic phosphate and yeast juice, this fact suggesting a common intermediate. Mannose-1-phosphate has been synthesized (Colowick, 1938) and apparently it is not attacked by the enzyme phosphoglucomutase which converts glucose-1-phosphate to the glucose-6-phosphate (Cori *et al.*, 1938a). On the other hand, mannose-6-phosphate has been isolated when either glucose, fructose, or mannose is treated with dried yeast (Robison, 1932; Jephcott and Robison, 1934; Neuberg and Ostendorf, 1930). This phospho-sugar can be formed as follows:

$$\text{Mannose} + \text{ATP} \rightleftharpoons \text{Mannose-6-phosphate} + \text{ADP}$$

It may then be converted by phosphomannose isomerase to fructose-6-phosphate (Slein, 1950, 1954) which is a normal constituent of the glycolytic pathway. Another possibility for its breakdown is the epimerization of mannose-6-phosphate to glucose-6-phosphate and fructose-6-phosphate (Slein, 1950) with subsequent dissimilation along known routes. Thus it appears that mannose is fermented as follows:

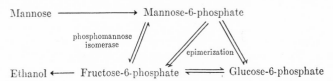

(*b*) *Galactose.* Adapted yeasts or their extracts can ferment galactose (Harden and Norris, 1910; Grant, 1935; Kosterlitz, 1943) and galactose-1-phosphate (Kosterlitz, 1943; Wilkinson, 1949) but are unable to attack galactose-6-phosphate. Kosterlitz (1943) proposed the following transformations, to explain how galactose is converted into one of the known

$$\text{Galactose} \xrightarrow{(1)} \text{Galactose-1-phosphate} \xrightarrow{(2)} \text{Glucose-1-phosphate} \rightarrow \text{Glucose-6-phosphate}$$

intermediates but gave no convincing proof to support his contention. Such studies were forthcoming from the laboratory of Leloir and his collaborators who demonstrated that reaction (1) occurred as follows (Trucco *et al.*, 1948; Caputto *et al.*, 1949):

$$\text{Galactose} + \text{ATP} \xrightarrow[\text{galactokinase}]{\text{Mg}^{++}} \text{Galactose-1-phosphate} + \text{ADP}$$

Unlike the hexokinases which catalyze the phosphorylation of fructose, glucose, and mannose to the corresponding 6-phosphohexose, galactokinase catalyzes the transphosphorylation to the 1-position of galactose. The second step (2), consisting of a Walden inversion of C_4, is catalyzed by the enzyme galactowaldenase and the coenzyme uridine diphosphate glucose (UDPG) (Caputto *et al.*, 1950; Cardini *et al.*, 1950).

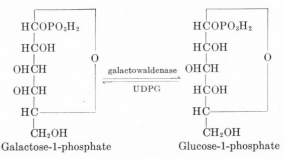

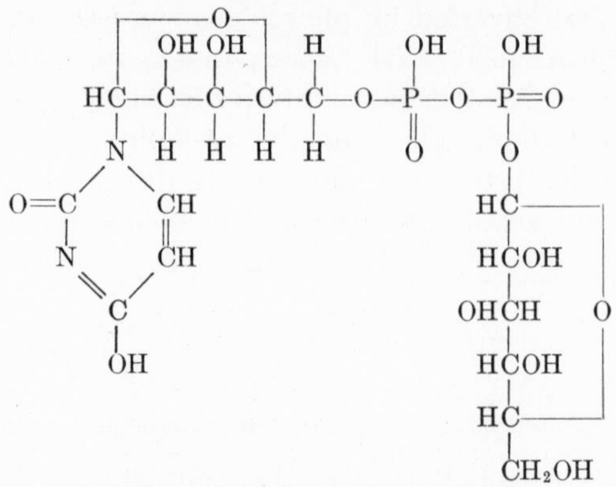

Uridine diphosphate glucose (UDPG)

Further studies (Leloir, 1951a) showed that when UDPG is incubated with enzyme extracts from yeast, about 25% of the glucose in UDPG is converted into galactose, yielding uridine diphosphate galactose (UDPGa). The postulation was that the inversion took place as follows:

(1)   Galactose-1-phosphate + UDPglucose $\rightleftharpoons$ Glucose-1-phosphate + UDPgalactose
(2)   UDPgalactose $\rightleftharpoons$ UDPglucose

Or, summing the two reactions, Galactose-1-phosphate $\rightleftharpoons$ Glucose-1-phosphate. Experimental evidence for reaction (1) was obtained (Kalckar and associates, 1953) in dialyzed extracts of *Saccharomyces fragilis* freed from the inversion enzyme concerned with reaction (2) above. These results received additional support from radioactive tracer studies (Trucco, 1954), for if the proposed reaction proceeded as follows: UDPglucose + Galactose-1-phosphate $\rightleftharpoons$ UDPgalactose + glucose-1-phosphate, C^{14}-glucose-1-phosphate, but not glucose-C^{14} should be incorporated into UDPglucose. This was found to be the case.

Another possible pathway for the conversion of galactose to glucose in yeast utilizes uridine triphosphate (UTP) (Kalckar *et al.*, 1953; Munch-Peterson *et al.*, 1953) by the following series of reactions:

(1)   UDPglucose + Pyrophosphate $\rightleftharpoons$ UTP + Glucose-1-phosphate
(2)   UTP + Galactose-1-phosphate $\rightleftharpoons$ UDPgalactose + Pyrophosphate

The resultant of these reactions is therefore as follows:

UDPglucose + Galactose-1-phosphate $\rightleftharpoons$ UDPgalactose + Glucose-1-phosphate

This is the same over-all equation expressed previously except that here UTP participates in the reaction. UTP can react with galactose-1-phosphate as depicted above, but further studies (Hansen and Freedland,

1955) have indicated that this is not the main pathway for the formation of UDPgalactose in yeast. While the data presented show how galactose enters the fermentation pathway, the exact mechanism of just how C^4 of galactose is inverted in the presence of the enzyme galactowaldenase is not yet known. The first hint concerning how this reversal of hydroxyl groups could occur was the recent finding (Maxwell, 1956) that DPN is a cofactor of a purified galactowaldenase preparation from calf liver. The inversion is presumed to proceed via a dehydrogenation of the carbon 4 hydroxyl group of glucose and subsequent specific reduction of the keto group to galactose. So far, the galactowaldenase from yeast has not been purified to the same extent to test whether the reaction proceeds in an analogous manner, but the above experiment points towards a possible solution to this problem.

(c) *Disaccharides.* The fermentation of disaccharides such as maltose, lactose, and sucrose by yeast has been extensively reviewed elsewhere (Hestrin, 1953; Leibowitz and Hestrin, 1945; Hassid *et al.*, 1951) and will be discussed here only briefly. The main problem to be solved concerns the initial phase of the fermentation. That is, just exactly how are these sugars cleaved to the hexose stage, for once they give rise to the known monosaccharides, usually consisting of glucose, fructose, or galactose or some combination thereof, the route to the end product, alcohol, follows known metabolic pathways.

Initially (Fischer and Lindner, 1895; Fischer, 1898), it was maintained that only one way existed for yeast to split disaccharides and that was by direct hydrolysis of the sugar into 2 hexoses in the presence of the corresponding hydrolytic enzyme. For example:

$$\text{Maltose} + \text{H}_2\text{O} \xrightarrow{\text{maltase}} 2 \text{ Molecules of Glucose}$$

This type of reaction became known as an indirect fermentation since the carbohydrate must first be cleaved into simpler units prior to being enzymatically degraded.

However, subsequent investigations by Willstätter, Hassid, Hestrin, Leibowitz, and others have provided ample evidence that yet other metabolic routes are available to the yeast. For example, maltose can not only be fermented under conditions where the hydrolytic enzyme, maltase cannot function, but may even be metabolized at a faster rate than glucose itself (Leibowitz and Hestrin, 1945). Such a finding may be explained by assuming a phosphorolytic rather than hydrolytic cleavage of the disaccharide as follows:

$$\text{Maltose} + \text{H}_3\text{PO}_4 \xrightarrow{\text{phosphorylase}} \text{Glucose-1-phosphate} + \text{Glucose}$$

This reaction is analogous to the formation of the Cremer-Cori ester from glycogen and, in the above cited example, may account for the increase in the observed rate of maltose as compared to glucose.

Further studies (Hehre, 1948, 1951; Hassid, 1951) have revealed that the dissimilation of disaccharides can also occur in the presence of enzymes known as transglucosidases, transfructosidases, and transgalactosidases. As the name implies, the reaction proceeds by the transfer of an intact glucose, fructose, or galactose unit from the substrate to a suitable acceptor such as phosphate or another sugar, as in the following sequence:

$$\text{Glucose-1-fructoside (sucrose)} + \text{Arabinose} \xrightarrow{\text{transglucosidase}} \text{Glucosido-1-arabinose} + \text{Fructose}$$

These transfer reactions are not quite as simple as the above equation would imply, for when paper chromatography has been used to follow the course of some of these reactions, many intermediates, some of them more complex than the initial substrate, have been detected. If the phosphate group can be an acceptor in these transfer reactions, then the end product would be a phosphohexose, indistinguishable in many cases, from the action of phosphorylase on the same substrate.

These enzymes have been found in plants, molds, and bacteria as well as in yeast, and some recent experiments with lactose (Aronson, 1952; Pazur, 1953, 1954), sucrose (Bacon, 1954), and maltose (Blau and Pigman, 1954) appear to favor this type of mechanism for cleavage of the disaccharides over that of hydrolysis or phosphorolysis. It is difficult to evaluate exactly to what extent each of the proposed mechanisms participate *in vivo* during the fermentation of a given disaccharide by yeast as no conclusive data have as yet been forthcoming to provide this information.

The problem of the fermentability and the mechanism (Myrbäck *et al.*, 1937; Myrbäck, 1949) of fermentation of the nonreducing disaccharide trehalose (1-α-D-glucopyranosyl-α-D-glucopyranoside) by yeast still remains unsettled since the available evidence precludes any definite answer to this question. The picture is also complicated by the fact that this sugar itself is a natural component of yeasts (Harding, 1923). Apparently whether a given yeast can ferment trehalose depends on its genetic constitution for out of 133 strains of yeast tested, only 16 were able to ferment this disaccharide (Bouthilet *et al.*, 1949). In contrast to these results are those obtained with the mold *Fusarium lini* B. where it was clearly demonstrated that trehalose is dissimilated at a more rapid rate than glucose, indicating a *direct* fermentation (O'Connor, 1940).

4. Glycerol Fermentation

Alcohol and carbon dioxide do not entirely account for the carbon utilized during the dissimilation of glucose, for other metabolic products such as glycerol are also produced. Normally, this polyhydroxy alcohol is formed to the extent of 3%, but Connstein and Lüdecke (1915, 1916, 1917, 1919a,b) observed that by varying the experimental conditions, the yield of glycerol can be considerably increased. Thus, if the pH of the medium is increased by adding alkaline salts such as ammonium carbonate, sodium bicarbonate, sodium acetate, or disodium phosphate, the final glycerol content rose from 3 to 9–16%. On the other hand, an increase in bacterial contamination was also obtained under these conditions resulting in erratic yields. These difficulties were obviated by substituting sodium sulfite for the alkaline salts since in this case not only were greater quantities of glycerol obtained (23–37%), but the salt itself acted as an antiseptic. These workers utilized these findings for the commercial manufacture of glycerol.

Investigations, especially by Neuberg and associates, concerning the mechanism of this change, have revealed that there are essentially three different mechanisms to explain the increasing yields of glycerol, depending on whether sulfite salts, alkali, or neutral solutions are present. According to Neuberg's classification, considering ordinary alcoholic fermentation as the first form, these are known as the second, third, and fourth forms of fermentation, respectively.

A. *Second Form of Fermentation*

When sodium sulfite is present in the culture medium, the Gay-Lussac expression

$$C_6H_{12}O_6 \rightarrow 2C_2H_5OH + 2CO_2$$

is no longer valid, since glycerol and acetaldehyde accumulate at the expense of the ethanol (Connstein and Lüdecke, 1919a,b; Neuberg and Reinfurth, 1918a). The acetaldehyde is not present as such but is trapped as the bisulfite addition product. Further studies (Neuberg and Reinfurth, 1918b, 1919; Neuberg and Hirsch, 1919a) indicated that equimolar quantities of glycerol and acetaldehyde are formed throughout the fermentation period.

During the course of a normal fermentation, DPNH (formed during the oxidation of 3-phosphoglyceraldehyde to 3-phosphoglyceric acid) is reoxidized, when acetaldehyde is reduced to ethanol. However, in the presence of sodium sulfite, the acetaldehyde can serve no longer as the hydrogen acceptor for DPNH, since it combines with the sulfite salt to yield an addition compound. Under these altered conditions, dihydroxyacetone phosphate can become a suitable substrate for DPNH, resulting in the formation of glycerol phosphate which is then converted into glycerol:

$$
\begin{array}{ccc}
\mathrm{CH_2OH} & \mathrm{CH_2OH} & \mathrm{CH_2OH} \\
| & | & | \\
\mathrm{C{=}O} \quad + \mathrm{DPNH} + \mathrm{H^+} \rightarrow \mathrm{CHOH} \quad \xrightarrow{\text{phosphatase}} \quad \mathrm{CHOH} \\
| & | & | \\
\mathrm{CH_2OPO_3H_2} & \mathrm{CH_2OPO_3H_2} & \mathrm{CH_2OH} \\
\text{Dihydroxyacetone phosphate} & \text{Glycerol} & \text{Glycerol} \\
& \text{phosphate} &
\end{array}
$$

The reason why more glycerol is not produced under standard fermentation conditions is that acetaldehyde has a much greater affinity for DPNH than dihydroxyacetone phosphate (Negelein and Brömel, 1939a,b,c). The over-all relationships can be expressed as follows:

$$ C_6H_{12}O_6 \rightarrow CH_2OHCHOHCH_2OH + CH_3CHO + CO_2 $$

The total equation including the sodium sulfite then becomes:

$$ C_6H_{12}O_6 + Na_2SO_3 + H_2O \rightarrow CH_2OHCHOHCH_2OH + CH_3CH(OH)SO_3Na + NaHCO_3 $$

The more acetaldehyde that is trapped by the sodium sulfite, the greater the quantity of glycerol found (Connstein and Lüdecke, 1919a,b; Neuberg and Reinfurth, 1918a), but the yeast can tolerate only a certain percentage of this salt before the latter exerts a toxic effect (Polak, 1929). Sodium sulfite can be substituted by the corresponding magnesium, zinc, or calcium salt without any noticeable differences between them being observed (Neuberg and Reinfurth, 1919).

It is reasonable to assume that other metabolically active substances such as glucose and pyruvic acid can also react with sodium sulfite. Investigations have substantiated this, but in the case of glucose, the addition compound is unstable in aqueous solution and dissociates into its original components, while with pyruvate, the reaction product is easily fermented by yeast (Neuberg and Reinfurth, 1920a,b; Zerner, 1920).

Since the principle involved in increasing glycerol production is to prevent acetaldehyde from being reduced to ethanol, any fixing agent which will trap the aldehyde and at the same time not inhibit the *in vivo* enzymic reactions should lead to the same result. The following compounds have fulfilled these requirements and can be used to increase the yields of glycerol: dimedone (Neuberg and Reinfurth, 1920c), thiosemicarbazide (Neuberg and Kobel, 1927), charcoal (Abderhalden and Glaubach, 1922), different hydrazides (Neuberg and Kobel, 1928; Kobel and Tychowski, 1928; Klein and Fuchs, 1929), and phenylhydrazine oxalate (Bolcato, 1950).

B. *Third Form of Fermentation*

If the pH of the culture medium is raised into the alkaline region, the course of the yeast fermentation is changed, for under these conditions ethanol, acetic acid, glycerol, and carbon dioxide are produced. The mechanism of this reaction has been studied in detail (Neuberg and Färber, 1917; Neuberg and Hirsch, 1919b,c; Neuberg et al., 1920; Neuberg and Ursum, 1920).

Instead of being reduced to ethanol, the acetaldehyde undergoes a dismutation in the presence of an aldehyde mutase to form alcohol and acetic acid:

$$2CH_3CHO + H_2O \rightarrow C_2H_5OH + CH_3COOH$$

The reactions that follow are analogous to those described for the second form of fermentation. That is, since the acetaldehyde is unavailable as an acceptor for DPNH, the latter can be used to reduce dihydroxyacetone phosphate to glycerol phosphate which finally yields glycerol. The total equation can be expressed as follows:

$$2C_6H_{12}O_6 + H_2O \rightarrow 2CO_2 + CH_3COOH + C_2H_5OH + 2CH_2OHCHOHCH_2OH$$

This type of fermentation is due to the alkalinity of the medium since various salts or hydroxides can be used with practically the same results. It is interesting to note that a yeast, *Zygosaccharomyces acidifaciens*, has been observed to undergo this third form of fermentation as its normal glycolytic process (Nickerson and Carroll, 1945).

C. *Fourth Form of Fermentation*

A fourth type of fermentation has been demonstrated (Neuberg and Kobel, 1930a,b,c; Kobel and Scheuer, 1930; Kobel, 1931) to occur under special experimental conditions, for in this case no formation of carbon dioxide or ethanol takes place but instead equimolar amounts of pyruvic acid and glycerol are produced:

$$C_6H_{12}O_6 \rightarrow CH_3COCOOH + CH_2OHCHOHCH_2OH$$

The exact mechanism for the change has not as yet been elucidated, and further studies are necessary to clarify this problem.

These particular types of fermentation illustrate the effect of changing the environment on the course of a normal yeast fermentation. Yet another way exists to alter the normal dissimilatory processes and that is by switching from anaerobic to aerobic conditions.

5. Aerobic Oxidation

A. *Hexose Monophosphate Pathway*

Within recent years, a new metabolic pathway has been elucidated for the oxidation of glucose in yeast in which various carbohydrates, ranging from two to seven carbons, have been implicated as intermediates. This cyclic process assumes new importance in explaining the synthesis and degradation of pentoses since little information concerning this phase of the dissimilatory route has been available.

The early work of Warburg and his associates (1935a,b) established that glucose-6-phosphate could be enzymically oxidized by yeast preparations to 6-phosphogluconic acid and that TPN functions as a coenzyme in this conversion. Further studies on this reaction have revealed that the primary oxidation product of glucose-6-phosphate is not 6-phosphogluconate but 6-phospho-δ-gluconolactone which is subsequently hydrolyzed by a specific gluconolactonase to the phospho-acid (Cori and Lipmann, 1952; Brodie and Lipmann, 1955).

Glucose-6-phosphate   6-Phospho-δ-gluconolactone   6-Phosphogluconic acid

The formation of the lactone is catalyzed by the enzyme glucose-6-phosphate dehydrogenase and it is in this step that the coenzyme TPN is required. This reaction can be reversed (Horecker and Smyrniotis, 1953a) and, even though the total content of this enzyme in yeast is usually low, some degree of purification has been accomplished (Kornberg, 1950; Glaser and Brown, 1955). It is interesting to note that it is the pyranose form of glucose which undergoes dehydrogenation, giving the lactone directly without any further structural modifications in the molecule. The lactone must be hydrolyzed to the acid, since any further enzymic changes require the presence of an open chain compound as the substrate.

Initially, the 6-phosphogluconic acid was considered to be fermented by yeast extracts (Warburg *et al.*, 1935a,b), but Lipmann (1936) demonstrated the oxidative nature of this reaction and suggested on the basis of oxygen consumption and carbon dioxide formation that this phosphohexonic acid could be decarboxylated to yield arabinose-5-phosphate. However, subsequent experiments with Lebedew maceration juices (Dickens, 1938a,b) pointed towards ribose-5-phosphate as the probable pentose formed from 6-phosphogluconic acid since it is fermented much more rapidly than arabinose-5-phosphate. That this contention was true was proven more than 10 years later when ribose-5-phosphate was identified by paper chromatography as a product of the oxidation of 6-phosphogluconate (Cohen and McNair Scott, 1950).

More detailed studies of this transformation were undertaken by Horecker and Smyrniotis (1951) who purified an enzyme, 6-phosphogluconic acid dehydrogenase from yeast which catalyzed the decarboxylation of 6-phosphogluconate to ribose-5-phosphate and carbon dioxide. Now, ribose-5-phosphate is not the logical pentose expected from the direct decarboxylation of the phosphohexonic acid since an inversion of the hydroxyl group at carbon 2 of the pentose occurred during its formation. Further purification of the enzyme system provided the necessary explanation for this anomaly (Horecker *et al.*, 1951). The 6-phosphogluconate dehydrogenase preparations also contained a phosphopentose isomerase which converted the initially formed pentose, ribulose-5-phosphate into ribose-5-phosphate. Since the equilibrium of this reaction favors the formation of the latter pentose (ratio 3:1), this accounts for the identification of the ribose instead of the ribulose moiety. Utilizing both the information that TPN is the coenzyme for this transformation, indicative of a dehydrogenation mechanism, as well as previous knowledge of oxidative decarboxylations of compounds of similar type, it was postulated (Horecker and Smyrniotis, 1950) that the 6-phosphogluconic acid was oxidized first to 3-keto-6-phosphogluconate prior to being decarboxylated to ribulose-5-phosphate. However, as yet, no direct experimental evidence exists to prove this point since this compound has not as yet been detected. Another expressed possibility is that the same enzyme catalyzes both the dehydrogenation and subsequent decarboxylation, giving rise to the pentose directly without the necessity of having any transitory intermediate. Further studies are necessary to unravel the question as to which of the two postulations is correct. The formation of ribose-5-phosphate from 6-phosphogluconic acid can be depicted as follows:

$$
\begin{array}{ccccc}
\text{COOH} & \left[\begin{array}{c}\text{COOH}\end{array}\right. & \begin{array}{c}\text{CO}_2\\ +\\ \text{CH}_2\text{OH}\end{array} & & \text{CHO}\\
\text{H\overset{|}{C}OH} & \text{H\overset{|}{C}OH} & & & \text{H\overset{|}{C}OH}\\
\text{OH\overset{|}{C}H} & \text{C}=\text{O} & \text{C}=\text{O} & & \text{H\overset{|}{C}OH}\\
\text{H\overset{|}{C}OH} \rightarrow & \text{H\overset{|}{C}OH} \rightarrow & \text{H\overset{|}{C}OH} & \xrightarrow[\text{isomerase}]{\text{phosphopentose}} & \text{H\overset{|}{C}OH}\\
\text{H\overset{|}{C}OH} & \text{H\overset{|}{C}OH} & \text{H\overset{|}{C}OH} & & \text{CH}_2\text{OPO}_3\text{H}_2\\
\text{CH}_2\text{OPO}_3\text{H}_2 & \left.\begin{array}{c}\text{CH}_2\text{OPO}_3\text{H}_2\end{array}\right] & \text{CH}_2\text{OPO}_3\text{H}_2 & &
\end{array}
$$

6-Phospho-   3-Keto-6-phos-   Ribulose-5-   Ribose-5-
gluconic acid   phogluconic acid   phosphate   phosphate

Once the two pentoses are formed, they can undergo various transformations, ultimately yielding the hexoses, fructose-6-phosphate and glucose-6-phosphate. These conversions are not native only to yeast for they also occur in various plants, animals, and microorganisms and they have played an essential role in elucidating the intricate mechanism of photosynthesis. However, a discussion of these processes is outside the scope of this chapter. Nevertheless, while the substrates and intermediates may differ from genus to genus, the general over-all scheme remains essentially the same.

An enzyme was isolated from yeast which catalyzes the cleavage of ribulose-5-phosphate into glyceraldehyde-3-phosphate and a two-carbon compound, presumed to be "active" glycolaldehyde (Racker et al., 1953; de la Haba, et al., 1955). However, later studies (Srere et al., 1955) revealed that the pentose actually involved in this reaction is xylulose-5-phosphate and not ribulose-5-phosphate, the conversion of one to the other being catalyzed by a phosphopentoepimerase (Hurwitz, 1956). This splitting of the phosphopentose occurs only in the presence of a suitable acceptor such as ribose-5-phosphate, glyceraldehyde, or glycolaldehyde (de la Haba et al., 1955). Other metabolically active aldehydes such as acetaldehyde, formaldehyde, or glucose-6-phosphate do not react under the experimental conditions employed. The reaction with ribose-5-phosphate is of particular interest and can be depicted as shown at the top of page 345.

The enzyme bringing about this last reaction has been named transketolase since the first two carbon atoms of xylulose-5-phosphate (ketol

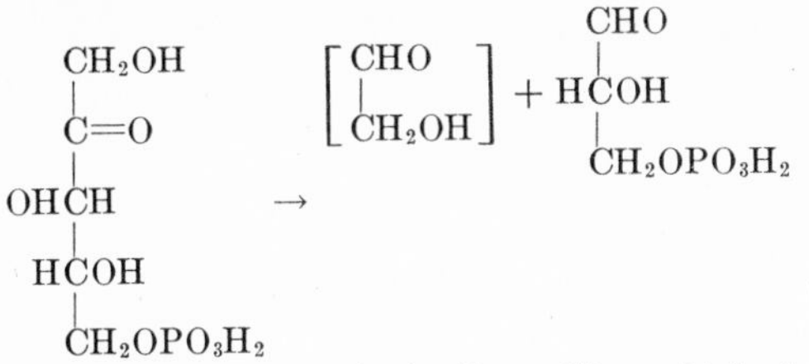

$$
\begin{array}{ccc}
\begin{array}{c}
\text{CH}_2\text{OH} \\
| \\
\text{C}=\text{O} \\
| \\
\text{OHCH} \\
| \\
\text{HCOH} \\
| \\
\text{CH}_2\text{OPO}_3\text{H}_2
\end{array}
& \rightarrow &
\left[\begin{array}{c}
\text{CHO} \\
| \\
\text{CH}_2\text{OH}
\end{array}\right]
+
\begin{array}{c}
\text{CHO} \\
| \\
\text{HCOH} \\
| \\
\text{CH}_2\text{OPO}_3\text{H}_2
\end{array}
\end{array}
$$

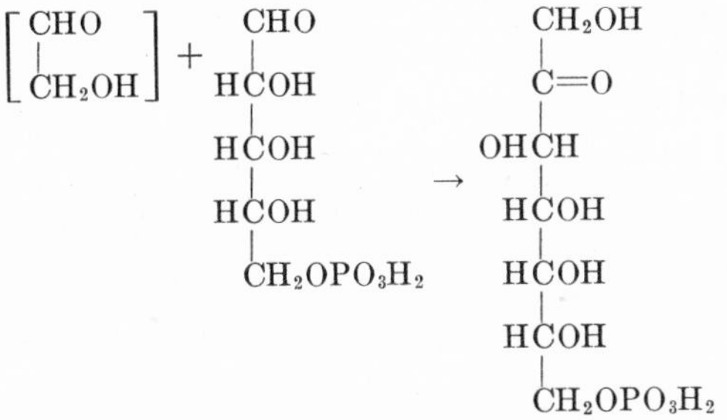

Xylulose-5-phosphate	"Active" glycol-aldehyde	Glyceraldehyde-3-phosphate

$$
\left[\begin{array}{c}
\text{CHO} \\
| \\
\text{CH}_2\text{OH}
\end{array}\right]
+
\begin{array}{c}
\text{CHO} \\
| \\
\text{HCOH} \\
| \\
\text{HCOH} \\
| \\
\text{HCOH} \\
| \\
\text{CH}_2\text{OPO}_3\text{H}_2
\end{array}
\rightarrow
\begin{array}{c}
\text{CH}_2\text{OH} \\
| \\
\text{C}=\text{O} \\
| \\
\text{OHCH} \\
| \\
\text{HCOH} \\
| \\
\text{HCOH} \\
| \\
\text{HCOH} \\
| \\
\text{CH}_2\text{OPO}_3\text{H}_2
\end{array}
$$

"Active" glycolaldehyde	Ribose-5-phosphate	Sedoheptulose-7-phosphate

Xylulose-5-phosphate + Ribose-5-phosphate → Sedoheptulose-7-phosphate
+ Glyceraldehyde-3-phosphate

grouping) are transferred to the aldehyde acceptor. It contains bound thiamine diphosphate as the coenzyme and requires magnesium ion for its activity. Xylulose-5-phosphate is not a specific substrate for transketolase as other compounds such as hydroxypyruvic acid (de la Haba *et al.*, 1955), fructose-6-phosphate (Racker *et al.*, 1954), or sedoheptulose-7-phosphate (Horecker *et al.*, 1953) are also capable of generating "active" glycolaldehyde units in the presence of the enzyme and an aldehyde acceptor. It is interesting to note that all of the phosphosugars which act as the source of "active" glycolaldehyde have the same stereoconfiguration of their first three carbon atoms indicated below:

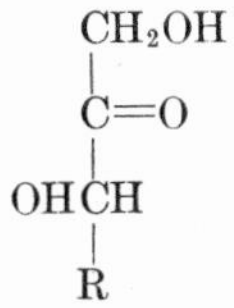

$$
\begin{array}{c}
\text{CH}_2\text{OH} \\
| \\
\text{C}=\text{O} \\
| \\
\text{OHCH} \\
| \\
\text{R}
\end{array}
$$

The seven carbon sugar, sedoheptulose-7-phosphate, obtained by the reaction depicted above, can also be synthesized by a transfer of the ketol grouping from fructose-6-phosphate to ribose-5-phosphate (Racker *et al.*, 1954) as in the scheme:

Fructose-6-phosphate + Ribose-5-phosphate → Sedoheptulose-7-phosphate
                                                         + Tetrose-4-phosphate

One of the intermediates of the glycolytic pathway, glyceraldehyde-3-phosphate, may also serve as a substrate acceptor of the ketol grouping from fructose-6-phosphate, yielding ribulose-5-phosphate which again can be made available for additional reactions in the cycle by epimerization to xylulose-5-phosphate.

Sedoheptulose-7-phosphate does not appear to be an artifact of the experimental conditions employed since its presence has been detected in photosynthetic processes, plants, microorganisms, and animals. Studies by Horecker and Smyrniotis (1953b, 1955) have provided the necessary clues to elucidate the further transformations of heptulose phosphate. Sedoheptulose-7-phosphate can react with glyceraldehyde-3-phosphate in the presence of a purified enzyme, transaldolase, from yeast to yield fructose-6-phosphate and a tetrose phosphate, presumably erythrose-4-phosphate.

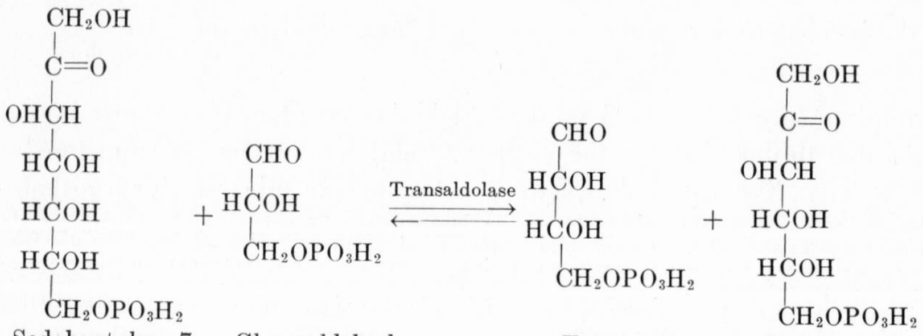

$$
\begin{array}{ccccc}
\text{CH}_2\text{OH} & & & & \text{CH}_2\text{OH} \\
\text{C=O} & & & & \text{C=O} \\
\text{OHCH} & & \text{CHO} & & \text{OHCH} \\
\text{HCOH} & \text{CHO} & \text{HCOH} & & \text{HCOH} \\
\text{HCOH} & + \text{HCOH} & \xrightarrow[\leftarrow]{\text{Transaldolase}} \text{HCOH} & + & \text{HCOH} \\
\text{HCOH} & \text{CH}_2\text{OPO}_3\text{H}_2 & \text{CH}_2\text{OPO}_3\text{H}_2 & & \text{HCOH} \\
\text{CH}_2\text{OPO}_3\text{H}_2 & & & & \text{CH}_2\text{OPO}_3\text{H}_2 \\
\text{Sedoheptulose-7-} & \text{Glyceraldehyde-} & \text{Tetrose-4-} & & \text{Fructose-6-} \\
\text{phosphate} & \text{3-phosphate} & \text{phosphate} & & \text{phosphate}
\end{array}
$$

In effect, it is the transfer of a dihydroxyacetone grouping from the seven-carbon sugar to the acceptor. There does not appear to be any prosthetic group necessary for transaldolase activity and so far only fructose-6-phosphate and sedoheptulose-7-phosphate can serve as donors of the three-carbon unit to the appropriate acceptor which must be present for the reaction to proceed. Moreover, glyceraldehyde or glycolaldehyde cannot be substituted for glyceraldehyde-3-phosphate.

The reaction mechanism depicted above was studied utilizing radioactive isotopes (Horecker and Smyrniotis, 1955). Uniformly labeled hexose diphosphate-C^{14} and aldolase provided the source for glyceraldehyde-3-phosphate-1,2,3,-C^{14} while the heptulose-7-phosphate employed was inactive. Analysis of the hexose obtained revealed that about 90% of the activity was present in C^4, C^5 and C^6 as would be expected if the reaction proceeded as shown. Furthermore, when sedoheptulose-1,3-C^{14} was incubated under the same conditions with inactive hexose diphosphate and aldolase either in the absence or presence of a large excess of dihydroxyacetone, the glucose so obtained in both cases had the same radioactivity. This meant that at no time could the dihydroxyacetone grouping from the sedoheptulose-7-phosphate exist in the free state during its transfer to the aldehyde acceptor, for otherwise it would have been diluted by the excess dihydroxyacetone present in the incubation mixture.

The other product of the transaldolase reaction is a tetrose phosphate, and, as mentioned above, the available evidence indicates that it is erythrose-4-phosphate. The difficulty encountered in demonstrating the presence of this carbohydrate rested on its reactivity since under experimental conditions where accumulation of the tetrose would have been expected, only traces were found. This was due primarily to the interaction of this phosphotetrose with other components in the system employed. However, evidence for its existence as a product of the reaction was furnished by paper chromatography (Horecker and Smyrniotis, 1955). Furthermore, when sedoheptulose was incubated with hexose diphosphate and aldolase (to furnish a source for trioses) along with transaldolase, sedoheptulose diphosphate was isolated and identified from the incubation medium (Horecker et al., 1955). This diphosphoheptose could only have been synthesized by a condensation of a four-carbon sugar having the stereo-configuration of erythrose. The reactions involved in its formation may be expressed as follows:

(1)   Hexose diphosphate $\xleftrightarrow{\text{aldolase}}$ Glyceraldehyde-3-phosphate
                                              + Dihydroxyacetone phosphate

(2)   Sedoheptulose-7-phosphate + Glyceraldehyde-3-phosphate
           $\xrightarrow{\text{transaldolase}}$ Fructose-6-phosphate + Erythrose-4-phosphate

(3)   Erythrose-4-phosphate + Dihydroxyacetone phosphate
           $\xrightarrow{\text{aldolase}}$ Sedoheptulose-1,7-diphosphate

The over-all result of these reactions therefore becomes:

Hexose diphosphate + Sedoheptulose-7-phosphate → Fructose-6-phosphate
                                              + Sedoheptulose-1,7-diphosphate

It is interesting to note that heptulose diphosphate is an excellent substrate for aldolase, yielding as noted above, dihydroxyacetone phosphate and erythrose-4-phosphate. More direct evidence for erythrose-4-phosphate formation came from the study of the enzymic synthesis of fructose-6-phosphate in a simplified system using sedoheptulose-1,7-diphosphate as the direct precursor of erythrose-4-phosphate and xylulose-5-phosphate as the source of "active" glycolaldehyde (Smyrniotis and Horecker, 1956) (although ribulose-5-phosphate was stated to be the source of the two-carbon unit, presumably there was sufficient phosphopentoepimerase present in the system to convert the ribulose-5-phosphate to xylulose-5-phosphate as the former sugar does not serve as a donor of the "active" glycolaldehyde):

$$\text{Sedoheptulose-1,7-diphosphate} \xrightarrow{\text{aldolase}} \text{Erythrose-4-phosphate}$$
$$+ \text{ Dihydroxyacetone phosphate}$$
$$\text{"Active" glycolaldehyde} + \text{Erythrose-4-phosphate} \xrightarrow{\text{transketolase}} \text{Fructose-6-phosphate}$$

Fructose-6-phosphate was also identified when the tetrose phosphate (generated from sedoheptulose-7-phosphate and glyceraldehyde-3-phosphate) was allowed to react with a source of "active" glycolaldehyde in the presence of transketolase (Horecker et al., 1955). Racker and associates (1954) had previously shown the reverse of this reaction in their investigations with the properties of transketolase.

Final confirmation came from the synthesis of D-erythrose-4-phosphate itself (Ballou et al., 1955) and the demonstration that when this phospho-sugar is incubated with dihydroxyacetone phosphate and aldolase, sedoheptulose diphosphate is formed.

Whether sedoheptulose diphosphate is a metabolically active intermediate in yeast is not known but if so, it would be a potential source of erythrose-4-phosphate. It would appear that this phosphotetrose can function as an important intermediate in biochemical transformations, since, for example, it is involved in the enzymic synthesis in E. coli of shikimic acid, the precursor of the aromatic ring (Srinivasan et al., 1955). In this particular experiment, sedoheptulose was used to generate the erythrose-4-phosphate.

Based on the reactions just presented, a hexose monophosphate cycle for glucose oxidation has been advanced (Racker, 1955; Horecker and Mehler, 1955) in which at least 7 enzymes participate: glucose-6-phosphate dehydrogenase, 6-phosphogluconic acid dehydrogenase, phosphopentose isomerase, phosphopentoepimerase, transketolase, transaldolase and phosphohexose isomerase.

6-Phosphogluconolactone $+ H_2O$ $\xrightarrow{\text{gluconolactonase}}$ 6-Phosphogluconic acid $\xrightleftharpoons[\text{dehydrogenase}]{\text{6-phosphogluconic acid}}$ $CO_2 +$ Ribulose-5-PO_4

6-Phosphogluconolactone:
$$\begin{array}{l} C=O \\ HCOH \\ OHCH \quad O \\ HCOH \\ HC \\ CH_2OPO_3H_2 \end{array}$$

6-Phosphogluconic acid:
$$\begin{array}{l} COOH \\ HCOH \\ OHCH \\ HCOH \\ HCOH \\ CH_2OPO_3H_2 \end{array}$$

Ribulose-5-PO_4:
$$\begin{array}{l} CH_2OH \\ C=O \\ HCOH \\ HCOH \\ CH_2OPO_3H_2 \end{array}$$

Glucose-6-PO_4:
$$\begin{array}{l} OH \\ HC \\ HCOH \\ OHCH \quad O \\ HCOH \\ HC \\ CH_2OPO_3H_2 \end{array}$$

$\xrightleftharpoons[\text{-2H}]{\text{TPN}}$ glucose-6-PO_4 dehydrogenase

$\xrightleftharpoons[\text{phosphohexose isomerase}]{}$

Fructose-6-PO_4:
$$\begin{array}{l} CH_2OH \\ C=O \\ OHCH \\ HCOH \\ HCOH \\ CH_2OPO_3H_2 \end{array}$$

$\xrightleftharpoons{\text{transketolase}}$

Erythrose-4-PO_4:
$$\begin{array}{l} CHO \\ HCOH \\ HCOH \\ CH_2OPO_3H_2 \end{array}$$

Xylulose-5-PO_4:
$$\begin{array}{l} CH_2OH \\ C=O \\ OHCH \\ HCOH \\ CH_2OPO_3H_2 \end{array}$$

Ribose-5-PO_4:
$$\begin{array}{l} CHO \\ HCOH \\ HCOH \\ HCOH \\ CH_2OPO_3H_2 \end{array}$$

phosphopentoepimerase   phosphopentose isomerase

transaldolase   transketolase

Glyceraldehyde-3-phosphate:
$$\begin{array}{l} CHO \\ HCOH \\ CH_2OPO_3H_2 \end{array}$$

Sedoheptulose-7-PO_4:
$$\begin{array}{l} CH_2OH \\ C=O \\ OHCH \\ HCOH \\ HCOH \\ HCOH \\ CH_2OPO_3H_2 \end{array}$$

Several features of this cycle are worth noting. First, a carbon balance reveals that 3 moles of ribulose-5-phosphate will provide two moles of fructose-6-phosphate and one mole of glyceraldehyde-3-phosphate. This, of course is on the assumption that these particular reactions proceeded exclusively *in vivo* which is unlikely. Furthermore, this cycle provides a means for pentose being formed in yeast in either of two ways: (a) by oxidative decarboxylation of 6-phosphogluconic acid to form ribulose-5-phosphate, or (b) by a transketolase reaction between fructose-6-phosphate and glyceraldehyde-3-phosphate, yielding again ribulose-5-phosphate. Since the first reaction requires aerobic conditions while the second may also proceed anaerobically, the latter route assumes importance for the synthesis of pentoses in yeast.

The complete hexose monophosphate cycle cannot operate anaerobically since formation of ribulose-5-phosphate from glucose-6-phosphate does not occur. However, the remainder of the enzymic steps apparently do not need aerobic conditions and potentially these reactions could proceed as described previously. Certainly it appears feasible to explain the fermentation of pentoses by the hexose monophosphate pathway. Thus ribose-5-phosphate could yield fructose-6-phosphate which then might be dissimilated anaerobically by the Embden-Meyerhof-Parnas pathway. Evidence has been accumulating through the years which supports this view. Ribose-5-phosphate is rapidly fermented by yeast (Dickens, 1938a,b) and *in vitro* anaerobic experiments with a yeast protein fraction indicate that as much as 89% of this pentose phosphate is accounted for as hexose mono- and diphosphate and triose phosphate (Sable, 1952). Furthermore, as early as 1938, the presence of a heptulose phosphate sugar was detected in a hexose monophosphate fraction isolated from fermenting yeast, and while final identification was not achieved, preliminary experiments indicated that the phosphate group was not attached to the oxygen of C_1 (Robison *et al.*, 1938). Experiments *in vivo* with radioactive ribose-5-phosphate should answer whether pentose fermentation arises in living yeast via a combination of the hexose monophosphate and Embden-Meyerhof-Parnas pathways.

Information pertaining to this question was provided by Gibbs and his associates (1955) who utilized ribose-1-C^{14} and found that the content and distribution of the C^{14} in the alcohol and carbon dioxide was in agreement with the concept that the pentose first formed hexose phosphate via the hexose monophosphate pathway and then underwent dissimilation by the regular anaerobic route to ethanol and carbon dioxide. This particular strain of yeast could ferment ribose as well as ribose-5-phosphate (most strains apparently do not metabolize the pentose itself) and the plausible assumption is made that the ribose is first phosphorylated by a pentokinase to ribose-5-phosphate prior to being acted upon.

The physiological importance of this pathway for the synthesis of pentoses has recently been demonstrated many times. Thus, when *T. utilis* was grown on glucose-1-C^{14}, only a small quantity of radioactivity was detected in the ribose isolated from the nucleic acid fraction (Sowden *et al.*, 1954). This result is to be expected if pentose formation occurs via the HMP pathway since C_1 becomes carbon dioxide. When glucose-2-C^{14} was utilized as the carbon source for *T. utilis*, the isolated ribose was radioactive and analysis showed that 92% of the radioactivity was distributed in the first three carbon atoms (David and Renault, 1954). This would imply that the ribose was synthesized not only by a direct decarboxylation of 6-phosphogluconate but perhaps also by a transketolase reaction of fructose-6-phosphate and glyceraldehyde-3-phosphate.

The elucidation of the HMP pathway was established by utilizing mainly a combination of isolated systems and purified enzyme preparations. However, the necessity of reconstituting these reactions in terms of the living organism, the intact yeast cell, remains. The question naturally arises as to what extent this metabolic route participates in the normal physiological processes occurring in yeast, for under aerobic conditions, glucose can also be enzymically degraded *in vivo* by the Embden-Meyerhof-Parnas pathway. Two different approaches were employed to estimate to what extent the HMP cycle is operating in yeast for dissimilation of glucose.

In the first method (Blumenthal *et al.*, 1954) glucose $1\text{-}C^{14}$ was utilized as the substrate and the radioactivity present in the carbon dioxide, ethanol, and acetate determined under both aerobic and anaerobic conditions. Since C_1 of glucose in the HMP cycle becomes carbon dioxide while in the Embden-Meyerhof-Parnas route it forms the methyl group of ethanol or acetate, and since the former pathway gives only one mole of triose per mole of hexose used while the latter gives two, a method for distinguishing between these two processes is available. Correction is made for endogenous metabolism by employing uniformly labeled glucose and it is assumed in these calculations that these two pathways are the ones mainly used by the yeast to dissimilate the glucose. Aerobically they found that in *Saccharomyces cerevisiae*, the HMP pathway accounted for 0–30% of the glucose catabolized while with *T. utilis* the values ranged from 30–50%. Different values would be expected between strains of yeast depending on their genetic constitution. Under anaerobic conditions, 95% or more of the glucose was dissimilated by the glycolytic route.

Another approach designed to test whether the HMP cycle functions *in vivo* under aerobic conditions was undertaken by Beevers and Gibbs (1954) who utilized both glucose-1-C^{14} and glucose-6-C^{14} as substrates and determined the amount of radioactivity in the respired carbon dioxide with time. If the Embden-Meyerhof-Parnas pathway were the sole route for the oxidation of the hexose, then the ratio:

$$\frac{\text{radioactivity in } CO_2 \text{ from glucose-1-}C^{14}}{\text{radioactivity in } CO_2 \text{ from glucose-6-}C^{14}}$$

would be unity irrespective of time since both of these carbons would be oxidized at the same rate (C_1 and C_6 in this case would form methyl groups of pyruvic acid). On the other hand, if the shunt pathway were operating to any extent, then the observed ratio should be greater than one during the early stages of the oxidation since relatively few enzymatic steps are involved in the conversion of C_1 to carbon dioxide while C_6 requires many more prior to becoming carbon dioxide. Ratios greater than one were observed indicative of the reality of the HMP route, but no evaluation of the contribution of each of these pathways was made in these experiments.

In a critical evaluation of isotopic experiments designed to estimate to what extent the HMP and EMP pathways participate *in vivo*, Wood (1955) has pointed out some of the features which must be carefully considered prior to interpreting the experimental data. For example, the question arises as to whether the triose phosphate produced from the EMP and HMP pathways form one homogeneous pool as is assumed, or whether they are dissimilated separately at different rates to ethanol as may be represented diagrammatically:

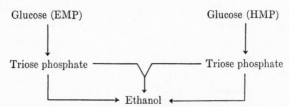

It is appropriate in this respect to note the results of some recent centrifugal studies (Newburgh and Cheldelin, 1956) with rabbit liver and kidney, when it was found that the enzymes of the HMP cycle were closely associated with each other. Such a finding may increase the possibility of separate degradation of the triose phosphates. The final calculation will depend on the extent to which the yeast uses these different routes.

Another possible source of error arises from the assumption of complete equilibration of dihydroxyacetone phosphate and glyceraldehyde-3-phosphate. From glucose-1-C^{14} there should initially be formed C^{14}-dihydroxyacetone phosphate and inactive glyceraldehyde-3-phosphate. If the former undergoes further reaction, e.g., for reduction to glycerol phosphate, prior to being equilibrated with glyceraldehyde-3-phosphate, then the latter will contain less radioactivity than expected. Hence the final products (which are formed from glyceraldehyde-3-phosphate) will have a lower specific activity than would be calculated.

The assumption is also made that there is no intermixing of the EMP and HMP pathways. However, the possibility exists (Horecker and Mehler, 1955) that this can occur. Thus C^{14}-fructose-6-phosphate (formed from glucose-1-C^{14} by the EMP pathway) can react with glyceraldehyde-3-phosphate (arising from either the EMP or HMP route) to yield ribulose-5-phosphate by a transketolase reaction. This pentose then can give C^{14}-glucose-6-phosphate which would lose its radioactive C_1 as carbon dioxide. This would raise the estimated value for the HMP cycle and lower the EMP contribution.

These and other assumptions (see Wood, 1955) suggest that data which have been obtained for estimating alternate pathways in living organisms should be carefully interpreted. However, there can be no doubt that the hexose monophosphate cycle does exist in yeast and that it plays an important role in the synthesis of the ribose moiety of nucleic acids as well as a route for the oxidation of hexoses and pentoses.

B. *Citric Acid Cycle*

Under aerobic conditions, at least two pathways are operative in yeast for the oxidation of carbohydrates: (1) the hexose monophosphate cycle and (2) the Embden-Meyerhof-Parnas scheme. If the sugar is enzymically degraded via the latter route, then alcohol, the normal anaerobic end product does not accumulate, for it is oxidized further to acetate. The following equations express the various ways in which it may be formed:

$$\text{Ca}^{++} \text{ or Mg}^{++} \text{ or Mn}^{++}, \text{TPN}$$

$$CH_3COCOOH \rightarrow CH_3CHO \rightarrow CH_3CH_2OH \rightarrow CH_3CHO \rightarrow CH_3COOH$$

$$\text{K}^+ \text{ DPN or TPN}$$

The acetaldehyde formed by decarboxylation of pyruvic acid may be reduced to alcohol, then dehydrogenated back to acetaldehyde, in presence of an alcohol dehydrogenase, and subsequently oxidized by an aldehyde dehydrogenase to acetate. Two different aldehyde dehydrogenases have been purified from yeast. One, can utilize either DPN or TPN as its coenzyme and has an absolute requirement for potassium ions. Either cysteine or glutathione must be present for maximum activity (Black, 1951). The other specifically requires TPN and is activated by divalent ions such as Ca, Mg, or Mn, potassium ions being ineffective (Seegmiller, 1953).

$$CH_3CHO + TPN + H_2O \xrightarrow[\text{aldehyde dehydrogenase}]{\text{Ca}^{++}} CH_3COOH + TPNH^+ + H^+$$

Since these two aldehyde dehydrogenases were obtained from the same type of yeast and apparently can function independently of each other, it is difficult to evaluate their efficiency *in vivo*. In the scheme presented above, the oxidation of acetaldehyde can either proceed directly without the intermediate formation of ethanol or else the aldehyde can undergo reduction to alcohol which is then oxidized to acetate. Acetate can be further catabolized and it is at this point in the oxidative pathway that divergent views exist.

When barium acetate is the substrate, succinate and citrate accumulate (Wieland and Sonderhoff, 1932), and apparently the presence of barium ions prevents the further oxidation of citrate by yeast (Virtanen and Sundman, 1942). On the basis of these results, Wieland and Sonderhoff (1932) proposed that acetate is oxidized via the Thunberg-Knoop cycle, citrate arising merely as a side reaction:

Citric Acid

ζ

$CH_3COCOOH \rightarrow CH_3CHO \rightarrow CH_3COOH \rightarrow HOOCCH_2CH_2COOH$

$\uparrow \qquad\qquad\qquad\qquad\qquad\qquad\qquad\qquad\qquad\qquad \downarrow$

$HOOCCOCH_2COOH \leftarrow HOOCCHOHCH_2COOH \leftarrow HOOCCH{=}CHCOOH$

However isotopic experiments with CH_3COOH revealed that the deuterium content of the succinate was lower than would be expected if the dicarboxylic acid arose by a direct condensation of two acetate molecules (Sonderhoff and Thomas, 1937). Lynen (1942a, 1943) proposed another scheme for the oxidation of acetate similar to the tricarboxylic acid cycle postulated for animal tissues and he reconciled the results obtained with deuterium on this basis. These and other findings (Lynen, 1947) employing deuterium containing substrates must be interpreted with due caution in the light of our present-day knowledge concerning the inactivity of deuterium in both oxidative processes and its effect on coenzyme–substrate complexes (Thorn, 1951; Abeles, 1955; Rachele et al., 1955).

On the other hand, Krebs (1943) was of the opinion that the tricarboxylic acid cycle was not the route for oxidative processes in yeast because of the apparent absence of individual members of the cycle. But Lynen and Neciullah (1939) showed that the reasons why these reactions could not be observed was due to the impermeability of the cell membrane, for if the walls were broken by freezing them in liquid air and then thawing, succinate, malate, α-ketoglutarate and citrate underwent rapid dehydrogenation. Many subsequent experiments bear out the contention that the tricarboxylic acid cycle is the major oxidative pathway in yeast. Thus Weinhouse and his associates (1947, 1948) have shown using barium and magnesium acetate with the carboxyl labeled with C^{13} that catabolism occurred via the tricarboxylic acid cycle. They further demonstrated that at least 50% of the glucose was oxidized via acetate and thus established the importance of the cycle for oxidative reactions in yeast. Foulkes (1951), employing cell-free extracts of baker's yeast found that citrate was rapidly catabolized and that, if the reaction is carried out in the presence of semicarbazide or cyanide as inhibitors, α-ketoglutarate accumulates.

It should not be assumed that the Krebs cycle operates exclusively in yeast, for isotopic data (Weinhouse and Millington, 1947) and other studies (Lynen, 1942a, 1943) indicate that another independent mechanism is also available for the formation of the dicarboxylic acids.

While the prevailing evidence demonstrates the scope and usefulness of the Krebs cycle in explaining the oxidation of various metabolically active intermediates, some investigators have expressed doubts as to whether this is its main function. Thus Krebs and his associates (1952), on the basis of their experimental findings, feel that the reactions of the tricarboxylic acid cycle can also provide intermediates for anabolic processes and not necessarily be utilized by the organism primarily for energetic purposes. Certainly it cannot be denied, as Krebs has pointed out, that the cycle can provide essential building bricks for numerous synthetic reactions. However, with the recent discovery of coenzyme A which provided a link between carbohydrate and fatty acid metabolism on the one hand and the citric acid cycle on the other, it appears that the latter serves as an important outpost for oxidative processes in microorganisms.

The tricarboxylic acid cycle, as conceived today, may be represented schematically as follows (Ochoa, 1954):

As mentioned previously, most of the components of the cycle have been demonstrated to occur in yeast. Interestingly enough, two enzymes have been purified from yeast which catalyze the conversion of isocitrate to α-ketoglutarate (Kornberg and Pricer, 1951). One is DPN specific and requires catalytic amounts of adenosine-5-phosphate and in this case, the α-ketoglutarate is formed directly without the necessity of passing through the intermediate stage of oxalosuccinate. The second enzyme system is TPN dependent and the isocitric acid is first dehydrogenated to oxalosuccinate which then loses a molecule of carbon dioxide to form the end product.

It has only been within the last decade that the investigations of Lipmann, Ochoa, Lynen, and others have clarified the initial condensation step in the cycle, the formation of citric acid. It was observed (Novelli and Lipmann, 1947, 1950) that yeasts deficient in pantothenic acid do not utilize acetate as effectively as normal yeasts and the view was expressed that coenzyme A was involved in the condensation of acetate and oxaloacetate to form citrate. The finding that the active center of coenzyme A was an SH group and that "active" acetate was in reality the S-acetyl derivative of coenzyme A (Lynen and Reichert, 1951) provided the additional and necessary information for the further study of this condensation reaction. The structure of coenzyme A (see also Chapter V) can be depicted as follows (Gregory et al., 1952; Novelli, 1953):

Coenzyme A

With the isolation of the highly purified condensing enzyme from pig's heart (Stern et al., 1950; Ochoa et al., 1951) and the demonstration that this reaction is reversible, the last link necessary to comprehend how itrate is formed from acetate and oxaloacetate became available. Yeast ontains this particular enzyme (Ochoa *et al.*, 1951) and since coenzyme A is also present, the essential components to form citrate presumably an react *in vivo*. A comprehensive review on the citric acid cycle has been provided by Ochoa (1954).

6. The Pasteur Effect

Pasteur first observed that the presence of oxygen resulted in an inhibition of anaerobic fermentation and a simultaneous increase in espiration. At the same time, less sugar is apparently utilized by the yeast. This phenomenon is known as the *Pasteur effect,* and although various theories have been expounded to explain this reversible relationship between respiration and fermentation (see Burk, 1939; Dickens, 951), as yet, no satisfactory answer exists which can account for all the acts.

One of the proposed possibilities is a special enzyme which would connect the processes of anaerobic and aerobic fermentation. Thus Melnick (1941), as the result of phytochemical evidence, believes that baker's yeast contains both a respiratory enzyme, which is involved in he oxidation of the substrates, and a so-called "Pasteur" enzyme which regulates the suppression of fermentation in the presence of oxygen. These enzymes, which contain hemin, are able to combine with oxygen and thus perhaps can control aerobic processes within the cell. In the light of our present-day knowledge of the various changes produced by he Pasteur effect, it does not appear likely that such an enzyme would be the sole agent in charge of the regulatory mechanism.

Since anaerobic fermentation is suppressed in yeast during aerobiosis, he question arises as to whether this is due to some impairment of the normal function of some of the enzymes responsible for the dissimilation of the carbohydrate. Engelhardt and Sakov (1943) found that the enzyme system responsible for the conversion of fructose-6-phosphate to ructose-1,6-diphosphate is extremely sensitive towards oxidation and hence would be practically completely inhibited under aerobic conditions. This suggests that the yeasts follow yet another pathway other than he Embden-Meyerhof-Parnas route to degrade the sugar. Fructose-6-phosphate can be catabolized via the Hexosemonophosphate cycle during aerobic oxidation, and if their contention is correct, this should be he main prevailing route for dissimilation of glucose. However, it is lifficult to reconcile their findings with the available evidence which ndicates that *in vivo*, the EMP route not the HMP pathway is the prevailing one for the utilization of glucose-1-C^{14} (Blumenthal *et al.*, 1954).

According to Lynen (1941, 1942b; Lynen and Reichert, 1951) and Johnson (1941), during aerobic oxidation, the concentration of inorganic phosphate in the cell is low due primarily to its utilization in oxidative phosphorylation reactions. If these oxidations can occur at a phosphate level lower than required for anaerobiosis, fermentation reactions should be suppressed and synthetic processes increased. Moreover, as was noted previously, more energy can be obtained aerobically and hence less carbohydrate need be degraded by the microorganism.

One of the enzymic steps in anaerobic fermentation involving inorganic phosphate is the oxidation of 3-phosphoglyceraldehyde to 3-phosphoglyceric acid. One would expect the concentration of 3-phosphoglyceraldehyde to be higher aerobically than anaerobically due to the absence of sufficient inorganic phosphate. Measurements in living yeast cells (Holzer and Holzer, 1953) have shown this to be true and these results suggest that the activity of the enzyme 3-phosphoglyceraldehyde dehydrogenase may be one of the limiting factors when the cell is exposed to oxygen. While this theory is attractive, it does not appear to be the core around which the yeast can reversibly switch its course of action when the environment is changed. Again, consideration must be given to the isotopic data (Blumenthal, et al., 1954; Weinhouse and Millington, 1947; Weinhouse et al., 1948) which strongly suggest the full participation of all the enzymes of the Embden-Meyerhof-Parnas pathway. To correlate their results with the radioactive tracer studies, it would be necessary to assume an alternate mechanism, as yet unknown, for the oxidation of 3-phosphoglyceraldehyde to the corresponding acid.

Moreover, results of recent studies (Stickland, 1956; Aisenberg and Potter, 1957) do not support the view that the level of inorganic phosphate is the limiting factor responsible for the Pasteur effect. The cause(s) apparently lies elsewhere. Aisenberg and co-workers (1957) are of the opinion that the phosphohexokinase and hexokinase systems are the ones inhibited in the presence of oxygen, in agreement with the views expressed previously by Engelhardt and Sakov (1943).

The above suggestions are but a few of the proposals made to explain the Pasteur effect in yeast. There are others (Lipmann, 1941, 1942; Meyerhof, 1942) but as yet, no direct proof for a *specific agent* or action has been forthcoming. It may be that there is no one agent responsible for the Pasteur effect and that several factors are operating simultaneously to produce the observed result.

7. General Considerations

While the fermentation of hexoses by living yeast can be expressed by the Gay-Lussac equation:

$$C_6H_{12}O_6 \rightarrow 2C_2H_5OH + 2CO_2$$

east extracts or juices on the other hand usually catabolize the carbohydrate in such a way that for every molecule of glucose which forms carbon dioxide and alcohol, one molecule is esterified to hexose diphosphate. This is referred to as the Harden-Young equation (Harden and Young, 1906):

$$2C_6H_{12}O_6 + 2Na_2HPO_4 \rightarrow 2C_2H_5OH + 2CO_2 + C_6H_{10}O_4(PO_4Na_2)_2$$

Although a plausible explanation has been advanced (Meyerhof, 1945; Meyerhof and Wilson, 1949) to clarify this particular difference between intact yeast cells and extracts, the basic question still remains as to whether information derived from *in vitro* experiments can be projected precisely into its exact place in the complex mechanics of the living cell.

The approach to this problem involves a consideration of some of the factors, both biophysical and nutritional, which distinguishes the whole organism from its homogenized counterpart. For example, a study of the carbon dioxide evolved and the energy liberated as heat during the fermentation of carbohydrates by living yeasts and Lebedew extracts shows significant differences in their mode of action (Hofstetter *et al.*, 1938). This experiment depicts the net result of all the reactions proceeding *in vitro* and *in vivo* and hence illustrates the presence of a qualitative difference between the intact cells and extracts. Such a finding is not unexpected, for it must be remembered that in the preparation of the latter, the cell wall has been ruptured, resulting in a distortion of the ratios of the various cellular components. Hence it follows that biophysical factors such as the speed of stirring (Nord and Weichherz, 1929a; Weichherz, 1931) or the presence of compounds like ethylene and acetylene which affect the permeability of cell membranes (Nord, 1929, 1932; Nord and Franke, 1928; Nord and Weichherz, 1929b) would have little effect on *in vitro* fermentation studies. Instead they would exert their action on the living cell, influencing the rate at which alcoholic fermentation can occur *in vivo*.

Other differences between the living organism and its extracts can readily be demonstrated, for basically it must be remembered that the former is a compact closely knit *organized* system whereas the latter is a conglomeration of different agents. Thus, in the homogenate, some reactions which normally occur at a certain velocity may decrease or even disappear while others which ordinarily would not predominate due to the inherent composition of the intact cell, will now come to the fore. In addition, some recent studies (Swartz *et al.*, 1956) have revealed yet other factors which must be considered in evaluating *in vitro* studies. These workers observed that sonic extracts of certain bacteria contain a DPN pyrophosphatase which normally does not function due to its binding with a nondialyzable, heat-labile inhibitor. When this inhibitor is removed either by treatment at acid pH or heating in a boiling-water bath, the heat-stable enzyme becomes active. Several other enzyme-inhibitor relationships have been observed and also studied. The important suggestion was made that the presence of such enzyme-inhibitors might be a method by which the cell regulates enzymic activities *in vivo*. Such a mechanism would act in conjunction with the well-established genetic control of enzyme production within the cell.

In the particular case just described, the inhibitor was noted due to its greater lability with heat than the enzyme. In the preparation of extracts where the cell wall is ruptured and the cellular contents allowed to intermingle freely, it is difficult to judge to what extent other enzyme-inhibitor bonds may be broken. The fact that an enzyme has been found active *in vitro* does not necessarily mean it functions *in vivo* to the same extent.

In vitro investigations are valuable in obtaining data on the possible presence or absence of certain enzymes occurring within the intact organism. Isolation and purification of individual enzymes have aided greatly in elucidating certain pathways such as the HMP cycle and the EMP route in yeast. But one should not lose sight of the ultimate goal of all *in vitro* studies: To fit the facts into its plausible place of action within the living cell. Nature in her various ways, makes it difficult for the experimenter to attain this goal. For example, by varying the nutritional background of the organism, different pictures of *in vivo* mechanisms are observed. Thus, in the case of the enzyme-inhibitor just described, it was found that the presence of yeast extract in the nutrient medium resulted in a DPN-pyrophosphatase practically devoid of any inhibitor.

The study of a purified enzyme system enables one to attain some idea of the specificity of the substrate and the rate of reaction but it does not yield accurate information on its relative activity *in vivo*. This would depend primarily on the nutrients available to the organism and the number of enzymic systems which can utilize a particular substrate.

It is also difficult at times to draw general conclusions based on results obtained with a particular species. Thus the results of studies on the utilization of glucose-1-C^{14} by *Saccharomyces cerevisiae* and *T. utilis* indicated that these yeasts differ with respect to the way they synthesized mannose for polysaccharide formation. From the radioactivity of the isolated mannose, it was concluded that *S. cerevisiae* utilizes the entire glucose-1-C^{14} chain directly for the formation of mannose (Gilvarg

952). On the other hand, no radioactivity was detected in the mannose
isolated from the mannan of *T. utilis,* showing that here, the mannose is
synthesized from smaller carbon fragments, none of which apparently
contain the C^1 of glucose (Sowden and associates, 1954). These opposite
results are naturally not true for all of the enzymic routes available to
the microorganism, since for example, all yeasts studied utilize the same
EMP pathway for alcohol formation under anaerobic conditions. What
such experiments do reveal is the presence of genetic and environmental
differences between species which merit consideration prior to formulat-
ing any general reaction scheme.

The observations and difficulties noted above are but a few of the
experiments described in the literature which attempt to correlate the
in vitro results to the precise mechanics of the intact cell. Usually by
combining the data from various sources, a scheme or pathway is proposed which the living organism supposedly uses for converting a given
substrate to a definite end product. Such a hypothesis is subject to experimental verification, and with the availability today of numerous
radioactive compounds, a sensitive tool becomes available to the investigator for testing such a proposed route *in vivo.* This approach has
proved fruitful not only in establishing the validity of the EMP pathway
Koshland and Westheimer, 1949, 1950) but also in detecting the
presence of alternate routes by which the organism might dissimilate
the same carbon source.

Multiple pathways in microorganisms are not a recent development in
biochemistry for such information has been known for many years. Thus,
in certain wood-destroying molds, two pathways were found for the
oxidation of acetic to oxalic acid (Nord and Vitucci, 1947). Hehre (1949)
observed that in the *same* enzyme extracts of some *Neisseria* bacteria,
there are two enzyme systems capable of synthesizing polysaccharides;
one which utilizes sucrose, the other glucose-1-phosphate. Moreover,
contrary to the assumption of Cori (1945), evidence has been accumulating (Hehre, 1951; Monod and Torriani, 1950) that polysaccharides of the
starch-glycogen class can also be synthesized without the direct participation of phosphates. In yeasts, early studies revealed the existance of
multiple pathways for the fermentation of disaccharides (Leibowitz and
Hestrin, 1945; Hestrin, 1948, 1949). These results and others (e.g.,
Effront, 1890; Nord and Mull, 1945), obtained prior to the general usage
of radioactive compounds as tracer indicators, established a basis for the
later studies.

It is not surprising therefore to find that although multiple pathways
exist in yeast, bacteria, and molds, the respective routes in each of these

microorganisms may differ from each other. In yeast, anaerobically the EMP route prevails while aerobically the hexose can be dissimilated via the HMP cycle and the EMP pathway. The extent to which each is utilized by the organism will depend on the particular species used.

On the other hand, depending on the strain and species employed, bacteria can degrade the glucose molecule by many different mechanisms, some of which involve phosphorylated intermediates while others do not (Gunsalus et al., 1955).

Since molds differ in their ability to dissimilate a given substrate, and since they are usually noted for their accumulation of one or more compounds, it is difficult to make any general statements regarding the availability of alternate pathways in these organisms. However, studies with such genera as Fusaria or certain wood-destroying molds (Nord and Weiss, 1951) have established the importance of dual pathways in these organisms. Moreover with the latter organisms, a heptulose sugar has been implicated in the synthesis of certain important aromatic compounds (Eberhardt and Nord, 1955; Nord and Schubert, 1957).

In conclusion, the ever-changing results obtained in the field of microbiology only reemphasize the need for continued research in this field.

References

Abderhalden, E., and Glaubach, S. (1922). Fermentforschung 6, 143.

Abeles, R. H. (1955). Federation Proc. 14, 170.

Aisenberg, A. C., and Potter, V. R. (1957). J. Biol. Chem. 224, 1115.

Aisenberg, A. C., Reinafarje, B., and Potter, V. R. (1957). J. Biol. Chem. 224, 1099.

Aronson, M. (1952). Arch. Biochem. and Biophys. 39, 370.

Bacon, J. S. D. (1954). Biochem. J. 57, 320.

Ballou, C. E., Fischer, H. O. L., and McDonald, D. L. (1955). J. Am. Chem. Soc. 77, 2658.

Bailey, K., and Webb, E. C. (1948). Biochem. J. 42, 60.

Bard, R. C., and Gunsalus, I. C. (1950). J. Bacteriol. 59, 387.

Beevers, H., and Gibbs, M. (1954). Nature 173, 640.

Berger, L., Slein, M. W., Colowick, S. P., and Cori, C. F. (1946). J. Gen. Physiol. 29, 379.

Black, S. (1951). Arch. Biochem. and Biophys. 34, 86.

Blau, M. G., and Pigman, W. (1954). Arch. Biochem. and Biophys. 48, 17.

Blumenthal, H. J., Lewis, K. F., and Weinhouse, S. (1954). J. Am. Chem. Soc. 76, 6093.

Bolcato, V. (1950). Nature 165, 814.

Bouthilet, R. J., Neilson, N. E., Mrak, E. M., and Phaff, H. J. (1949). J. Gen. Microbiol. 3, 282.

Brodie, A. F., and Lipmann, F. (1955). J. Biol. Chem. 212, 677.

Brown, D. H. (1951). Biochim. et Biophys. Acta 7, 487.

Bücher, T. (1947). Biochim. et Biophys. Acta 1, 292.

uchner, E. (1897). *Ber. deut. chem. Ges.* **30,** 117; Buchner, E., Buchner, H., and Hahn, M. (1903). "Die Zymasegärung." R. Oldenburg, Munchen.

urk, D. (1939). *Cold Spring Harbor Symposia Quant. Biol.* **7,** 420.

aputto, R., Leloir, L. F., Cardini, C. E., and Paladini, A. C. (1950). *J. Biol. Chem.* **184,** 333.

aputto, R., Leloir, L. F., Trucco, R. E., Cardini, C. E., and Paladini, A. C. (1948). *Arch. Biochem.* **18,** 201.

aputto, R., Leloir, L. F., Trucco, R. E., Cardini, C. E., and Paladini, A. C. (1949). *J. Biol. Chem.* **179,** 497.

ardini, C. E., Paladini, A. C., Caputto, R., Leloir, L. F., and Trucco, R. E. (1949). *Arch. Biochem.* **22,** 87.

ardini, C. E., Paladini, A. C., Caputto, R., and Leloir, L. F. (1950). *Nature* **165,** 191.

ohen, S. S., and McNair Scott, D. B. (1950). *Science* **111,** 543.

olowick, S. P. (1938). *J. Biol. Chem.* **124,** 557.

olowick, S. P., and Sutherland, E. W. (1942). *J. Biol. Chem.* **144,** 423.

onnstein, W., and Lüdecke, K., German Patents 298593 (1915): 298594-6 (1916); 343321 (1917); 347604 (1917).

onnstein, W., and Lüdecke, K. (1919a). *Ber. deut. chem. Ges.* **52,** 99.

onnstein, W., and Lüdecke, K. (1919b). *Ber. deut. chem. Ges.* **52,** 1385.

ori, C. F. (1945). *Federation Proc.* **4,** 226.

ori, C. F., Colowick, S. P., and Cori, G. T. (1937). *J. Biol. Chem.* **121,** 465.

ori, G. T., Colowick, S. P., and Cori, C. F. (1938a). *J. Biol. Chem.* **123,** 375.

ori, G. T., Colowick, S. P., and Cori, C. F. (1938b). *J. Biol. Chem.* **124,** 543.

ori, G. T., and Cori, C. F. (1939). *J. Biol. Chem.* **131,** 397.

ori, G. T., and Cori, C. F. (1940). *J. Biol. Chem.* **135,** 733.

ori, G. T., Slein, M. W., and Cori, C. F. (1948). *J. Biol. Chem.* **173,** 605.

ori, O., and Lipmann, F. (1952). *J. Biol. Chem.* **194,** 417.

ramer, F. B., and Woodward, G. E. (1952). *J. Franklin Inst.* **253,** 354.

remer, M. (1899). *Ber. deut. chem. Ges.* **32,** 2062.

avid, S., and Renault, J. (1954). *Compt. rend.* **239,** 369.

e la Haba, G., Leder, I. G., and Racker, E. (1955). *J. Biol. Chem.* **214,** 409.

ickens, F. (1938a). *Biochem. J.* **32,** 1626.

ickens, F. (1938b). *Biochem. J.* **32,** 1645.

ickens, F. (1951). In "The Enzymes" (J. B. Sumner and K. Myrbäck, eds.), Vol. II, Part 1, p. 672. Academic Press, New York.

rabkin, D. L., and Meyerhof, O. (1945). *J. Biol. Chem.* **157,** 571.

berhardt, G., and Nord, F. F. (1955). *Arch. Biochem. and Biophys.* **55,** 578.

ffront, J. (1890). *Bull. soc. chim. biol.* [3]4, 627.

mbden, G., Deuticke, H. J., and Kraft, G. (1933). *Klin. Wochschr.* **12,** 213.

ngelhardt, V. A., and Sakov, N. E. (1943). *Biokhimiya* **8,** 9.

ischer, E. (1898). *Hoppe-Seyler's Z. physiol. Chem.* **26,** 60.

ischer, E., and Lindner, P. (1895). *Ber. deut. chem. Ges.* **28,** 3034.

oulkes, E. C. (1951). *Biochem. J.* **48,** 378.

amble, J. L. Jr., and Najjar, V. A. (1954). *Science* **120,** 1023.

amble, J. L. Jr., and Najjar, V. A. (1955). *J. Biol. Chem.* **217,** 595.

ay-Lussac, L. J. (1815). *Ann. chim. et phys.* **95,** 311.

ibbs, M., Earl, J. M., and Ritchie, J. L. (1955). *J. Biol. Chem.* **217,** 161.

ilvarg, C. (1952). *J. Biol. Chem.* **199,** 57.

Glaser, L., and Brown, D. H. (1955). *J. Biol. Chem.* **216**, 67.

Gottschalk, A. (1943). *Australian J. Exp. Biol. Med. Sci.* **21**, 133.

Gottschalk, A. (1947). *Nature* **160**, 113.

Grant, G. A. (1935). *Biochem. J.* **29**, 1661.

Gregory, J. D., Novelli, G. D., and Lipmann, F. (1952). *J. Am. Chem. Soc.* **74**, 854.

Green, D. E., Needham, D. M., and Dewan, J. G. (1937). *Biochem. J.* **31**, 2327.

Green, D. E., Herbert D., and Subrahmanyan, V. (1940). *J. Biol. Chem.* **135**, 795.

Green, D. E., Herbert D., and Subrahmanyan, V. (1941). *J. Biol. Chem.* **138**, 327.

Guarino, A. J., and Sable, H. Z. (1954). *Federation Proc.* **13**, 222.

Gunsalus, I. C., Horecker, B. L., and Wood, W. A. (1955). *Bacteriol Revs.* **19**, 79.

Hanes, C. S. (1940a). *Proc. Roy. Soc.* **B128**, 421.

Hanes, C. S. (1940b). *Proc. Roy. Soc.* **B129**, 174.

Hansen, R. G., and Freedland, R. A. (1955). *J. Biol. Chem.* **216**, 303.

Harden, A., and Young, W. J. (1906). *Proc. Roy. Soc.* **B77**, 405.

Harden, A., and Young, W. J. (1909). *Proc. Roy. Soc.* **B81**, 336.

Harden, A., and Norris, R. V. (1910). *Proc. Roy. Soc.* **B82**, 645.

Harding, T. S. (1923). *Sugar* **25**, 476.

Hartung, J., and Chance, B. (1953). *Federation Proc.* **12**, 714.

Hassid, W. Z. (1951). In "Phosphorous Metabolism" (W. D. McElroy and B. Glass, eds.), Vol. I, p. 11. Johns Hopkins, Baltimore.

Hassid, W. Z., Doudoroff, M., and Barker, H. A. (1951). In "The Enzymes" (J. B. Sumner and K. Myrbäck, eds.), Vol. I, Part II, p. 1014. Academic Press, New York.

Hehre, E. J. (1948). *Trans. N.Y. Acad. Sci.* [2], **10**, 188.

Hehre, E. J. (1949). *J. Biol. Chem.* **177**, 267.

Hehre, E. J. (1951). *Advances in Enzymol.* **11**, 297.

Hestrin, S. (1948). *Wallerstein Lab. Comms.* **11**, 193.

Hestrin, S. (1949). *Wallerstein Lab. Comms.* **12**, 45.

Hestrin, S. (1953). *Ann. Rev. Biochem.* **22**, 85.

Hofstetter, H., Leichter, H., and Nord, F. F. (1938). *Biochem. Z.* **295**, 414.

Holzer, H., and Holzer, E. (1953). *Hoppe-Seyler's Z. physiol. Chem.* **292**, 232.

Hopkins, R. H., and Horwood, M. (1950). *Biochem. J.* **47**, 95.

Horecker, B. L., and Mehler, A. H. (1955). *Ann. Rev. Biochem.* **24**, 207.

Horecker, B. L., and Smyrniotis, P. Z. (1950). *Arch. Biochem.* **29**, 232.

Horecker, B. L., and Smyrniotis, P. Z. (1951). *J. Biol. Chem.* **193**, 371.

Horecker, B. L., and Smyrniotis, P. Z. (1953a). *Biochim. et Biophys. Acta* **12**, 98.

Horecker, B. L., and Smyrniotis, P. Z. (1953b). *J. Am. Chem. Soc.* **75**, 2021.

Horecker, B. L., and Smyrniotis, P. Z. (1955). *J. Biol. Chem.* **212**, 811.

Horecker, B. L., Smyrniotis, P. Z., Hiatt, H. H., and Marks, P. A. (1955). *J. Biol Chem.* **212**, 827.

Horecker, B. L., Smyrniotis, P. Z., and Klenow, H. (1953). *J. Biol. Chem.* **205**, 661.

Horecker, B. L., Smyrniotis, P. Z., and Seegmiller, J. E. (1951). *J. Biol. Chem.* **193**, 383.

Hurwitz, J. (1956). *Federation Proc.* **15**, 278.

Jagannathan, V., and Luck, J. M. (1949). *J. Biol. Chem.* **179**, 569.

Jephcott, C. M., and Robison, R. (1934). *Biochem. J.* **28**, 1844.

Johnson, M. J. (1941). *Science* **94**, 200.

Kalckar, H. M., Braganca, B., and Munch-Petersen, A. (1953). *Nature* **172**, 1038

Kiessling, W. (1939). *Biochem. Z.* **302**, 50.

Klein, G., and Fuchs, W. (1929). *Biochem. Z.* **213**, 40.
Klenow, H. (1953). *Arch. Biochem. and Biophys.* **46**, 186.
Klenow, H., and Emberland, R. (1955). *Arch. Biochem. and Biophys.* **58**, 276.
Kluyver, A. J., and Custers, M. T. J. (1940). *Antonie van Leeuwenhoek. J. Microbiol. Serol.* **6**, 121.
Kobel, M. (1931). *Biochem. Z.* **243**, 406.
Kobel, M., and Scheuer, M. (1930). *Biochem. Z.* **229**, 238.
Kobel, M., and Tychowski, A. (1928). *Biochem. Z.* **199**, 218.
Kornberg, A. (1950). *J. Biol. Chem.* **182**, 805.
Kornberg, A., and Pricer, W. E., Jr. (1951). *J. Biol. Chem.* **189**, 123.
Koshland, D. E., Jr., and Westheimer, F. H. (1949). *J. Am. Chem. Soc.* **71**, 1139.
Koshland, D. E., Jr., and Westheimer, F. H. (1950). *J. Am. Chem. Soc.* **72**, 3383.
Kosterlitz, H. W. (1943). *Biochem. J.* **37**, 322.
Krebs, H. A. (1943). *Advances in Enzymol.* **3**, 191.
Krebs, H. A., Gurin, S., and Eggleston, L. V. (1952). *Biochem. J.* **51**, 614.
Krebs, E. G., Rafter, G. W., Junge, J. M. (1953). *J. Biol. Chem.* **200**, 479.
Krimsky, I., and Racker, E. (1952). *J. Biol. Chem.* **198**, 721.
Krimsky, I., and Racker, E. (1955). *Science* **122**, 319.
Kunitz, M., and McDonald, M. R. (1946). *J. Gen. Physiol.* **29**, 143.
Leibowitz, J., and Hestrin, S. (1945). *Advances in Enzymol.* **5**, 87.
Leloir, F. (1951a). *Arch. Biochem. and Biophys.* **33**, 186.
Leloir, L. F. (1951b). *In* "Phosphorous Metabolism" (W. D. McElroy and B. Glass, eds.), Vol. I, p. 75. Johns Hopkins, Baltimore.
Leloir, L. F., Trucco, R. E., Cardini, C. E., Paladini, A. C., and Caputto, R. (1948). *Arch. Biochem.* **19**, 339.
Ling, K. H., and Lardy, H. A. (1954). *J. Am. Chem. Soc.* **76**, 2842.
Lipmann, F. (1936). *Nature* **138**, 588.
Lipmann, F. (1941). *Advances in Enzymol.* **1**, 99.
Lipmann, F. (1942). *In* "Symposium on Respiratory Enzymes," p. 48. Univ. of Wisconsin Press, Madison.
Lohmann, K. (1933). *Biochem. Z.* **262**, 137.
Lohmann, K., and Meyerhof, O. (1934). *Biochem. Z.* **273**, 60.
Lutwak-Mann, C., and Mann, T. (1935). *Biochem. Z.* **281**, 140.
Lynen, F. (1941). *Ann. Chem. Justus Liebigs* **546**, 120.
Lynen, F. (1942a). *Ann. Chem. Justus Liebigs* **552**, 270.
Lynen, F. (1942b). *Naturwiss.* **30**, 398.
Lynen, F. (1943). *Ann. Chem. Justus Liebigs* **554**, 40.
Lynen, F. (1947). *Ann. Chem. Justus Liebigs* **558**, 47.
Lynen, F., and Koenigsberger, R. (1951). *Ann. Chem. Justus Liebigs* **573**, 60.
Lynen, F., and Neciullah, N. (1939). *Ann. Chem. Justus Liebigs* **541**, 203.
Lynen, F., and Reichert, E. (1951). *Angew. Chem.* **63**, 47.
Massart, L., and Dufait, R. (1942). *Hoppe-Seyler's Z. physiol. Chem.* **272**, 157.
Maxwell, E. S. (1956). *J. Am. Chem. Soc.* **78**, 1074.
Melnick, J. L. (1941). *J. Biol. Chem.* **141**, 269.
Meyerhof, O. (1942). *In* "Symposium on Respiratory Enzymes," p. 3. Univ. of Wisconsin Press, Madison.
Meyerhof, O. (1945). *J. Biol. Chem.* **157**, 105.
Meyerhof, O. (1948). *Experientia* **4**, 169.
Meyerhof, O., and Junowicz-Kocholaty, R. (1942). *J. Biol. Chem.* **145**, 443.

Meyerhof, O., and Kiessling, W. (1935a). *Biochem. Z.* **279**, 40.
Meyerhof, O., and Kiessling, W. (1935b). *Biochem. Z.* **276**, 239.
Meyerhof, O., and Lohmann, K. (1934). *Biochem. Z.* **271**, 89.
Meyerhof, O., and Schulz, W. (1938). *Biochem. Z.* **297**, 60.
Meyerhof, O., and Oesper, P. (1947). *J. Biol. Chem.* **170**, 1.
Meyerhof, O., and Wilson, J. R. (1949). *J. Biol. Chem.* **180**, 575.
Meyerhof, O., Lohmann, K., and Schuster, P. (1936). *Biochem. Z.* **286**, 301.
Meyerhof, O., Schulz, W., and Schuster, P. (1937). *Biochem. Z.* **293**, 309.
Meyerhof, O., Ohlmeyer, P., and Möhle, W. (1938a). *Biochem. Z.* **297**, 90.
Meyerhof, O., Ohlmeyer, P., Gentner, W., and Maier-Leibnitz, H. (1938b). *Biochem. Z.* **298**, 396.
Monod, J., and Torriani, A. M. (1950). *Ann. Inst. Pasteur* **78**, 65.
Munch-Petersen, A., Kalckar, H. M., Cutolo, E., and Smith, E. E. B. (1953). *Nature* **172**, 1036.
Myrbäck, K. (1949). *Ergeb. Enzymforsch.* **10**, 168.
Myrbäck, K., Örtenblad, B., and Ahlborg, K. (1937). *Enzymologia* **3**, 210.
Najjar, V. A. (1948). *J. Biol. Chem.* **175**, 281.
Najjar, V. A., and Pullman, M. E. (1954). *Science* **119**, 631.
Needham, D. M., and Pillai, R. K. (1937). *Biochem. J.* **31**, 1837.
Negelein, E., and Brömel, H. (1939a). *Biochem. Z.* **301**, 135.
Negelein, E., and Brömel, H. (1939b). *Biochem. Z.* **303**, 132.
Negelein, E., and Wulff, H. J. (1937). *Biochem. Z.* **293**, 351.
Negelein, E., and Brömel, H. (1939c). *Biochem. Z.* **303**, 231.
Neubauer, O. (1910). *Hoppe-Seyler's Z. physiol. Chem.* **70**, 350.
Neuberg, C., and Färber, E. (1917). *Biochem. Z.* **78**, 238.
Neuberg, C., and Hirsch, J. (1919a). *Biochem. Z.* **98**, 141.
Neuberg, C., and Hirsch, J. (1919b). *Biochem. Z.* **96**, 175.
Neuberg, C., and Hirsch, J. (1919c). *Biochem. Z.* **100**, 304.
Neuberg, C., and Karczag, L. (1911). *Biochem. Z.* **36**, 68.
Neuberg, C., and Kobel, M. (1927). *Biochem. Z.* **188**, 211.
Neuberg, C., and Kobel, M. (1928). *Biochem. Z.* **199**, 230.
Neuberg, C., and Kobel, M. (1930a). *Ber. deut. chem. Ges.* **63**, 1986.
Neuberg, C., and Kobel, M. (1930b). *Biochem. Z.* **219**, 490.
Neuberg, C., and Kobel, M. (1930c). *Biochem. Z.* **229**, 446.
Neuberg, C., and Reinfurth, E. (1918a). *Biochem. Z.* **92**, 234.
Neuberg, C., and Reinfurth, E. (1918b). *Biochem. Z.* **89**, 365.
Neuberg, C., and Reinfurth, E. (1919). *Ber. deut. chem. Ges.* **52**, 1677.
Neuberg, C., and Reinfurth, E. (1920a). *Ber. deut. chem. Ges.* **53**, 462.
Neuberg, C., and Reinfurth, E. (1920b). *Ber. deut. chem. Ges.* **53**, 1039.
Neuberg, C., and Reinfurth, E. (1920c). *Biochem. Z.* **106**, 281.
Neuberg, C., and Ursum, W. (1920). *Biochem. Z.* **110**, 193.
Neuberg, C., Hirsch, J., and Reinfurth, E. (1920). *Biochem. Z.* **105**, 307.
Neuberg, I. S., and Ostendorf, C. (1930). *Biochem. Z.* **221**, 154.
Newburgh, R. W., and Cheldelin, V. H. (1956). *J. Biol. Chem.* **218**, 89.
Nickerson, W. J., and Carroll, W. R. (1945). *Arch. Biochem.* **7**, 257.
Novelli, G. D. (1953). *Federation Proc.* **12**, 675.
Novelli, G. D., and Lipmann, F. (1947). *J. Biol. Chem.* **171**, 833.
Novelli, G. D., and Lipmann, F. (1950). *J. Biol. Chem.* **182**, 213.
Nord, F. F. (1929). *Z. angew. Chem.* **42**, 1022.

Nord, F. F. (1932). *Ergeb. Enzymforsch.* **1**, 77.
Nord, F. F. (1940). *Chem. Rev.* **26**, 423.
Nord, F. F., and Franke, K. W. (1928). *J. Biol. Chem.* **79**, 27.
Nord, F. F., and Mull, R. P. (1945). *Advances in Enzymol.* **5**, 165.
Nord, F. F., and Schubert, W. J. (1957). *Advances in Enzymol.* **18**, 349.
Nord, F. F., and Vitucci, J. C. (1947). *Arch. Biochem.* **14**,229.
Nord, F. F., and Weichherz, J. (1929a). *Z. Elektrochem.* **35**, 612.
Nord, F. F., and Weichherz, J. (1929b). *Hoppe-Seyler's Z. physiol. Chem.* **183**, 191.
Nord, F. F., and Weiss, S. (1951). *In* "The Enzymes" (J. B. Sumner and K. Myrbäck, eds.), Vol. II, Part I, p. 684. Academic Press, New York.
Ochoa, S. (1954). *Advances in Enzymol.* **15**, 185.
Ochoa, S., Stern, J. R., and Schneider, M. C. (1951). *J. Biol. Chem.* **193**, 691.
O'Connor, R. C. (1940). *Biochem. J.* **34**, 1008.
Oesper, P. (1954). *J. Biol. Chem.* **207**, 421.
Ostern, P., Guthke, J. A., and Terszakowec, J. (1936). *Hoppe-Seyler's Z. physiol. Chem.* **243**, 9.
Parnas, J. K. (1936). *Bull. soc. chim. biol.* **18**, 53.
Parnas, J. K. (1937). *Ergeb. Enzymforsch.* **6**, 57.
Parnas, J. K., and Baranowski, T. (1935). *Compt. rend. soc. biol.* **120**, 307.
Parnas, J. K., Ostern, P., and Mann, T. (1934). *Biochem. Z.* **272**, 64.
Pasteur, L. (1872). *Ann. chim. et phys.* [4] **25**, 145.
Pasteur, L. (1876). "Études sur la Bière," Gauthier-Villars, Paris.
Pazur, J. H. (1953). *Science* **117**, 355.
Pazur, J. H. (1954). *J. Biol. Chem.* **208**, 439.
Polak, F. (1929). *Biochem. Z.* **212**, 363.
Rachele, J. R., Kuchinskas, E. J., Kratzer, F. H., and du Vigneaud, V. (1955). *J. Biol. Chem.* **315**, 593.
Racker, E. (1951). *J. Biol. Chem.* **190**, 685.
Racker, E. (1954). *Advances in Enzymol.* **15**, 141.
Racker, E. (1955). *In* "Methods in Enzymology" (S. P. Colowick and N. O. Kaplan, eds.), Vol. I, p. 500. Academic Press, New York.
Racker, E., de la Haba, G., and Leder, I. G. (1953). *J. Am. Chem. Soc.* **75**, 1010.
Racker, E., de la Haba, G., and Leder, I. G. (1954). *Arch. Biochem. and Biophys.* **48**, 238.
Robison, R. (1932). *Biochem. J.* **26**, 2191.
Robison, R., Macfarlane, M. G., and Tazelaar, A. (1938). *Nature* **142**, 114.
Sable, H. Z. (1952). *Biochim. et Biophys. Acta* **8**, 687.
Schäffner, A., and Specht, H. (1938). *Naturwiss.* **26**, 494.
Seegmiller, J. E. (1953). *J. Biol. Chem.* **201**, 629.
Segal, H. L., and Boyer, P. D. (1953). *J. Biol. Chem.* **204**, 265.
Slator, A. (1908). *J. Chem. Soc.* **93**, 217.
Slein, M. W. (1950). *J. Biol. Chem.* **186**, 753.
Slein, M. W. (1954). *Federation Proc.* **13**, 299.
Smyrniotis, P. Z., and Horecker, B. L. (1956). *J. Biol. Chem.* **218**, 745.
Somers, G. F., and Cosby, E. L. (1945). *Arch. Biochem.* **6**, 295.
Sonderhoff, R., and Thomas, H. (1937). *Ann. Chem. Justus Liebigs* **530**, 195.
Sowden, J. C., Frankel, S., Moore, B. H., and McClary, J. E. (1954). *J. Biol. Chem.* **206**, 547.

Srere, P. A., Cooper, J. R., Klybas, V., and Racker, E. (1955). *Arch. Biochem. and Biophys.* **59**, 535.

Srinivasan, P. R., Katagiri, M., and Sprinson, D. B. (1955). *J. Am. Chem. Soc.* **77**, 4944.

Stern, J. R., Shapiro, B., and Ochoa, S. (1950). *Nature* **166**, 403.

Stickland, L. H. (1956). *Biochem. J.* **64**, 515.

Stumpf, P. K. (1948). *J. Biol. Chem.* **176**, 233.

Sutherland, E. W., Cohn, M., Posternak, T., and Cori, C. F. (1949a). *J. Biol. Chem.* **180**, 1285.

Sutherland, E. W., Posternak, T., and Cori, C. F. (1949b). *J. Biol. Chem.* **181**, 153.

Sutherland, E. W., Colowick, S. P., and Cori, C. F. (1941). *J. Biol. Chem.* **140**, 309.

Swartz, M. N., Kaplan, N. O., and Frech, M. E. (1956). *Science* **123**, 50.

Taylor, J. F. (1951). *In* "Phosphorous Metabolism" (W. D. McElroy and B. Glass, eds.), Vol. I, pp. 104–116. Johns Hopkins, Baltimore.

Taylor, J. F., Green, A. A., and Cori, G. T. (1948). *J. Biol. Chem.* **173**, 591.

Thorn, M. B. (1951). *Biochem. J.* **49**, 602.

Trucco, R. E. (1954). *Nature* **174**, 1103.

Trucco, R. E., Caputto, R., Leloir, L. F., and Mittelman, N. (1948). *Arch. Biochem.* **18**, 137.

Utter, M. F., and Werkman, C. H. (1942a). *J. Biol. Chem.* **146**, 289.

Utter, M. F., and Werkman, C. H. (1942b). *Biochem. J.* (*London*) **36**, 485.

Vallee, B. L., and Hoch, F. L. (1955). *J. Am. Chem. Soc.* **77**, 821.

Velick, S. F., and Hayes, J. E. Jr. (1953). *J. Biol. Chem.* **203**, 545.

Virtanen, A. I., and Sundman, J. (1942). *Biochem. Z.* **313**, 236.

von Euler, H., and Adler, E. (1935). *Hoppe-Seyler's Z. physiol. Chem.* **235**, 122.

Warburg, O. (1948). "Schwermetalle als Wirkungsgruppen von Fermenten," 2nd ed., p. 163. W. Saenger, Berlin.

Warburg, O., and Christian, W. (1939a). *Biochem. Z.* **301**, 221.

Warburg, O., and Christian, W. (1939b). *Biochem. Z.* **303**, 40.

Warburg, O., and Christian, W. (1942). *Biochem. Z.* **310**, 384.

Warburg, O., and Christian, W. (1943). *Biochem. Z.* **314**, 149.

Warburg, O., Christian, W., and Griese, A. (1935a). *Biochem. Z.* **279**, 143.

Warburg, O., Christian, W., and Griese, A. (1935b). *Biochem. Z.* **282**, 157.

Weichherz, J. (1931). *Biochem. Z.* **238**, 325.

Weinhouse, S., and Millington, R. H. (1947). *J. Am. Chem. Soc.* **69**, 3089.

Weinhouse, S., Millington, R. H., and Lewis, K. F. (1948). *J. Am. Chem. Soc.* **70**, 3680.

Wieland, H., and Sonderhoff, R. (1932). *Ann. Chem. Justus Liebigs* **499**, 213.

Wilkinson, J. F. (1949). *Biochem. J.* **44**, 460.

Wood, H. G. (1955). *Physiol. Revs.* **35**, 841.

Young, W. J. (1909). *Proc. Roy. Soc.* **B81**, 528.

Zerner, E. (1920). *Ber. deut. chem. Ges.* **53**, 325.

CHAPTER VIII

Synthesis and Degradation of Cellular Carbohydrates by Yeasts

W. E. Trevelyan

> *If I am to be quite honest, there are many points on
> these subjects still open to doubt; questions can be raised
> which I confess I am not competent to solve or to dis-
> entangle; this is not because they have not got definite
> natural explanations, but because I am ignorant of them.*
> John Ray, 1627–1705

1. Introduction

A. *Function of Cell Carbohydrates*

 The gross chemical composition of the yeast cell shows that carbohydrates play an important part in its economy. Most of the cell is, of
course, water: of the other constituents, protein bulks largest, accounting
for about a half of the dry matter of commercial baker's yeasts, but carbohydrate is not far behind making up, as it does, one-third of the dry
matter. (The exact fraction varies within quite wide limits according to
the way the yeast has been grown.) (See also Chapter V.)

 The role of protein needs no emphasis. The astonishing rapidity of the
complex chemical reactions which occur in the living cell is due to the
catalytic activity of specialized proteins, the enzymes: their extreme
specificity explains, in part, the linking together of reactions into an
ordered and balanced pattern. These ideas, commonplace nowadays, had
a long historical development, which has been documented by Walden
(1949).

 Present understanding of the function of cellular carbohydrates is not
so precise, nor does it go so deep. The presence in brewer's yeast of reserve food material in the form of glycogen was discovered in 1885 by
Errera; but the conditions under which glycogen is utilized, and the detailed mechanism of its synthesis and breakdown, are still obscure. Some
years later, Salkowski (1894a,b) described other polysaccharides which
had no storage function, but were on the other hand important components of the cell structure, particularly of the cell wall. The presence

in yeast of carbohydrates is therefore not adventitious, but essential. Indeed, if their formation is obstructed by sodium fluoride, the growth of the yeast cells is inhibited (Nickerson and Chung, 1952; Chung and Nickerson, 1954).

It must not be thought that the term *structural* implies a purely mechanical role. Enzymes of yeast cells, as of other cells, appear to be organized on a "federal" basis, the individual members of a metabolic sequence being closely associated—a concept which has been held, in a nebulous form, for a long time, but which is being brought into increasingly better definition by recent experimentation. Particulate elements of the cell, such as microsomes and mitochondria (for references on yeast mitochondria see Linnane and Still, 1955; see also Chapter IV) have been separated by differential centrifugation, and their associated multienzyme sequences studied; even these small sub-units may be structurally complex, for example in possessing selectively permeable membranes. The organization and regulation of metabolic processes rests, therefore, not only upon the molecular architecture of the proteins, but upon their grouping and disposition in space, and upon the physico-chemical properties of the membranes and surfaces upon which they are oriented. In this, it may be conjectured that cellular carbohydrates will prove to play an important part.

These considerations are not merely of purely theoretical interest. Experience in the manufacture of baker's yeasts has shown that nitrogen (protein) content parallels metabolic activity, e.g., fermentation rate, but that a high carbohydrate content confers on the cell *stability*, for example towards storage (Joslyn, 1955), towards attack by acids (Henneberg and Böhmer, 1921), or towards the drying process used in the manufacture of active dried yeast (Pollock and Holmstrom, 1951).

B. Carbohydrate Synthesis as a Growth Process

The function of carbohydrates, then, is of sufficient practical and theoretical importance to arouse interest in the paths by which these materials are formed and degraded in the yeast cell. Apart from this, the synthetic process commands interest in its own right as contributing to the understanding of growth. Growth is a deceptively simple word, whose associations and overtones change with the progress of biological science: from one aspect it may be considered as the orderly synthesis of the macromolecules of which the cell is largely made up. The steps by which a living cell transforms, let us say, glucose into one of the simpler polysaccharide macromolecules such as glycogen are (relatively) few and straightforward. The enzymes involved have been isolated from various sources and purified, offering, as Stacey (1954) points out, an impressive *in vitro* demonstration of growth. There is no doubt that the chemical and physico-chemical concepts evolved during the study of these enzymes will be of great assistance in unravelling the far more complex processes of protein and nucleic acid synthesis.

By using yeast as one's experimental material, the synthesis of polysaccharides in a living system can be studied virtually as an isolated process. Protein and nucleic acid formation can be minimized by suspending the yeast in a medium which does not contain a source of assimilable nitrogen, for example a simple buffer solution. Synthesis of lipids, though not exclusively an aerobic process (Klein, 1955), proceeds to only a small extent during the anaerobic fermentation of sugars such as glucose (Smedley-Maclean, 1922; Kleinzeller, 1948; Klein and Lipmann, 1953). On the other hand, under such conditions cellular carbohydrates are laid down at rates equal to, or even greater than, the rates of their formation when yeast is cultivated aerobically in a complete growth medium.

C. Regulation of Carbohydrate Synthesis and Breakdown in the Yeast Cell

Surprisingly little is definitely known about the nature of the enzyme reactions involved in the synthesis or breakdown of yeast carbohydrates. Glycogen metabolism has been most studied, but even in this case the usual assumption that a phosphorylase system plays a major part rests to some extent on analogy with other, better known, plant or animal enzymes. Some of these problems of mechanism, for example the way in which the β-linkages of the glucose polymer glucan (yeast "cellulose") are formed, are of general as well as special interest.

However, attention has been focused on problems of the *regulation* of synthetic reactions, and particularly on the extent of assimilation during carbohydrate storage—that is to say, the ratio between the amount of sugar polymerized and retained by the yeast cell and that converted during fermentation or respiration into carbon dioxide and ethanol, or carbon dioxide and water.

Early work (see Clifton, 1946 for a review) showed that the fraction of metabolized sugar assimilated was strikingly constant, not only with respect to time (at least for some hours), but also as between different samples of yeast under comparable conditions. Discussion in thermodynamic terms has often been appended to reports of experimental work on assimilation: perhaps "constant ratio" leads one quite naturally to think of equilibrium; perhaps thermodynamic argument, being independent of mechanism, is attractive when the nature of the intermediate stages in a transformation is largely unknown. It is, however, becoming generally realized that thermodynamic considerations must be applied with caution to the reaction networks found in living systems. For example, calculations are sometimes made of the "available free energy" resulting from say the fermentation of one mole of glucose to two moles each of ethanol and carbon dioxide; however, the figures mean little when one considers that some of the reactions involved, for example, the decarboxylation of pyruvate, catalyzed by carboxylase, are irreversible.

In fact, when dealing with the synthesis of cellular carbohydrates as one of the major assimilatory processes, we are concerned with a problem in *kinetics:* the relative rates at which some intracellular intermediate is transformed by two or more multi-enzyme systems (Dixon, 1949) which result on the one hand in the production of diffusible end-products such as carbon dioxide, on the other hand in the storage of glycogen, mannan, and so on.

D. *Concentration of Intermediates and Structural Organization of Enzymes as Factors in the Regulation of Cell Kinetics*

The most striking aspect of cell kinetics is that the net result, for example in terms of substrate metabolized and cell material formed, is not variable or capricious, in spite of the complexity of the system. Indeed, the regulation of reaction rates inside the yeast cell is of the same degree of precision as some commonly used analytical techniques. Moreover, the systems show stability, in the sense of resistance to small changes in external conditions.

How is this achieved? One important factor governing the kinetics of an enzyme is probably the intracellular concentration of its specific substrate when this is below saturation level for the particular enzyme concerned. Beck (1955), studying the glycolytic system of leukocytes, found that the over-all rate of glycolysis was less than the maximum rate *in vitro* of the individual enzyme systems which therefore could not have been saturated with respect to their substrates when operating in the cell. The saturation of carboxylase by pyruvate in fermentation by baker's yeast (Trevelyan and Harrison, 1954) is thought to be a special case (Trevelyan and Harrison, 1956b). In general, it is tentatively suggested that the normal intracellular concentration of an intermediate in a multi-enzyme sequence approximates the Michaelis constant of the enzyme following it.

From this point of view, the function of the metabolic systems of fermentation and respiration is not so much the provision of energy, but the maintenance inside the cell of definite concentrations of intermediates which form the starting points of other reaction chains leading to the synthesis notably of the macromolecules of which the cell is largely formed.

It may be argued that the structural organization of yeast enzyme systems makes nonsense of any attempt to treat cell kinetics in the light of principles strictly applicable only to homogeneous reactions. That may be so: but possibly it will be precisely from the failure of such attempts that the significance of structure will become apparent. The anaerobic assimilation of glucose by yeast would seem to offer one of the less complex examples of the interrelation between growth and catabolism, the study of which may throw light upon these controversial and ill-defined questions of the basis of kinetic regulation.

E. *Present Status of Knowledge of Carbohydrate Synthesis and Degradation in Yeast*

It would be idle to pretend that material exists for even a tentative outline of a complete physiology of yeast cellular carbohydrate. Many studies have been made, often by investigators using yeast as a convenient experimental tool, but not interested in it as such. They range over a wide field, giving hints on all the problems raised in this introduction, but few definite answers. The selection and method of presentation of experimental facts in this review is intended to draw attention to the gaps in our present knowledge of an important aspect of yeast metabolism, as much as to suggest possible answers to the many interesting problems which have arisen.

2. Yeast Carbohydrates

A. *Preparations from Baker's and Brewer's Yeast*

Most work on the chemistry and metabolism of yeast carbohydrates concerns varieties of *Saccharomyces cerevisiae,* which is readily available in quantity as commercial baking or brewing yeast. Four carbohydrates have been purified from this source (Neuberg, 1950; Whistler and Smart, 1953). Three are high molecular weight polysaccharides namely glycogen, mannan (yeast gum), and glucan (yeast cellulose) (see Chapter V). The nonreducing disaccharide trehalose occurs in baker's yeast, but not in brewer's yeast.

The term *glycogen* originally referred to a polysaccharide found in the cell plasma, particularly of animal cells, which yields glucose as the end product of hydrolysis and which gives a reddish color with iodine (Meyer, 1943). The staining properties of yeast under various conditions led Errera (1885) to suggest the presence of glycogen, and its function as a carbohydrate reserve. Its preparation is not entirely straightforward, since the yeast cell is enclosed by a tough membrane of insoluble glucan through which the glycogen molecule diffuses with difficulty. Harden and Young (1902, 1912) broke this barrier by grinding yeast with sand. Glycogen and mannan were then extracted with boiling water, and separated by fractionation with ammonium sulfate. Later investigators have preferred to remove mannan by precipitation (as the copper complex) with Fehling's solution (Stockhausen and Silbereisen, 1936a; Jeanloz, 1944). Protein contaminating glycogen preparations may be removed by Sevag's technique of shaking with chloroform (Stockhausen and Silbereisen, 1936a) or by precipitation with picric acid (Jeanloz, 1944). A more usual procedure is to destroy protein by Pflüger's method, that is, treatment with hot 60% potassium hydroxide, towards which glycogen is stable (Bell, 1948).

Treatment with alkali, though useful in purifying glycogen, is not successful as a method of *extraction* from either fresh or dried yeast, owing to the resistance of the glucan envelope. Much early work on yeast glycogen was done at a time when glycogen could not be defined in terms of its molecular structure, and investigators tended to assume that any polysaccharide not extracted by alkali could not be glycogen. Salkowski (1894a,b) first showed that alkaline extracts contained principally mannan: although the cell debris was stained with iodine he considered glycogen to be absent from yeast, which contained instead "erythrocellulose." Ling and his collaborators (Ling *et al.*, 1925; Daoud and Ling, 1931a,b) thought that the glycogen of the yeast cell existed in two distinct forms, one (extracted by alkali) a constituent of the plasma, the other intimately connected with the cell wall which was a complex of mannan and glycogen esterified with silicic and phosphoric acids.

Erythrocellulose (now known to be glycogen) can be extracted from the alkali-insoluble residue by autoclaving with water (Salkowski, 1894b). This is more effective if the cell debris is first treated with cold 1 N hydrochloric acid, when magnesium salts and phosphates dissolve (McAnally and Smedley-Maclean, 1937, who cautiously termed the polysaccharide "pseudoglycogen"). Hot 0.5 N acetic acid has been used in a recent procedure for extracting glycogen (Bell and Northcote, 1950; Northcote, 1953).

That "erythrocellulose" is indeed glycogen follows from the work of Northcote (1953). He found that 3% sodium hydroxide extracted no glycogen from fresh baker's yeast. Glycogen preparations could be made (a) from dried yeast by extraction with sodium hydroxide, when about one-quarter of the glycogen dissolved, (b) from the alkali-insoluble residue of fresh or dried yeast by extraction with acetic acid, or (c) from cells after mechanical disintegration by extracting with boiling water (procedure of Harden and Young, 1902). They had identical chemical properties.

Glycogen, whether obtained from animal tissues, yeast, or bacteria (for bacterial glycogen see Levine *et al.*, 1953), is a branched α-1,4-glucosan, as is the amylopectin component of starch. Glycogen has fewer glucose residues in the unit chains—twelve in the case of glycogen from commercial baker's yeast (Northcote, 1953) or brewer's yeast (Manners and Maung, 1955a). By partial acid hydrolysis of glycogen from baker's yeast only oligosaccharides containing α-1,4 links (e.g., maltose) or α-1,6 links (e.g., isomaltose) are obtained, showing that the branch points are all of the α-1,6 type (Peat *et al.*, 1955a). Yeast glycogen will serve as a substrate for crystalline muscle phosphorylase, by which it can be degraded to the extent of 23% (Manners and Maung, 1955a).

These figures apply to glycogen prepared from commercial yeast samples. As the glycogen content of yeast slowly diminishes, even when stored in the refrigerator, it is possible that glycogen in fresh yeast, or in yeast enriched by fermentation, may show minor differences. This consideration applies to the question of how much glycogen can be extracted by alkali. Trevelyan and Harrison (1956c) agreed with Northcote (1953) in finding little in extracts from pressed baker's yeast, but the amount increased after the yeast had fermented glucose. Throughout, the ratio of glycogen extracted by alkali to that subsequently dissolved from the residue by dilute acetic acid was constant at 0.4.

Yeast glycogen is polydisperse, that is, not made up of molecules of uniform size. Jeanloz (1944) separated a "soluble" (27%) from an "insoluble" fraction (73%) by electrodialysis, while Northcote (1954) identified at least two components after paper electrophoresis.

Trehalose (1-(α-D-glucopyranose)-α-D-glucopyranoside), the other reserve carbohydrate of yeast, was first prepared from this source in 1925 (Koch and Koch, 1925). It had long been known as a constituent of fungi, and was early sought in yeast (Müntz, 1876): it is usually absent from brewer's yeast, because of the way in which it is grown (Stewart *et al.*, 1950) and until Koch and Koch examined baker's yeast, trehalose was thought to be absent altogether from the yeast cell.

The chemistry, occurrence in nature, and enzymology of trehalose has been reviewed by Myrbäck (1949). It apparently occurs in yeast as the free sugar, there being so far no evidence of complexes such as the treha-lose-containing lipids of acid-fast bacteria. Trehalose is readily extracted by ethanol (Koch and Koch, 1925), dilute sulfuric acid (Steiner and Cori, 1935), or cold trichloroacetic acid (Trevelyan and Harrison, 1952). It will diffuse from the cell when the permeability of the cell wall is altered by treatment with a cationic detergent (Trevelyan and Harrison, 1956c).

The reserve carbohydrates of yeast, glycogen and trehalose, are based on glucose residues united by three types of linkage. These are of differ-ent degrees of stability, as may be seen by comparing the rate of hy-drolysis by acid of the disaccharides maltose (α-1,4 linkage), isomaltose (α-1,6 linkage, more stable according to Wolfrom et al., 1951), and trehalose (most stable, see Moelwyn-Hughes, 1929). This may be rele-vant to any consideration of the various enzymic transformations glycogen and trehalose undergo in the yeast cell.

Mannan is usually extracted from yeast with hot, dilute potassium hydroxide, and then precipitated as the copper complex, as described originally by Salkowski (1894a). Strong (75%) sulfuric acid has also been used to extract the polysaccharide (Garzuly-Janke, 1940a). Part of the mannan may be brought into solution with boiling water (Salkowski, 1894a; Garzuly-Janke, 1940a). Even when yeast is dispersed in cold water, a small amount is dissolved; tap water is less effective than dis-tilled water, and more mannan is removed in this way from brewer's yeast than from baker's yeast (Stockhausen and Silbereisen, 1936b). Brewer's yeast contains less mannan than distillery or wine yeasts, and these less than baker's yeast, due to their different conditions of growth (Stockhausen and Silbereisen, 1935a,b,c). Kraut and Eichorn (1927), and Kraut et al. (1927) set about the preparation of mannan quite differently. They removed nitrogenous substances by autolyzing yeast with ethyl acetate and digesting the residue with pepsin. Mannan was brought into solution by the action of diastase or papain, and purified by fractional adsorption on kaolin and aluminum hydroxide.

Mannan yields only D-mannose on hydrolysis (Haworth et al., 1937, Garzuly-Janke, 1940a). Haworth et al. (1941) found the molecule to be made up of 200–400 mannose units. The highly branched structure ap-peared to be based on a repeating unit consisting of 6 mannose residues, three of which were joined by α-1,2 linkages, two by α-1,6 linkages, and one by an α-1,3 linkage. These findings were confirmed by Lindstedt (1945).

Yeast glucan—Salkowski's "achroocellulose"—was obtained by Zech-meister and Tóth (1934) as the insoluble residue left after the cell had been treated successively with dilute alkali and acid. Since the glucose residues of the molecule were linked in the 1,3 position, it was not in fact a cellulose at all. To rebut the charge of Sevag *et al.* (1935) that their glucan was an artifact resulting from the action of acid and alkali, Zechmeister and Tóth (1936) evolved a second method of preparation, whereby pressed yeast was killed with acetic acid and digested with papain and diastase, the residue being washed with water, alcohol, and ether.

The 1,3 linkages in yeast glucan are of the β configuration, as shown by Hassid *et al.* (1941), who prepared the polysaccharide in 7.9% yield from baker's yeast by the successive action of 3% sodium hydroxide and 3% hydrochloric acid. A demonstration of the β-1,3 linkage is provided by the preparation (by partial acid hydrolysis of glucan) of the disaccharide laminaribiose, 3-β-D-glucosyl-D-glucose (Barry and Dillon, 1943).

As they were not satisfied with the methylation technique Hassid had used, Bell and Northcote (1950) reopened the question of the molecular structure of yeast glucan. Their polysaccharide proved to be highly branched, with 10% of 1,2 linkages. The unit chain length was about 10 glucose residues; a previous estimate, by Barry and Dillon (1943), was 28.

Starting with the extraction of unwanted material from yeast by alkali, Bell and Northcote had removed glycogen from the residue with the comparatively mild reagent dilute acetic acid, instead of using hydrochloric acid as Hassid *et al.* (1941) had done. This is why Hassid could find no evidence of molecular branching, unlike Bell and Northcote, according to Kreger and Meeuse (1952). These investigators (see also Houwink and Krege, 1953) consider that "alkali-insoluble" glucan (which they made by treating the mechanically separated cell walls of yeast with sodium hydroxide) is a complex of two types of glucan. Half is dissolved by dilute boiling mineral acid, leaving a polysaccharide they have termed "hydroglucan" and which, by itself, is soluble in cold alkali (see McAnally and Smedley-Maclean, 1937).

B. *The State of Carbohydrates in Living Baker's and Brewer's Yeasts*

The microscopic appearance of yeast cells stained with iodine suggests that glycogen is dispersed in the cytoplasm as granules as illustrated and discussed by Lindegren (1949). More definite information is provided by Northcote and Horne (1952) in examining the composition and structure of the yeast cell wall. They disrupted the cell by agitation with fine glass beads, and separated the cell walls by centrifuging at 1500 × g; these were glycogen-free. Glycogen was sedimented in a fraction consisting of fine particles collected at 14,000 × g.

Particulate glycogen is present in mammalian liver cells, from preparations of which it can be separated in pure form by differential centrifugation (Lazarow, 1942; Claude, 1954). The glycogen is dispersed by agents commonly used for extraction of the polysaccharide from the cell, such as trichloroacetic acid or potassium hydroxide (Lazarow, 1942).

How much of the glycogen of the yeast cell is present in particulate form is not known. More information on this question may resolve the controversy on the significance of the division of glycogen into alkalisoluble and -insoluble fractions (see Section 2A, above). A possibly related issue, also controversial, is the distinction suggested by Willstätter between free glycogen and that combined with protein (lyo- and desmoglycogen), which is discussed by Meyer (1943).

As already mentioned, trehalose appears to exist in the yeast cell as the free sugar, which is prevented from diffusing out of the cell by an osmotic barrier near the surface. Yeast may simultaneously contain trehalose and the hydrolytic enzyme trehalase (Myrbäck, 1949), which raises interesting questions of the relative location within the cell of this enzyme and its specific substrate.

More is known about the location and state of combination in the yeast cell of the polysaccharides mannan and glucan. Garzuly-Janke (1940a) suggested that mannan was associated, in vivo, with protein, and was a constituent of the cell wall. Macromolecular complexes containing polysaccharide have been extracted by Lindquist (1953a,b) from baker's and brewer's yeasts using mild procedures, and their physico-chemical properties studied. Protein linked to mannan may include enzymes. Invertase, after purification, was found by Fischer and Kohtès (1951; see also Cifonelli and Smith, 1955) to be a complex of specific protein and mannan. The polysaccharide acted as a stabilizer, for when the components were resolved by electrophoresis enzyme activity was rapidly lost. Yeast hexokinase is reported to be a glycoprotein containing 50% of mannose; it separates into two components after paper electrophoresis (Boser, 1955).

In acid solutions, yeast loses its invertase activity more readily than its capacity to ferment glucose (Willstätter and Lowry, 1925; Myrbäck and Willstaedt, 1955), and this has been held to imply that invertase is located near the cell surface (Mandels, 1953; Myrbäck and Willstaedt, 1955). Hexokinase is also a surface enzyme, according to arguments presented by Rothstein (1954a,b).

Recently, direct evidence has been obtained that the yeast cell wall contains mannan and glucan as major components, together with protein and lipid. Cell wall material, prepared after mechanical disintegration of the yeast cell, is seen in electron microscope photographs (for which see Northcote and Horne, 1952) to consist of at least two membranes: the appearance is made more distinct when lipid has been first extracted with methanol and ether. After mannan and protein have been removed in dilute sodium hydroxide, only one layer remains, containing glucan. The multiple nature of membranes of the yeast cell wall has also been demonstrated by electron microscopy of ultra-thin sections (Bartholomew and Levin, 1955; Agar and Douglas, 1955). Glucan has a characteristic infrared spectrum, which resembles the spectrum of the whole yeast cell (*Saccharomyces* and *Hansenula* spp.), the constancy of which under varied conditions of growth is noteworthy (Simon and Hedrick, 1955). Electron diffraction methods have been applied in a study of the structure and orientation of the lipids of the cell wall (Hurst, 1952). The cell wall of baker's yeast contains a small amount of chitin (Houwink *et al.,* 1951; Roelofsen and Hoette, 1951).

Recently a mannan-protein which is thought to play a role in cellular division has been prepared from yeast (Nickerson and Falcone, 1956). An alkaline solution of the cell wall fraction was dialyzed, and then lyophilized to give a product which was separated into a water-soluble mannan-protein and an insoluble gel, apparently a glucan-protein. The mannan complex contained 6.8% protein, a pseudokeratin of high sulfur content. Its disulfide groups could be reduced to sulfhydryl by enzymes present in the mitochondria of baker's yeast.

Whether glucan, and more particularly mannan, are found exclusively in the cell wall is not known. The structure of the yeast cell is complex, and several interior membranes have been distinguished by Bartholomew and Mitwer (1952).

The cell wall of baker's yeast occupies a considerable part of the total cell volume. Northcote and Horne (1952) found that cell wall material accounted for 15% of the cell dry weight. Roelofsen (1953) gives a figure of 20%, his preparation containing 34% each of mannan and glucan, and 1% chitin. By studying the extent of penetration of various solutes into the yeast cell, Conway and Downey (1950a) distinguished an *outer metabolic region,* which they identified with the cell wall. The cell wall may include enzymes, some possibly concerned in polysaccharide synthesis. According to Rothstein (1954a), enzymes of the cell surface may be expected to be concerned with the production and maintenance of the surface itself, and with activities related to interactions between the cell and its environment, such as digestion of extracellular substances, synthesis of extracellular enzymes, and active transfer of substances into the cell.

Structural investigations on the cell wall of yeast (and of other types of cell) will eventually link up with kinetic studies directed toward evaluating the part played by active transport mechanisms concerned with the uptake of metabolites into the cell. This subject, which at present is receiving a good deal of attention, appears to be in somewhat confused state, and will probably continue to be so as long as evidence adduced for one or other mechanism remains largely indirect.

Polysaccharides of the cell surface may be responsible for the flocculation of yeast induced by borates (Van Laer, 1906; Lindquist, 1953c; see Chapter XIII). Highly polymerized polysaccharides such as yeast mannan form gels with borates *in vitro* (Zittle, 1951) and are also important determinants of immunological properties (Tomcsik, 1930; Sevag *et al.*, 1935; Klopstock and Vercellone, 1936; Vendrely and Sarciron, 1945; Rawson and Norris, 1947; Vogel, 1954).

It should be evident from this brief account that a description of yeast cell carbohydrates in their natural state will require detailed knowledge of cell structure. In all probability, the action of enzymes concerned in carbohydrate synthesis and breakdown will have to be related to structure, through evidence in this field is meager at the present time.

C. Polysaccharides from Yeasts Other than Saccharomyces

The composition of the cell walls of various species has been elucidated by x-ray diffraction (Kreger, 1954). *Rhodotorula glutinosa* and *Sporobolomyces roseus* were found to lack both glucan and mannan. Garzuly-Janke (1940b) had previously observed that *Rhodotorula* was an exception to the rule that budding fungi (in contradistinction to filamentous fungi) contained mannan. Other mannan-deficient species, *Nadsonia fulvescens* and *Schizosaccharomyces octosporus*, contained glucan. Except in the last-named species, mannan deficiency was associated with an increased chitin content. In *Schizosaccharomyces*, an unknown alkali-soluble microcrystalline component was detected.

Of more immediate interest (as bearing on the mechanism of glycogen synthesis) is the finding that the capsulated nonfermenting asporogenous yeasts (Mager and Aschner, 1947), including the pathogenic species *Cryptococcus* (*Torulopsis*) *neoformans*, liberate into the growth medium not only the capsular material which contains xylose, mannose, and glucuronic acid (Evans and Theriault, 1953) and has antigenic properties (Neill *et al.*, 1948), but also a starchlike polysaccharide, provided the medium is allowed to become acid during growth (Aschner *et al.*, 1945; Mager, 1947). Hehre *et al.* (1949) succeeded in preparing a crystalline amylose, using Schoch's technique of starch fractionation with amyl alcohol mixtures. Left in solution were the serologically active capsular pentosan, and a glycogenlike polysaccharide.

3. Enzymes Which Catalyze the Formation or Degradation of Yeast Cell Carbohydrates *in Vitro*

A. *Enzymes Acting on Mannan or Glucan*

Neither mannan nor glucan forms part of the endogenous food reserve. Thus the former, unlike glycogen, is not utilized when yeast is stored (Hashitani, 1927). Even when yeast autolyzes, mannan and glucan are not broken down (Joslyn, 1955) and microscopic examination shows that after autolysis the glucan membrane still retains the shape of the cell.

It seems that no enzyme has been prepared from yeast which will degrade these carbohydrates, much less accomplish their synthesis, though an early report (Kraut *et al.*, 1927) presents evidence for the occurrence in yeast of a "yeast-gum splitting enzyme." Manners (1955), in reviewing the enzymic degradation of polysaccharides, does not mention any enzyme (from any source) which has been shown to attack yeast mannan although enzymes from barley and other plant sources are known which partially hydrolyze yeast glucan to glucose and laminaribiose. Enzymes in the digestive juice of the snail, *Helix pomatia*, attack glucan (Holden and Tracey, 1950) and can even dissolve away the membrane from whole yeast without disorganizing the cell (Giaja, 1919, 1922). The effect on fermentation rate, a decrease, is said to resemble that produced by toluene, and both agents induce autofermentation.

B. *Glycogen Metabolism: Phosphorylase and Related Enzymes*

Cremer (1899) first demonstrated the occurrence in yeast of enzymes capable of breaking down and synthesizing glycogen. Press juice from very fresh yeast, he found, had a high glycogen content and gave, after deproteinization, a red coloration with iodine but juice which had been kept for 6 to 12 hours no longer reacted in this way. If then sugar were added to glycogen-free juice, a positive reaction with iodine became evident, in most cases, after a further 12 to 24 hours. Polysaccharide formation accompanying the fermentation of glucose or fructose by yeast maceration juice was studied by Harden and Young (1913). As long as free phosphate was present, the sugar disappearing was found to be completely accounted for as carbon dioxide, ethanol, and hexose diphosphate. If, however, fermentation were prolonged for 17 hours after the phosphate had been esterified, a proportion of the sugar was converted into a dextrorotatory carbohydrate. Although a test for glycogen was positive, subsequent work (Naganishi, 1926) showed that only a small fraction of the carbohydrate synthesized was glycogen. The major fraction was presumably trehalose, not then known to occur in yeast (see Section 3, B).

In the inter-war period attention became concentrated on the breakdown of glycogen by the glycolytic systems found in yeast and muscle extracts. At an early stage, the basic similarity in the reaction mechanism of the two systems became apparent. Work up to 1931 with yeast preparations is described by Harden (1932). In 1927, Meyerhof showed that when glycogen was fermented, more phosphate was esterified per mole of carbon dioxide formed than was the case with glucose. A further step was taken three years later by Nilsson, who observed that glycogen could induce the esterification of phosphate by apozymase preparations which could not, in the absence of coenzyme I, ferment glucose. These, and other findings, are now seen as a prelude to the announcement by Parnas (see Parnas, 1937) that the initial step in glycogen breakdown was to be formulated as a *phosphorolysis*. The reaction was demonstrated in muscle extracts and shortly afterwards (1936) followed the Coris' discovery that the product of phosphorolysis was a new phosphate ester, glucose-1-phosphate. The reaction was shown to occur, not only in muscle preparations, but also in dialyzed yeast extract (Cori *et al.*, 1938; Lehmann, 1938). *En passant*, it may be observed that in most experiments with yeast enzymes the glycogen was of animal origin; some work with yeast glycogen (so-called erythrocellulose) was however reported by Gottschalk (1926).

Although Kiessling (1939a) demonstrated the reversibility of the reaction with the aid of a phosphorylase from yeast, and thus opened up the study of glycogen *synthesis*, recent work has been based on enzymes prepared from other sources—muscle, plants, especially the potato, and bacteria. It therefore seems best to summarize first the modern understanding of the phosphorylase reaction, so as better to assess what little is known of the yeast system. For a more detailed account, one of several recent reviews may be consulted. The enzymology of starch and glycogen has been reviewed by Bernfeld (1951) and by Myrbäck and Neumüller (1951). Phosphorylases are treated by Hassid, Doudoroff, and Barker (1951). Barker and Bourne (1953) write on the synthesis of polysaccharides, Manners (1955) on their degradation. Hassid (1951, 1954) is the author of two articles of which the second, on the biosynthesis of complex saccharides, is particularly clear and concise. The mechanism of transglycosidation, including the transfer of sugar residues to a receptor molecule to form higher saccharides, is considered by Kalckar (1954).

The synthesis of the branched glycogen (or amylopectin) molecule is believed to occur in two stages, corresponding to the two types of linkage present, 1,4-α and 1,6-α. In the first stage, the glucosyl radical is regarded as transferred reversibly from combination in a donor molecule to a receptor molecule, which must be a complex saccharide such as glycogen itself, though the minimum degree of complexity necessary for reaction differs from enzyme to enzyme. The donor molecule may be α-D-glucose-1-phosphate, in which case the enzyme is a phosphorylase, or the disaccharides sucrose and maltose. Amylosucrase and amylomaltase, as the corresponding enzymes are called, have not as yet been detected in yeast. The repetition of this process builds up to a long, straight chain of 1,4-α-linked glucose residues, as in amylose;[1] and, in fact, the purified phosphorylases from muscle and potato synthesize from glucose-1-phosphate (and a trace of priming polysaccharide) carbohydrates which, like amylose, stain blue with iodine and show the phenomenon of retrogradation. In the absence of a receptor molecule no reaction takes place.

Provided the external chains of a polysaccharide comprise more than a certain minimum number of 1,4-α-linked glucose residues, and less than a rather indefinite maximum number, both the rate of the forward reaction (in which glucosyl radicals are transferred from glucose-1-phosphate to the nonreducing end of a chain) and of the back reaction are proportional to the number of nonreducing end groups in the polysaccharide receptor molecule. Consequently, the equilibrium state, when forward and back reactions proceed equally fast, is not affected by the amount of receptor polysaccharide.

Equilibrium is characterized by the ratio of orthophosphate to glucose-1-phosphate and is little affected by temperature. In the physiological pH range, solutions of phosphates contain mainly the monovalent and divalent ions, for example $H_2PO_4^-$ and HPO_4^{--}, and the actual substrate for phosphorylase is one of these ionic species, though which one is not known. At equilibrium, where a_H denotes the antilog of pH (hydrogen

$$\frac{[\text{orthophosphate}]}{[\text{glucose-1-phosphate}]} = K_a \cdot \frac{a_H + K'_P}{a_H + K'_G} = K_b \cdot \frac{K'_G}{K'_P} \cdot \frac{a_H + K'_P}{a_H + K'_G}$$

ion activity), K'_P and K'_G the apparent second dissociation constants of phosphoric and glucose-1-phosphoric acids, respectively. Thus the equilibrium ratio of phosphate/glucose-1-phosphate depends upon pH, but not the ratio of the monovalent ions (K_a) or of the divalent ions (K_b). K_a has a value of about 12, which is therefore the limiting value of the

[1] The structure of amylose still presents some problems (see Neufeld and Hassid, 1955).

equilibrium ratio phosphate/glucose-1-phosphate reached as the pH is lowered. As pH is increased, a limit of 2.4 (K_b, the ratio of the divalent ions) is approached. Acid conditions thus favor glycogen synthesis. The pH at the site of phosphorylase action in the yeast cell is not known; the over-all pH of the cell (Conway and Downey, 1950b) is 6–6.5, when the equilibrium ratio would be about 6.

Equilibrium conditions are of course independent of the source from which phosphorylase has been derived. The same cannot be said of reaction kinetics, especially in their quantitative aspect and, unfortunately, little appears to be known regarding the kinetics of the yeast enzyme.

Weibull and Tiselius (1945) reported that the reaction catalyzed by the potato enzyme was characterized by three independent Michaelis constants, corresponding to the three substrates glucose-1-phosphate, phosphate, and polysaccharide. The rate of transformation of glucose-1-phosphate can therefore be written

$$ -\frac{dG}{dt} = \frac{A}{K_a + A} \left\{ \frac{V \dfrac{G}{K_g} - V' \dfrac{P}{K_p}}{1 + \dfrac{G}{K_g} + \dfrac{P}{K_p}} \right\} $$

where A stands for the concentration of polysaccharide, G and P stand for the concentrations of glucose-1-phosphate and phosphate respectively, the K's for Michaelis constants and the V's for the maximum (saturation) rates of the forward and back reactions.

From this equation the equilibrium ratio phosphate/glucose-1-phosphate is seen to equal $VK_p/V'K_g$, so that the relative maximum rates for forward and back reactions cannot be deduced from the equilibrium constant without knowing the Michaelis constants.

The decomposition of glucose-1-phosphate, using either potato or muscle phosphorylase with sufficient priming polysaccharide, follows first-order kinetics. If the reaction is accurately described by the equation we have written, it follows that the Michaelis constants with respect to phosphate and glucose-1-phosphate are equal. This may be seen by writing the initial glucose-1-phosphate concentration as G_0, and the phosphate produced after time t as x, and then recasting the kinetic equation; it will be found that the denominator contains no x term only when $K_p = K_g$. This is not the case with figures quoted by Weibull and Tiselius (1945). The potato enzyme has been reinvestigated (Trevelyan, unpublished data), in a system containing amylopectin, with maleate buffers pH 5.4–6.8 at 30°C., ionic strength 0.2. K_p/K_g varied from about 2 at pH 5.4 to 0.5 at pH 6.8, and was unity only at pH 6.2, when both constants were about 10^{-3} M.

The detailed mechanism of the phosphorylase reaction has not yet been elucidated. In the absence of polysaccharide, the enzyme, either muscle or potato phosphorylase, will catalyze neither exchange between inorganic P^{32} and glucose-1-phosphate nor the arsenolysis of glucose-1-phosphate (Cohn and Cori, 1948) (see below). The initial step in the reaction cannot therefore be formulated as:

$$\text{Glucose-1-phosphate} + \text{Enzyme} \rightleftharpoons \text{Enzyme–glucose complex} + \text{Phosphate}$$

as it can in the case of sucrose phosphorylase.

Polysaccharides of which the molecule is made up of an unbranched, linear chain of 1,4-α-linked glucose residues are completely degraded to glucose-1-phosphate by phosphoylase in the presence of excess of phosphate. If the latter is replaced by arsenate, the end product is free glucose (arsenolysis). The enzyme cannot, however, break or by-pass the 1,6-α-linkage of a branched polysaccharide such as glycogen; thus, the glycogen of brewer's yeast is only partially converted into glucose-1-phosphate (to the extent of 23% according to Manners and Maung, 1955a). The other product of the reaction, a phosphorylase-resistant dextrin, is attacked by enzymes such as amylo-1,6-glucosidase from muscle or R-enzyme from potato (which differ in specificity): 1,6-α-linkages are broken, exposing the dextrin to further degradation by phosphorylase.

Phosphorylase, then, can neither break nor form 1,6 linkages. The second step in the synthesis of glycogen or amylopectin is brought about by an enzyme (Q-enzyme from potato and other plant sources, and from bacteria, "branching factor" from animal tissues) which has a transglucosylase action upon the amylose chains built up by phosphorylase. These are broken up into smaller units by the conversion of about one in every twenty 1,4 linkages into the 1,6 configuration. The reaction catalyzed by Q-enzyme has been written (Barker and Bourne, 1953):

$$\overset{A}{\longrightarrow} + \text{Q-enzyme} = \overset{B}{-} \text{Q-enzyme} + \overset{C}{\longrightarrow} \tag{1}$$

$$\overset{B}{-} \text{Q-enzyme}_{-}^{"} + \overset{D}{\longrightarrow} = \frac{|B}{D} + \text{Q-enzyme} \tag{2}$$

Here A is an amylose-type substrate, the arrows indicate chains of 1,4-α-linked glucose residues with the reducing group at the arrowhead, and the branch points are through the 1,6-α positions. The reaction is apparently irreversible, possibly reflecting the greater energy content of the 1,4 linkage (see Section 2, A above).

Recently Manners and Maung (1956c) succeeded in preparing a

branching enzyme by ethanol-citrate fractionation of an extract of brewer's yeast at $-5°C$. When amylose was incubated for 20 hours with the enzyme, the end product gave a reddish-brown coloration with iodine. The branch points synthesized by yeast-branching enzyme were hydrolyzed by yeast isoamylase (see below) and were therefore of the $1,6$-α type.

Before leaving the subject of phosphorylases from sources other than yeast, it is worth mention that the enzymes from liver and muscle can be inactivated by other enzymes present in these tissues. This has been discussed by Sutherland (1951), who points out that the amount of active phosphorylase in liver and muscle represents a balance between inactivation and resynthesis of the active form. The change from the inactive to the active form can be extremely rapid, so that the active enzyme can be doubled in a few minutes. Phosphorylase b of muscle (arising from the action of the PR-enzyme on phosphorylase a, the active form) requires adenylic acid as a coenzyme. Adenylic acid has no action on the inactivated form of the liver enzyme. Inactivation of liver phosphorylase is paralleled by the release of inorganic phosphate from the enzyme, 1 mole from about 124,000 g. Also, when liver slices are incubated with radioactive phosphate, the latter is rapidly incorporated into phosphorylase (Sutherland and Wosilait, 1955).

More details of the properties of liver phosphorylase, and of the inactivating and reactivating enzymes have appeared (Sutherland and Wosilait, 1956; Wosilait and Sutherland, 1956; Rall et al., 1956a). The interconversion of phosphorylase a and b (inactive form) from muscle has been investigated by Rall et al. (1956b) and by Krebs and Fischer (1956). Adenosine triphosphate is a cofactor for enzymic reactivation of either liver or muscle phosphorylase. It now seems clear that the amount of phosphorylase present in the active form is a major factor in the regulation of glycogen metabolism in muscle (Cori, 1956). The existence of a similar mechanism in yeast has not been established, but would go far to explain many of the apparent anomalies of glycogen metabolism in this organism.

Turning now to yeast phosphorylase and related enzymes, a suitable point of departure is the paper by Schäffner and Specht (1938a). Studying the breakdown of glycogen by cell-free yeast extracts, they found that phosphorolysis was not affected by dialysis (so no coenzyme appeared to be involved), by exposure to a pH of 8.6 for 3 hours (which destroyed hexokinase), or by keeping the extract for 8 days in the refrigerator. After such treatment the extract lost the power of phosphorylating glucose. Enzymes which brought about the phosphorylation of glucose could be freed from phosphorylase by fractional precipitation with acetone. Phosphorolysis was accompanied by a hydrolytic splitting of glycogen, a reaction which, initially, was slower. Subsequently Schäffner and Specht (1938b) found that when dialyzed maceration juice was acidified to pH 5.5, phosphorylase was precipitated and could in this way be freed from amylase. When their preparation acted on glucose-1-phosphate at pH 6.6, inorganic phosphate was rapidly split off. Simultaneously a glycogenlike substance was formed, but after 10 minutes this slowly disappeared.

Isoelectric precipitation at pH 5.3 was also used by Meyer and Bernfeld (1942) to separate phosphorylase from "amyloglucosidase." Their preparation clearly was a mixture of several enzymes; it degraded limit dextrin as well as glycogen and starch and therefore could split 1,6 linkages. Maltose and isomaltose were also hydrolyzed by the enzyme. The precipitate contains phosphorylase and other enzymes complexed with nucleic acid (Trevelyan, unpublished data); the ribonucleoproteins of yeast have been studied, from the chemical aspect, by Khouvine and de Robichon-Szulmajster (1951, 1952).

A different method of preparation—fractionation of Lebedew juice with ammonium sulfate at pH 6.5—was adopted by Kiessling (1939b). The reversibility of the reaction was established, and its equilibrium constant determined, though it was not realized to be pH dependent. By calorimetry, the heat of reaction was shown to be small, 1200 cal./mole phosphate. By further purification steps, Kiessling obtained an enzyme which would phosphorolyze glycogen but not synthesize polysaccharide from glucose-1-phosphate. At this time the necessity for traces of preformed polysaccharide "primer" to be present was not appreciated, and Kiessling thought he had separated a specific phosphorolyzing enzyme. No kinetic data were given, though it appears from one of the figures that the forward reaction (substrate, glucose-1-phosphate) was several times faster than the back reaction. The enzyme was noted as being rather sensitive to heat.

The yeast amylases described by Schäffner and Specht were further studied by Meyer and Bernfeld (1941), who found them to possess properties which distinguished them from both α- and β-amylase. According to Hopkins (1955) brewer's yeasts contain small amounts of the latter. In particular, β-amylase residual dextrin was attacked. These findings are explained by the presence, in brewer's yeast, of "isoamylase" (Maruo and Kobayashi, 1951) an enzyme originally described by Nishimura (1930) as "amylosynthease" who found it produced from amylopectin polysaccharides which stained blue with iodine. However, this action is a degradation, not a synthetic one, since the products have a much smaller molecular weight than amylopectin (Maruo and Kobayashi, 1951). The enzyme actually splits 1,6 linkages in the branched amylopectin molecule to give straight-chain products which resemble amylose in reaction with iodine and in liability to retrogradation. Recently isoamylase has been prepared from brewer's yeast extract by fractionation with acetone (Manners and Maung, 1955b). Its action on glycogen is incomplete, and limited to A-chains, which are chains of 1,4-α-linked glucose residues with a non-reducing group at the free end, and attached by a 1,6-α linkage to the rest of the polysaccharide molecule, but which have no other chains attached to them (Manners, 1955). Isoamylase also catalyzed the hydrolysis of terminal 1,6-α linkages; it hydrolyzed both isomaltose and a glycogen preparation which contained a number of single glucose residues attached 1,6 to the rest of the molecule, these being split off as glucose. In so doing, the enzyme exhibited a wider specificity than either R-enzyme (potato) or amylo-1,6-glucosidase (muscle).

Certain "super-attenuating" yeasts, such as S. *diastaticus*, are capable of setting up fermentation in starch solutions. This is due to their ability to secrete *glucamylase*, an enzyme which splits β-glucose from the non-reducing ends of starch chains and proceeds along the chains in the same manner as β-amylase. The enzyme can diffuse out of the cell (see review by Hopkins, 1955).

Yeast phosphorylases so far described have synthesized, from glucose-1-phosphate, polysaccharides which like glycogen stain reddish brown with iodine (see, e.g., Kiessling, 1939b). They presumably contained enzymes resembling Q-enzyme, or the branching factor. It is therefore of interest that Mager (1947) reported that dried preparations of the capsulated yeast *Torulopsis rotundata* yielded, after grinding with glass powder, an enzyme which synthesized amylose-type polysaccharides from glucose-1-phosphate between pH 4.5 and 5.9, the acid conditions apparently causing the destruction of a postulated branching factor (see Section 2, C above).

C. Trehalose Fermentation and Trehalase

Trehalose is fermented by certain strains of yeast, though not at all by lactose-fermenting types (Myrbäck, 1949). Myrbäck and Örtenblad (1936) found that a Swedish baker's yeast fermented the disaccharide very slowly indeed; brewer's bottom yeast, however, fermented trehalose about 15% as fast as it did glucose. Dried yeast (of both types), and Lebedew juice, fermented trehalose at 25% of the rate at which glucose was attacked. Put this way the result is perhaps a little misleading, since from the figures given it would appear that on drying, the power to ferment glucose was reduced to about one-quarter.

Although suggestions have been advanced in favor of the "direct" fermentation of trehalose (Leibowitz and Hestrin, 1945), there is little doubt that the first step in fermentation is the hydrolysis of the sugar (Myrbäck, 1949; Gottschalk, 1949; Doudoroff, 1951). The enzyme

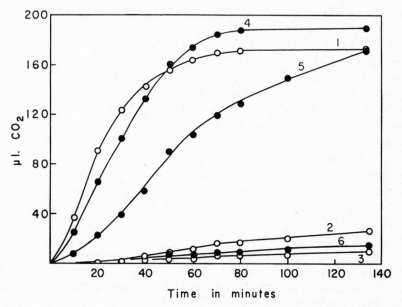

FIG. 1. The adaptive fermentation of trehalose by *Candida tropicalis*. (1) Glucose-grown cells, 5 μM of glucose; (2) glucose-grown cells, 2.5 μM of trehalose; (3) glucose-grown cells, endogenous; (4) trehalose-grown cells, 5 μM of glucose; (5) trehalose-grown cells, 2.5 μM of trehalose; (6) trehalose-grown cells, endogenous. Temperature 30°C.; $M/30 KH_2PO_4$ buffer. o—o, glucose-grown cells; ●—●, trehalose-grown cells (from Bouthilet *et al.*, 1949).

trehalase is a specific one: trehalose, though an α-glucoside, is not split by maltase (Myrbäck, 1949). It is possibly located at the surface of the yeast cell (Rothstein, 1954a).

Of a large number of yeasts examined by Bouthilet *et al.* (1949), very few were strong trehalose fermenters. *Candida tropicalis* was an outstanding strain in this respect. Washed cells of this organism fermented trehalose rapidly after growth in a medium containing trehalose. Glucose-grown cells, however, fermented trehalose only slowly. The enzyme, therefore, appeared to be adaptive (Fig. 1). No adaptation was noticed when *Candida* cells, grown on glucose, were exposed to trehalose for 2½ hours anaerobically, as they were when fermentation rate was determined. Myrbäck and Örtenblad (1936) had observed that bottom yeast sometimes fermented trehalose rapidly from the beginning, at other times only after an induction period. They did not consider trehalase to be an adaptive enzyme, since it was present in dried bottom yeast which had not been exposed to the disaccharide. Trehalase has been extracted from *Candida tropicalis* and purified by fractionation with ethanol (Lukes and Phaff, 1952).

What part trehalase plays in the utilization by baker's yeast of its endogenous trehalose is not known. Enzyme and sugar may be spatially separated in the cell (Myrbäck, 1949). One may also consider the possibility that modified forms of the enzyme exist, by analogy with the case of yeast catalase (Kaplan, 1955). It is unlikely to be involved in the synthesis of endogenous trehalose though it is interesting that, in recent years, many disaccharide-splitting enzymes have been shown to possess transglycosidase activity (Wallenfels and Bernt, 1952). Indeed, among the products obtained with an enzyme from *Aspergillus niger* is trehalose itself (Peat *et al.*, 1955b).

D. Trehalose and Trehalose Phosphate Formation by Dried Yeast and Lebedew Juice

The synthesis (and possibly the endogenous utilization) of trehalose by *Saccharomyces cerevisiae* probably proceeds through the intermediate stage of trehalose-6-phosphate. The existence of a new phosphate ester was suspected by Robison and Morgan (1928) when they found that analytical data on the phosphate esters obtained from fermenting suspensions of dried yeast did not agree with the assumption that these were mixtures of fructose diphosphate together with glucose and fructose monophosphates. This led to the isolation of trehalose monophosphate from the products of the fermentation of glucose or fructose using dried yeast. The ester, which was nonreducing and strongly dextrorotatory, was split by bone phosphatase to free trehalose and it was readily fermented by dried yeast. Robison and Morgan showed that the ester did not arise from the phosphorylation of trehalose previously existing in the dried yeast. Trehalose phosphate was not at first detected when yeast press juice was used in place of dried yeast but analysis later showed that small amounts were formed (Robison and Morgan, 1930).

Boyland (1929) found that if graded amounts of inorganic phosphate were added during fermentation by dried yeast, then the rate of fermentation after esterification was complete was proportional to the ester phosphate concentration provided a certain maximum level was not exceeded. Under such conditions, the diphosphate and monophosphate fractions bore a constant ratio to each other. The latter fraction was mainly trehalose monophosphate. If fructose diphosphate or trehalose monophosphate were added to fermenting yeast suspensions, the ratio was only temporarily upset: this equilibrium between the two suggested to Boyland that one ester was derived from the other.

Not only trehalose phosphate, but also, and notably, free trehalose are formed during fermentation by yeast maceration juice. It will be recalled (Section 3, B above) that Harden and Young (1913) had observed the accumulation of a dextrorotatory carbohydrate. That this was trehalose was indicated by the work of Sobotka and Holzman (1936), and confirmed by later studies (Nilsson and Alm, 1949; Elander and Myrbäck 1949). Trehalose accumulates during the fermentation of fructose as well as glucose, hence free glucose is unlikely to be involved in its synthesis. Trehalose is not formed as long as free phosphate is present (Nilsson and Alm, 1949). The instability of the hydrolytic enzyme trehalase may be important in allowing the accumulation of trehalose (Elander and Myrbäck, 1949).

Trehalose accumulated when glucose was fermented by acetone-dried yeast (Elander, 1956), the trehalose formed after various times being proportional to the amount of glucose which had been metabolized. Arsenate inhibited the synthesis of trehalose, whereas fluoride inhibited both trehalose formation and glucose fermentation.

The simplest explanation of the formation of trehalose in these experiments is that trehalose-6-phosphate appears first, to be then split by a phosphatase. If this mechanism were to apply to whole yeast, it would seem necessary either to postulate a phosphatase with a high degree of specificity towards trehalose phosphate, or in some other way to explain why other phosphate esters arising during metabolism are apparently not so split.

E. Trehalose Phosphate Formation from Uridine Diphosphoglucose

Leloir and Cabib (1953) have presented evidence that yeast enzymes can bring about the reaction:

Uridine diphosphoglucose + Glucose-6-phosphate → Uridine diphosphate
+ Trehalose-6-phosphate

Brewer's yeast was disintegrated by shaking with sand, and an enzyme preparation separated by precipitation with half-saturated ammonium

ulfate. The dialyzed precipitate was incubated at 37°C. and pH 7 for
.00 minutes with (a) 4×10^{-3} M glucose-6-phosphate, (b) 6×10^{-3} M
uridine diphosphoglucose, or (c) a mixture of both. In case (c) the
uridine diphosphoglucose was partly converted into uridine diphosphate
1.4×10^{-3} M), and simultaneously the reducing power of the solution
ell, indicating the loss of a similar amount of glucose-6-phosphate. From
c), but not from (a) or (b) trehalose-6-phosphate was isolated by
paper electrophoresis of the water-soluble, alcohol-insoluble barium salts.
The data, unfortunately, do not permit any calculation of the rate of this
eaction as compared with the rate of trehalose synthesis in the intact
east cell. Nor has the reversibility of the reaction been assessed (see,
however, Section 4, E below).

4. Reaction Pathways by Which Glucose and Other Substrates Are Transformed to Cell Carbohydrates

A. General

It is probable that the cellular carbohydrates of yeast, at least those of
accharomyces cerevisiae, are derived by reaction sequences of relatively
ew stages from hexose-6-phosphates generated as intermediates during
metabolism. This is almost certainly the case for glycogen and trehalose
(see preceding section) while evidence relating to the origin of the
hexose units of mannan and glucan is still meager (see this Section, B
nd C below).

From recent reviews of glucose and fructose metabolism (Racker,
954), and of carbohydrate metabolism by microorganisms (Gunsalus
t al., 1955), it appears that during the metabolism of sugars by yeast,
hexose-6-phosphates could arise in two ways (for fuller discussion see
Chapter VII). The first, direct pathway involves the hexokinase reaction
n which phosphate is irreversibly transferred from adenosine triphosphate to glucose, fructose, or mannose. Galactose is transformed to
galactose-1-phosphate by a specific kinase, and then by galactowaldenase
o glucose-1-phosphate. The second path leads from ribulose-5-phosphate
o fructose-6-phosphate by reactions catalyzed by phosphopentose isomerase, transketolase, and transaldolase. Since ribulose-5-phosphate may
rise from glucose-6-phosphate itself, which is oxidized first to 6-phos-
phogluconate (glucose-6-phosphate dehydrogenase or Zwischenferment),
fter which the latter is further oxidized by the enzyme 6-phospho-
gluconate dehydrogenase, the significance of the second pathway for cell
arbohydrate synthesis is problematical. A point which is interesting in
iew of the occurrence in yeast glucan of β-linked glucose residues is that

glucose-6-phosphate dehydrogenase is apparently specific for the β-anomer (Bentley, 1955).

When glucose-1-C^{14} is fermented by yeast, radioactivity appears mainly in the methyl carbon of ethanol, and only 3% in the carbon dioxide evolved. This is what would be expected if at least 95% of the glucose was catabolized via the Embden-Meyerhof pathway (Koshland and Westheimer, 1950). Similar experiments on the aerobic utilization of glucose (Blumenthal et al., 1954) suggest that the Embden-Meyerhof scheme again plays a major part, 0–30% of the glucose being metabolized by the hexose monophosphate dehydrogenase "shunt" process. In agreement with this, only small amounts of glucose-6-phosphate dehydrogenase were found by Glaser and Brown (1955) in brewer's yeast. In Torulopsis utilis, 30–50% of glucose may be oxidized by the "shunt" mechanism (Blumenthal et al., 1954).

B. Studies with Labeled Glucose

Gilvarg (1952) grew S. cerevisiae on a medium containing glucose-1-C^{14} as principal carbon source, together with acetate-1-C^{13} as an indicator of C_2 metabolism. The results suggested that the direct pathway (Section 4, A above) from glucose to its phosphate and mannose phosphate, and thence to glycogen and mannan, was followed.

Lipids were removed from the yeast with alcohol and ether, and protein by 0.2% sodium hydroxide, leaving 43% of the dry weight, largely a insoluble polysaccharides. Glucose and mannose derived from these polysaccharides had no C^{13}. The C^{14} activity (mainly in carbon 1) was the same as in the glucose of the medium. A small activity was found in position 6 of the hexose molecule (rather more in mannose than in glucose), which was taken as a measure of the degree of resynthesis of hexose from triose.

From the details given, the glucose apparently came from acid-soluble glycogen, since glucan itself would not be hydrolyzed under Gilvarg' conditions. The mannose came from part only of the yeast mannan, since only about 76 mg. mannose/g. (dry weight) of yeast was recovered in the polysaccharide hydrolysate, as may be calculated from the data given.

Quite different results were obtained by Sowden et al. (1954) using Torulopsis utilis grown on a medium containing glucose-1-C^{14} as the sole source of carbon. Crude mannan (67 mg./g.) was precipitated by ethanol from 24-hour aqueous extracts of lipid-free yeast. Mannose from the polysaccharide was not radioactive, which appeared to indicate derivation from a ribose unit arising during the operation of the glucose

6-phosphate shunt. This, as we have already seen, is more important in *Torulopsis utilis* than in *S. cerevisiae*.

Sowden *et al.* pointed out that their mannan was prepared by a procedure different from that of Gilvarg (1952), which raised the possibility that the yeast cell contained two mannan fractions of different origin. It may be added that the two series of experiments were not compatible in another respect, since the yield of yeast from 1 g. of glucose was four times greater in the later study.

More recently (Sowden and Frankel, 1956) the presence of two types of mannan in *T. utilis* has been confirmed. Evidence for the existence of another polysaccharide, a glucomannan, has also been presented.

In earlier experiments by Günther and Bonhoeffer (1937), yeast was grown in heavy water media, and samples of glycogen, mannan, and cell wall glucan isolated. When the medium contained glucose or fructose, least deuterium was found in glycogen. Growth on mannose, however, resulted in less deuterium being found in mannan than in the other polysaccharides. It was concluded that mannan was formed most directly from mannose, and glycogen from fructose.

C. Synthesis of Hexose Units of Cell Carbohydrates from Intermediates Containing a Smaller Number of Carbon Atoms

Since yeasts grow in media containing, as sole carbon source, ethanol or acetic acid, it follows that these two-carbon molecules can be converted in the cell into hexose phosphates and these in turn to cellular carbohydrates. Smedley-Maclean and Hoffert (1926) showed, moreover, that yeast stored carbohydrate when aerated in solutions of ethanol or acetate; Brücke (1933) showed that glycogen was formed from ethanol, though only half as much as from an equivalent amount of glucose. More recently White and Werkman (1947) demonstrated that brewer's yeast aerated in carboxyl-labeled acetate incorporated C^{13} into positions 3 and 4 of the glucose derived from cell carbohydrate.

The exact mechanism of such transformations is still obscure. Reactions of the Embden-Meyerhof sequence leading from fructose diphosphate to pyruvate are reversible, but are preceded and immediately followed by irreversible steps. How pyruvate arises in any given case, or how glucose-1-phosphate (from which glycogen is formed) is derived from fructose diphosphate, we do not definitely know. Some interesting information has, however, recently been published by Aubert and Milhaud (1955a,b; Milhaud and Aubert, 1955a). They prepared paper chromatograms of the alcohol-soluble metabolic intermediates of baker's yeast after it had assimilated isotopically-labeled glucose or ethanol, and measured the distribution of radioactivity between the various intermediates. Since these included *inter alia* intermediates of glycolysis and of the tricarboxylic acid cycle, the relative contribution of each of these major metabolic sequences could be assessed. Also in the alcohol-soluble fraction was trehalose. This was labeled when yeast had assimilated uniformly labeled glucose or ethanol, but not when the latter was supplied together with unlabeled glucose. Trehalose derived from $CH_3C^{14}H_2OH$ was hydrolyzed to glucose, and the distribution of activity between the six carbon atoms determined. The results showed that the hexose had been synthesized by the condensation of identical C_3 fragments, activity distribution in which was the same as in 3-phosphoglyceric acid, phosphopyruvate, and alanine, and which suggested a double origin for the fragments: carboxylation of a C_2 fragment, and formation via the citric acid cycle.

Further studies by these authors (Milhaud and Aubert, 1955b; Aubert and Milhaud, 1956) deal with the order in which the various intermediates appear when glucose or ethanol is metabolized by yeast.

D. *Fluoride Inhibition: Hexose-1-phosphates as Intermediates in the Synthesis of Mannan and Glucan*

Studies of the mechanism by which fluoride interferes with the growth of yeast have led to some interesting suggestions concerning the reaction sequences between glucose and cellular carbohydrates. An effect of fluoride on glycogen synthesis had been previously noted which, when low concentrations of inhibitor were used, could be counteracted by the simultaneous addition of phosphate (McAnally and Smedley-Maclean 1935b).

Growth of *Candida albicans, Zygosaccharomyces acidifaciens,* and *Saccharomyces cerevisiae* in a synthetic medium (containing glucose 0.11 M) was inhibited by fluoride (Nickerson and Chung, 1952). Growth in the presence of fluoride was normal, provided glucose-1-phosphate was added as well but not when this was replaced by glucose-6-phosphate. Fluoride therefore appeared to hinder growth by inhibiting the enzyme phosphoglucomutase and so preventing the synthesis of cell polysaccharides.

Concentrations of fluoride less than 5×10^{-4} M were ineffective: from this level to 0.1 M concentration, the dry weight of cells after 48 hour growth was proportional to $[NaF]^{-1/2}$. This was held to suggest the formation of an inhibitor-enzyme complex of the magnesium-fluoride-phosphate-enzyme type shown by Najjar (1948) to be involved in the inhibition, *in vitro*, of muscle phosphoglucomutase. However, according to

Najjar's equation, it appears that when phosphoglucomutase is severely inhibited by fluoride, the residual activity is proportional to $[NaF]^{-2}$, not $[NaF]^{-\frac{1}{2}}$.

Zygosaccharomyces cells tended to clump in fluoride-containing media, perhaps due to an effect on surface polysaccharides, and did not stain normally with Gram stain. The yield of yeast from media with 0.01 M fluoride was proportional to glucose-1-phosphate added in the range $6-50 \times 10^{-4}$ M.

Subsequently Chung and Nickerson (1954) proved that mannose-1-phosphate as well as glucose-1-phosphate could counteract the effect of fluoride on yeast growth. Analysis for trehalose, glycogen, mannan, and glucan showed that *Zygosaccharomyces* cells had the same amount per unit weight whether they had been grown with fluoride or not. Normal amounts of glucan were found in *Saccharomyces cerevisiae* when its growth was inhibited: the cells were deficient in the other three carbohydrates. Mannose-1-phosphate had the effect of restoring to normal the mannan content, and increasing the amount of glycogen and trehalose. In another experiment, fluoride produced cells completely lacking trehalose, but normal as regards glucan and mannan. Glycogen, but not trehalose, was increased when glucose-1-phosphate was added to the growth medium.

It was concluded that the yeast cell could not tolerate marked deficiencies in glucan and mannan, and that the synthesis of these carbohydrates was the rate-limiting step during growth in media to which fluoride had been added. Mannan was assumed to be synthesized via the intermediate mannose-1-phosphate, whereas glucose-1-phosphate was an intermediate on the routes to trehalose, glycogen, and cell wall glucan. Since inhibition could be relieved by either ester, Chung and Nickerson suggested that one was converted into the other by an unspecified process not involving phosphoglucomutase.

Interesting as these experiments are, it should be pointed out that an unequivocal answer is rarely to be hoped for from experiments involving complicated biological systems and a nonspecific inhibitor such as fluoride. Usually it is the case that as knowledge of the action of the inhibitor extends, the more doubtful does the interpretation of any particular experimental effect become.

E. *Relation of Uridine Diphosphoglucose and Similar Compounds to Cellular Carbohydrate Metabolism*

Although the role of UDPG (uridine diphosphoglucose) as the coenzyme of glucose-1-phosphate–galactose-1-phosphate isomerization

(Leloir, 1953), and its conversion in yeast extracts into trehalose phosphate (Section 3, E), go some way towards explaining the presence in yeast of this compound, the feeling remains that the nuceloside diphosphohexoses will eventually be revealed as having a common and probably important biochemical function. It has so far eluded definition, though Kalckar (1954) has raised some intriguing possibilities. In the cells of pressed baker's yeast, the only low-molecular weight phosphorylated hexose compounds present in appreciable quantity are those related to UDPG (Trevelyan *et al.*, 1954) and this is perhaps a hint of their importance.

Uridine diphosphoglucose, guanosine diphosphomannose, and uridine diphosphoacetylglucosamine are all to be found in baker's yeast (Cabib and Leloir, 1954; Cabib *et al.*, 1953). So are structural polysaccharides, in the cell wall and possibly elsewhere, based on glucose, mannose, and acetylglucosamine, a consideration leading Cabib and Leloir (1954) to propose that guanosine diphosphomannose and uridine diphosphoacetylglucosamine are involved in the synthesis, respectively, of mannan and chitin. Glucan was not mentioned, presumably because of the known relation of UDPG to trehalose.

Another indication of the connection between this class of nucleotide and the synthesis of structural elements of the yeast cell, many of which contain phospholipid, is the presence in yeast of cytidine diphosphocholine, a coenzyme of lecithin synthesis (Liebermann *et al.*, 1956). A recent report by Park and Strominger (1957), though concerned with *Staphylococcus aureus* rather than with yeast, is of interest as it clearly points to a relation between cell wall biosynthesis in this organism and the metabolism of uridine diphosphate compounds. This conclusion was arrived at as a result of studies on the action of penicillin on *S. aureus*: it is suggested that the antibiotic inhibits a transglycosidase located on or outside the cytoplasmic membrane.

Kalckar (1954) points out that the transfer of say glucosyl from UDPG to a carbohydrate receptor molecule is presumably attended by a large change in free energy, i.e., that carbohydrate synthesis by such a mechanism would be irreversible. So apparently is the synthesis of mannan and glucan by the yeast cell (Section 3, A above).

In addition to the above speculations on the role of UDPG and similar compounds, the author would like to advance two further suggestions. Firstly, they may be involved in the active *transfer* of glucose-1-phosphate (and other intermediates) across selectively permeable membranes in the yeast cell, thus permitting the synthesis of glycogen, for example, in some compartment of the cell though the over-all glucose-1-phosphate/phosphate ratio is unfavorable. Secondly, UDPG and guanosine diphosphomannose, together possibly with other similar compounds yet unknown, may be involved in a simultaneous polymerization process analogous to protein synthesis, whereby a structural mannan-glucan-nucleic acid complex is laid down.

A brief note may be in place on the origin of UDPG-like compounds themselves. Yeast contains enzymes which catalyze the reversible transfer of glucose, galactose, or glucosamine radicals from the respective 1-phosphates to uridine triphosphate to give the uridine diphospho-compounds and pyrophosphate; mannose is transferred from mannose-1-phosphate to guanosine triphosphate in a similar way (Munch-Petersen et al., 1953; Kalckar et al., 1953; Smith et al., 1953; Munch-Petersen, 1955).

Trehalose phosphate synthesis via UDPG would proceed from adenosine triphosphate (ATP) and from glucose-6-phosphate generated by glycolysis, by the following series of reactions:

$$\text{Glucose-6-phosphate} \rightleftharpoons \text{Glucose-1-phosphate}$$
$$\text{ATP} + \text{UDP} \rightleftharpoons \text{UTP} + \text{ADP}$$
$$\text{UTP} + \text{Glucose-1-phosphate} \rightleftharpoons \text{UDPG} + \text{Pyrophosphate}$$
$$\text{UDPG} + \text{Glucose-6-phosphate} \rightarrow \text{Trehalose-6-phosphate} + \text{UDP}$$

$$\text{ATP} + 2 \text{ Glucose-6-phosphate} \rightarrow \text{ADP} + \text{Pyrophosphate} + \text{Trehalose Phosphate}$$

When yeast is dried (in the manufacture of "active dried yeast") part of its glycogen is converted into trehalose (Payen, 1949; Pollock and Holmstrom, 1951). The possibility exists of a second pathway to trehalose, starting from glycogen. A consideration of the stability of the linkages between glucose units in glycogen and trehalose (Section 2, A above) suggests that such a reaction would be thermodynamically feasible.

F. Summing Up

While numerous speculations have appeared in this Section, the familiar phosphorylase reaction remains the only one we are reasonably sure of; certainly it is the only one which can be discussed in relation to the kinetics of glycolysis.

5. Coupling of the Phosphorylase Reaction to Reactions of the Embden-Meyerhof Fermentation System

When the individual enzymes of what Dixon (1949) calls a multi-enzyme system have been separated and studied in vitro, the knowledge of mechanism so gained makes possible qualitative prediction concerning events in the living cell. Quantitative prediction, even of the sketchiest kind, is immensely more difficult. Given the amount of each enzyme, it is theoretically possible to set up a mathematical expression describing the kinetics of a homogeneous system of any number of enzymes and giving, in particular, the steady-state concentration of each intermediate for a given over-all reaction rate. Such expressions (see e.g., Hearon,

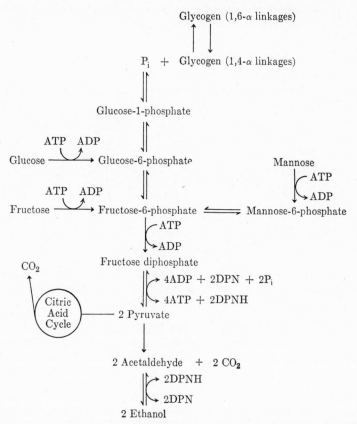

SCHEME I. Reactions by which glycogen is formed during the metabolism of glucose, fructose, or mannose by yeast. P_i, free phosphate. ATP, ADP adenosine-5'-tri- and diphosphate. DPN, DPNH, oxidized and reduced diphosphopyridine nucleotide (coenzyme I). ⇋ potentially reversible, → irreversible reactions.

1949a,b) are so complex as often to defeat their own purpose: consequently many authors have looked for some single reaction which would act as a "bottleneck," analogous to Burton's "master reaction" (Johnson et al., 1954). The variety of suggestions which have been advanced as to the nature of the limiting reaction shows this approach to be an oversimplification.

Even if the homogeneous system can be satisfactorily handled, the hardest problems are yet to come in making a transition to the living cell itself. There is, firstly, the question as to whether the enzymes themselves are altered in any fundamental way by the processes of extraction and purification: in this respect, the results of Chance (1954), who studied the kinetics of certain groups of enzymes of the cell *in situ* by an ingenious spectrophotometric technique, are encouraging. Secondly, one has to consider the possible inhomogeneous distribution of substrates within the cell. The location of enzymes at different sites may set up concentration gradients, due to a finite speed of diffusion, while actual discontinuities may exist at the surfaces of particulate elements such as the mitochondria. The result is that over-all concentrations of substrates, derived by chemical analysis of cell extracts, may be misleading.

In Scheme I are presented the reactions by which glucose (fructose or mannose) is partly transformed into glycogen during metabolism of the sugar by yeast. At the present time, the kinetics of these reactions *in vivo* can only be discussed tentatively. Nevertheless, certain results of value emerge, even if, in what follows, one could wish for more matter and less art.

A. *Theoretical Maximum Conversion of Glucose to Glycogen*

The maximum yield of glycogen when 1 mole of glucose has been fermented may readily be calculated from the fact that glycogen synthesis utilizes 1 mole of ATP per mole of glucose stored as polysaccharide, whereas when 1 mole of glucose is degraded to carbon dioxide and ethanol, 2 moles of ATP are generated. It follows that if glycogen synthesis were the only ATP-utilizing reaction accompanying fermentation, then $2/3$ of the glucose taken up could be assimilated. In respiration, as much as 38 moles of ATP/mole of glucose may be formed (see, e.g., Table 2 in Bücher, 1953), and the theoretical maximum conversion is correspondingly greater.

In practice (Section 6), no figures approaching the theoretical have been recorded, an indication that carbohydrate storage is limited by the relatively low rate of the enzyme reactions concerned and not by the stoichiometry of the processes generating and utilizing ATP.

B. *The Phosphorylase Equilibrium in Vivo*

From the discussion in Section 3, B above it follows that provided sufficient polysaccharide receptor molecules are present in the yeast cell, glycogen synthesis can occur if, at the site of phosphorylase, the ratio phosphate/glucose-1-phosphate is less than, at a rough estimate, 6. Since glucose-1-phosphate is derived from glucose-6-phosphate, it similarly follows that the ratio glucose-6-phosphate/glucose-1-phosphate must be greater than 20, the equilibrium constant of the phosphoglucomutase reaction.

During fermentation by baker's yeast, the intracellular concentration of glucose-6-phosphate was found to be roughly 10^{-3} M (Trevelyan et al., 1954). Glucose-1-phosphate could not be accurately measured, but was less than 10^{-4} M. This corresponds to expectation, though it must be pointed out that, after incubation with glucose for 15 minutes when the measurements were made, synthesis of glycogen had not reached its peak rate (Section 6). However, about 10 times the theoretical maximum phosphate concentration of 3×10^{-4} M was found.

This was the over-all concentration, but probably not that at the site of phosphorylase action. Studies on the uptake by yeast of P^{32} show that the intracellular phosphate is not homogeneous (Kamen and Spiegelman, 1948; Zetterström et al., 1951). The former authors found, indeed, that the apparent phosphate content of yeast depended upon whether extraction had been with trichloroacetic acid or cationic detergents; however, this may not have the significance they attributed to it, since after treatment of the cell with cationic detergents, enzymes, e.g., phosphatases, are still active (Trevelyan, unpublished data).

The existence in yeast of mitochondria to which respiratory enzymes and the oxidative phosphorylation system are bound (Nossal, 1954) is significant, since these elements possess a membrane showing selective permeability towards certain compounds, the adenine nucleotides being the subject of a recent study (Siekevitz and Potter, 1955a,b).

Can it be taken that at the phosphorylase surface the phosphate concentration is only 3×10^{-4} M or less? This question cannot be directly answered but one can enquire whether—assuming phosphorylase and the enzymes of the Embden-Meyerhof scheme occur in the same region of the cell—it is possible for fermentation to proceed at such low phosphate levels.

Referring to Scheme I, it is seen that fructose diphosphate (FDP) is transformed by the fermentation system to pyruvate by a group of reversible enzymes. The over-all equilibrium constant

$$\frac{[\text{pyruvate}^-]}{[\text{FDP}^{4-}]^{1/2}[\text{phosphate}^{2-}]} \left\{ \frac{[\text{ATP}^{4-}]}{[\text{ADP}^{3-}]} \right\}^2 \frac{[\text{DPNH}]}{[\text{DPN}]}$$

is about 1000 (Table I). The over-all concentration of pyruvate in fermenting yeast has been found to be 2×10^{-2} M or less (Trevelyan and Harrison, 1954), and of fructose diphosphate 2×10^{-3} M (Trevelyan

TABLE I

FREE ENERGY DATA FOR REACTIONS OF THE EMBDEN-MEYERHOF SCHEME BY WHICH
FRUCTOSE DIPHOSPHATE (FDP) IS TRANSFORMED TO PYRUVATE[a]

Reaction	ΔG^{0} [b]
$\frac{1}{2}$ FDP^{4-} → $\frac{1}{2}$ glyceraldehyde 3-P^{2-} + $\frac{1}{2}$ dihydroxyacetone 3-P^{2-}	+2.75
$\frac{1}{2}$ dihydroxyacetone 3-P^{2-} → $\frac{1}{2}$ glyceraldehyde 3-P^{2-}	+0.92
Glyceraldehyde 3-P^{2-} + DPN^{+} + HPO$_4$$^{2-}$ glyceroyl-P 3-P^{4-} + DPNH + H^{+}	+11.05
Glyceroyl-P 3-P^{4-} + ADP^{3-} → glycerate 3-P^{3-} + ATP^{4-}	−4.75
Glycerate 3-P^{3-} → glycerate 2-P^{3-}	+1.06
Glycerate 2-P^{3-} → enolpyruvate 2-P^{3-} + H$_2$O	−0.64
Enolpyruvate 2-P^{3-} + ADP^{3-} + H$_2$O + H^{+} → pyruvate^{-} + ATP^{4-}	−14.5
$\frac{1}{2}$ FDP^{4-} + DPN^{+} + HPO$_4$$^{2-}$ + 2ADP^{3-} → pyruvate^{-} + DPNH + 2ATP^{4-}	−4.11

$$\text{Equilibrium constant} = \text{antilog} \left(\frac{-\Delta G^{0}}{1.364} \right) = 1030$$

[a] Data from Burton and Krebs (1953).
[b] ΔG^{0}, change in standard free energy at 25°C. in kcal.

et al., 1954; Holzer and Holzer, 1953). DPNH/DPN appears to be about
0.3 (Holzer *et al.*, 1954), and the over-all ratio ATP/ADP around 0.25
(P. F. E. Mann, private communication). Substituting these values (actually the concentration of the ionic species as written should be used
although the accuracy of the data hardly warrants the correction), one
finds that the reactions can proceed in the direction of pyruvate with
phosphate less than 10^{-5} *M*. It may be objected that, at a high rate of
fermentation, these reactions are far from the equilibrium position. Actually, there is evidence that this is not the case; and all the reversible
reactions of fermentation, with the possible exception of that catalyzed
by pyruvate kinase, operate close to equilibrium. Measurements of intracellular substrate concentrations support the hypothesis (Trevelyan
et al., 1954; Holzer and Holzer, 1953; Holzer *et al.*, 1955) as do the high
activities of certain of these enzymes, 3-phosphoglyceraldehyde dehydrogenase, for example, being present in yeast in relatively enormous amount
(Krebs *et al.*, 1953; Chance, 1954).

It thus appears that glycogen synthesis in the yeast cell may, in fact,
be discussed in relation to the equilibrium constant of the phosphorylase
reaction. It may be added, though this is not the place to develop the
idea in detail, that the near-equilibrium hypothesis considerably simpli-
fies the kinetics of fermentation. Since fermentation rate closely parallels
the intracellular concentration of pyruvate (Trevelyan and Harrison,

1954; Holzer *et al.*, 1955), the influence of various factors on fermentation rate can be deduced from the equilibrium expression written above. The ratio ATP/ADP is seen to be particularly important, as it is raised to the second power.

C. Kinetic Aspects of Glycogen Synthesis from Glucose-6-phosphate

Phosphoglucomutase. The reaction catalyzed by this enzyme requires glucose-1,6-diphosphate as coenzyme (Leloir, 1951, 1953). The reaction mechanism involves the phosphorylated form of the enzyme, which reversibly transfers its phosphate to either glucose-1- or -6-phosphate to form glucose diphosphate (Najjar and Pullman, 1954). The enzyme will act on mannose-1-phosphate (Leloir, 1951; Posternak and Rosselet, 1954) and mannose diphosphate will serve as coenzyme (Posternak and Rosselet, 1954). Mannose-1-phosphate is transformed much more slowly than glucose-1-phosphate, at about $\frac{1}{40}$th the rate according to Leloir (1951).

The coenzyme requirement of phosphoglucomutase is of great interest, since the possibility exists that variation of glucose diphosphate concentration in the yeast cell may be one way by which glycogen synthesis or degradation is controlled. In yeast, the coenzyme is synthesized from ATP and glucose-1-phosphate by the enzyme glucose-1-phosphate kinase, which is present in only small quantity; in yeast extracts, the rate of reaction is about 1% of phosphoglucomutase activity (Paladini *et al.*, 1949).

Since yeast may be adapted to ferment galactose by a mechanism which passes through the stage of glucose-1-phosphate, it follows that in certain cases the rate of the reaction: glucose-1-phosphate → glucose-6-phosphate must be of the same order as the over-all fermentation rate. For the *synthesis* of glycogen, it is the rate of the back reaction which is important and, provided the Michaelis constants of the two esters are the same, this will be only 5% as fast. A *priori* the phosphoglucomutase reaction seems likely to be the rate-limiting step in glycogen synthesis. This is, however, not the case with the enzyme system of liver or muscle, where it is the amount of active phosphorylase which governs the rate of synthesis (see Section 3, B).

Phosphorylase: Forward and Back Reactions. The reverse applies to phosphorylase for glycogen synthesis by this enzyme can proceed much faster than breakdown, possibly, in yeast, 6 times faster.

An interesting point concerns the Michaelis constants of the yeast enzyme. If the figure of 10^{-4} M, quoted as the over-all intracellular concentration of glucose-1-phosphate (Trevelyan *et al.*, 1954), actually represents the concentration of this ester at the site of phosphorylase action, then either the yeast enzyme must have a much smaller K_m than the potato enzyme (10^{-3} M) or yeast, during glycogen synthesis, must contain a great excess of enzyme.

Steady-State Concentration of Glucose-6-phosphate. When glucose is metabolized by yeast, a definite concentration of glucose-6-phosphate will be established within the cell in equilibrium with fructose-6-phosphate (Trevelyan *et al.*, 1954). The level of glucose-6-phosphate will be determined by the requirement that the reactions catalyzed by hexokinase and phosphohexokinase + phosphoglucomutase should proceed at equal rates. In fermentation though not in respiration, the rate of the side reaction catalyzed by phosphoglucomutase is relatively small.

When excess of glucose is supplied to yeast, the steady-state level of glucose-6-phosphate probably depends mainly on the relative amounts present of the enzymes hexokinase and phosphohexokinase, both of which catalyze irreversible reactions. When the external glucose concentration is insufficient to saturate the yeast, the intracellular glucose-6-phosphate concentration would be expected to be lowered also, in order to keep the rate of the two kinases in step. Moreover, one might then expect the rate of glycogen synthesis to vary in a similar way, with the result that the fraction of glucose assimilated remains relatively constant.

Since hexokinase is, as far as is known, responsible for the uptake of glucose (fructose or mannose) into the yeast cell, it would be advantageous to know the Michaelis constants of this enzyme with respect to the three monosaccharides. Unfortunately, published figures relate to the optimum pH of this enzyme *in vitro*, which is considerably more alkaline than the pH of the cell. Also, according to Rothstein (1954b) there may be two hexokinases of different pH optima in yeast.

For a similar reason, the degree to which the two kinases are saturated by the ATP level prevailing intracellularly is difficult to assess. When, during aerobic metabolism, the Pasteur effect (see Chapter VII) is in operation it would appear that hexokinase action must be slowed due to a lowered ATP concentration, since its rate depends upon the amount of enzyme, the concentration of glucose (both presumed unaltered) and the concentration of coenzyme. This may be due to concentration of adenine nucleotides within the mitochondria, in which the respiratory systems are located (a conclusion arrived at independently by Prof. Lynen; private communication from H. Holzer). The effect on the concentration of glucose-6-phosphate would presumably depend upon the relative dissociation constants (unknown) of the hexokinase-ATP and phosphohexokinase-ATP complexes. However, recent work on the inhibition of glycolysis in a mammalian system, brought about by the addition of a suspension of mitochondria, does not support this hypothesis (Aisenberg et al., 1957; Aisenberg and Potter, 1957).

6. Synthesis and Breakdown of Cell Carbohydrates during Metabolism by Yeast (Mainly *Saccharomyces*)

A. *Endogenous Utilization of Glycogen and Trehalose*

When the organization of the yeast cell is disrupted, for example by toluene and other autolytic agents, glycogen and trehalose are broken down and fermented (review: Joslyn, 1955). The rate is rapid in relation to the rate at which carbohydrate reserves disappear from stored yeast, though this is measurable even at 4°C., when pressed baker's yeast loses about 1% of its glycogen and trehalose each day (Trevelyan and Harrison, 1956c). Intact yeast, then, uses its reserve only sparingly, though enzymes potentially capable of a much more rapid rate of breakdown are present in the cell. One would like to know (a) what organizational factors make this possible; (b) what conditions permit utilization of storage carbohydrate; (c) what pathway is followed when reserves are metabolized, and (d) what then is the biological advantage to the cell, e.g., whether carbohydrate carbon is built into new cell material. On all these points evidence is very scanty and often controversial.

Brandt (1941) found that autorespiration was temporarily increased when yeast which contained trehalose was warmed to 50°C. Coupling this with the observation that trehalose disappeared quickly when yeast was incubated in a full growth medium (see Section 6, B below), he surmised that trehalose utilization was specifically linked with protein synthesis, including the regeneration of destroyed protein. More recently, Yemm and Folkes (1954) investigated the relation between endogenous respiration, utilization of cell carbohydrate, and nitrogen assimilation. *Torulopsis utilis*, grown in the laboratory, had a total carbohydrate amounting to 18% of its dry weight. Its endogenous respiration (oxygen taken up in 3 hours at 25°C.) was little affected by the addition of ammonium salts to the suspension medium. The cell carbohydrate could be increased six fold by incubation with sucrose (nitrogen-deficient medium). As a result, the autorespiration rate in sodium phosphate buffer was trebled, and in ammonium phosphate buffer increased as much as 7 times. On the addition of ammonium salts to a suspension of carbohydrate-rich *T. utilis*, respiration rate rose sharply to a level which decreased slowly with time. Nitrogen was assimilated by the yeast and this uptake was accompanied by a diminution of glycogen, and, to a smaller extent, of mannan.

Several reports have appeared on the anaerobic utilization of glycogen though they are not easy to evaluate. Harden and Rowland (1901) found that carbon dioxide was evolved by brewer's top yeast when this was kept in an atmosphere of nitrogen or carbon dioxide. The rate increased with temperature but the total volume recorded was unaltered between 14 and 39°C. as shown in Fig. 2. At 26°C., 17% of the dry weight of the

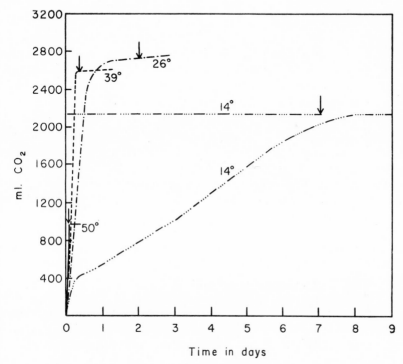

FIG. 2. Effect of temperature on the endogenous fermentation of brewer's yeast. The arrowhead shows the time of liquefaction (from Harden and Rowland, 1901).

yeast was recovered as carbon dioxide, and an equal amount of alcohol was produced, presumably by the normal fermentation mechanism. Concurrently, glycogen disappeared from the cell, as shown by an iodine staining technique, and the cell vacuole enlarged. After gas evolution ceased, the yeast liquefied, due apparently to discharge of the contents of the vacuole. At 50°C., however, liquefaction set in before all the carbon dioxide had been evolved. Stored aerobically, brewer's yeast took up oxygen and generated 20% more carbon dioxide.

Scott *et al.* (1951), in a paper on potassium retention by yeast (the amount retained after fermentation depends on the formation of reserve carbohydrate, as shown by Rothstein and Enns, 1946), reported on the anaerobic utilization of cell carbohydrate. They determined hydrolyzable polysaccharide (glycogen and mannan?) by extracting the yeast with alcoholic potassium hydroxide, and estimating the reducing sugar after the residue had been heated for 2 hours at 100°C. with 1 N hydrochloric acid. This decreased slowly—by 10 μg./mg. of yeast in the first hour— when *Saccharomyces cerevisiae* was stored anaerobically although no carbon dioxide was formed.

Harden and Rowland (1901) had used pressed yeast. This may be significant, as several investigators have found *suspensions* of yeast to have a negligible rate of output of carbon dioxide when shaken in an atmosphere of nitrogen in the Warburg manometric apparatus (see Stier and Stannard, 1936a,b; Spiegelman and Nozawa, 1945). Moreover, as shown by Winzler and Baumberger (1938) suspensions of yeast under nitrogen generate no detectable heat after 90 minutes at 25°C.; they used a sensitive adiabatic calorimeter in these studies. The suspension medium in all these experiments was phosphate buffer.

It appeared, however, that yeast suspensions could utilize reserve carbohydrate when the gas phase contained oxygen. The respiratory quotient during autorespiration was 1 (Stier and Stannard, 1936a,b) and the loss of glycogen could be demonstrated by the appearance of the cells after staining with iodine. With young cultures of yeast, the kinetics of the process were of the first order, suggesting that the determining factor was the concentration of substrate. With older cultures, the rate was lower, and remained steady for 2 hours. That the cells contained the enzyme systems for fermentation of carbohydrate reserve was shown by grinding them with sand, or by adding 1% of toluene, when carbon dioxide and alcohol were produced anaerobically. In Spiegelman and Nozawa's experiments, the initial Q_{O_2} (30°C.) was 30, which fell to 1% of this figure after 25 hours incubation in air. $Q_{CO_2}^{N_2}$ did not exceed 0.2 over the 25-hour period. Respiration of endogenous reserves produced heat (Winzler and Baumberger, 1938). When oxygen was admitted to a suspension of yeast which had been incubated anaerobically, there was a burst of heat production lasting for a time proportional to the length of anaerobic incubation. This suggested that an intermediary metabolite had accumulated which was rapidly oxidized when oxygen became available. This metabolite, the molecule of which apparently contained less than six carbon atoms, originated from reserve carbohydrate, as shown by the small but definite decrease in carbohydrate which occurred when a yeast suspension was made anaerobic (Brady *et al.*, 1956).

Stickland (1956) believes that the substrate utilized by pressed baker's yeast during autorespiration is not carbohydrate, as shown by the constancy of hydrolyzable polysaccharide. This applied whether the yeast had first been starved by aeration, untreated, or enriched in carbohydrate by fermentation of glucose. Moreover, the R.Q. in these experiments was less than unity. The yeast cells were treated with trichloroacetic acid before hydrolysis and determination of reducing substances, and no data were obtained on the acid-extractable carbohydrate (trehalose).

Fales (1951, see Section 6, B below) presented results which show how complex this problem of the fermentability of carbohydrate reserves really is. He enriched baker's yeast in carbohydrate by fermentation (of glucose), and determined the rate of endogenous oxygen uptake, and of anaerobic production of carbon dioxide, in cells withdrawn after graded intervals and washed free from glucose. The rate of endogenous metabolism, anaerobic as well as aerobic, increased after fermentation, the increase being correlated with the increase in a carbohydrate which was not extracted from the yeast cell by hot 30% potassium hydroxide (Figs. 3, 4).

Assuming this carbohydrate to be glycogen (it is not proved, see Section 6, B below) Fales' results may be interpreted as follows: only a part of yeast glycogen can be readily fermented or respired. From commercial baker's yeast about 8 μg. of glycogen/mg. can be isolated (Northcote, 1953) after extraction with acetic acid. Trevelyan and Harrison (1956c) found by an anthrone method of analysis 10 μg./mg. of a carbohydrate (glycogen) soluble in acetic acid and insoluble in alkali. In Fales' experiments, fermentation for 30 minutes sufficed to increase glycogen by 16 μg./mg. of yeast (Fig. 3), presumably about doubling it, but the endogenous fermentation rate actually went up some 8 times (Fig. 4). The fermentable material was apparently exhausted after 30 minutes (Fig. 4), but other results quoted show that alkali-insoluble carbohydrate did not return to the original level even after 48 hours, either in air or nitrogen. Glycogen contains a highly branched molecule and, as already mentioned (Section 2, B above), only 23% of the polysaccharide in brewer's yeast is available to phosphorylase. That formed during fermentation, however may, initially, consist of straight chains which could be more completely degraded.

In mammalian systems the turnover of glycogen *in vivo* can not be represented as the replacement of pre-existing by newly-formed molecules. Rather, peripherally situated glucosyl residues of glycogen are displaced by glucose from the body fluid, due to phosphorylase action. This is followed by a slower process, attributed to the action of a branching enzyme, by which peripheral glucosyl residues progressively enter the more centrally located tiers of the polysaccharide. Glycogen molecules of different sizes enter into the process at different rates (Stetten *et al.*, 1956).

It is, of course, only surmise that phosphorylase is concerned in the

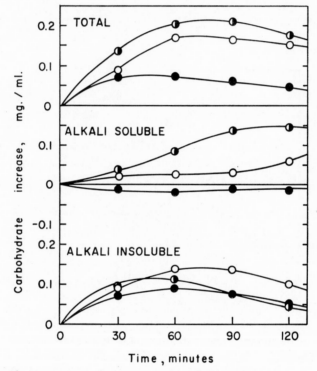

Fig. 3. The increase in the concentration of the carbohydrates in yeast cells during the fermentation of 500 mg. of anhydrous glucose by 500 ml. of 0.5% yeast at 27°C. ○, Fleischmann; ◑, Peerless; and ●, Consumer baker's yeast. The alkali-soluble fraction equals that portion dissolved in 30% potassium hydroxide in ½ hour of digestion at 100°C. (from Fales, 1951).

endogenous breakdown of glycogen. If so, several factors may be concerned in restricting the rate of this process. These include the relatively low rate of breakdown relative to synthesis (Section 5, C above), possible inactivation of the enzyme itself, and the retention of phosphate in some restricted compartment of the cell. The last would ensure the relation of glycogen utilization to maintenance of the integrity of the cell.

Trehalose is not utilized to any measurable extent when baker's yeast is incubated at 30°C. for 2 hours, even if assimilable nitrogen is supplied

(Trevelyan and Harrison, 1956a). It is respired slowly (Brandt, 1941). Possibly the initial steps involve trehalase, again separated from its substrate in the intact cell.

Since yeast can be grown so as to be free of trehalose, this carbohydrate is not essential to the cell. One wonders why two reserve carbohydrates should be found in the yeast cell under some conditions. As trehalose can occur in concentrations of around 0.1 M, it is possible that the maintenance of a correct osmotic pressure may play an important

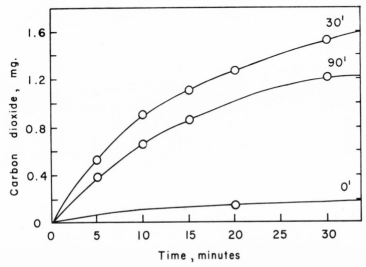

FIG. 4. The endogenous production of carbon dioxide by washed cells withdrawn from a fermentation mixture containing Peerless yeast and glucose at the concentrations given in Fig. 3. The samples were withdrawn at the times indicated after the sugar was added (from Fales, 1951).

part. Indeed, the labeling of glycogen and trehalose as "reserve" carbohydrates should not be allowed to obscure the possibility that their most important role may be quite different and that, for example, glycogen may be part of some cell structure. It may be noted in passing that the level of trehalose in the cell may affect the ability of baker's yeast to ferment maltose (Suomalainen and Oura, 1956).

B. *Synthesis of Cell Carbohydrate When Glucose (and Other Sources of Carbon) Are Metabolized by Nongrowing Yeast Cells*

A Note on the Determination of Glycogen. When yeast is incubated in a solution of glucose, its glycogen is usually increased more than are the other carbohydrates. Many investigators have interpreted their results exclusively in terms of changes in this polysaccharide. Its analysis is, however, far from simple and, especially in earlier studies, the term "glycogen" must be understood with reference to the particular technique used. Historically, the first method to be used was based on the microscopic appearance of cells after staining with iodine. Then followed chemical methods the most favored being (a) determination of hydrolyzable carbohydrate after hydrolysis of yeast by dilute acid for various periods of time, and (b) some variant of Pflüger's method. Method (a) suffered from the drawback that not only glycogen, but in part other carbohydrates are included, while (b) determined only that part of glycogen extracted by alkali (Section 2, A above). These methods were often inconvenient and time consuming, and hence tended to be applied to yeast which had been incubated for a relatively long period, and showed gross changes in glycogen content.

A swing of interest to short-term changes which could be conveniently followed by a manometric technique led to the use of more reproducible indirect methods, by which changes in yeast glycogen were inferred from gas exchange, or alteration of either dry weight or optical density (Stier et al., 1939).

The introduction of procedures using Dreywood's anthrone reagent makes the estimation of total yeast carbohydrate very simple (Fales, 1951; Trevelyan and Harrison, 1952). By successively extracting yeast with trichloroacetic acid or ethanol, alkali, and acetic acid or a mineral acid (sulfuric or perchloric acid), the cell carbohydrates are roughly partitioned into trehalose, mannan, glycogen, and glucan (Trevelyan and Harrison, 1952; Chung and Nickerson, 1954; Yemm and Folkes, 1954). The neat separation of glycogen still offers difficulty (Trevelyan and Harrison, 1956c) for mineral acid extracts, for example, presumably include some cell wall glucan (see Section 2, A above).

Glycogen Synthesis from Glucose, etc. (a) General. Pavy and Bywaters (1907) showed that yeast kept suspended in water lost a little glycogen whereas in glucose solutions the amount of polysaccharide doubled after two hours. Cell growth was considered responsible, but Lundin (1923a,b) found that glycogen was formed without any increase in cell number, as later authors (e.g., Stier et al., 1939) agree. Carbohydrate was laid down in the cell when yeast was aerated with ethanol (Lundin, 1923c) or lactic acid (Fürth and Lieben, 1922a,b). Aeration increases fat as well as carbohydrate. Aerated yeast suspensions form fat at the expense of cell carbohydrate (Smedley-Maclean and Hoffert, 1923) but if sugar is added both carbohydrate and fat are formed.

(b) *Effect of Vitamins.* McAnally and Smedley-Maclean (1935a) found that *Saccharomyces cerevisiae* (but not S. *frohberg,* McAnally and Smedley-Maclean, 1934) laid down more carbohydrate when glucose was replaced by an equivalent amount of maltose. This, Williams *et al.* (1936) ascribed to contamination of the maltose with pantothenic acid, but Swanson and Clifton (1948) were unable to find any effect on glycogen storage of this vitamin. Riboflavin also has been implicated in carbohydrate assimilation, especially under aerobic conditions (Stier, 1939; Stier and Sprince, 1941; Nickerson and Mullins, 1948).

(c) *Influence of Phosphate.* Addition of phosphate to the suspension medium has been reported to increase both fat and carbohydrate storage during glucose metabolism (Smedley-Maclean and Hoffert, 1923, 1924). Nickerson (1949; see Nickerson and Mullins, 1948) found that S. *cerevisiae* which had been cultured in a medium deficient in phosphate contained little glycogen. When transferred to a medium which had phosphate added as well as glucose, the yeast rapidly took up phosphate and synthesized glycogen. As about 1 mole of glucose was polymerized to glycogen for each mole of phosphate stored as metaphosphate, it was suggested that glucose-1-phosphate was first formed and then converted into glycogen metaphosphate. Trevelyan (1956) also found that a strain of baker's yeast grown in a phosphate-deficient medium had a low glycogen content: the cells moreover contained virtually no trehalose, though normal amounts of cell wall polysaccharides were present. The rate of glycogen synthesis during anaerobic fermentation was greater than normal.

Nickerson's suggested mechanism has not received confirmation. A change in the balance of enzymes in yeast as a result of growth with inadequate phosphate seems to offer an explanation more in accord with what is known of the mechanism of glycogen synthesis. It has been shown that the phosphatase activity of *Torulopsis utilis* is inversely related to the phosphate supplied in the growth medium (Rautanen and Kärkkäinen, 1951), and other enzymes which generate free phosphate such as phosphorylase may be similarly affected.

The influence of a given constituent of the suspension medium is liable to be complex, and to depend upon the concentration of other constituents. Pressed baker's yeast synthesized glycogen rapidly from glucose when incubated anaerobically in succinate buffer, but less rapidly when potassium phosphate was included (Trevelyan and Harrison, 1956c). It was suggested that metaphosphate formation resulted in the binding of intracellular magnesium, since magnesium supplied together with phosphate offset the effect on glycogen synthesis. Magnesium added to phosphate-free buffer solutions had no effect, probably because magnesium is transported into the yeast cell as a phosphate complex (Rothstein, 1954b).

(d) *Effect of pH*. Sussman *et al.* (1947) found that, when fermentation was studied at pH 4.5, only 79% of the theoretical maximum yield of carbon dioxide was recorded when 3 mg. of glucose had been metabolized by yeast. At pH 8.5 the yield was 93%; this indicated that the fraction of glucose stored by the cell as glycogen had been reduced, due, the authors suggested, to the effect of pH on the equilibrium position of the phosphorylase reaction (Section 3, B above). Rothstein (1954b) has briefly noted that glycogen synthesis is reduced at pH values between 8 and 10.

Wiggins *et al.* (1952) thought that a pH effect might be due to the location of enzymes concerned in glycogen synthesis at the cell surface. However, with their yeast, both fermentation rate and the rate of glycogen synthesis were reduced at pH 8.5, with the result that the fraction of glucose stored as glycogen remained unaltered. They pointed out that, in any event, a pH effect required a complicated kinetic explanation, and that to consider only the equilibrium of the phosphorylase was to oversimplify the problem.

The author (unpublished data) incubated baker's yeast for 2 hours in succinate-phosphate buffer containing glucose, supplemented with sources of Mg^{++} and K^+ (see Trevelyan and Harrison, 1956c), and determined glucose uptake, carbon dioxide output, and change in the cell trehalose, glycogen, mannan, and glucan. The pH ranged, in five steps, from 2 to 7.5. The dependence on pH of fermentation rate (see Rothstein, 1954a,b) and rate of glycogen synthesis was very slight, but trehalose formation was reduced in the more acid buffers. The effect of first exposing the yeast to 0.1 M HCl (see Section 2, B above) was complex, and offered no clear evidence for location at the cell surface of rate-limiting steps in the synthesis of mannan or glucan. It seems likely that pH affects the action of hexokinase (Rothstein, 1954b) and if an alteration in the steady-state concentration of glucose-6-phosphate in the cell is thereby produced, carbohydrate synthesis may well be disturbed (Section 5, C above).

Changes in Cell Carbohydrates during the Initial Period of Sugar Metabolism. Several investigators have noted that when yeast is incubated in sugar solutions, cell carbohydrate may actually decrease in the initial stage. The disappearance and subsequent resynthesis of glycogen was observed in 1900 by Meissner (Meissner, 1900), and some years later by Kullberg (1914). Smedley-Maclean and Hoffert (1924) found that aeration of yeast suspended in sugar solutions resulted in a temporary fall in cell carbohydrate, when the yeast was initially rich in carbohydrate.

Trehalose similarly is first broken down, and then resynthesized

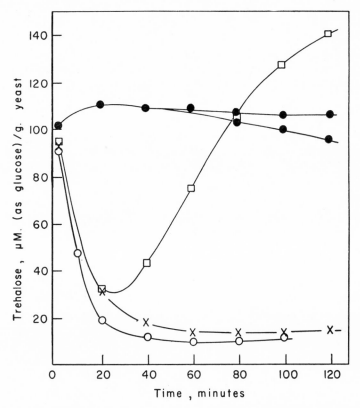

Fig. 5. Effect of constituents of the medium on trehalose breakdown and resynthesis during fermentation by baker's yeast. ○, full medium + glucose (0.3 M); ×, phosphate-free medium + glucose; □, nitrogen-free medium + glucose; ● (upper curve), nitrogen-free medium + maltose (0.15 M); ● (lower curve), full medium + maltose. The full medium contained both phosphate and ammonium ion (from Trevelyan and Harrison, 1956a).

(Trevelyan and Harrison, 1956a, Fig. 5). Resynthesis during the experimental period of 2 hours was prevented by ammonium salts, and trehalose resynthesis was reversed when NH_4^+ was added to a suspension of yeast which had metabolized glucose for 80 minutes, by which time the process of resynthesis had restored trehalose to its initial level. Yeast washed, after a period of fermentation with or without ammonium salts added, and transferred to fresh suspension medium free from nitrogen started to synthesize trehalose immediately glucose was added, with no initial breakdown. Initial breakdown followed by resynthesis was observed also when sucrose, fructose, or mannose were metabolized, with some differences in detail, but not during the initially slow fermentation of maltose (Fig. 5).

A slight initial breakdown of glycogen under similar conditions was occasionally noted (Trevelyan and Harrison, 1956c). Mannan and glucan formation were characterized by an initial induction period, but no actual breakdown occurred. Glycogen synthesis, but not mannan or glucan synthesis, was reduced by ammonium salts. Later (Trevelyan, 1956) the effect of a 30 minute period of fermentation was studied, using a pure strain of *S. cerevisiae*. The results from 34 laboratory-grown cultures were described by the equation

$$(G_{30} - G_0) = 288 - 0.77G_0$$

where G_0 represents the initial glycogen, in μM of glucose/g. of dry weight, and G_{30} the glycogen content after fermentation. (Note: 1 μM of glucose $\equiv$ 0.16 mg. of glycogen.) In other words, an initial breakdown was not observed when less than 370 $\mu M/g$. of glycogen was originally present in the cell.

An initial fall in glycogen during glycolysis is not confined to yeast since it has been observed with heart homogenates (Meyer *et al.*, 1955). An adequate explanation of this phenomenon must await further research. Meanwhile it may be pointed out that the rate of breakdown of trehalose or glycogen at the start of fermentation can be of the same order as the rate of subsequent resynthesis, and thus much greater than published figures for the rate of utilization during autofermentation. It is interesting that the presence of substrate accelerates the production of $C^{14}O_2$ from yeast cells containing reserve material labeled by C^{14} (Reiner *et al.*, 1949) though this can happen even when there is no *net* breakdown of the endogenous reserves (Moses and Syrett, 1955).

Fraction of Glucose Assimilated by Yeast. When a microorganism grows, part of the carbon supplied in the medium is converted into new cell substance, i.e., it is assimilated. For a short time at least, assimilation can also occur even when conditions do not permit reproduction, for example when the medium lacks a source of nitrogen and in general the phenomenon is most striking when the ratio of *substrate metabolized/weight of organism* is small. As a result, there is a shortfall in the carbon dioxide evolved during metabolism, or in oxygen taken up, which can be conveniently measured manometrically. The subject has been reviewed in detail by Clifton (1946, 1952). Part of the substrate "deficit" can be accounted for by an increase in cell carbohydrates and here manometric results are of interest as at any rate an approximate index of carbohydrate synthesis under various conditions.

Lundin (1923a,b) found that at the point when small amounts of glucose or fructose just disappeared from yeast suspensions, only 33% of the sugar carbon was recovered as carbon dioxide. The remainder appeared as alcohol and cell carbohydrate while no protein or fat was formed. The cells increased in size, but not in number. Wertheimer (1929) observed that a small quantity of glucose added to a suspension of yeast disappeared before fermentation set in. Up to 50% of the sugar could be recovered in the form of glycogen (not soluble in 60% potassium hydroxide). Similar observations of the changes accompanying the first few minutes of glucose metabolism led Willstätter and Rohdewald (1937) to advance the idea that the first step in fermentation was the formation of glycogen. Though this is not generally accepted, the results are noteworthy particularly as other investigators (see preceding subsection) have found a net *breakdown* of glycogen at the beginning of fermentation, due probably to using different experimental conditions, particularly as regards substrate concentration.

Meyerhof and Schulz (1936) determined by the Warburg manometric method the carbon dioxide produced after a quantity varying from 2–20 mg. of glucose or fructose had been completely fermented by a suspension of yeast (20–200 mg.) in phosphate buffer. In an atmosphere of nitrogen, only 72–78% of the carbon dioxide expected from complete conversion was obtained, the higher yields corresponding to higher initial ssugar concentration. Carbon analysis revealed that $\frac{1}{3}$ of the deficit was due to the appearance in the medium of nonvolatile compounds while the remainder was retained by the cells. Alcohol equivalent to the carbon dioxide was produced. Addition of ammonium sulfate raised the yield of carbon dioxide in one case from 74 to 86%. When carbon dioxide was used to fill the manometric flasks in place of nitrogen, the yield rose to 80%. With air as the gas phase, the fraction of sugar assimilated was more than doubled as compared with that in anaerobic experiments.

Many investigations of a similar type have been carried out. In general, assimilation is more marked the more dilute the substrate, as follows not only from the yield of carbon dioxide, but also from the alcohol resulting from fermentation (Dumazert and Penet, 1938). A much greater proportion of glucose is retained by the cell in aerobic conditions, as shown by manometric data and by calorimetric measurement of heat production

(Winzler and Baumberger, 1938). By the latter technique, 30% of the glucose metabolized was found to be assimilated anaerobically, 74% aerobically. Assimilation occurs during the respiration of nonsugar substrates, e.g., acetate (Winzler, 1940).

Since fermentation of glucose by yeast results in equal quantities of alcohol and carbon dioxide (Meyerhof and Schulz, 1936; Van Niel and Anderson, 1941), the over-all process can be written

$$C_6H_{12}O_6 \rightarrow \frac{x}{n}(C_6H_{10}O_5)_n + 2(1-x)CO_2 + 2(1-x)C_2H_6O$$

where x is the fraction of glucose unaccounted for as carbon dioxide and alcohol, and $(C_6H_{10}O_5)_n$ the formula of a hypothetical polysaccharide assimilation product. The manometric data on respiration by yeast and indeed by many other microorganisms (Clifton, 1946) are similarly summed up by the equation

$$C_6H_{12}O_6 + 6(1-x)O_2 \rightarrow \frac{x}{n}(C_6H_{10}O_5)_n + 6(1-x)CO_2$$

These results seemed to indicate that a definite fraction of a given substrate was converted into cell material, initially mainly carbohydrate, and that the explanation for this might lie in the stoichiometry or energetics of the metabolic processes. However, it was soon found that the results of manometric experiments were deceptively simple. In the first place, not all the substrate unaccounted for as carbon dioxide is retained by the cells. A portion is recoverable from the medium as nonvolatile products after fermentation (Meyerhof and Schulz, 1936; Van Niel and Anderson, 1941) and especially after respiration, when the carbon of glucose is found approximately equally distributed between carbon dioxide, the cells themselves, and the medium (Pickett and Clifton, 1943a). Similar results follow from direct analysis of the increase in cell carbohydrate, Gottschalk (1942), for example, finding that about half the deficit of glucose, fructose, or mannose after fermentation can be ascribed to polysaccharide synthesis. Fales and Baumberger (1948) determined the disappearance of glucose, carbon dioxide, and ethanol production, and increase in hydrolyzable cell carbohydrate during fermentation. Up to 40% of the glucose metabolized could not be accounted for.

Thus manometric data give only an upper limit for the fraction of substrate converted into cell carbohydrate, though it is interesting that this is less than the theoretical maximum calculated from the stoichiometry of ATP generation and utilization (Section 5, A above). The constancy of the fraction "assimilated" may reflect the constancy, over short experimental periods, of the enzyme make-up of yeast; and, as suggested in Section 1, an acceptable explanation of such findings will probably have to be based on the kinetics of the enzyme systems involved.

Nature of the Cell Carbohydrates Synthesized. Fales (1951) applied the anthrone reagent to determine total yeast carbohydrate, alkali-soluble carbohydrate (extracted in 30 minutes at 100°C. by 30% potassium hydroxide), alkali-insoluble carbohydrate, and alkali-labile carbohydrate, obtained by difference. When glucose was fermented, no change in the alkali-soluble fraction occurred with one of three strains of baker's yeast, whereas they all stored alkali-insoluble carbohydrate. This partly disappeared after glucose had vanished from the medium. This transient reserve carbohydrate was considered to be different from glycogen because it was not extracted by potassium hydroxide; however, this apparent difference probably relates more to the impermeability of the cell membrane than to the chemical properties of the reserve carbohydrate (Section 2, A above). Fales' polysaccharide was therefore, in all likelihood, glycogen although as the chemical studies have not been extended to yeast enriched in carbohydrate by fermentation, some small doubt remains.

The concentration of glucose in these experiments was initially 1 mg./ml. (5.6×10^{-3} M). Trevelyan *et al.* (1952) used the same concentration and also found that baker's yeast stored mainly acid-soluble glycogen. With excess of glucose (0.3 M) an initial induction period, when trehalose partially breaks down, is followed by an increase not only in glycogen, but also in trehalose, mannan, and glucan (Table II). When air, instead of nitrogen, is bubbled through the yeast suspension, the synthesis of trehalose and glycogen, but not of the cell wall polysaccharides, is reduced (Table II). This is only in apparent contradiction to manometric findings that aerobic assimilation is greater than anaerobic, since (a) the rate of glucose uptake is reduced under these conditions (see Fales, 1951), (b) fat may have been formed as well as carbohydrate, and (c) fully aerobic metabolism, i.e., respiration, occurs only at low glucose levels (Aldous *et al.*, 1950).

How long yeast can continue to store carbohydrate during fermentation has not, apparently, been studied. Yeast metabolism slows when carbohydrate storage proceeds beyond a certain point (Stier and Newton, 1939; Sperber, 1944; Lindegren 1945, 1946) though whether the connection is direct seems doubtful. Trevelyan and Harrison (1956b) have pointed out that, if cells metabolizing sugar in a nitrogen-free medium divide, the activity of an enzyme might be expected to remain unaltered although coenzymes would be diluted and thereby made less

TABLE II

CARBOHYDRATE SYNTHESIS BY COMMERCIAL BAKER'S YEASTS (*Saccharomyces cerevisiae*) METABOLIZING EXCESS GLUCOSE AT 30°C.[a]

Yeast strain	S	H	G	K	K(aerobic)
	Rate of carbohydrate synthesis				
Trehalose	3.8	5.4	3.2	3.7	2.2
Glycogen	6.4	5.4	8.2	5.8	2.8
Mannan	1.4	1.0	1.5	1.8	2.0
Glucan	1.3	1.2	1.3	1.1	1.5
	Fermentation rate				
	241	263	249	252	223

[a] Glucose 0.3 M, yeast 2.5 g. wet weight in 100 ml. medium (succinate buffer, pH 5.5, supplemented with K^+, Mg^{++}, and phosphate). Anaerobic experiments: suspension stirred with nitrogen. Aerobic experiment: stirred with air, 200 ml./minute. Rates of carbohydrate synthesis are averages between 30 and 120 minutes, and are given as μM of glucose or mannose/minute/g. of dry weight. 1 $\mu M \equiv 0.16$ mg. of polysaccharide. Fermentation rates are given as μM of carbon dioxide/minute/g. of dry weight. For the anaerobic experiments only, 2 μM of carbon dioxide $\equiv 1 \mu M$ of glucose. From Trevelyan and Harrison (1956c and unpublished data).

effective, since it is their concentration rather than their total amount which is kinetically relevant.

C. The Effect of Dinitrophenol and Other Cell Poisons on Carbohydrate Synthesis and Breakdown

The action of nitrophenols (usually 2,4-dinitrophenol), sodium azide, and arsenate has been studied not only with yeast, but with metabolic systems from many different sources. The number of papers is so large that no complete coverage is possible here; for the effect of these inhibitors on assimilation in yeast and other microorganisms one may consult the review by Clifton (1946), while for the part they have played in the development of general concepts of energy transfer in the cell, Spiegelman and Sussman (1952). Since the appearance of the paper by Loomis and Lipmann (1948, see below), a widely held view has been that these inhibitors interfere with synthetic reactions in the cell by reducing the supply of adenosine triphosphate. This may prove to be so but it is unfortunately also the case that many authors have burdened their papers with discussions of almost theological subtlety in an effort to fit fact to theory.

Action of Nitrophenols and Azide on Assimilation by Yeast. Krahl and lowes (1935) observed that, below a certain limiting concentration, 4-dinitro-o-cresol accelerated the endogenous oxygen uptake of yeast, nd also its oxygen uptake when respiring 0.01 M glucose in phosphate uffer. Higher concentrations of inhibitor reduced the rate of oxygen ptake and caused an increase in the proportion of glucose fermented. urthermore, assimilation was reduced, the substrate being more com-letely converted into carbon dioxide. Assimilation during anaerobic rmentation of glucose was likewise reduced. The effect on fermentation te was interesting; thus, with one sample of commercial yeast little effect as observed, while with another there was up to 200% stimulation. This st type had in the absence of inhibitor an unusually low fermentation te $Q_{CO_2}^{N_2}$ 85). When the first sample of yeast ($Q_{CO_2}^{N_2}$ 170) was in-bated for 12 hours in 1% glucose (phosphate buffer), its rate ropped to $Q_{CO_2}^{N_2}$ 110, and moreover was now stimulated by dinitrocresol. The action of dinitrocresol on yeast metabolism had thus several spects: (a) The rate of oxygen uptake was increased; (b) the rate of tilization of glucose was increased still more, so that the Pasteur effect as abolished and aerobic fermentation set in; (c) assimilation, presum-ly including glycogen formation, was abolished when glucose was etabolized aerobically or anaerobically; and (d) in the special case of carbohydrate-rich yeast, anaerobic fermentation rate increased.

Pickett and Clifton (1941, 1943b) studied the action of the more mmonly used 2,4-dinitrophenol when oxidative assimilation during the etabolism of yeast of glucose or acetate was found to be reduced. Glu-se metabolism was similarly affected by sodium azide. However, respi-tion was inhibited as well as synthesis, due to the action of azide on the tochrome system, so that aerobic fermentation was established.

Trevelyan et al. (1952) found that, in the fermentation of glucose (1 g./ml. in phosphate buffer, pH 4.5), concentrations of azide below 5 × 10⁻⁵ M increased the yield of carbon dioxide from 73 to 86%. Since e rate of carbon dioxide production was increased proportionately, it llowed that the rate of glucose uptake was unaffected. Higher concen-ations of azide, which increased carbon dioxide output to nearly 100% theoretical, did however inhibit glucose uptake. Furthermore, the rbohydrate of the yeast cell then showed an actual decrease, due to e disappearance of a large part of the trehalose fraction. Later (1956a), revelyan and Harrison studied the effects of azide on the fermentation y baker's yeast of excess glucose (0.3 M). Trehalose was found to de-ease in the initial stages of fermentation but after about 20 minutes synthesis started, the latter being prevented by 10⁻³ M sodium azide. he addition of inhibitor after fermentation had proceeded normally for

1 hour caused resynthesized trehalose to break down again. Azide als
stopped the synthesis of mannan and glucan (Trevelyan and Harrisor
1956c), and induced a slight breakdown of glycogen.

Fales (1951) found the synthesis of his "transient reserve carbohydrate
(glycogen ?) to be blocked by azide. This was shown by direct analysi
and also by the effect of azide on the endogenous respiration of sample
of yeast withdrawn from the fermentation system after various time
Similar effects of graded concentrations of azide on glucose uptake t
those reported by Trevelyan et al. (1952) were observed by Fales (1953
He also showed that though, at the end of fermentation, carbon dioxid
and ethanol were present in equimolecular amounts, the carbon dioxid
ethanol ratio varied during the course of the fermentation and was a
fected by azide. He found no decrease in yeast carbohydrate induced b
10^{-3} M azide, as had Trevelyan et al. (1952). However, according t
Sussman and Bradley (1953) different strains of yeast vary in their sens
tivity to azide and, in fact, some resistant mutants were isolated.

As noted by early workers on these inhibitors, the action of nitr
phenols on the yeast cell depends upon the pH of the medium; thi
together with the effect of the chemical structure of a number of nitr
phenols has been recently considered by De Deken (1955). In genera
inhibitors which are weak acids, including azide, appear to penetrate th
cell in the undissociated form, which explains the effect of pH (Simc
and Beevers, 1951).

Stimulation of Endogenous Fermentation of Glycogen by Dinitr
phenol and Azide. Reiner and Spiegelman (1947) found that a suspe
sion of *Saccharomyces cerevisiae* which normally fermented glucose t
give 80% of the theoretical yield of carbon dioxide evolved 100% in th
presence of dinitrophenol or azide. If azide were added only after glucos
had disappeared from the medium, no additional carbon dioxide wa
evolved whereas dinitrophenol (10^{-3} M) caused renewed evolution
gas until recovery reached 100%. A higher concentration was required
produce this action than to prevent assimilation, and it was suggeste
that the structural integrity of the cell was attacked. An interesting poir
is that the yeast, before being enriched in glycogen by fermentatio
contained little carbohydrate capable of endogenous fermentation in th
presence of dinitrophenol, unless the cells had been rapidly harveste
and washed in the cold, when about 5% of the dry weight could b
metabolized. Rothstein and Berke, (1952), who used commercial baker
yeast, found that concentrations of azide or dinitrophenol greater tha
2.5×10^{-5} M induced endogenous fermentation to carbon dioxide an

hanol, azide being less effective. There was a definite limit to the total
ıtput of carbon dioxide induced by dinitrophenol. Analysis for glycogen
modified Pflüger procedure), or hydrolyzable carbohydrate, showed a
ecrease. Brady and Duggan (1954) also reported that high concentra-
ons of azide induced endogenous fermentation by baker's yeast, the
ɔncentration required to prevent assimilation during the fermentation
: glucose being very much less.

*Comparison between the Action of Dinitrophenol or Azide and of
mmonium Ions.* It will be seen that there are some resemblances be-
veen the actions of dinitrophenol, azide, and ammonium ions as far as
ıe metabolism of the carbohydrates of yeast cells is concerned. For in-
ance, ammonium salts prevent glycogen synthesis or trehalose resyn-
ıesis during fermentation (Trevelyan and Harrison, 1956a,c) though
ıe formation of mannan or glucan is not stopped, as it is by azide.
•initrophenol increased the endogenous respiration of *Torulopsis utilis,*
; did ammonium ions (Yemm and Folkes, 1954). Ammonium salts re-
ɛmble dinitrophenol in their capacity to abolish the Pasteur effect;
.olzer *et al.* (1955) has recently examined the mechanism of these
ʃects.

*Other Synthetic Activities of Yeast Inhibited by Azide and Dini-
ophenol.* Both inhibitors prevent many general synthetic processes of
ıe yeast cell including nitrogen assimilation (Winzler *et al.,* 1944; Yemm
ıd Folkes, 1954), synthesis of adaptive enzymes (Spiegelman, 1947),
ıosphate uptake (Hotchkiss, 1944), and potassium uptake (Conway
: *al.,* 1954).

*Other Inhibitors which Similarly Affect Assimilation during Metabolism
f Glucose, etc., by Yeast.* Somewhat similar effects, presumably includ-
ıg inhibition of glycogen formation, are shown by a miscellany of sub-
ances, examples being 2,4-dichlorophenoxyacetic acid (Swanson, 1955),
iethylstilbestrol and related compounds (Schacter, 1953), phenan-
ıroline (Dische, 1940), and cysteine (Runnström and Sperber, 1938).
.ike azide, the last two form complexes with many metal ions.

Arsenate is another inhibitor in this class but its action deserves
ɛparate mention (see below).

Action of Inhibitors of Assimilation on Some Enzyme Systems in vitro.
•initrophenols inhibit carboxylase (Massart and Vandendriessche, 1940),
ʰhich is possibly why they reduce the fermentation rate of yeast as well
; assimilation, if present in more than very small amount. The phos-
ʰorolysis of glycogen by dialyzed maceration juice is not affected
Vandendriessche, 1941), so presumably phosphorylase is not inhibited.

Phosphorylase from potato is not affected by azide (Trevelyan, unpul lished data). Azide inhibits many metallo-enzymes including the cyt chromes (Keilin, 1936) and the zinc-containing enzyme, carbonic ar hydrase (Keilin and Mann, 1940) which, in mammalian systems, ma be concerned in potassium and sodium regulation (Davies *et al.*, 1955 In view of the suggested interference of azide with the formation of AT during metabolism, it is interesting that Meyerhof and Ohlmeyer (1952 found an inhibitory action on an enzyme which breaks down AT adenosinetriphosphatase. Unlike the purified enzyme, a crude extra was unaffected.

These findings do not suggest any mechanism whereby assimilation reduced, though they indicate that both dinitrophenol and azide ar liable to have many loci of action in the cell.

Action of Arsenate on Yeast Metabolism. Arsenate, like azide, inte feres with assimilation (glycogen synthesis), during the metabolism (glucose, and also with nitrogen assimilation and enzymatic adaptatio These effects are competitively reversed by phosphate (Reiner, 194 Sussman and Spiegelman, 1950a,b). Beraud (1943) showed that arsena interferes with glycogen synthesis with the result that yeast which ha been induced by serial transfer to grow in the presence of arsenate lo its power to store glycogen.

In vitro, arsenate can replace phosphate as a substrate for 3-phosph glyceraldehyde dehydrogenase. The product of the modified reaction i however, not 1,3-diphosphoglyceric acid, but 3-phosphoglyceric ac (Warburg and Christian, 1939). The result of this action of arsena during fermentation by cell-free extracts of yeast is to prevent net ge. eration of ATP; the processes of phosphorylation and dephosphorylatic are in balance and the Harden-Young effect is abolished.

Although this action has been advanced as an explanation of the actic of arsenate on metabolism by whole yeast, other inhibitory effects arsenate on individual enzymes are equally pertinent. For exampl arsenate can replace phosphate in phosphorylase systems, causing tl arsenolysis of glycogen. Phosphoglucomutase is inhibited (Leloir *et a* 1952), an action which is not only of significance where cell carbohydra synthesis is concerned, but also probably accounts for the inhibition galactose fermentation by galactose-adapted yeast observed by Sussma and Spiegelman (1950a).

Effects of 2,4-Dinitrophenol, Azide, and Arsenate on Phosphorylatic Processes. Loomis and Lipmann (1948) measured the ATP generate during the oxidation of glutamate by a kidney homogenate by includi

the system fructose and yeast hexokinase. 2,4-Dinitrophenol "un-
coupled" phosphorylation from oxidation, i.e., it reduced the formation
of ATP without affecting oxidation itself. The inhibitor could replace the
inorganic phosphate requirement of the experimental system and, consequently, a strong stimulation of oxygen uptake was observed when the
inhibitor was added in the absence of inorganic phosphate. It appears
Hunter, 1951) that this last effect may be due to a release of phosphate
from ATP, itself caused by an acceleration of the action of mitochondrial
adenosinetriphosphatase. Later Loomis and Lipmann (1949) showed
that azide had also an uncoupling action; in this case, inhibition of oxidation due to the action of azide on the cytochrome system was avoided by
using ferricyanide as a hydrogen acceptor.

These findings provided powerful support for a generalization advanced by Brockmann and Stier (1947), among others. They suggested
that the rate of glucose consumption by yeast was limited by the enzyme
systems which regenerated adenosine diphosphate and free phosphate
from ATP formed during fermentation or respiration. From this standpoint, glycogen synthesis could be considered as a mechanism whereby
excess ATP was utilized. The rate-accelerating action of ammonium ion
was due to increased utilization of ATP, and that of inhibitors such as
azide and dinitrophenol to reduction of ATP generated during metabo-
sm.

This scheme, attractive in its brilliant simplicity, had two flaws. In the
first place, not all strains of yeast reacted in accord with its predictions.
That studied by Trevelyan et al. (1952), for example, increased its fermentation rate, but not the rate of glucose utilization during anaerobic
metabolism of low concentrations of glucose, when azide was added. But
high concentrations of glucose were present, fermentation rate was
scarcely affected (Trevelyan, unpublished data), and under these conditions carboxylase was shown to be one limiting enzyme system
Trevelyan and Harrison, 1954). Secondly, it was purely descriptive, and
contained no hint of the mechanism whereby azide and dinitrophenol
reduced the generation of ATP.

Loomis and Lipmann's experiments were an advance towards finding
mechanism for the action of azide and dinitrophenol on aerobic metabo-
ism but failed to explain their effect on anaerobic yeast metabolism.
Spiegelman et al. (1948) saw azide as analogous in its mode of action to
arsenate, which was assumed to exert its effects on yeast metabolism by
interfering with the 3-phosphoglyceraldehyde oxidation system. Azide
was found to have no action comparable to that of arsenate on the en-

zyme *in vitro,* and it was postulated that azide acted *after* the formatio of diphosphoglycerate. Azide apparently interfered with the esterificatio of inorganic phosphate. However, measurement was made not of th steady-state level of phosphate during fermentation, but of the free pho phate in the cell *after* fermentation. What was inhibited, therefore, ma have been the transfer of phosphate from inorganic to *stable* forms, no to the transient intermediates of fermentation and in this connection it noteworthy that Wiame (1949) found that azide inhibited metapho phate formation.

Recently it has become evident that dinitrophenol prevents phosphe rylation coupled with electron transfer from reduced diphosphopyridin nucleotide to oxygen (Hunter, 1951), but has no effect on phosphoryla tion below that level. Azide has a similar action: it does not interfer with phosphorylation associated with glycolysis in yeast extracts (Rober son and Boyer, 1955), but does prevent the exchange of P^{32} of inorgani phosphate with ATP normally catalyzed by liver mitochondria, an indica tion that azide prevents the initial uptake of inorganic phosphate couple with electron transport. Trevelyan *et al.* (1954) examined the effect azide on the intracellular concentration of intermediates established du ing fermentation, but could find no evidence for a specific interferenc with the generation of ATP. They did, however, find that the marke decrease in the level of adenosine-5'-phosphate which occurs durin normal fermentation was prevented by azide.

Conclusion. A cautious view is that carbohydrate synthesis in the yea cell depends, not only upon a relatively few specific enzymes such a phosphorylase and phosphoglucomutase, but also on the maintenance o a suitable steady-state concentration of the substrates of these enzyme perhaps in a particular part of the cell. This process—as affecting th free phosphate concentration, for example—may well involve the con certed action of many enzymes, and the integrity of selectively permeabl membranes and other structural components. The failure of any secto may then destroy the conditions for carbohydrate synthesis, withou necessarily affecting the action of the enzymes directly involved. Schacte (1955), it is interesting to note, found that one effect of dinitrophenol o Ehrlich ascites tumor cells was to make the cell membrane more perme able to phosphate compounds.

It may seem that a good deal of space has been devoted to discussin experiments which have led to no definite conclusions. One must no forget that these investigations have been courageously directed toward uncovering the very fundamentals of cell metabolism; and there is n doubt that when the action of azide, for example, on yeast fermentatio

s fully understood, that a tremendous advance in our understanding of
arbohydrate physiology of cells generally will have been made.

D. *Carbohydrate Synthesis by Growing Yeast*

Relatively few studies have been made of the effect of growth condi-
ions on the synthesis of cellular carbohydrates. Since these constitute
n appreciable fraction of the dry weight of the cell, conditions which
esult in a high yield of yeast may be those most suitable to carbohydrate
torage. An important factor is the concentration of sugar, for White
1954) has shown that, at a fixed rate of aeration, the yield of yeast
lecreases as the concentration of sugar in the growth medium is raised.
ield also depends inversely on the rate of growth.

Trevelyan (1956) grew a strain of *Saccharomyces cerevisiae* by feeding
synthetic medium at a constant rate to an inoculum contained in a 450
nl. cylinder and aerated by air at a rate of 1 l./minute. Excess medium
vas allowed to overflow, so that the yeast grew in a medium of approxi-
nately constant composition for 15 hours. The yeast was analyzed for
itrogen, nucleic acid, phosphate, and cell carbohydrates. The rate at
vhich the yeast, after harvesting, would store carbohydrate during the
ermentation of 0.3 M glucose was also determined. The effect was de-
ermined of varying the concentration of the following constituents of the
nedium: glucose, ammonium chloride, and phosphate.

With a medium containing *inter alia* 0.075 M glucose, and 0.03 M as-
imilable nitrogen, the effect was studied of supplementing the medium
vith iron and other trace metals, yeast extract, and several vitamins and
ucleosides. Under these conditions, it was found that all the nitrogen
vas taken up from the medium, and variations in yield were due largely
o variation in the carbohydrate stored by the yeast.

The nitrogen content of 37 cultures (nitrogen insoluble in trichloro-
cetic acid, i.e., mainly protein and nucleic acid) varied between 4340
nd 6170 μM/g. of dry weight (1000 μM N $\equiv$ 14 mg. $\equiv$ 1.4%). The range
f cell carbohydrate composition, in μM of glucose or mannose per gram
1000 $\mu M \equiv$ 162 mg. polysaccharide $\equiv$ 16%) was: total, 1440–2700; tre-
alose, 8–727; glycogen, 292–772; mannan, 615–1048; glucan, 383–625. A
ommercially grown sample of the same strain contained 2140 total carbo-
ydrate, 452 trehalose, 467 glycogen, 737 mannan, 419 glucan.

The most important determinant of yeast trehalose and glycogen was
ound to be, under these conditions, the rate of growth. This could be
ltered by varying the rate at which the medium was added (Table III).
)ne result of this was that the reserve carbohydrate (sum of glycogen
nd trehalose) was synthesized at approximately the same *rate* during

TABLE III

THE EFFECT OF GROWTH RATE ON THE CARBOHYDRATE CONTENT OF YEAST[a]

	Carbohydrate (μM hexose/g. dry weight)				
Feed rate (ml. medium/min.)	Total	Trehalose	Glycogen	Mannan	Glucan
0.75	2700	727	772	760	427
1.5	2150	100	492	1004	494
3.0	1440	12	292	769	383

[a] From Trevelyan (1956).

growth; thus for 13 comparable experiments, the rate was 1.3 ± 0.2 μM of glucose/minute/g. of yeast, though the amount per g. of yeast was variable.

When the yeast, after harvesting, was transferred to 0.3 M glucose, it continued to synthesize glucan and mannan anaerobically, the former at about the same rate as during aerobic growth, the latter much more slowly. After an initial breakdown, trehalose and glycogen were synthesized about 5 times faster than they had been during growth, the precise figure varying from culture to culture. The fermentation rate varied only slightly from one culture to another.

With a slightly different strain of yeast, it was shown that the maximum rate of growth in the medium corresponded to a mean generation time of 2 hours. By analyzing the contents of a dialysis sac suspended in the growth vessel for 24 hours while yeast was growing with a mean generation time of 4 hours, it was shown that the steady-state concentration of glucose during growth was 2×10^{-3} M. It is probably the concentration of glucose which is important in determining the effects of growth rate.

References

Agar, H. D., and Douglas, H. C. (1955). *J. Bacteriol.* **70**, 427.

Aisenberg, A. C., and Potter, V. R. (1957). *J. Biol. Chem.* **224**, 1115.

Aisenberg, A. C., Reinafarje, B., and Potter, V. R. (1957). *J. Biol. Chem.* **224**, 1099.

Aldous, J. G., Fisher, K. C., and Stern, J. R. (1950). *J. Cellular Comp. Physiol.* **3**, 303.

Aschner, M., Mager, J., and Leibowitz, J. (1945). *Nature* **156**, 295.

Aubert, J. P., and Milhaud, G. (1955a). *Compt. rend.* **240**, 1943.

Aubert, J. P., and Milhaud, G. (1955b). *Compt. rend.* **240**, 2451.

Aubert, J. P., and Milhaud, G. (1956). *Ann. inst. Pasteur* **90**, 320.

Barker, S. A., and Bourne, E. J. (1953). *Quart. Revs. (London)* **7**, 56.

Barry, V. C., and Dillon, T. (1943). *Proc. Roy. Irish Acad.* **B49**, 177.

Bartholomew, J. W., and Levin, R. (1955). *J. Gen. Microbiol.* **12**, 473.

Bartholomew, J. W., and Mittwer, T. (1952). *J. Bacteriol.* **64**, 1.

Beck, W. S. (1955). *J. Biol. Chem.* **216**, 333.
Bell, D. J. (1948). *Biol. Revs. Cambridge Phil. Soc.* **23**, 256.
Bell, D. J., and Northcote, D. H. (1950). *J. Chem. Soc.* **1950**, 1944.
Bentley, R. (1955). *Nature* **175**, 870.
Beraud, P. (1943). *Ann. inst. Pasteur* **69**, 230, 275, 349.
Bernfeld, P. (1951). *Advances in Enzymol.* **12**, 379.
Blumenthal, H. J., Lewis, K. F., and Weinhouse, S. (1954). *J. Am. Chem. Soc.* **76**, 6093.
Boser, H. (1955). *Hoppe-Seyler's Z. physiol. Chem.* **300**, 1.
Bouthilet, R. J., Neilson, N. E., Mrak, E. M., and Phaff, H. J. (1949). *J. Gen. Microbiol.* **3**, 282.
Boyland, E. (1929). *Biochem. J.* **23**, 219.
Brady, T. G., and Duggan, P. F. (1954). *Biochem. J.* **58**, xxii.
Brady, T. G., McGann, C., and Tully, E. (1956). *Biochem. J.* **64**, 44P.
Brandt, K. (1941). *Biochem. Z.* **309**, 190.
Brockmann, M. C., and Stier, T. J. B. (1947). *J. Cellular Comp. Physiol.* **29**, 159.
Brücke, F. T. (1933). *Biochem. Z.* **264**, 157.
Bücher, T. (1953). *Advances in Enzymol.* **14**, 1.
Burton, K., and Krebs, H. A. (1953). *Biochem. J.* **54**, 94.
Cabib, E., and Leloir, L. F. (1954). *J. Biol. Chem.* **206**, 779.
Cabib, E., Leloir, L., and Cardini, C. E. (1953). *J. Biol. Chem.* **203**, 1055.
Chance, B. (1954). *In* "The Mechanism of Enzyme Action" (W. D. McElroy and B. Glass, eds.), p. 399. Johns Hopkins Press, Baltimore.
Chung, C. W., and Nickerson, W. J. (1954). *J. Biol. Chem.* **208**, 395.
Cifonelli, J. A., and Smith, F. (1955). *J. Am. Chem. Soc.* **77**, 5682.
Claude, A. (1954). *Proc. Roy. Soc.* **B142**, 177.
Clifton, C. E. (1946). *Advances in Enzymol.* **6**, 269.
Clifton, C. E. (1952). *In* "The Enzymes" (J. B. Sumner and K. Myrbäck, eds.), Vol. II, Part 2, p. 912. Academic Press, New York.
Cohn, M., and Cori, G. T. (1948). *J. Biol. Chem.* **175**, 89.
Conway, E. J., and Downey, M. (1950a). *Biochem. J.* **47**, 347.
Conway, E. J., and Downey, M. (1950b). *Biochem. J.* **47**, 355.
Conway, E. J., Ryan, H., and Carton, E. (1954). *Biochem. J.* **58**, 158.
Cori, C. F. (1956). *In* "Enzymes: Units of Biological Structure and Function" (O. H. Gaebler, ed.), p. 573. Academic Press, New York.
Cori, G. T., Colowick, S. P., and Cori, C. F. (1938). *J. Biol. Chem.* **123**, 375.
Cremer, M. (1899). *Ber. deut. chem. Ges.* **32**, 2062.
Daoud, K. M., and Ling, A. R. (1931a). *J. Soc. Chem. Ind.* (*London*) **50**, 365T.
Daoud, K. M., and Ling, A. R. (1931b). *J. Soc. Chem. Ind.* (*London*) **50**, 379T.
Davies, R. E., Galston, A. W., and Whittam, R. (1955). *Biochim. et Biophys. Acta* **17**, 434.
De Deken, R. H. (1955). *Biochim. et Biophys. Acta* **17**, 494.
Dische, Z. (1940). *Compt. rend. soc. biol.* **133**, 380.
Dixon, M. (1949). "Multi-Enzyme Systems." Cambridge Univ. Press, London and New York.
Doudoroff, M. (1951). *In* "Phosphorus Metabolism" (W. D. McElroy and B. Glass, eds.), Vol. I, p. 42. Johns Hopkins Press, Baltimore.
Dumazert, C., and Penet, G. (1938). *Compt. rend. soc. biol.* **127**, 75.
Elander, M. (1956). *Arkiv Kemi* **9**, 191.

Elander, M., and Myrbäck, K. (1949). *Arch. Biochem.* **21**, 249.
Errera, L. (1885). *Compt. rend.* **101**, 253.
Evans, E. E., and Theriault, R. J. (1953). *J. Bacteriol.* **65**, 571.
Falcone, G., and Nickerson, W. J. (1956). *Science* **124**, 273.
Fales, F. W. (1951). *J. Biol. Chem.* **193**, 113.
Fales, F. W. (1953). *J. Biol. Chem.* **202**, 157.
Fales, F. W., and Baumberger, J. P. (1948). *J. Biol. Chem.* **173**, 1.
Fischer, E. H., and Kohtès, L. (1951). *Helv. Chim. Acta* **34**, 1132.
Fürth, O., and Lieben, F. (1922a). *Biochem. Z.* **128**, 144.
Fürth, O., and Lieben, F. (1922b). *Biochem. Z.* **132**, 165.
Garzuly-Janke, R. (1940a). *J. prakt. Chem.* **156**, 45.
Garzuly-Janke, R. (1940b). *Zentr. Bakteriol. Parasitenk. Abt. II* **102**, 361.
Giaja, J. (1919). *Compt. rend. soc. biol.* **82**, 719.
Giaja, J. (1922). *Compt. rend. soc. biol.* **86**, 708.
Gilvarg, C. (1952). *J. Biol. Chem.* **199**, 57.
Glaser, L., and Brown, D. H. (1955). *J. Biol. Chem.* **216**, 67.
Gottschalk, A. (1926). *Hoppe-Seyler's Z. physiol. Chem.* **153**, 215.
Gottschalk, A. (1942). *Australian J. Exptl. Biol. Med. Sci.* **20**, 201.
Gottschalk, A. (1949). *Wallerstein Labs. Communs.* **12**, 55.
Gunsalus, I. C., Horecker, B. L., and Wood, W. A. (1955). *Bacteriol. Revs.* **19**, 79.
Günther, G., and Bonhoeffer, K. F. (1937). *Z. physik. Chem.* **A180**, 185.
Harden, A. (1932). "Alcoholic Fermentation." Longmans Green, London.
Harden, A., and Rowland, S. (1901). *J. Chem. Soc.* **1901**, 1227.
Harden, A., and Young, W. J. (1902). *J. Chem. Soc.* **1902**, 1224.
Harden, A., and Young, W. J. (1912). *J. Chem. Soc.* **1912**, 1928.
Harden, A., and Young, W. J. (1913). *Biochem. J.* **7**, 630.
Hashitani, Y. (1927). *J. Inst. Brewing* **33**, 347.
Hassid, W. Z. (1951). In "Phosphorus Metabolism" (W. D. McElroy and B. Glass eds.), Vol. I, p. 11, Johns Hopkins Press, Baltimore.
Hassid, W. Z. (1954). In "Chemical Pathways of Metabolism" (D. M. Greenberg ed.), Vol. I, p. 235. Academic Press, New York.
Hassid, W. Z., Doudoroff, M., and Barker, H. A. (1951). In "The Enzymes" (J. B Sumner and K. Myrbäck, eds.), Vol. I, Part 2, p. 1014. Academic Press, New York.
Hassid, W. Z., Joslyn, M. A., and McCready, R. M. (1941). *J. Am. Chem. Soc.* **63**, 295.
Haworth, W. N., Heath, R. L., and Peat, S. (1941). *J. Chem. Soc.* **1941**, 833.
Haworth, W. N., Hirst, E. L., and Isherwood, F. A. (1937). *J. Chem. Soc.* **1937**, 784
Hearon, J. Z. (1949a). *Bull. Math. Biophys.* **11**, 29.
Hearon, J. Z. (1949b). *Bull. Math. Biophys.* **11**, 83.
Hehre, E. J., Carlson, A. S., and Hamilton, D. M. (1949). *J. Biol. Chem.* **177**, 289.
Henneberg, W., and Böhmer, M. (1921). *Wochschr. Brau.* **38**, 237, 245.
Holden, M., and Tracey, M. V. (1950). *Biochem. J.* **47**, 407.
Holzer, H. (1955). Private Communication.
Holzer, H., and Holzer, E. (1953). *Hoppe-Seyler's Z. physiol. Chem.* **292**, 232.
Holzer, H., and Holzer, E., and Schultz, G. (1955). *Biochem. Z.* **326**, 385.
Holzer, H., Goldschmidt, S., Lamprecht, W., and Helmreich, E. (1954). *Hoppe-Seyler's Z. physiol. Chem.* **297**, 1.

Hopkins, R. H. (1955). *Proc. European Brewery Conv. 5th Congr. Baden-Baden 1955*, p. 452.

Hotchkiss, R. D. (1944). *Advances in Enzymol.* 4, 153.

Houwink, A. L., and Kreger, D. R. (1953). *Antonie van Leeuwenhoek J. Microbiol. Serol.* 19, 1.

Houwink, A. L., Kreger, D. R., and Roelofsen, P. A. (1951). *Nature* 168, 693.

Hunter, F. E. (1951). *In* "Phosphorus Metabolism" (W. D. McElroy and B. Glass, eds.), Vol. I, p. 297. Johns Hopkins Press, Baltimore.

Hurst, H. (1952). *J. Exptl. Biol.* 29, 30.

Jeanloz, R. (1944). *Helv. Chim. Acta* 27, 1501.

Johnson, F. H., Eyring, H., and Polissar, M. J. (1954). "The Kinetic Basis of Molecular Biology," p. 187. Wiley, New York.

Joslyn, M. A. (1955). *Wallerstein Labs. Communs.* 18, 107.

Kalckar, H. M. (1954). *In* "The Mechanism of Enzyme Action" (W. D. McElroy and B. Glass, eds.), p. 675. Johns Hopkins Press, Baltimore.

Kalckar, H. M., Braganca, B., and Munch-Petersen, A. (1953). *Nature* 172, 1038.

Kamen, M. D., and Spiegelman, S. (1948). *Cold Spring Harbor Symposia Quant. Biol.* 13, 151.

Kaplan, J. G. (1955). *Exptl. Cell Research* 8, 305.

Keilin, D. (1936). *Proc. Roy. Soc.* B121, 165.

Keilin, D., and Mann, T. (1940). *Biochem. J.* 34, 1163.

Khouvine, Y., and De Robichon-Szulmajster, H. (1951). *Bull. soc. chim. biol.* 33, 1508.

Khouvine, Y., and De Robichon-Szulmajster, H. (1952). *Bull. soc. chim. biol.* 34, 1056.

Kiessling, W. (1939a). *Naturwissenschaften* 27, 129.

Kiessling, W. (1939b). *Biochem. Z.* 302, 50.

Klein, H. P. (1955). *J. Bacteriol.* 69, 620.

Klein, H. P., and Lipmann, F. (1953). *J. Biol. Chem.* 203, 95.

Kleinzeller, A. (1948). *Advances in Enzymol.* 8, 299.

Klopstock, F., and Vercellone, A. (1936). *Z. Immunitätsforsch.* 88, 446.

Koch, E. M., and Koch, F. C. (1925). *Science* 61, 570.

Koshland, D. E., Jr., and Westheimer, F. H. (1950). *J. Am. Chem. Soc.* 72, 3383.

Krahl, M. E., and Clowes, G. H. A. (1935). *J. Biol. Chem.* 111, 355.

Kraut, H., and Eichorn, F. (1927). *Ber. deut. chem. Ges.* 60, 1639.

Kraut, H., Eichorn, F., and Rubenbauer, H. (1927). *Ber. deut. chem. Ges.* B60, 1644.

Krebs, E. G., and Fischer, E. H. (1956). *Biochim. et Biophys. Acta* 20, 150.

Krebs, E. G., Rafter, G. W., and Junge, J. M. (1953). *J. Biol. Chem.* 200, 479.

Kreger, D. R. (1954). *Biochim. et Biophys. Acta* 13, 1.

Kreger, D. R., and Meeuse, B. J. D. (1952). *Biochim. et Biophys. Acta* 9, 699.

Kullberg, S. (1914). *Hoppe-Seyler's Z. physiol. Chem.* 92, 340.

Lazarow, A. (1942). *Anat. Record* 84, 31.

Lehmann, H. (1938). *Nature* 141, 470.

Leibowitz, J., and Hestrin, S. (1945). *Advances in Enzymol.* 5, 87.

Leloir, L. F. (1951). *In* "Phosphorus Metabolism" (W. D. McElroy and B. Glass, eds.), p. 67. Johns Hopkins Press, Baltimore.

Leloir, L. F. (1953). *Advances in Enzymol.* 14, 193.

Leloir, L. F., and Cabib, E. (1953). *J. Am. Chem. Soc.* 75, 5445.

Leloir, L. F., Cardini, C. E., and Cabib, E. (1952). *Anales asoc. quim. argentina* **40,** 228.

Levine, S., Stevenson, H. J. R., Tabor, E. C., Bordner, R. H., and Chambers, L. A. (1953). *J. Bacteriol.* **66,** 664.

Liebermann, I., Berger, L., and Gimenez, W. T. (1956). *Science* **124,** 81.

Lindegren, C. C. (1945). *Arch. Biochem.* **8,** 119.

Lindegren, C. C. (1946). *Arch. Biochem.* **9,** 353.

Lindegren, C. C. (1949). "The Yeast Cell, Its Genetics and Cytology." Educational Publishers, St. Louis.

Lindquist, W. (1953a). *Biochim. et Biophys. Acta* **10,** 580.

Lindquist, W. (1953b). *Biochim. et Biophys. Acta* **11,** 90.

Lindquist, W. (1953c). *J. Inst. Brewing* **59,** 59.

Lindstedt, G. (1945). *Arkiv Kemi, Mineral. Geol.* **A20,** No. 13.

Ling, A. R., Nanji, D. R., and Paton, F. J. (1925). *J. Inst. Brewing* **31,** 316.

Linnane, A. W., and Still, J. L. (1955). *Arch. Biochem. and Biophys.* **59,** 383.

Loomis, W. F., and Lipmann, F. (1948). *J. Biol. Chem.* **173,** 807.

Loomis, W. F., and Lipmann, F. (1949). *J. Biol. Chem.* **179,** 503.

Lukes, T. M., and Phaff, H. J. (1952). *Antonie van Leeuwenhoek J. Microbiol. Serol.* **18,** 323.

Lundin, H. (1923a). *Biochem. Z.* **141,** 310.

Lundin, H. (1923b). *Biochem. Z.* **142,** 454.

Lundin, H. (1923c). *Biochem. Z.* **142,** 463.

McAnally, R. A., and Smedley-Maclean, I. (1934). *Biochem. J.* **28,** 495.

McAnally, R. A., and Smedley-Maclean, I. (1935a). *Biochem. J.* **29,** 1872.

McAnally, R. A., and Smedley-Maclean, I. (1935b). *Biochem. J.* **29,** 2236.

McAnally, R. A., and Smedley-Maclean, I. (1937). *Biochem. J.* **31,** 72.

Mager, J. (1947). *Biochem. J.* **41,** 603.

Mager, J., and Aschner, M. (1947). *J. Bacteriol.* **53,** 283.

Mandels, G. R. (1953). *Exptl. Cell Research* **5,** 48.

Mann, P. F. E. (1956). Private Communication.

Manners, D. J. (1955). *Quart. Revs. (London)* **9,** 73.

Manners, D. J., and Maung, K. (1955a). *J. Chem. Soc.* **1955,** 867.

Manners, D. J., and Maung, K. (1955b). *Chemistry & Industry* **1955,** 950.

Manners, D. J., and Maung, K. (1956). *Biochem. J.* **63,** 16P.

Maruo, B., and Kobayashi, T. (1951). *Nature* **167,** 606.

Massart, L., and Vandendriessche, L. (1940). *Naturwissenschaften* **28,** 781.

Meissner, R. (1900). *Centr. Bakteriol. Parasitenk.* **6,** 517.

Meyer, D. K., Russell, R. L., Platner, W. S., Purdy, F. A., and Westfall, B. A. (1955). *Proc. Soc. Exptl. Biol. Med.* **90,** 15.

Meyer, K. H. (1943). *Advances in Enzymol.* **3,** 109.

Meyer, K. H., and Bernfeld, P. (1941). *Helv. Chim. Acta* **24,** 1400.

Meyer, K. H., and Bernfeld, P. (1942). *Helv. Chim. Acta* **25,** 399.

Meyerhof, O., and Ohlmeyer, P. (1952). *J. Biol. Chem.* **195,** 11.

Meyerhof, O., and Schulz, W. (1936). *Biochem. Z.* **287,** 206.

Milhaud, G., and Aubert, J. P. (1955a). *Compt. rend.* **240,** 2178.

Milhaud, G., and Aubert, J. P. (1955b). *Compt. rend.* **241,** 525.

Moelwyn-Hughes, E. A. (1929). *Trans. Faraday Soc.* **25,** 81.

Moses, V., and Syrett, P. J. (1955). *J. Bacteriol.* **70,** 201.

Munch-Petersen, A. (1955). *Arch. Biochem. and Biophys.* **55,** 592.

Munch- Petersen, A., Kalckar, H. M., Cutolo E., and Smith, E. E. B. (1953). *Nature.* 172, 1036.

Müntz, A. (1876). *Ann. chim. et phys.* 8, 56, 61.

Myrbäck, K. (1949). *Ergeb. Enzymforsch.* 10, 168.

Myrbäck, K., and Neumüller, G. (1951). *Ergeb. Enzymforsch.* 12, 1.

Myrbäck, K., and Örtenblad, B. (1936). *Biochem. Z.* 288, 329.

Myrbäck, K., and Willstaedt, E. (1955). *Arkiv Kemi* 8, 367.

Naganishi, H. (1926). *Biochem. J.* 20, 856.

Najjar, V. A. (1948). *J. Biol. Chem.* 175, 281.

Najjar, V. A., and Pullman, M. E. (1954). *Science* 119, 631.

Neill, J. M., Castillo, C. G., Smith, R. H., and Kapros, C. E. (1948). *J. Exptl. Med.* 89, 93.

Neuberg, C. (1950). *Am. Brewer* 83, 35.

Neufeld, E. F., and Hassid, W. Z. (1955). *Arch. Biochem. and Biophys.* 59, 405.

Nickerson, W. J. (1949). *Experientia* 5, 202.

Nickerson, W. J., and Chung, C. W. (1952). *Am. J. Botany* 39, 669.

Nickerson, W. J., and Falcone, G. (1956). *Science* 124, 318.

Nickerson, W. J., and Mullins, L. J. (1948). *Nature* 161, 939.

Nilsson, R., and Alm, F. (1949). *Acta Chem. Scand.* 3, 213.

Nishimura, S. (1930). *Biochem. Z.* 225, 264.

Northcote, D. H. (1953). *Biochem. J.* 53, 348.

Northcote, D. H. (1954). *Biochem. J.* 58, 353.

Northcote, D. H., and Horne, R. W. (1952). *Biochem. J.* 51, 232.

Nossal, P. M. (1954). *Biochem. J.* 57, 62.

Paladini, A. C., Caputto, R., Leloir, L. F., Trucco, R. E., and Cardini, E. (1949). *Arch. Biochem.* 23, 55.

Park, J. T., and Strominger, J. L. (1957). *Science* 125, 99.

Parnas, J. K. (1937). *Ergeb. Enzymforsch.* 6, 57.

Pavy, F. W., and Bywaters, H. W. (1907). *J. Physiol. (London)* 36, 149.

Payen, R. (1949). *Can. J. Research* 27, 749.

Peat, S., Whelan, W. J., and Edwards, T. E. (1955a). *J. Chem. Soc.* 1955, 355.

Peat, S., Whelan, W. J., and Hinson, K. A. (1955b). *Chemistry & Industry* 1955, 385.

Pickett, M. J., and Clifton, C. E. (1941). *Proc. Soc. Exptl. Biol. Med.* 46, 443.

Pickett, M. J., and Clifton, C. E. (1943a). *J. Cellular Comp. Physiol.* 21, 77.

Pickett, M. J., and Clifton, C. E. (1943b). *J. Cellular Comp. Physiol.* 22, 147.

Pollock, G. E., and Holmstrom, C. D. (1951). *Cereal Chem.* 28, 498.

Posternak, T., and Rosselet, J. P. (1954). *Helv. Chim. Acta* 37, 246.

Racker, E. (1954). *Advances in Enzymol.* 15, 141.

Rall, T. W., Sutherland, E. W., and Wosilait, W. D. (1956a). *J. Biol. Chem.* 218, 483.

Rall, T. W., Wosilait, W. D., and Sutherland, E. W. (1956b). *Biochim. et Biophys. Acta* 20, 69.

Rautanen, N., and Kärkkäinen, V. (1951). *Acta Chem. Scand.* 5, 1216.

Rawson, A. J., and Norris, R. F. (1947). *Am. J. Clin. Pathol.* 17, 807.

Reiner, J. M. (1948). *Arch. Biochem.* 19, 218.

Reiner, J. M., and Spiegelman, S. (1947). *J. Cellular Comp. Physiol.* 30, 347.

Reiner, J. M., Gest, H., and Kamen, M. D. (1949). *Arch. Biochem.* 20, 175.

Robertson, H. E., and Boyer, P. D. (1955). *J. Biol. Chem.* 214, 295.

Robison, R., and Morgan, W. T. J. (1928). *Biochem. J.* 22, 1277.

Robison, R., and Morgan, W. T. J. (1930). *Biochem. J.* **24**, 119.

Roelofsen, P. A. (1953). *Biochim. et Biophys. Acta* **10**, 477.

Roelofsen, P. A., and Hoette, I. (1951). *Antonie van Leeuwenhoek J. Microbiol Serol.* **17**, 297.

Rothstein, A. (1954a). In "Protoplasmatologia," Vol. II, E4. Springer Verlag, Vienna

Rothstein, A. (1954b). *Symposia Soc. Exptl. Biol.* **8**, 165.

Rothstein, A., and Berke, H. (1952). *Arch. Biochem. and Biophys.* **36**, 195.

Rothstein, A., and Enns, L. H. (1946). *J. Cellular Comp. Physiol.* **28**, 231.

Runnström, J., and Sperber, E. (1938). *Nature* **141**, 689.

Salkowski, E. (1894a). *Ber. deut. chem. Ges.* **27**, 497.

Salkowski, E. (1894b). *Ber. deut. chem. Ges.* **27**, 3325.

Schacter, B. (1953). *Arch. Biochem. and Biophys.* **46**, 312.

Schacter, B. (1955). *Arch. Biochem. and Biophys.* **57**, 387.

Schäffner, A., and Specht, H. (1938a). *Hoppe-Seyler's Z. physiol. Chem.* **251**, 144.

Schäffner, A., and Specht, H. (1938b). *Naturwissenschaften* **26**, 494.

Scott, G. T., Jacobson, M. A., and Rice, M. E. (1951). *Arch. Biochem.* **30**, 282.

Sevag, M. G., Cattaneo, C., and Maiweg, L. (1935). *Ann. Chem. Justus Liebigs* **519** 111.

Siekevitz, P., and Potter, V. R. (1955a). *J. Biol. Chem.* **215**, 221.

Siekevitz, P., and Potter, V. R. (1955b). *J. Biol. Chem.* **215**, 237.

Simon, E. W., and Beevers, H. (1951). *Science* **114**, 124.

Simon, S., and Hedrick, L. R. (1955). *J. Bacteriol.* **69**, 4.

Smedley-Maclean, I. (1922). *Biochem. J.* **16**, 370.

Smedley-Maclean, I., and Hoffert, D. (1923). *Biochem. J.* **17**, 720.

Smedley-Maclean, I., and Hoffert, D. (1924). *Biochem. J.* **18**, 1273.

Smedley-Maclean, I., and Hoffert, D. (1926). *Biochem. J.* **20**, 343.

Smith, E. E. B., Munch-Petersen, A., and Mills, G. T. (1953). *Nature* **172**, 1038.

Sobotka, H., and Holzman, M. (1936). *Enzymologia* **1**, 168.

Sowden, J. C., and Frankel, S. (1956). *J. Biol. Chem.* **221**, 587.

Sowden, J. C., Frankel, S., Moore, B. H., and McClary, J. E. (1954). *J. Biol. Chem.* **206**, 547.

Sperber, E. (1944). *Arkiv Kemi, Mineral. Geol.* **A18**, No. 4.

Spiegelman, S. (1947). *J. Cellular Comp. Physiol.* **30**, 315.

Spiegelman, S., and Nozawa, M. (1945). *Arch. Biochem.* **6**, 303.

Spiegelman, S., and Sussman, M. (1952). *Ann. Rev. Physiol.* **14**, 97.

Spiegelman, S., Kamen, M. D., and Sussman, M. (1948). *Arch. Biochem.* **18**, 409.

Stacey, M. (1954). *Advances in Enzymol.* **15**, 301.

Steiner, A., and Cori, C. F. (1935). *Science* **82**, 422.

Stetten, M. R., Katzen, H. M., and Stetten, D. (1956). *J. Biol. Chem.* **222**, 587.

Stewart, L. C., Richtmyer, N. K., and Hudson, C. S. (1950). *J. Am. Chem. Soc.* **72**, 2059.

Stickland, L. H. (1956). *Biochem. J.* **64**, 498.

Stier, T. J. B. (1939). *Cold Spring Harbor Symposia Quant. Biol.* **7**, 385.

Stier, T. J. B., and Newton, M. I. (1939). *J. Cellular Comp. Physiol.* **13**, 345.

Stier, T. J. B., and Sprince, H. (1941). *J. Cellular Comp. Physiol.* **18**, 135.

Stier, T. J. B., and Stannard, J. N. (1936a). *J. Gen Physiol.* **19**, 461.

Stier, T. J. B., and Stannard, J. N. (1936b). *J. Gen. Physiol.* **19**, 479.

Stier, T. J. B., Newton, M. I., and Sprince, H. (1939). *Science* **89**, 85.

Stockhausen, F., and Silbereisen, K. (1935a). *Wochschr. Brau.* **52**, 145.

Stockhausen, F., and Silbereisen, K. (1935b). *Wochschr. Brau.* **52**, 257.

Stockhausen, F., and Silbereisen, K. (1935c). *Wochschr. Brau.* **52**, 393.

Stockhausen, F., and Silbereisen, K. (1936a). *Biochem. Z.* **287**, 276.

Stockhausen, F., and Silbereisen, K. (1936b). *Wochschr. Brau.* **53**, 281.

Suomalainen, H., and Oura, E. (1956). *Biochim. et Biophys. Acta* **20**, 538.

Sussman, M., and Bradley, S. G. (1953). *J. Bacteriol.* **66**, 52.

Sussman, M., and Spiegelman, S. (1950a). *Arch. Biochem.* **29**, 54.

Sussman, M., and Spiegelman, S. (1950b). *Arch. Biochem.* **29**, 85.

Sussman, M., Spiegelman, S., and Reiner, J. M. (1947). *J. Cellular Comp. Physiol.* **29**, 149.

Sutherland, E. W. (1951). *In* "Phosphorus Metabolism" (W. D. McElroy and B. Glass, eds.), Vol. I, p. 53. Johns Hopkins Press, Baltimore.

Sutherland, E. W., and Wosilait, W. D. (1955). *Nature* **175**, 169.

Sutherland, E. W., and Wosilait, W. D. (1956). *J. Biol. Chem.* **218**, 459.

Swanson, C. R. (1955). *Iowa State Coll. J. Sci.* **29**, 511.

Swanson, W. H., and Clifton, C. E. (1948). *J. Bacteriol.* **56**, 115.

Tomcsik, T. (1930). *Z. Immunitätsforsch.* **66**, 8.

Trevelyan, W. E. (1956). To be published.

Trevelyan, W. E., and Harrison, J. S. (1952). *Biochem. J.* **50**, 298.

Trevelyan, W. E., and Harrison, J. S. (1954). *Biochem. J.* **57**, 556.

Trevelyan, W. E., and Harrison, J. S. (1956a). *Biochem. J.* **62**, 177.

Trevelyan, W. E., and Harrison, J. S. (1956b). *Biochem. J.* **62**, 183.

Trevelyan, W. E., and Harrison, J. S. (1956c). *Biochem. J.* **63**, 23.

Trevelyan, W. E., Mann, P. F. E., and Harrison, J. S. (1954). *Arch. Biochem. and Biophys.* **50**, 81.

Trevelyan, W. E., Gammon, J. N., Wiggins, E. H., and Harrison, J. S. (1952). *Biochem. J.* **50**, 303.

Vandendriessche, L. (1941). *Enzymologia* **10**, 69.

Van Laer, H. (1906). *Bull. soc. chim. Belges* **20**, 277.

Van Niel, C. B., and Anderson, E. H. (1941). *J. Cellular Comp. Physiol.* **17**, 49.

Vendrely, R., and Sarciron, R. (1945). *Ann. inst. Pasteur* **71**, 327.

Vogel, R. A. (1954). *Proc. Soc. Exptl. Biol. Med.* **86**, 373.

Walden, P. (1949). *Ergeb. Enzymforsch.* **10**, 1.

Warburg, O., and Christian, W. (1939). *Biochem. Z.* **303**, 40.

Wallenfels, K., and Bernt, E. (1952). *Angew. Chem.* **64**, 28.

Weibull, C., and Tiselius, A. (1945). *Arkiv Kemi, Mineral. Geol.* **A19**, No. 19.

Wertheimer, E. (1929). *Fermentforschung* **11**, 22.

Whistler, R. L., and Smart, C. L. (1953). "Polysaccharide Chemistry." Academic Press, New York.

White, A. G. C., and Werkman, C. H. (1947). *Arch. Biochem.* **13**, 27.

White, J. (1954). "Yeast Technology." Wiley, New York.

Wiame, J. M. (1949). *J. Biol. Chem.* **178**, 919.

Wiggins, E. H., Mann, P. F. E., Trevelyan, W. E., and Harrison, J. S. (1952). *Biochim. et Biophys. Acta* **8**, 537.

Williams, R. J., Mosher, W. A., and Rohrmann, E. (1936). *Biochem. J.* **30**, 2036.

Willstätter, R., and Lowry, C. D. (1925). *Hoppe-Seyler's Z. physiol. Chem.* **150**, 287.

Willstätter, R., and Rohdewald, M. (1937). *Hoppe-Seyler's Z. physiol. Chem.* **247**, 269.

Winzler, R. J. (1940). *J. Cellular Comp. Physiol.* **15**, 343.

Winzler, R. J., and Baumberger, J. P. (1938). *J. Cellular Comp. Physiol.* **12**, 183.

Winzler, R. J., Burk, D., and du Vigneaud, V. (1944). *Arch. Biochem.* **5**, 25.

Wolfrom, M. L., Lassetre, E. N., and O'Neill, A. W. (1951). *J. Am. Chem. Soc.* **73**, 595.

Wosilait, W. D., and Sutherland, E. W. (1956). *J. Biol. Chem.* **218**, 469.

Yemm, E. W., and Folkes, B. F. (1954). *Biochem. J.* **57**, 495.

Zechmeister, L., and Tóth, G. (1934). *Biochem. Z.* **270**, 309.

Zechmeister, L., and Tóth, G. (1936). *Biochem. Z.* **284**, 133.

Zetterström, R., Ernster, L., and Lindberg, O. (1951). *Arch. Biochem. and Biophys.* **31**, 113.

Zittle, C. A. (1951). *Advances in Enzymol.* **12**, 493.

Nitrogen Metabolism[1]

G. Harris

For the continued survival of yeast cells as biological and biochemical entities a great number of substances must be elaborated including structural materials, such as the cell walls, nuclei, etc., and the various vehicles for the production of energy and for reproduction, including nucleic acids, enzymes, and many other substances. Many of these compounds, e.g., the proteins and nucleic acids, are of great molecular size and complexity (see Chapter VI) and some of the most challenging problems with which we are confronted at the present time are concerned with how these macromolecules are built up from simpler substances and in what form the latter compounds are themselves assimilated and translated by the yeast.

[1] It is convenient to consider the metabolism of nitrogen compounds and sulfur compounds by yeasts together as many of these substances contain both elements. Indeed, in yeast most of the important compounds which contain sulfur also contain nitrogen; these include, for example, cystine, methionine, glutathione, adenosylmethionine, and most proteins and enzymes. These sulfur derivatives are considered in the appropriate sections dealing with amino acids and these sections should therefore be taken in conjunction with the short concluding article on the general metabolism of sulfur.

1. Assimilation of Nitrogen

Earlier reports in the literature suggested that yeast is able to fix atmospheric nitrogen itself. Thus, Zikes (1909) claimed that the yeast, *Torula wiesneri*, and all aerobic film-forming yeasts took up nitrogen. This claim was supported by Lipmann (1911) and by Kossowicz (1912) who apparently demonstrated the incorporation of gaseous nitrogen into *Saccharomyces* sp. and into *Monilia candida*. However, the latter author soon reversed his claim (Kossowicz, 1914) and Lindner and Naumann (1913) enunciated the view, which is now most commonly accepted, that yeasts cannot assimilate nitrogen which is free from ammonia or oxides of nitrogen. On the other hand, Ingram (1955) has commented recently that yeasts can exchange isotopic nitrogen with the atmosphere, thus indicating that atmospheric nitrogen can find its way into the nitrogen compounds of the yeast. However, there is presumably no net increase of the total nitrogen content of the cell population under these conditions and hence no net assimilation of nitrogen.

Like many other organisms, yeasts can assimilate nitrate presumably by reduction to derivatives of ammonia in a coupled energy-yielding and hydrogen-donating system. Nickerson (1944) identified nitrite as an intermediate in cultures of *Hansenula* assimilating nitrate but found that *Pichia* was unable to utilize this source of nitrogen. The ability to assimilate nitrate was employed by Stelling-Dekker (1931) as a systematic test for yeasts but Ingram has pointed out that the growth medium used in the test contains no vitamins and that, in the presence of these substances, it is probable that all yeasts can metabolize nitrate. The energy required to effect the reduction is most readily available in cells grown under aerobic conditions. Thus, Sakamura and Maeda (1950) found that the utilization of nitrate by *Hansenula anomala* was most efficient under aerobic conditions in a glucose medium at pH 3.8 and a similar effect was noted for *Torulopsis utilis* by Virtanen *et al.* (1949). The last-named authors found that hydroxylamine was formed under these conditions and that this reacted with pyruvic acid to yield the oxime which was then reduced to alanine:

$$CH_3COCO_2H + NH_2OH \rightarrow CH_3C(=NOH)CO_2H \rightarrow CH_3CHNH_2CO_2H$$
$$\uparrow$$
$$NO_3^-$$

This latter amino acid can presumably then give rise to ammonia and other amino acids by the routes described below and, indeed, Virtanen *et al.* state that the rate of synthesis of protein achieved in this way is as great as that using ammonia (cf. McElroy and Glass, 1956).

The most readily utilizable form of nitrogen for yeasts, however, is ammonia, from which the organism is able to build up by means of the requisite energy-donating reactions all the complex nitrogenous substances necessary for growth and reproduction. Yeasts will also assimilate amino acids, amines, amides, and even complex nitrogenous substances, such as polypeptides and proteins, but the fate of the majority of these materials upon assimilation lies in their degradation and conversion into ammonia which is then incorporated into the cell substance. The mechanisms whereby these degradations are brought about are of considerable interest since the compounds so degraded form common substrates for yeast in many industries, for example in brewing and baking.

A. *Catabolism of Proteins and Peptides*

The breakdown of proteins and polypeptides by yeast is brought about by the proteolytic enzymes of the yeast cell. In general, yeasts possess only poor ability to attack proteins and so, for example, when they grow on wort gelatin the liquefaction of the gelatin is very slow. Unlike bacteria, therefore, the yeasts excrete little extracellular protease but, nevertheless, contain a full complement of proteolytic enzymes which can be liberated when the cells are broken down by autolysis (see Joslyn, 1955). These enzymes were first studied by Willstätter, Grassmann and their co-workers (1926, 1927, 1928, 1934), who classified them as proteases, polypeptidases, and dipeptidases according to their ability to hydrolyze their respective substrates.

Yeast protease (Grassmann, et al., 1934) is able to degrade many proteins, e.g., casein, gelatin, and egg albumin, and has optimal activity for this degradation at pH 5.0. It is activated by thiols such as cysteine and, although it has been isolated only from yeast autolysates, it is supposed that it is responsible for the extracellular degradation of proteins. Yeast protease has recently been shown to consist of two enzymes (Lenney, 1956), an observation previously made by Dernby (1917) but lost sight of in the intervening years. Lenney observed that the preparations studied by Grassmann *et al.* contained peptidase activity and that they probably underwent partial inactivation under the incubation conditions employed. He found that the two proteinases, A and B, are liberated by autolysis with chloroform of four different strains of *Saccharomyces cerevisiae*. One of them (A) has an optimal pH of 3.7 for splitting acid-denatured hemoglobin and the other (B) exhibits an optimal pH of 6.2 on urea-denatured proteins. Proteinase A is extremely labile in urea solutions and contains no essential sulfhydryl groups but proteinase B is stable to urea and possesses essential sulfhydryl groups. Both enzymes are activated by urea but differ in stability to heating at 50°C. The yeast polypeptidase is liberated from the cells only with difficulty, even under the conditions of autolysis, and it is therefore supposed that both this enzyme and an associated dipeptidase function normally only inside the cell. These enzymes do, in fact, have optimal activity at pH values close to that of the interior of the cell. Johnson (1941) isolated from auto-lysates of *Saccharomyces cerevisiae* a polypeptidase which he regarded as a single protein of molecular weight 670,000. This protein behaved as a single component on electrophoresis and in the ultracentrifuge and had an enzyme activity 1000 times as great as that of the original yeast extract. It had an isoelectric point at pH 4.5–4.8 and functioned opti-mally at pH 7.9 for the hydrolysis of leucylglycylglycine. The enzyme showed greatly enhanced activity in the presence of zinc ions and to some extent of cobaltous and halogen ions and was of true aminopeptidase nature since it did not catalyze the fission of N-methylleucylglycylglycine (I) but brought about the hydrolysis of leucylmethylamine (II). Since

$$\begin{array}{cc}
CH_3 & CH_3 \\
\diagdown & \diagdown \\
\quad CHCH_2CHCONHCH_2CONHCH_2CO_2H & \quad CHCH_2CHCONHCH_3 \\
\diagup \qquad\quad | & \diagup \qquad\quad | \\
CH_3 \qquad\quad NHCH_3 & CH_3 \qquad\quad NH_2 \\
(I) & (II)
\end{array}$$

it catalyzed the hydrolysis of tripeptides containing a free terminal amino group, whether of the leucyl, alanyl, or glycyl residue, it resembled the aminotripeptidase of animal tissues but, unlike this tripeptidase, it had a considerable action on dipeptides. In this latter respect it differed from the aminopolypeptidase first isolated from yeast by Grassmann and his co-workers (Willstätter and Grassmann, 1926; Grassmann, 1927; Grass-mann and Dyckerhof, 1928; Grassmann et al., 1934), which hydrolyzed leucylglycylglycine much more rapidly than leucylglycine. Smith (1951) remarks that the general mode of action of Grassmann's polypeptidase appears to resemble that of the well-studied mammalian tripeptidase whereas that of Johnson's enzyme does not. He suggests that it would be desirable to learn more of the homogeneity of the enzymes by ascertain-ing whether their actions on di- and tripeptides are increased in the same way by zinc and halogen ions and reduced in parallel fashion by partial inactivation.

Grassmann et al. were able to separate the enzyme system catalyzing the decomposition of dipeptides from the above polypeptidase. This en-zyme system was able to split only dipeptides and since it did not hydrolyze acylated dipeptides (III), polypeptides, or amino acid amides (IV), it was concluded that it requires both a free amino group and a free carboxyl group adjacent to the peptide bond in order to exercise its activity. Maschmann (1943) showed that the activity of a dipeptidase, which he isolated from yeast, was very weak but was increased two-thou-

$$RCONHCHR'CONHCHR''CO_2H$$

(III)

$$RCHCONH_2$$
$$|$$
$$NH_2$$

(IV)

sand-fold by the addition of manganous or cobaltous ions. It was suggested that the enzyme was activated by forming a metal bridge between

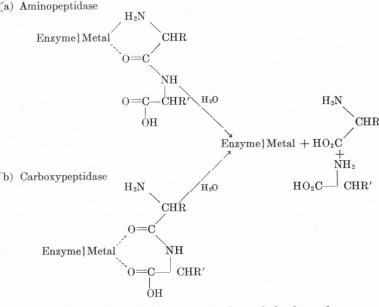

(a) Aminopeptidase

(b) Carboxypeptidase

FIG. 1. Schematic hydrolysis of a dipeptide by dipeptidases.

itself and the substrate and Smith has elaborated a general scheme explaining the activity of the metallo-enzymes as arising through the chelation of the metal ion on the one hand with active sites on the enzyme, e.g., thiol groups, and on the other hand with the carbonyl group of the peptide bond and an active grouping of the substrate. The latter grouping consists, for reactions involving aminopeptidases, of an amino group or, for reactions with carboxypeptidases, of a carboxyl group. In the structure of the resulting complex (Fig. 1) the electrons are so redistributed that the peptide bond is labilized and its hydrolysis facilitated. It is well known that individual peptides and enzymes show considerable specificity in their affinities for metallic ions and that the complexes formed between the metals, enzymes, and peptides may be very stable whereas those formed between the metallo-enzyme and amino acids are quite weak. Thus the product of the hydrolytic reaction dissociates readily and the metallo-enzyme is made available for the hydrolysis of more peptide. In this connection it is of much interest that one peptidase, leucine amino-peptidase, isolated by Vescia (1956) from swine kidney, brings about the hydrolysis of different peptides individually in the presence of different added metals. No such experiments have been effected with the proteolytic enzymes of yeast and it is apparent that the further purification of these enzymes and comparison of their properties as suggested above by Smith is needed to further our understanding of their action. Furthermore, little comparative work has been carried out on the enzymes of different strains of yeast.

The ultimate products of the degradation of the proteins and polypeptides by the proteolytic enzymes, namely the amino acids, are dealt with by yeasts in a number of different ways and the modes of degradation will now be considered individually.

B. *Catabolism of Amino Acids*

Single Amino Acids: the Ehrlich Mechanism. Yeasts degrade most of the common amino acids and perhaps the best-known method whereby this is brought about is that involving deamination and decarboxylation followed by reduction to yield an alcohol containing one carbon atom less than the original amino acid. The breakdown of amino acids to alcohols by yeast in this way was first described by Ehrlich (1907, 1909, 1911, 1912) for the amino acids leucine and isoleucine and was later found by Thorne (1937) to apply to a number of other amino acids. The latter author isolated the alcohols corresponding to the individual amino acids used in growth media for yeast. The mixture of alcohols formed from the fermentation of a normal growth medium containing several amino acids is, of course, known as fusel oil. Ehrlich found that the addition of ammonia to such growth media depressed the production of fusel oils, showing that the yeasts preferentially assimilate nitrogen in the form of ammonia. The over-all mechanism of the conversion of amino acids to alcohols by the Ehrlich mechanism is as follows (Neubauer and Fromherz, 1911; Neuberg and Hildesheimer, 1911):

$$(1) \qquad RCHNH_2CO_2H \rightarrow RC \begin{smallmatrix} OH \\ \diagup \\ -NH_2 \\ \diagdown \\ CO_2H \end{smallmatrix} \rightarrow RCOCO_2H + NH_3$$

(2)   RCOCO$_2$H → RCHO + CO$_2$
(3)   RCHO + 2H → RCH$_2$OH

Presumably the α-keto acids formed in the initial stages of the reaction are readily decarboxylated by the enzyme carboxylase, which is very active in yeasts, and the aldehyde so produced is reduced by mechanisms analogous to those which yield alcohol. Under aerobic conditions the α-keto acid is the primary product, e.g., α-ketoglutaric acid is formed from glutamic acid and may then be utilized by respiration while the ammonia is incorporated into yeast protein.

$$\begin{array}{cc} \text{Respiration} & \text{Protein} \\ \uparrow & \uparrow \end{array}$$

(4)   CO$_2$HCH$_2$CH$_2$CHNH$_2$CO$_2$H + H$_2$O → CO$_2$HCH$_2$CH$_2$COCO$_2$H + NH$_3$
         Glutamic acid

Thorne (1946b) classified the amino acids according to their efficiency as nitrogen sources for yeast and this type of classification has been applied to the differentiation of yeast genera and species (see Chapter II). Brewer's yeasts generally deaminate only the L-amino acids with the exception of glutamic acid, aspartic acid, and asparagine of which both optical isomers are utilized (Nielsen, 1936, 1938, 1943; Nielsen and Hartelius, 1938). These three amino acids were found to be the best nutrients, aspartic acid and asparagine (and glutamine) being slightly superior to ammonia supplied in the form of ammonium phosphate (Thorne, 1941; Nielsen and Hartelius, 1938). Most single amino acids, including α-alanine, α-aminobutyric acid, arginine, isoleucine, leucine, methionine, ornithine, phenylalanine, proline, serine, tyrosine, and valine, are about 60–70% as efficient as ammonium phosphate in promoting growth and fermentation while hydroxyproline and tryptophan are very poor nutrients and histidine, glycine, cystine, and lysine alone are non-nutrients although lysine can function as a growth factor (Nielsen and Hartelius, 1938). Nielsen (1943) reported that threonine was not assimilated by the yeast which he employed. This grading of the amino acids parallels generally that based upon their ease of deamination, those amino acids utilized which are most easily deaminated being the best single sources of nitrogen for yeast. Confirmation that the amino acids so utilized are converted into ammonia is afforded by the fact that they must contain the grouping —CHNH$_2$. Amino acids such as α-amino-isobutyric acid, Me$_2$C(NH$_2$)CO$_2$H, which do not contain this grouping, are not assimilable (Nielsen, 1943). The alcohols produced from the amino acids are sometimes toxic to the yeast, e.g., tryptophol produced from tryptophan inhibits yeast growth and hence accounts for the poor utilization of the amino acid. However, that part of the molecule of the amino acid remaining after deamination can be respired away as mentioned above and this is borne out by the fact that the uptake of nitrogen in the absence of carbohydrate gives rise to enhanced respiration. In this connection also it is of interest that Massart and Horens (1953) have shown that during the growth of yeast in glucose-phosphate medium the addition of ammonium sulfate causes increased respiration accompanied by assimilation of nitrogen. An equivalent effect is caused by glutamic acid, aspartic acid, and alanine but no such effect is induced by other amino acids, and cystine inhibits respiration under the conditions of the experiment.

Mixtures of Amino Acids: (*a*) *the Stickland Mechanism.* When mixtures of amino acids are used as the nitrogen source for yeast, growth is often greater than that produced by the equivalent amount of either of the amino acids alone. Thorne explained this effect as being due to the Stickland reaction between the two amino acids. This reaction, first studied in detail for the strict anaerobe, *Clostridium sporogenes,* by Stickland (1934, 1935), consists of the oxidation of one amino acid (the hydrogen donor) by another (the hydrogen acceptor) according to the over-all reaction:

(5) $R'CHNH_2CO_2H + 2R''CHNH_2CO_2H + 2H_2O \rightarrow R'CO_2H + 2R''CH_2CO_2H$
$$+ CO_2 + 3NH_3$$

In this way three molecules of ammonia are made available from three molecules of amino acid despite the fact that one of the amino acids may not readily undergo deamination by the Ehrlich mechanism. Thorne (1944) was in fact able to demonstrate the formation of acetic acid from glycine in yeast when alanine was added to the medium. The first step in the reaction is probably catalyzed by a type of L-amino acid oxidase which is capable of transferring hydrogen atoms from a donor amino acid either to another amino acid or to oxygen or a dye in an appropriate test system. Nisman and Mager (1952) found that diphosphopyridine nucleotide (DPN) was readily reduced in cell-free extracts of *Clostridia* by hydrogen-donating amino acids. The keto acid so produced is then oxidized by a keto acid oxidase thus making available two more hydrogen atoms on the coenzyme. These reactions may be summarized thus:

(6) $R'CHNH_2CO_2H + H_2O \rightarrow R'COCO_2H + NH_3 + 2H$ (L-amino acid oxidase)
(7) $R'COCO_2H + H_2O \rightarrow R'CO_2H + CO_2 + 2H$ (Keto acid oxidase)
(8) $2R''CHNH_2CO_2H + 4H \rightarrow 2R''CH_2CO_2H + 2NH_3$

to give the over-all reaction (5) shown above. The hydrogen-donating amino acids for yeast comprise, according to Thorne, α-alanine, aspartic acid, cysteine, glutamic acid, histidine, leucine, phenylalanine, serine, and valine while the hydrogen acceptors include arginine, glycine, hydroxy-proline, ornithine, proline, and tryptophan. By the use of twenty-six different binary mixtures of amino acids of these groups Thorne observed (1944) a mean enhancement of 19% in the growth of yeast.

(b) *Intact Assimilation.* Some enhancement of growth was observed (8%) when yeast was grown on a binary mixture composed of two hydrogen-donating amino acids, e.g., alanine and leucine, a fact which is not explained by the Stickland reaction. Even greater growth was observed when ternary mixtures of amino acids were used (Thorne, 1945, 1946a, b), a mixture of the three amino acids, arginine, aspartic acid, and leucine, for example, giving 28% more growth than any single one. This type of investigation was extended to include mixtures of eight amino acids, on which the yeast showed a 60% enhancement of growth, although in certain instances the assimilation of one amino acid was hindered by another (Thorne, 1946a; Nielsen and Hartelius, 1938). Further increases in the extent of incorporation of nitrogen into yeast are shown in even more complex mixtures such as those which occur in protein hydrolysates or brewer's wort. In these cases the amino acids are taken up very much more quickly than ammonia itself (Thorne, 1949; Schultz and Pomper, 1948) and it is apparent that a mechanism of assimilation not involving deamination is operative. It is believed that the amino acids are assimilated intact in these circumstances, the units required for protein synthesis being built directly into the protein structure. Thus, the whole amino acid skeleton will, if this belief is true, form part of the cell substance since sufficient carbon, which would normally have to be supplied from another source, will already be present. In fact, Thorne has observed a sugar-sparing effect in the growth of yeast on complex mixtures of amino acids and he and Barton-Wright (1949, 1950) have adduced a considerable body of evidence in support of the hypothesis of intact assimilation. The contributions of the various mechanisms of assimilation to the growth of yeast in wort are summarized diagrammatically in Fig. 2 (from Thorne, 1950). It will be noted that Thorne considers that peptides are broken down to amino acids before incorporation into yeast protein either via ammonia or by intact assimilation. This is because the growth and fermentation of yeast are less when the yeast is assimilating nitrogen from a peptide than when it is assimilating the nitrogen from the constituent amino acids (Damlé and Thorne, 1949; Hartelius, 1939; Nielsen, 1943). Thus the growth of yeast on the tripeptide, leucylglylcyl-glycine, was found to be less rapid than that on the appropriate dipeptides although the whole of the nitrogen was eventually assimilated. The metabolism of the amino acids liberated from the peptides follows the normal course, since, for example, the dipeptide, leucyltyrosine, gave good yields of isoamyl alcohol and tyrosol produced by the Ehrlich mechanism. Peptides containing D-amino acids were not assimilated by yeast even in presence of manganous ions which stimulate the hydrolysis or such peptides by animal tissues (Nielsen, 1943).

It would thus appear that the main routes, at least, for the utilization of the amino acids and peptides by yeast have been uncovered. However, the intact assimilation of amino acids remains to be unequivocally

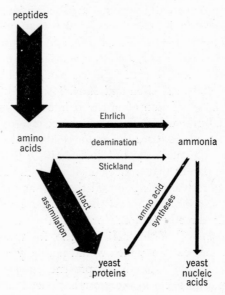

Fig. 2. An over-all view of the nitrogen assimilation mechanisms operating in yeast growing in wort (from Thorne, 1950).

demonstrated and this might be achieved quite readily now by means of isotopes. It would be necessary to demonstrate that the α-C-N linkages of labeled amino acids were not broken during assimilation into yeast protein so that the possibility of deamination could be ruled out. This might be achieved simply by labeling the α-carbon atom with C^{14} and the attached nitrogen atom with N^{15}. If the specific activity of the amino acid, isolated from the yeast protein, with respect to both C^{14} and N^{15} were identical with that of the added amino acid it could be concluded that the amino acid had been assimilated intact. Similar experiments with labeled peptides might well be made as the utilization by yeast of only a very limited number of these compounds has been studied (Damlé and Thorne, 1949) and work with other organisms has suggested that peptides may be assimilated intact in some circumstances or at least yield ammonia more rapidly than asparagine and glutamine (Miller and Waelsch, 1952).

Decarboxylase. Yeasts can bring about the decarboxylation of amino acids as suggested first by the identification of γ-aminobutyric acid in the cells (Giri, 1953; Bair *et al.*, 1952). This amino acid is well known to arise in various animals, plants, and bacteria by the decarboxylation of glutamic acid (Schales, 1951):

$$(9) \qquad HO_2CCH_2CH_2\underset{\underset{NH_2}{|}}{CH}CO_2H \rightarrow HO_2CCH_2CH_2CH_2NH_2 + CO_2$$

and can participate further in the nitrogen metabolism of these organisms via transamination reactions (Roberts *et al.*, 1953) as described later. This decarboxylation is brought about by cell-free extracts of *Rhodotorula glutinis* quantitatively at pH 4.5 and 30°C., but these extracts lose their activity on dialysis (Krishnaswamy and Giri, 1956). The activity can be restored by the addition of pyridoxal phosphate, is inhibited by silver, mercury, and cyanide ions but is insensitive to copper, fluoride, or iodoacetate ions. These properties of the enzyme are markedly similar to those of the well-known bacterial decarboxylases (see Meister, 1955a) but it has not been possible so far to obtain the enzyme in a purified condition and to assess its importance in the over-all metabolism of the yeast cell.

Glutamic Acid Dehydrogenase. By contrast to that brought about by decarboxylase, the metabolism of glutamic acid mediated by the enzyme glutamic acid dehydrogenase occupies a uniquely important position (v. Euler *et al.*, 1938). This enzyme catalyzes the removal of two hydrogen atoms from each molecule of glutamic acid according to equation (10) and the imino compound which results is then hydrolyzed presumably spontaneously to α-ketoglutaric acid and ammonia as in equation (11) (Schlenk, 1951). It is of considerable interest that this or

$$(10) \qquad CO_2HCH_2CH_2CHNH_2CO_2H \underset{+2H}{\overset{-2H}{\rightleftharpoons}} CO_2HCH_2CH_2C(=NH)CO_2H$$

$$(11) \qquad CO_2HCH_2CH_2C(=NH)CO_2H \underset{-H_2O}{\overset{+H_2O}{\rightleftharpoons}} CO_2HCH_2CH_2COCO_2H + NH_3$$

analogous enzymes occur widely in the plant and animal kingdoms although the enzymes from various sources require different coenzymes to link them to the respective oxidation-reduction systems. Thus the coenzyme for the enzyme of yeast is coenzyme II (Adler *et al.*, 1938a) as for *Escherichia coli* (Adler *et al.*, 1938b) while for higher plants coenzyme I is required (Adler *et al.*, 1938b) and for mammals either coenzyme I or coenzyme II is effective (Dewan, 1938; von Euler *et al.*, 1938). Glutamic acid dehydrogenase is highly stereospecific, having a very slow action on D-glutamic acid although, as mentioned earlier, whole yeast can metabolize this unnatural isomer. It is inhibited by L-aspartic acid. Although the enzyme is considered here in relation to the catabolism of amino acids, the equilibrium in reactions (10) and (11) in living yeast cells is in favor of the synthesis of glutamic acid. A mechanism therefore exists here for the fixation of inorganic nitrogen, in the form of ammonia, into an organic molecule derived from the breakdown of sugars and this synthetic aspect of the reaction will be discussed later (cf. Olson and Anfinsen, 1952).

Aspartase and Other Anaerobic Deaminases. A mechanism of nitrogen fixation similar to that induced by glutamic acid dehydrogenase but in this case producing aspartic acid, is provided by the enzyme aspartase, which occurs not only in yeast but also in a number of microorganisms, including *Escherichia coli, Pseudomonas fluorescens, Serratia marcescens, Proteus vulgaris,* and *Lactobacillus casei* (Woolf, 1929; Cook and Woolf, 1928; Erkama and Virtanen, 1951). In the reaction catalyzed by this enzyme a molecule of ammonia is removed from aspartic acid to yield fumaric acid:

(12) $$CO_2HCH_2CHNH_2CO_2H \xrightleftharpoons{-NH_3} CO_2HCH{=}CHCO_2H$$

By inhibiting the conversion of fumaric acid into succinic acid or malic acid in cells treated with cyclohexanol, it is found that the equilibrium favors the formation of aspartic acid, thus providing another important means of fixing inorganic nitrogen which operates, moreover, under anaerobic conditions. The synthesis of aspartic acid from fumaric acid and ammonia in brewer's yeast has been reported by Sumiki (1928) and the degradation of aspartic acid to fumaric acid was demonstrated in an autolysate of a bottom yeast by Haehn and Leopold (1937), but Virtanen and Tarnanen (1932, 1935) were unable to find aspartase activity in dried top yeast. The biochemical significance of aspartase has been reviewed by Erkama and Virtanen (1951) against the background of the reactions catalyzed by other enzymes involved in the synthesis and degradation of aspartic acid. These authors comment that if the Stickland and transamination reactions (see below) are excluded from consideration it is generally assumed that the amino acids are most commonly deaminated oxidatively to keto acids but that the enzyme, analogous to glutamic acid dehydrogenase, which would effect such a reaction with aspartic acid, is not known [reaction (b), Fig. 3]. The reaction (c) shown in Fig. 3 is considered improbable since it involves a direct oxidation-reduction system, but the deamination of aspartic acid involving an

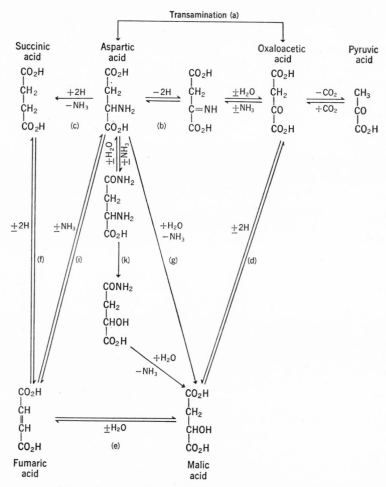

Fig. 3. Possible modes of synthesis and degradation of aspartic acid (from Erkama and Virtanen, 1951).

oxidation-reduction mechanism is readily visualized if it is assumed that the amino acid is first converted into fumaric acid or malic acid of which the latter is oxidized and the former reduced in the presence of fumarase [reaction (e)]. The reactions (g) and (h), which do not involve an oxidation-reduction system, are discounted by Virtanen and Erkama since they have not been demonstrated in cell-free preparations. Consequently, the formation of fumaric acid by the intervention of aspartase [reaction (i)] is for the present the only deamination reaction of aspartic acid known to be present in the cell-free systems and, furthermore, the reverse reaction is the only one known leading to the synthesis of aspartic acid apart from that catalyzed by transaminase reaction a (see below).

The anaerobic deamination of other amino acids in a manner analogous to that of aspartic acid is also known to occur in various microorganisms. For example, serine and threonine yield pyruvic acid and α-ketobutyric acid, respectively, presumably by the initial loss of the elements of water followed by the spontaneous decomposition of the resultant imino compounds as in the breakdown of glutamic acid by glutamic acid dehydrogenase (Chargaff and Sprinson, 1943). A similar reaction is undergone by cysteine in the presence of the enzyme cysteine desulfurase to yield pyruvic acid, ammonia, and hydrogen sulfide (Fromageot, 1951):

(13) $CH_2SHCHNH_2CO_2H + H_2O \rightarrow CH_3COCO_2H + NH_3 + H_2S$

In this case the primary step consists of the removal of the elements of hydrogen sulfide instead of those of water. Although much of the investigation of the various anaerobic α-deaminases, aspartase, serine and threonine deaminases and cysteine desulfurase, has been concerned with microorganisms other than yeast, the activities of these enzymes are dependent on cofactors which occur in yeast and hence it is pertinent to consider them here. It was found by Gale and his co-workers (Gale, 1940; Gale and Stephenson, 1938) that the anaerobic α-deaminase activity of Escherichia coli was lost in water but that this could be prevented by adding adenosine monophosphate (AMP) or inorganic phosphate in the presence of a reducing agent, e.g., cysteine, formate, or lactate. Similarly, Lichstein (1949) found that the aspartase and serine deaminase activity of several microorganisms was, after being allowed to decay, restored by yeast extract or biotin in the presence of adenosine monophosphate. Stokes et al. (1947) also suggested that biotin may participate in aspartic acid metabolism as a result of the observation that strains of lactobacilli and Streptococcus faecalis, which required aspartic acid for growth, grew well in the absence of this amino acid if they were well supplied with biotin. However, these authors were unable to show that biotin was a cofactor for aspartase. On the other hand, a biotin derivative, ϵ-N-biotinyl-L-lysine, known as biocytin (V), has been isolated from yeast extract (Wright et al., 1951) and shown to be a cofactor for aspartase, although it cannot be the natural coenzyme as its activity is only equivalent to that of biotin, itself a hundred times less active than

$$
\begin{array}{c}
O \\
\parallel \\
C \\
\diagup \quad \diagdown \\
NH \qquad NH \\
| \qquad\quad | \\
CH———CH \\
| \qquad\quad | \\
CH_2 \qquad CH(CH_2)_4CONH(CH_2)_4CHCO_2H \\
\diagdown \;\; \diagup \qquad\qquad\qquad\qquad | \\
S \qquad\qquad\qquad\qquad\qquad NH_2
\end{array}
$$

(V) Biocytin

the most active concentrates isolated from yeast (Lichstein, 1949; Wright *et al.*, 1950). That biotin is not always necessary for the activity of the anaerobic α-deaminases was shown by Wood and Gunsalus (1949) who prepared a cell-free extract of *Escherichia coli* which did not require biotin to deaminate serine or threonine although gluta-thione and AMP were necessary. For the mold *Neurospora*, none of the above mentioned cofactors, AMP, glutathione, or biotin, is required for D- and L-amino acid deaminase activity but the enzymes are activated by pyridoxal phosphate (Yanofsky, 1952; Yanofsky and Reissig, 1953) (see, however, section on transamination below). Similarly biotin is not present in the aspartase system isolated from *Bacterium cadaveris* by Christman and Williams (1952), who found, however, that a prod-uct obtained by heating glucose with mineral acid was as effective as yeast extract in activating the enzyme. Nevertheless, Winzler *et al.* (1944) were able to demonstrate that washed cells of biotin-deficient yeast (*Saccharomyces cerevisiae*) could not assimilate ammonia until biotin was added and it is therefore assumed that the vitamin is an essential component of the systems, including aspartase, in yeast responsible for incorporating ammonia into organic molecules.

2. Synthesis and Interconversion of Amino Acids

It has already been mentioned that yeasts can synthesize all their amino acids from certain inorganic sources of nitrogen, primarily am-monia, and that among the most important mechanisms for the incorpora-tion of this nitrogen into organic structures are those provided by the enzyme systems, glutamic acid dehydrogenase and aspartase. Of these two systems the former is probably the more important. The formation of glutamic acid and aspartic acid in this way occurs at the expense of α-ketoglutaric acid and oxaloacetic acid which are themselves partici-pants in the respiratory cycle, known as the Krebs cycle or the citric acid cycle. It is known that yeasts contain a considerable pool of free amino acids among which glutamic acid, aspartic acid, and also alanine predominate (Gale, 1947; Gale and Freeland, 1947; Bair *et al.*, 1952). The latter amino acid may possibly arise from pyruvic acid in a manner analogous to the formation of glutamic acid and aspartic acid. Thus a

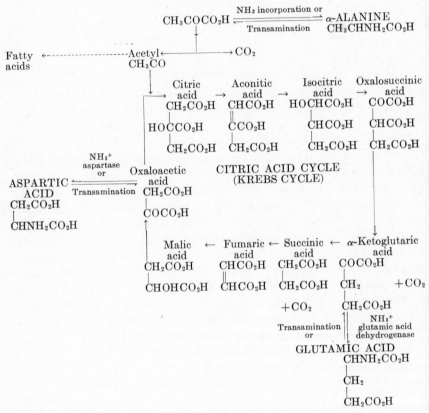

FIG. 4. Relationship of amino acid metabolism to carbohydrate metabolism via the citric acid cycle.

dynamic state may be visualized in which the citric acid cycle generates the α-keto acids which in turn combine with ammonia (or undergo transamination as discussed in a later section of this chapter) as shown in Fig. 4. When the metabolism of the yeast occurs largely through the Krebs cycle, for example under aerobic conditions of growth, the production of energy is increased and protein synthesis is enhanced largely via glutamic acid and aspartic acid.

This view of the connection between carbohydrate and nitrogen metabolism of yeast has only recently been justified by establishing that the Krebs cycle exists in yeasts in addition to operating, as has long been known, in mammals. All the reaction steps of the cycle have now been demonstrated in baker's yeast (Nossal, 1954a,b; Foulkes, 1951; Krebs *et al.*, 1952; Lynen and Neciullah, 1939; Barron *et al.*, 1950; Novelli and Lipmann, 1950; Weinhouse and Millington, 1947) and respiring particles regarded as mitochondria have been isolated from the cells (Linnane and Still, 1955). It is still not certain whether the citric acid cycle is the only terminal respiratory system in yeast but there can be no doubt that it plays a major role. Indeed, even before its existence in yeast was established with certainty a number of investigators were able to explain various aspects of the biosynthesis of amino acids by invoking the reactions of this cycle (Abelson and Vogel, 1955; Ehrensvärd, 1955; Vavra and Johnson, 1956). The general experimental technique which was used involved supplying yeasts, which were actively synthesizing amino acids and proteins, with sources of carbon containing radioactive isotopes of carbon (C^{14} or C^{13}), isolating the yeast protein and degrading it to its constituent amino acids. The amino acids were broken down in turn to afford a picture of the extent of isotopic labeling of individual carbon atoms or groups of carbon atoms and in this way certain conclusions could be drawn as to the mechanism of their synthesis. It is of great interest to trace out the development of this work, not only as it has been applied to yeast but also for other microorganisms as well as plants and animals, since it is in this way that much of our present knowledge on the general biosynthesis of amino acids has been obtained.

In general the amino acids, constituting the proteins of yeasts or other microorganisms after growth on a radioactive carbon source, fall into several distinct families according to their degree of labeling with the radioactive isotope (Abelson and Vogel, 1955; Abelson *et al.*, 1953; McQuillen and Roberts, 1954). These groups comprise: (1) the glutamic acid family, consisting of glutamic acid, proline and arginine; (2) the aspartic acid family, containing aspartic acid, methione, threonine, and isoleucine; (3) lysine; (4) the pyruvic acid family, including α-alanine, valine, and leucine; (5) histidine (Levy and Coon, 1954; Ames *et al.*, 1953); (6) the serine family, namely serine, glycine and cysteine; and (7) the aromatic family consisting of phenylalanine, tyrosine, and tryptophan (Tatum and Perkins, 1950). Thus, Ehrensvärd (1955) and Abelson and Vogel (1955) found that this classification applied to the organisms, *Torulopsis utilis, Neurospora crassa,* and *Escherichia coli* with the sole exception that lysine is derived in the latter from aspartic

TABLE I

INCORPORATION OF C^{14} OF TRACER COMPOUNDS INTO AMINO ACIDS OF YEAST PROTEIN

Tracer compound	Amino acid							
	Glutamic acid	Arginine	Proline	Aspartic acid	Threonine	Isoleucine	Methionine	Lysine
C^{14}-Carbon dioxide	100	500	95	230	230	240	220	0
Acetic acid-1-C^{14}	100	250	129	33	30	30	35	200
C^{14}-Aspartic acid	100	100	105	167	160	170	170	70
C^{14}-Glutamic acid	100	80	67	26	25	24	22	40
Glutamic acid-1-C^{14}	100	90	70	0	0	0	0	0

acid via α,ε-diaminopimelic acid (Abelson, 1954) an amino acid which has not been detected at all in the fungi (Work and Dewey, 1953). Abelson and Vogel commented that their results are in conformity with the existence of the Krebs cycle in both *T. utilis* and *Neurospora* and the evidence for this is discussed in the following sections dealing with the biosynthesis of each of the members of the families of amino acids enumerated above.

(1) *The Glutamic Acid Family*. The relative activities of the amino acids isolated from *T. utilis* after growth in the presence of various tracer compounds labeled with C^{14} is shown in Table I (Abelson and Vogel, 1955). This shows quite clearly the division of these particular amino acids into three (1, 2, and 4) of the seven families mentioned above when

TABLE II

EFFECT OF COMPETITORS ON THE RADIOACTIVITY OF THE AMINO ACIDS OF THE GLUTAMIC ACID FAMILY IN *Torulopsis utilis*

Competitor	Amino acid		
	Glutamic acid	Arginine	Proline
None	100	100	100
Ornithine	75	12	4
Citrulline	95	25	25
Arginine	95	15	15
Glutamic acid semialdehyde	65	70	6
Proline	100	100	0

allowance is made for the fact that the relative activity of arginine is increased by direct incorporation of C^{14} from carbon dioxide or acetate into the amidine moiety. The data are consistent with the view that the five-carbon skeletons of proline and arginine are derived from glutamic acid. Evidence for the actual biosynthetic sequence of these compounds is yielded by isotopic competition experiments in which unlabeled compounds which are presumed intermediates in their synthesis are allowed to compete with the added labeled compounds. Any reduction in the radioactivity of the products as compared with that of the products of the control experiments may be taken as evidence of the participation of the nonradioactive competitors in the biosynthesis and hence that these compounds are natural intermediates. The results of such experiments are illustrated in Table II, in which it may be seen that ornithine, citrulline, and arginine compete effectively as sources of arginine and proline while added proline suppresses the radioactivity of the proline of the yeast protein but not that of glutamic acid or arginine. Glutamic acid semialdehyde contributes to proline and, to some extent, to glutamic acid and arginine. On the basis of both these results and parallel studies with mutants of *T. utilis* and of *Neurospora,* Abelson and Vogel propose the following sequence of reactions for the biosynthesis of the members of the glutamic acid family:

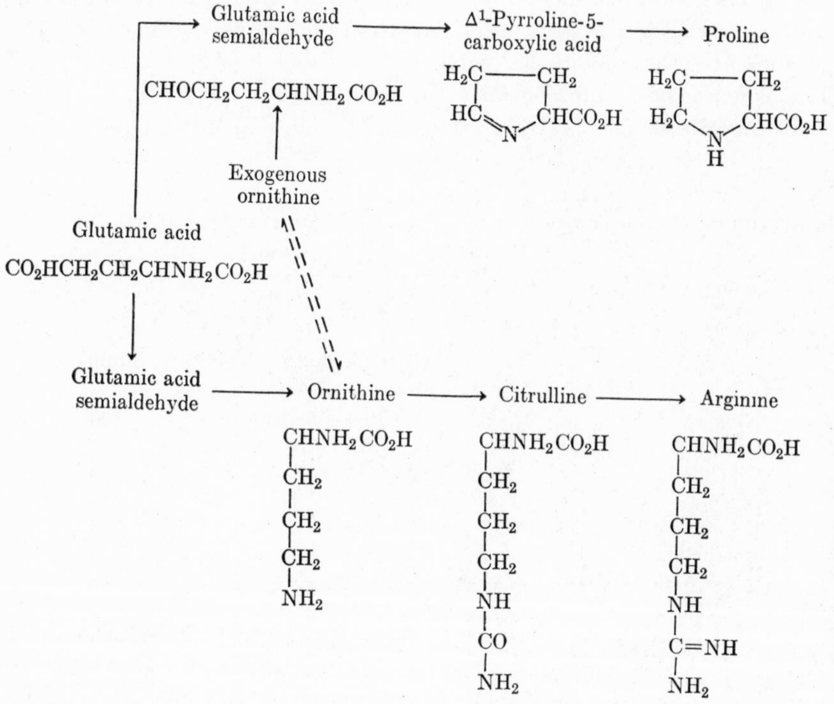

This scheme is not consistent with the earlier postulation by Strassman and Weinhouse (1952) that proline plays a major role as a precursor of ornithine and of arginine in *T. utilis* and the similar contention by Fincham (1953) for *Neurospora crassa.* The contribution of the semialdehyde to arginine indicates that it is an ornithine precursor, a biosynthetic sequence which was proposed earlier for *Neurospora* (Vogel and Bonner, 1954), but in view of its conversion to glutamic acid (Table II) it appears that part of the exogenous material does not form ornithine directly and the two biosynthetic pathways leading, on the one hand, to proline and, on the other hand, to arginine may well be physically separated in the cell. Similarly, there is a distinction between endogenous and exogenous ornithine in *T. utilis* a phenomenon also noted by Vogel and Bonner for *Neurospora*. Thus, when only traces of highly radioactive ornithine were used in the growth medium the specific activities of the recovered proline and arginine were in the ratio 100:6 but when the added ornithine was diluted with carrier this ratio was 100:80, indicating that exogenous ornithine as a source of proline does not equilibrate with endogenous ornithine acting as a source of arginine. Added ornithine also appears to function as a source of the amidine carbon atom of arginine, possibly by decarboxylation to carbon dioxide which is readily incorporated. The added ornithine also contributes to glutamic acid, probably via the semialdehyde, and presumably mediates the contribution of citrulline and arginine to proline by way of the ornithine cycle (Srb and Horowitz, 1944) and glutamic acid semialdehyde (Fincham, 1955). The relationship between glutamic acid, proline, and ornithine in the yeast cell thus resembles that in *Neurospora* but differs from that in *Escherichia coli*, in which ornithine is formed via a series of acetylated intermediates (Vogel, 1953, 1955; Vogel *et al.*, 1953). These latter intermediates appear to play no part in yeast metabolism since N^α-acetylornithine, a precursor of ornithine in *E. coli*, did not reduce the radioactivity of arginine in isotopic competition experiments with *T. utilis*. It is noteworthy that an enzyme catalyzing the reduction of Δ^1-pyrroline-5-carboxylic acid to proline has been observed in *Neurospora* and in rat liver (Smith and Greenberg, 1956). This enzyme requires DPNH to effect the reduction.

Vogel (1955) has drawn attention to a parallelism, of particular interest from the point of view of comparative biochemistry, between the interrelationship of glutamic acid, proline, and ornithine in *T. utilis* or *N. crassa* and that in mammals as found by Stetten (1951). The two fungi resemble mammals more than the bacterium, *E. coli*, and Vogel also points out the similar observation by Yanofsky (1955b) that the relationship between tryptophan and nicotinic acid in *N. crassa* resembles that in mammals but differs from that in bacteria (see below). As regards the formation of ornithine it has been shown that the transamination of glutamic acid semialdehyde is a reversible reaction favoring the semialdehyde, presumably because of cyclization of the latter. Thus, in the fungi and possibly in mammals a mechanism has been evolved, namely the above-mentioned physical separation of intermediates, which permits an adequate rate of synthesis of ornithine in spite of the unfavorable equilibrium. In *E. coli*, however, the goal of ornithine synthesis is achieved by the use of *N*-acetylation which prevents the cyclization of the semialdehyde and hence maintains the equilibrium.

The details of the conversion of ornithine into arginine in yeast have not yet been worked out, but since this transformation proceeds via citrulline it is presumably brought about by a mechanism analogous to that which operates in mammals. Ratner (1955) has shown that this latter mechanism, which forms part of the Krebs ornithine cycle (Krebs and Henseleit, 1932), involves several stages. The first is the addition of carbon dioxide and ammonia to ornithine in an endergonic reaction for which ATP furnishes the driving force and in which carbamylglutamic acid or other acylglutamic acids function catalytically (Grisolia, 1955). In mammals the utilization of ATP results in the formation of an unstable intermediate, compound "X"* (Grisolia, 1951, 1955; Grisolia *et al.*, 1955), which then reacts with ornithine to form citrulline with the liberation of carbamylglutamic acid and inorganic phosphate. These reactions may be summarized as follows:

(14)   Carbamylglutamic acid + ATP + NH_3 + CO_2 $\xrightarrow{Mg^{++}}$ Compound X + ADP

Compound X + Ornithine → Citrulline + Carbamylglutamic acid + H_3PO_4

The citrulline so formed is then converted into arginine in two stages which involve formally the addition of ammonia and the removal of water. The ammonia can only be donated by aspartic acid, however, and

(15)   Citrulline   +   Aspartic acid   + ATP $\xrightarrow{Mg^{++}}$ Arginosuccinic acid   + ADP + H_3PO_4

$$
\begin{array}{lll}
\underset{\displaystyle\overset{\displaystyle\|}{\text{COH}}}{\text{NH}} & \underset{\displaystyle\overset{\displaystyle|}{\text{H}_2\text{NCH}}}{\text{CO}_2\text{H}} & \underset{\displaystyle\overset{\displaystyle|}{\text{C—NH—CH}}}{\text{NH}\quad\text{CO}_2\text{H}}
\end{array}
$$

once again the energy from ATP is required to drive the condensation reaction 15. The phosphate bond energy is thereby incorporated into the

(16)

Arginosuccinic acid   Arginine   Fumaric acid

---

* Compound X has been shown to be a derivative of carbamyl phosphate which is the active donor of the carbamyl group (Jones *et al.*, 1955; Grisolia *et al.*, 1955; Marshall *et al.*, 1955) to ornithine.

amidine moiety of arginosuccinic acid which is readily cleaved to form arginine and fumaric acid (reaction 16). Two enzymes are required to effect the condensation reaction yielding arginosuccinic acid (Ratner, 1955) and it was found that one was lost during purification of the other. It is of particular interest from our present standpoint that the lost activity can be replaced by a purified fraction from baker's yeast. Furthermore, both the condensing enzyme and that causing cleavage of arginosuccinic acid are present in yeast as well as in *Neurospora* and a number of bacteria which utilize citrulline (Newmeyer and Ratner, 1955; Fincham, 1955). It will be seen that the action of the latter enzyme is analogous to that of aspartase (see above) in yielding fumaric acid and a base, but in mammals no aspartase activity was associated with preparations of the other enzymes. It is conceivable that in yeast, as in mammalian liver, the ammonia required for arginine synthesis is fixed by α-ketoglutaric acid to yield glutamic acid via glutamic acid dehydrogenase (see above). Some α-ketoglutaric acid is oxidized to oxaloacetic acid in the citric acid cycle and the latter ketoacid can then transaminate with further glutamic acid (see below) to form aspartic acid which in turn donates ammonia to citrulline with the formation of arginine. Arginine can also be degraded to ornithine in a cyclic process which, in mammals, can be diverted to urea formation. It is of considerable interest that both yeast and bacteria contain the enzyme, arginine desimidase, which brings about the reversal of the above-described formation of arginine from citrulline (Korzenovsky, 1955; Roche and Lacombe, 1952). In the further degradation of citrulline, ATP is generated, thus:

$$(17) \quad RNHCONH_2 + H_3PO_4 + ADP \xrightarrow{Mg^{++}} RNH_2 + CO_2 + NH_3 + ATP$$
$$\text{Citrulline} \qquad\qquad\qquad\qquad \text{Ornithine}$$

This reaction is of importance since it provides for the first time a method whereby the cell can use arginine for the production of energy in the absence of carbohydrate. In bacteria, carbamylglutamic acid and its analogues are not involved in this reaction which is not, therefore, simply a reversal of the formation of citrulline as it occurs in mammals. Roche and Lacombe (1952) reported that they were unable to detect arginase (arginine dihydrolase) in the extracts of yeast which they examined and attribute the finding of this enzyme, which yields ornithine directly from arginine, by Edlbacher and Baur (1938) to confusion with arginine desimidase.

(2) *The Aspartic Acid Family.* The close relationship which exists between the members of this group is well brought out in Table I, in which it may be seen that the relative radioactivities observed in aspartic

acid, threonine, isoleucine, and methionine are almost identical in yeast grown on a variety of labeled substrates. The function of aspartic acid as a precursor of threonine was demonstrated for baker's yeast by Black and Wright (1954, 1955) and for both *T. utilis* and *Neurospora* by Abelson and Vogel (1955). The former workers showed that aspartic acid is phosphorylated in the presence of adenosine triphosphate (ATP) to yield β-L-aspartyl phosphate (equation 18), which in the presence of triphos-

(18)

$$CO_2HCH_2CHNH_2CO_2H + ATP \xrightarrow[\text{Mg}^{++}]{\text{aspartokinase}} H_2O_3POCOCH_2CHNH_2CO_2H + ADP$$
$$\beta\text{-L-Aspartyl phosphate}$$

(19) $H_2O_3POCOCH_2CHNH_2CO_2H \xrightarrow{\substack{\text{L-aspartic-}\beta\text{-semi-}\\ \text{aldehyde dehydrogenase}}} CHOCH_2CHNH_2CO_2H$
$$\text{L-Aspartic acid-}\beta\text{-}$$
$$\text{semialdehyde}$$

$$\Big\updownarrow \substack{\text{L-homoserine}\\ \text{dehydrogenase}+\\ \text{TPNH}}$$

$$CH_2OHCH_2CHNH_2CO_2H$$
$$\text{Homoserine}$$

phopyridine nucleotide (TPN) is reduced to aspartic acid β-semialdehyde (equation 19). This compound is converted in turn to L-homoserine which is then transformed to threonine by a series of reactions which so far remains unelucidated. A dialyzed yeast extract was prepared which on incubation with C^{14}-labeled aspartic acid, ATP, TPN, and magnesium chloride yielded C^{14}-labeled threonine. In other experiments Wang *et al.* (1955) found that the pattern of labeling of threonine, determined by degradation of this amino acid isolated from yeast grown on pyruvic acid-2-C^{14}, was identical with that of aspartic acid. This accords well with the relationship which exists between aspartic acid, oxaloacetic acid (see Fig. 4) and threonine in *E. coli* (Delluva, 1953) and with the labeling pattern of threonine when acetic acid, $C^{13}H_3C^{14}O_2H$, is used as the sole carbon source for both *E. coli* and yeasts (Ehrensvärd *et al.*, 1951a). The formation of threonine from homoserine has been demonstrated in *Neurospora* and *E. coli* as well as in yeast and hence appears to be a general sequence in microorganisms (Teas *et al.*, 1948; Abelson *et al.*, 1952; Cohen and Hirsch, 1954; Nisman *et al.*, 1954). The further fate of threonine in both *T. utilis* and *Neurospora* was elucidated by Abelson and Vogel (1955) by isotopic competition experiments analogous to those described above for the glutamic acid family. The results clearly establish the following sequences:

Aspartic acid $\quad\rightarrow\quad$ Homoserine $\quad\rightarrow\quad$ Threonine $\quad\rightarrow$
$CO_2H\,CH_2\,CHNH_2\,CO_2H \qquad CH_2OH\,CH_2\,CHNH_2\,CO_2H \qquad CH_3\,CHOH\,CHNH_2\,CO_2H$

$\downarrow$

Methionine
$CH_3SCH_2CH_2CHNH_2CO_2H$

α-Keto-β-methyl-
α-Ketobutyric $\quad\rightarrow\quad$ valeric acid $\quad\rightarrow\quad$ Isoleucine
acid $\qquad\qquad CH_3 \qquad\qquad\qquad CH_3$
$\qquad\qquad\qquad\qquad\quad | \qquad\qquad\qquad\qquad |$
$CH_3CH_2COCO_2H \qquad CH_3CH_2CHCOCO_2H \qquad CH_3CH_2CHCHNH_2CO_2H$

The mechanism of the conversion of homoserine to threonine involves the transfer of a hydroxyl group from the γ- to the β-position and has been shown in baker's yeast to be catalyzed by an ATP-dependent enzyme (Watanabe and Shimura, 1954), while the transformation of threonine into α-ketobutyric acid involves a reduction followed by deamination. Incidentally, a stimulating suggestion has been made recently by Umbarger (1956) that the specific inhibition of the deamination which has been observed to be caused by isoleucine in *E. coli* is an example of a negative feedback mechanism in a biological system. Thus, when the organism has sufficient isoleucine its requirement for threonine is reduced. Consequently the isoleucine exerts a regulating effect on the whole biosynthetic system such that the synthesis of isoleucine can only proceed when its level in the medium or metabolic pool has been reduced to a very low level. The production of α-keto-β-methylvaleric acid from α-ketobutyric acid is a less direct reaction and isotopic studies indicate that it might occur via a ketol condensation of the α-ketobutyric acid with acetaldehyde (Strassman *et al.*, 1956b) yielding acetohomolactic acid (VI). This latter compound is then postulated to undergo intramolecular migration of the α-ethyl group to give a hydroxyketo acid which undergoes reduction to the dihydroxy acid (VII), followed by dehydration and transamination (see below) to isoleucine (Myers and Adelberg, 1954).

$CH_3 \qquad\qquad\qquad\qquad\qquad O \qquad\qquad CH_3CH_2C(OH)CH_3 \qquad CH_3CH_2CHCH_3$
$|\qquad\qquad\qquad\qquad\qquad\qquad ||\qquad\qquad\qquad\qquad |\qquad\qquad\qquad\qquad\quad |$
$CH_2 \quad + \quad CH_3 \quad\longrightarrow\quad \overset{\nearrow}{C}CH_3 \quad +2H \quad CHOH \quad\longrightarrow\quad CHNH_2$
$|\qquad\qquad |\qquad\qquad\qquad\quad |\qquad\qquad\qquad\qquad\quad |\qquad\qquad\qquad\qquad\quad |$
$CO \qquad CHO \qquad CH_3CH_2COH \qquad\qquad CO_2H \qquad\qquad\qquad CO_2H$
$|\qquad\qquad\qquad\qquad\qquad\quad |$
$CO_2H \qquad\qquad\qquad\qquad CO_2H$

$\qquad\qquad\qquad\qquad\qquad (VI) \qquad\qquad\qquad\qquad\qquad (VII)$

A similar mechanism has been proposed by Adelberg (1954) for the biosynthesis of isoleucine in *Neurospora* on the basis of further isotopic competition experiments. In this case it was found that threonine suppressed the incorporation of the radioactivity into carbon atoms, 1, 2, 4, and 5 of isoleucine when uniformly labeled acetic acid was used as the carbon source for the organism. In addition, threonine-1,2-C^{14} yielded the dihydroxy acid-1,2-C^{14} (VII) showing that C_4 and C_5 of isoleucine came from C_3 and C_4 of threonine. Adelberg proposed that the primary product (VIII), derived from α-ketobutyric acid and acetaldehyde, is produced by an aldol condensation followed by hydration and that this trihydroxy acid then undergoes a pinacol rearrangement to the keto-

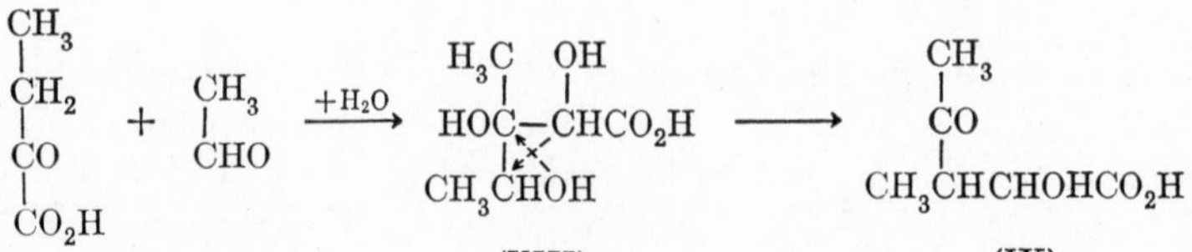

$$
\begin{array}{c}
\text{CH}_3 \\
| \\
\text{CH}_2 \\
| \\
\text{CO} \\
| \\
\text{CO}_2\text{H}
\end{array}
+
\begin{array}{c}
\text{CH}_3 \\
| \\
\text{CHO}
\end{array}
\xrightarrow{+\text{H}_2\text{O}}
\begin{array}{c}
\text{H}_3\text{C} \quad \text{OH} \\
| \quad\quad | \\
\text{HOC}-\text{CHCO}_2\text{H} \\
| \\
\text{CH}_3\text{CHOH}
\end{array}
\longrightarrow
\begin{array}{c}
\text{CH}_3 \\
| \\
\text{CO} \\
| \\
\text{CH}_3\text{CHCHOHCO}_2\text{H}
\end{array}
$$

(VIII)   (IX)

hydroxy acid (IX). The latter is then supposed to be hydrated and reduced in turn to give the dihydroxy acid (VII) and finally isoleucine. It is not possible at the moment to distinguish between the above two mechanisms and a final decision will probably be reached only by isolating the intermediates and studying the changes involved in them by the appropriate enzyme systems.

This type of synthesis of isoleucine is paralleled by that of valine (see below) in which pyruvic acid condenses with acetaldehyde to form acetolactic acid (Singer and Pensky, 1954) which then rearranges in the above manner to give a hydroxyketo acid (Strassman et al., 1953, 1955; McManus, 1954). A biochemical relationship between valine and isoleucine was first indicated earlier by Bonner et al. (1943), who found a single mutant of Neurospora which required both amino acids for growth. Later, Broquist and Stiffey (1956) showed that the synthesis both of isoleucine and of valine in Torula cremoris is inhibited by thioctic acid analogues and attributed this behavior to the blocking of a common or at least a similar step in the biosynthesis of these amino acids. The investigations of Bonner et al. (1943) revealed that the Neurospora mutants accumulated the two α,β-hydroxy acids having the carbon chains of valine and isoleucine (Adelberg and Tatum, 1950; Adelberg et al., 1951; Umbarger and Adelberg, 1951) and the above schemes provide a ready explanation of this since the formation of these hydroxyacids, e.g. VII, only requires that the hydroxyketo acid precursors should be reduced. The generality of the schemes proposed for the formation of threonine and isoleucine in various microorganisms is borne out by observations on other isoleucineless mutants of Neurospora, which will grow on the four-carbon acids, α-ketobutyric acid, α-aminobutyric acid, and threonine (Umbarger and Adelberg, 1951; Myers and Adelberg, 1954; Teas, 1948), and on *E. coli*, in which these four-carbon acids suppress the radioactivity of isoleucine formed from C^{14}-glucose (Abelson, 1954). In the latter organism Umbarger (1956) has shown that L-threonine is an *obligatory* precursor of isoleucine.

At this point it may, perhaps, be of interest to follow the details of the isotope incorporation experiments as these provide a good example of the techniques now widely used for the elucidation of biosynthetic mechanisms while the results obtained in the present application illustrate the part played by the Krebs cycle in amino acid metabolism. Thus, from *Torulopsis utilis* grown on the appropriately labeled acetate or lactate a mixture of isoleucine and leucine is isolated by chromatography of the

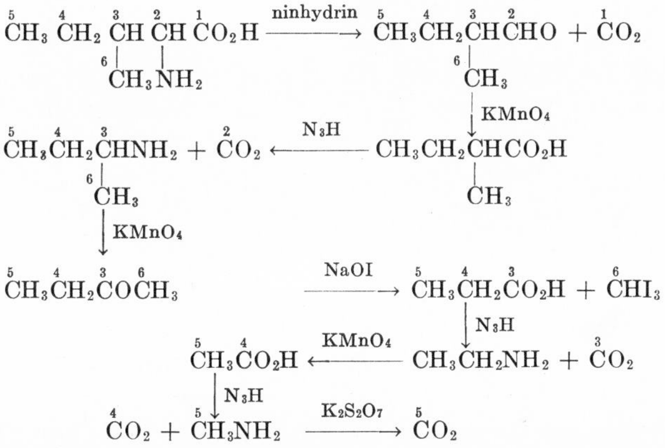

$$\overset{5}{C}H_3\ \overset{4}{C}H_2\ \overset{3}{C}H\ \overset{2}{C}H\ \overset{1}{C}O_2H \xrightarrow{\text{ninhydrin}} \overset{5}{C}H_3\overset{4}{C}H_2\overset{3}{C}H\overset{2}{C}HO + \overset{1}{C}O_2$$
$$\underset{\overset{6}{C}H_3NH_2}{|\quad|} \qquad\qquad \underset{\overset{6}{C}H_3}{|}$$

$$\left\downarrow \text{KMnO}_4\right.$$

$$\overset{5}{C}H_3\overset{4}{C}H_2\overset{3}{C}HNH_2 + \overset{2}{C}O_2 \xleftarrow{\text{N}_3\text{H}} CH_3CH_2CHCO_2H$$
$$\underset{\overset{6}{C}H_3}{|} \qquad\qquad\qquad \underset{\overset{6}{C}H_3}{|}$$

$$\left\downarrow \text{KMnO}_4\right.$$

$$\overset{5}{C}H_3\overset{4}{C}H_2\overset{3}{C}O\overset{6}{C}H_3 \xrightarrow{\text{NaOI}} \overset{5}{C}H_3\overset{4}{C}H_2\overset{3}{C}O_2H + \overset{6}{C}HI_3$$
$$\left\downarrow \text{N}_3\text{H}\right.$$
$$\overset{5}{C}H_3\overset{4}{C}O_2H \xleftarrow{\text{KMnO}_4} \overset{5}{C}H_3\overset{4}{C}H_2NH_2 + \overset{3}{C}O_2$$
$$\left\downarrow \text{N}_3\text{H}\right.$$
$$\overset{4}{C}O_2 + \overset{5}{C}H_3NH_2 \xrightarrow{\text{K}_2\text{S}_2\text{O}_7} \overset{5}{C}O_2$$

FIG. 5. Degradation of labeled isoleucine isolated from yeast protein.

protein hydrolysate on the ion exchange resin, Dowex 50. The two amino acids are then separated by chromatography on starch and the pure isoleucine degraded according to the foregoing scheme (Strassman *et al.*, 1956b; Strassman and Weinhouse, 1955) to give the radioactivity associated with each carbon atom (Fig. 5). In this scheme carbon atoms 1–5 of the isoleucine are obtained as carbon dioxide and carbon 6 as iodoform. In this way it is found that the distribution of C^{14} in isoleucine from the yeast grown on methyl-labeled acetate, on carboxyl-labeled acetate, and on symmetrically labeled and α-carbon-labeled lactate is as shown in Table III.

Consideration of the fate of the carbon atoms of acetic acid, for example, in their passage through the citric acid cycle yields the picture shown in Fig. 6 in which the carbon atoms originating in the methyl group are shown in bold letters and the carbon atoms derived from the carboxyl group are shown in normal print. In the steady state of oxidation of acetic acid which is maintained while the yeast is growing, two origins of oxaloacetic acid may be discerned. In one the β-carboxyl group is derived from the carboxyl group of acetic acid and the remaining three carbon atoms are formed from the methyl group, while in the other the β-carboxyl group and the two central carbon atoms are produced from the methyl group of acetic acid and the α-carboxyl group arises from the acetic acid carboxylic function. These two "types" of oxaloacetic acid can condense with acetic acid to yield two "different" citric acid molecules which, in turn, give rise to "different" α-ketoglutaric acid molecules which both produce succinic acid. The succinic acid molecule is symmetrical but on oxidation through malic acid two forms of oxaloacetic acid are regenerated and it therefore follows that the distribution of the

TABLE III

DISTRIBUTION OF C^{14} IN ISOLEUCINE FROM YEAST GROWN ON VARIOUS SUBSTRATES

Substrate	Carbon number					
	1	2	3	4	5	6
$C^{14}H_3CO_2H$	17	39	4	19	18	3
$CH_3C^{14}O_2H$	47	1	3	0	46	3
Lactate	5	15	5	27	7	41
Lactate-1-C^{14}	9	43	36	4	7	1

carbon atoms of the original acetic acid in α-ketoglutaric acid will be represented by the mean of the forms, A and B (Fig. 6). In other words, if the acetic acid is initially labeled with a radioactive isotope in the methyl group the distribution of activity in the five carbon atoms of the derived α-ketoglutaric acid will be 72, 143, 143, 143, 0 while if the original acetic acid is labeled in the carboxyl group the corresponding distribution will be 167, 0, 0, 0, 333, assuming that a specific activity of 100 is allotted to the α-ketoglutaric acid. Furthermore, if isoleucine is formed by the reaction sequence described above, C_1 and C_2 would be derived from C_1 and C_2 of oxaloacetic acid, C_4 and C_5 (the carbon atoms of the ethyl group) would arise from C_3 and C_4 of oxaloacetic acid and C_3 and C_6 would be produced from the carbonyl and methyl carbon atoms, respectively, of acetaldehyde. It follows that the isoleucine formed from acetic acid, labeled in the carboxyl group, through the citric acid cycle would be radioactive exclusively and equally in carbon atoms 1 and 5. On the other hand the isoleucine formed from acetic acid, labeled in the methyl group, would be radioactive in C_1, C_2, C_4, and C_5, the specific activity of C_2 and C_4 being double that in C_1 and C_5. Reference to Table III shows that the activity distributions in isoleucine, experimentally determined by Strassman *et al.* (1956b), conform fairly well with those predicted although C_2 had a higher and C_4 a lower activity than expected in the isoleucine derived from acetic acid labeled in the methyl group. There is strong presumptive evidence, therefore, that the general mechanism of isoleucine synthesis outlined above is essentially correct although only one or two of the earlier stages have been characterized by the

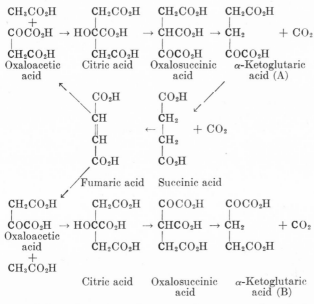

FIG. 6. Fate of the carbon atoms of acetic acid on passage through the citric acid cycle (see Fig. 4) (from Strassmann and Weinhouse, 1953).

isolation of either the intermediates or the enzymes responsible for their interconversion. It is possible that the citric acid cycle is not the sole source of the carbon atoms of aspartic acid since, apart from the slight discrepancies in the above comparisons of the activities of isoleucine with those predicted, Wang *et al.* (1952) found that the distribution of C^{14} in aspartic acid from yeast grown on pyruvic acid-2-C^{14} differed from that predicted.

The fact that the formation of methionine in yeast proceeds via homoserine suggests that it occurs by a mechanism similar to that which operates in *Neurospora* (Horowitz, 1947) and in mammals, i.e., by the condensation of the homoserine with cysteine (see section on serine family) to yield cystathione (X) which gives rise in turn to homocysteine (XI) and finally methionine. Cystathione has been shown to be a highly

$$
\begin{array}{ccccccc}
\text{CH}_2\text{SH} & \text{CH}_2\text{OH} & \text{CH}_2\!-\!\text{S}\!-\!\text{CH}_2 & & \text{CH}_2\text{SH} & \text{CH}_2\text{SCH}_3 \\
| & | & | \qquad\quad | & & | & | \\
\text{CHNH}_2 + & \text{CH}_2 & \text{CHNH}_2 \quad \text{CH}_2 & \xrightarrow{\text{Thionase}} & \text{CH}_2 & \text{CH}_2 \\
| & | \quad\rightarrow & | \qquad\quad | & & | & | \\
\text{CO}_2\text{H} & \text{CHNH}_2 & \text{CO}_2\text{H} \quad \text{CHNH}_2 & & \text{CHNH}_2 & \text{CHNH}_2 \\
& | & \qquad\quad | & & | & | \\
& \text{CO}_2\text{H} & \qquad\quad \text{CO}_2\text{H} & & \text{CO}_2\text{H} & \text{CO}_2\text{H} \\
\text{Cysteine} & \text{Homo-} & \text{Cystathione} & & \text{Homo-} & \text{Methionine} \\
& \text{serine} & \text{(X)} & & \text{cysteine} & \\
& & & & \text{(XI)} &
\end{array}
$$

effective competitor in the synthesis of radioactive methionine in *T. utilis* (Abelson *et al.*, 1953) as well as in *Neurospora* and is thus implicated as a methionine precursor. The reverse process, namely the incorporation of the sulfur of methionine into the cysteine of proteins and into glutathione has also been observed in yeast. Methionine can take part in transmethylation reactions so that it is formed from homocysteine by the transfer of a methyl group from an energy-rich "onium" pole, such as that present in betaine, thetins, and similar compounds, or can form homocysteine by the transfer of its methyl group to acceptor molecules (Stekol, 1955). Whether the methionine always functions as a methyl donor *per se* or is present as an activated complex is not certain. Such an activated compound has been found in yeast in the form of S-adenosylmethionine (Cantoni, 1953). It is formed from methionine and ATP and its structure has been unequivocally established (XII) by synthesis (Baddiley and Jamieson, 1954). By donating its methyl group to an acceptor molecule it presumably forms S-adenosylhomocysteine and this is possibly the active form of homocysteine in yeast which actually accepts methyl groups to form methionine (Cantoni, 1955). The adenosylhomocysteine has been found in animal tissues and its structure proved by complete synthesis (Baddiley and Jamieson, 1955). It is possible that the methylation of homocysteine occurs by the intermediate addition of formaldehyde from the "one-carbon pool" (see section on serine family) to yield S-hydroxymethylhomocysteine a compound which has been found in pigeon liver homogenates (Berg, 1953).

McRorie *et al.* (1956) have observed, however, that certain mutants of *Neurospora* yield compounds intermediate between homocysteine and methionine which have chemical and biological properties different from those of the S-hydroxymethyl compound and from the alternative *m*-thiazane-4-carboxylic acid. The position is still open, therefore, and as regards yeast little is known at the moment of this area of the metabolism of the cell.

It is noteworthy that S-adenosyl homocysteine has been shown to be formed from adenosine and L-homocysteine by direct condensation rather than via methionine. This reaction has only been demonstrated so far in animal tissues (De la Haba and Cantoni, 1957). In bacteria, methionine is also formed from homocysteine and S-methylmethionine (Shapiro, 1956).

In addition to transferring methyl groups the active form of methionine can yield up its S-methyl grouping intact, e.g., a mutant strain of *Aerobacter* has been found in which S-adenosylmethionine transfers its S-methyl group to α-aminobutyric acid, a direct reversal of one path of methionine degradation in yeast. In this connection it is of considerable interest that Schlenk and Tillotson (1954) and Schmidt *et al.* (1954) have shown that methyl mercaptan and ethyl mercaptan can give rise to methylthioadenosine and ethylthioadenosine in yeast presumably via adenosylmethionine and adenosylethionine. Since both of the mercaptans may be formed in the normal metabolism of the cell (see final section of this chapter) these reactions may well be of importance in the general economy of the sulfur compounds.

$$
\begin{array}{c}
\text{N—CNH}_2 \\
\text{HC C—N} \\
\text{CH} \\
\text{N=C—N} \\
\text{CHCHOHCHOHCHCH}_2\overset{+}{\text{S}}\text{CH}_2\text{CH}_2\text{CHNH}_2\text{CO}_2^- \\
\text{O} \qquad \text{CH}_3
\end{array}
$$

S-Adenosylmethionine

(XII)

(3) *Lysine.* The scheme discussed above (see Fig. 6) for the formation of the four-carbon acids via the citric acid cycle may be followed further to explain the biosynthesis of lysine in *T. utilis* (Strassman and Weinhouse, 1952, 1953; Weinhouse *et al.*, 1951). The distribution of radioactivity in carbon 3, 4, 5, and 6 of lysine, isolated from the yeast after growth on acetic acid labeled either in the carboxyl group or in the methyl group, accords well with that expected in the succinic acid moiety of α-ketoglutaric acid (Fig. 6). The radioactivity of the C_1 and C_2 of the lysine suggests that these carbon atoms find their origin in an intact acetate radical (Ehrensvärd *et al.*, 1951a,b; Gilvarg and Bloch, 1951) and Strassman and Weinhouse therefore postulate that this radical condenses with the ketonic grouping of α-ketoglutaric acid to yield homocitric acid (XIII) as the first stage in the biosynthesis. This reaction is analogous to that giving citric acid by the condensation of oxaloacetic acid with acetic acid (Fig. 6) or that producing compound (VI) from α-ketobutyric acid

$$
\begin{array}{c}
CH_3CO_2H \\
+ \\
COCO_2H \\
| \\
CH_2 \\
| \\
CH_2 \\
| \\
CO_2H
\end{array}
\rightarrow
\begin{array}{c}
CH_2CO_2H \\
| \\
HOCCO_2H \\
| \\
CH_2 \\
| \\
CH_2 \\
| \\
CO_2H \\
\text{Homocitric} \\
\text{acid} \\
XIII
\end{array}
\rightarrow
\begin{array}{c}
HOCHCO_2H \\
| \\
CHCO_2H \\
| \\
CH_2 \\
| \\
CH_2 \\
| \\
CO_2H \\
\text{Homoisocitric} \\
\text{acid}
\end{array}
\rightarrow
\begin{array}{c}
COCO_2H \\
| \\
CHCO_2H \\
| \\
CH_2 \\
| \\
CH_2 \\
| \\
CO_2H \\
\text{Oxalo-} \\
\text{glutaric} \\
\text{acid}
\end{array}
\rightarrow
\begin{array}{c}
COCO_2H \\
| \\
CH_2 \\
| \\
CH_2 \\
| \\
CH_2 \\
| \\
CO_2H \\
\alpha\text{-Keto-} \\
\text{adipic} \\
\text{acid} \\
XIV
\end{array}
\rightarrow
$$

$$
\begin{array}{c}
CHNH_2CO_2H \\
| \\
CH_2 \\
| \\
CH_2 \\
| \\
CH_2 \\
| \\
CO_2H \\
\alpha\text{-Aminoadipic} \\
\text{acid} \\
XV
\end{array}
\rightarrow
\begin{array}{c}
CHNH_2\ CO_2H \\
| \\
CH_2 \\
| \\
CH_2 \\
| \\
CH_2 \\
| \\
CH_2NH_2 \\
\text{Lysine}
\end{array}
$$

and acetic acid. The further reactions postulated are again analogous to those of the citric acid cycle yielding α-ketoadipic acid (XIV), the homologue of α-ketoglutaric acid, which is then supposed to yield α-aminoadipic acid (XV) presumably by transamination (see below). This amino acid is known to be a precursor of lysine in various microorganisms (Mitchell and Houlalan, 1948; Windsor, 1951; Work, 1955) and is presumed to be converted into lysine by a series of reactions resembling that involved in the transformation of glutamic acid to ornithine previously described. No evidence has as yet been adduced for the presence of the seven-carbon acids proposed in yeast, however, and the confirmation of this biosynthetic pathway must await their isolation and the demonstration that they can function as precursors of lysine. The isolation of pipecolic acid, piperidine-2-carboxylic acid, from a number of sources (Morrison, 1952; Zacharias et al., 1952; Harris and Pollock, 1952) suggests that the α-aminoadipic semialdehyde, the expected analogue of glutamic acid semialdehyde, is present and can yield tetrahydropyridine-2-carboxylic acid in a manner similar to the formation of Δ^1-pyrrolinecarboxylic acid. It would appear that the pathway to lysine in T. utilis is similar to that in Neurospora with the exception that in the latter the α-ketoglutaric acid condenses with a molecule other than acetate (Abelson and Vogel, 1955). It is quite different from that in E. coli, in which lysine is formed by decarboxylation of α,ϵ-diaminopimelic acid and not via aspartic acid as in the present instance (Strassman et al., 1956a).

(4) *The Pyruvic Acid Family.* The incorporation of radioactive tracers into a further series of amino acids of *T. utilis* is shown in Table IV (see Abelson and Vogel, 1955). It is apparent that α-alanine functions as a precursor both of valine and of leucine and this presumably occurs via pyruvic acid as an intermediate. Isotopic competition experiments reveal that unlabeled pyruvic acid depresses the incorporation of radioactivity (shown in Table IV) into alanine, valine and leucine, thus confirming

TABLE IV

INCORPORATION OF RADIOACTIVE TRACERS INTO THE AMINO ACIDS
OF THE PROTEIN OF *Torulopsis utilis*

Tracer	Protein amino acid					
	α-Alanine	Valine	Leucine	Serine	Glycine	Cystine
α-Alanine	100	40	60	5	5	
Serine	0	0	0	100	100	100
Glycine	0	0	0	15	100	15

that it fills the above-presumed function as a precursor of these amino acids. Similar experiments with α-ketoisovaleric acid show the suppression of the radioactivity of valine and leucine while α-ketoisocaproic acid suppresses only the activity of leucine. Competition experiments show that added nonradioactive valine affects both the valine and leucine of the yeast protein while added leucine affects only the leucine. These findings support the following reaction sequences:

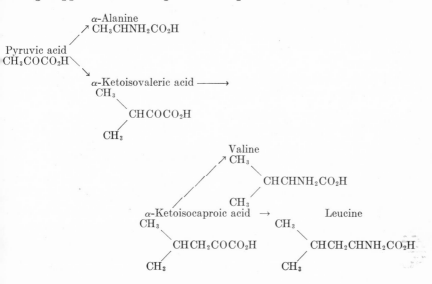

As mentioned earlier, the role of pyruvic acid as a precursor of valine in *T. utilis* was established by Strassman *et al.* (1953) and in *E. coli* by Abelson (1954) while the function of α-ketoisovaleric acid as a forerunner of valine in *Neurospora* was revealed by Bonner *et al.* (1943). Further more, the mediation of α-ketoisocaproic acid in the biosynthesis of leucine in other organisms is exemplified in *Neurospora* and *E. coli* (Abelson and Vogel, 1955). The conversion of α-ketoisovaleric acid to α-ketoiso caproic acid appears to involve the loss of a fragment containing a single carbon atom and the replacement of this by a fragment containing two carbon atoms. In view of the finding by Ehrensvärd *et al.* (1951a,b) that the carboxyl group of leucine in both *T. utilis* and *E. coli* appears to arise in the carboxyl group of acetate it seemed probable that the two-carbon fragment was closely related to acetic acid. This probability was realized when Reiss and Bloch (1955) showed that C_1 and C_2 of leucine in *Saccharomyces cerevisiae*, grown on labeled glucose or acetate, are de rived directly from an acetyl unit. A similar conclusion was reached by Strassman *et al.* (1956c) from the examination of the activity of each carbon atom of leucine derived from *T. utilis* after growth on glucose in the presence of tracer amounts of variously labeled acetic acid and lactic acid. These workers also found that the labeling of the isobutyl group of leucine matched that of the corresponding group of valine thus con firming that the carbon chain of the latter amino acid arises from the same source as that of the former as shown by Abelson's isotopic compe tition experiments. By analogy with the reactions of the citric acid cycle Strassman *et al.* propose the following reactions as a working hypothesis to explain leucine synthesis:

$$
\begin{array}{ccccccc}
\text{CH}_3\text{COSCoA} & & \text{CH}_2\text{CO}_2\text{H} & & \text{CHCO}_2\text{H} & & \text{CHOHCO}_2\text{H} \\
+ & \xrightarrow{\ -\text{CoA}\ } & | & \xrightarrow{\ -\text{H}_2\text{O}\ } & \| & \xrightarrow{\ +\text{H}_2\text{O}\ } & | \\
\text{O} & & \text{HOCCO}_2\text{H} & & \text{CCO}_2\text{H} & & \text{CHCO}_2\text{H} \\
\| & & | & & | & & | \\
\text{CCO}_2\text{H} & & \text{CH(CH}_3)_2 & & \text{CH(CH}_3)_2 & & \text{CH(CH}_3)_2 \\
| & & & & & & | \downarrow {-2\text{H}} \\
\text{CH(CH}_3)_2 & & \text{CHNH}_2\text{CO}_2\text{H} & & \text{COCO}_2\text{H} & & \text{COCO}_2\text{H} \\
& & | & & | & \xleftarrow{\ -\text{CO}_2\ } & | \\
& & \text{CH}_2 & \leftarrow & \text{CH}_2 & & \text{CHCO}_2\text{H} \\
& & | & & | & & | \\
& & \text{CH(CH}_3)_2 & & \text{CH(CH}_3)_2 & & \text{CH(CH}_3)_2
\end{array}
$$

Acetic acid is assumed to be activated by combination with coenzyme A (CoA) as in the citric acid cycle, which is now considered to be one example of a general process in nature for the production of α-keto acids However, the full details of leucine biosynthesis in yeast have not yet been worked out and the above hypothesis is being tested at the present time. It seems probable that the last step involves transamination of α

ketoisocaproic acid since this compound is known to be an active substrate for transamination. Adelberg (1955) has commented that, if this is so, there must be more than one leucine transaminase (see below) since loss of one such transaminase activity did not result in a nutritional requirement for leucine, at least in a mutant strain of E. coli.

The results of the detailed determination of the extent of labeling of the individual carbon atoms both of valine and of α-alanine from baker's yeast, grown on pyruvic acid either aerobically or anaerobically (Wang et al., 1955), suggest that α-alanine is formed directly from pyruvic acid by transamination. Thus, administration of pyruvic acid-2-C^{14} resulted in heavy labeling of C_2 of the alanine. However, the C_1 and C_3 positions in the alanine were also labeled to some extent probably as a result of equilibration with oxaloacetic acid since the ratio of the activities in these carbon atoms was very similar to that observed for the corresponding carbon atoms of aspartic acid. Comparison of the extent of labeling of the carboxyl group of alanine formed under aerobic conditions with that of the same amino acid synthesized under anaerobic conditions indicates that the equilibrium between pyruvic acid and oxaloacetic acid favors the former under anaerobic conditions. The studies of Wang et al. confirmed generally the pattern of labeling in valine found, as mentioned above, by Strassman and his co-workers (1953), but in their experiments equal labeling in C_2 and C_3 of the amino acid was not fully realized. These authors therefore suggest in common with McManus (1954) that this might be explained if the two molecules which condense to form acetolactic acid are not equivalent in labeling. They also found that the ratio of labeling between C_1 and C_2 of valine differed from that of alanine and comment that, if the pinacol type of rearrangement described earlier is the only mechanism for the formation of valine (and isoleucine), these ratios should be similar. It therefore appears that a mechanism additional to that postulated earlier for valine biosynthesis is operative after the formation of acetolactic acid.

(5) *Histidine.* Isolation of histidine from the cellular protein of *Saccharomyces cerevisiae, T. utilis,* or *Pseudomonas fluorescens* grown in the presence of formic acid-C^{14}, followed by degradation shows that C_2 of the imidazole ring (XIX) is derived exclusively from formic acid (Levy and Coon, 1951; Tabor et al., 1952). Neither glycine-1-C^{14} nor bicarbonate-C^{14} was incorporated into histidine and since yeast incorporates the former directly into the imidazole ring of purines (see below) it was apparent that the imidazole ring in the latter compounds is synthesized by a different route from that appertaining to histidine. The observation by Broquist and Snell (1949) that *Lactobacillus casei* shows an increased

requirement for purines when grown in the absence of histidine is not to be interpreted therefore to mean that the purines serve as histidine precursors. More probably these purines serve as sources of formic acid or single carbon intermediates in the formation of C_2 of the new imidazole ring in histidine (see, however, p. 475). As in the case of many other reactions involving the transfer of units containing one carbon atom it appears probable that the incorporation of formic acid into the histidine ring is mediated by the citrovorum factor (CF) (see section on serine family). Thus, Broquist (1952) showed that when a strain of the yeast, *Torula cremoris*, was grown on a synthetic medium, the addition of 4-aminopteroylglutamic acid (aminopterin) caused a strong inhibition of growth which was reversed competitively by CF. The inhibition could be overcome noncompetitively by the addition either of methionine, methionine together with purine, or methionine together with purine and histidine.

Studies on the breakdown of histidine in either liver or microorganisms revealed that one product consisted of a compound which yielded formic acid and glutamic acid on hydrolysis (Edlbacher, 1943; Abrams and Borsook, 1952; Fournier and Bouthillier, 1952; Wolf, 1953; Tabor and Hayaishi, 1952). This substance proved to be formamidinoglutamic acid and the formic acid produced by degradation therefore originated in C_2 of the imidazole ring (Sprinson, 1951; Sprinson and Rittenberg, 1952; Reid and Landefeld, 1951; Soucy and Bouthillier, 1951; Toporek *et al.*, 1952; Magasanik and Bowser, 1955; Waelsch and Miller, 1955). This fact suggested that the synthesis of histidine might occur by reversal of the degradation reactions described, possibly from glutamic acid. Investigation of this hypothesis by Levy and Coon (1954) showed it to be untenable, at least for yeast. When this organism was grown on acetic acid-2-C^{14} the derived histidine had low specific activity, all the C^{14} again being located at C_2 of the ring and having been derived presumably from the acetic acid via formic acid. The acetic acid did not contribute to the five-carbon chain of the histidine molecule either directly or indirectly via glutamic acid as the latter amino acid was heavily labeled. On the other hand, when the yeast was grown on glucose-1-C^{14} the specific activity of the histidine equaled that of the glucose but C_2 of the ring contained only 9% of the total radioactivity of the molecule. Hence, the five-carbon chain is derived more or less directly from glucose. In passing, it may be mentioned that the failure of acetic acid to participate in the formation of this chain in these experiments does not appear to accord with the finding by Ehrensvärd *et al.* (1949) that the carboxyl group of histidine originates in the methyl group of acetic acid. However, these apparently contradictory results may be reconciled when it is recalled that the latter workers used organisms adapted to acetic acid and grown on it as the sole source of carbon. It may be assumed, therefore, that the acetic acid-2-C^{13} in their experiments gave rise to glucose labeled at C_1, C_2, C_5, and C_6 (White and Werkmann, 1947; Lifson et al., 1948) which served in turn as the precursor of histidine, in which the carboxyl group was labeled.

The probability that a sugar functions as the source of the carbon chain of histidine is enhanced by the findings that mutants of E. coli (Vogel et al., 1951) and of Neurospora (Ames et al., 1953) accumulate compounds, which are related to histidine but which contain one to three hydroxyl groups in the side chain. Compounds of this type are formed in the nonenzymic reaction of D-arabinose or D-ribose with ammonia and formaldehyde in the presence of copper, thus,

(20)

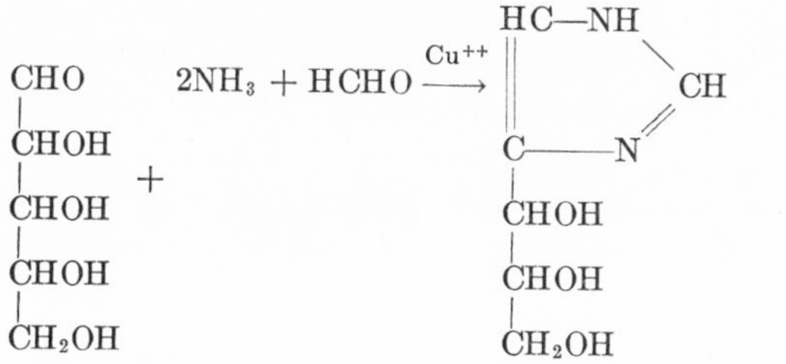

$$\text{CHO} \atop \text{CHOH} \atop \text{CHOH} \atop \text{CHOH} \atop \text{CH}_2\text{OH}} + \quad 2\text{NH}_3 + \text{HCHO} \xrightarrow{\text{Cu}^{++}}$$

$$\begin{array}{c} \text{HC---NH} \\ \| \qquad \diagdown \\ \text{C----N} \qquad \text{CH} \\ | \qquad \diagup \\ \text{CHOH} \\ | \\ \text{CHOH} \\ | \\ \text{CH}_2\text{OH} \end{array}$$

D-*Erythrotrihydroxy-propylimidazole*

and it seemed probable that an enzymic reaction of similar nature might occur in Neurospora (Ames, 1955). Working with this organism, Ames and Mitchell (1955) isolated three phosphate esters from various mutants, which proved to be derived from hydroxy compounds of the above type, and on the basis of this evidence were able to propose the following reactions for the later stages in the biosynthesis of histidine:

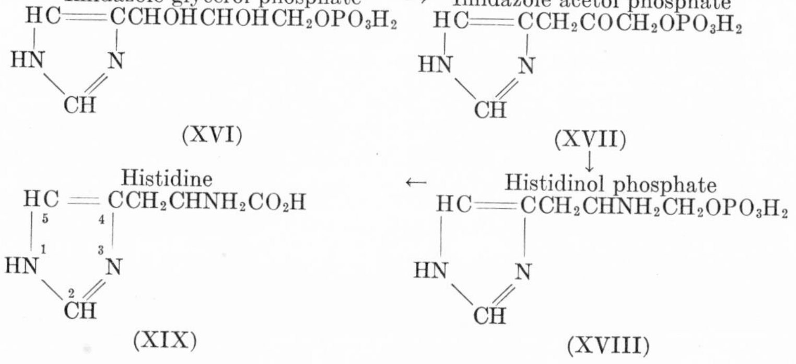

Imidazole glycerol phosphate → Imidazole acetol phosphate

$$\begin{array}{c} \text{HC===CCHOHCHOHCH}_2\text{OPO}_3\text{H}_2 \\ | \qquad | \\ \text{HN} \qquad \text{N} \\ \diagdown \quad \diagup \\ \text{CH} \end{array}$$

(XVI)

$$\begin{array}{c} \text{HC===CCH}_2\text{COCH}_2\text{OPO}_3\text{H}_2 \\ | \qquad | \\ \text{HN} \qquad \text{N} \\ \diagdown \quad \diagup \\ \text{CH} \end{array}$$

(XVII)

Histidine ← Histidinol phosphate

$$\begin{array}{c} \text{HC} = \text{CCH}_2\text{CHNH}_2\text{CO}_2\text{H} \\ |^{5} \quad ^{4}| \\ |^{1} \qquad ^{3}| \\ \text{HN} \qquad \text{N} \\ \diagdown ^{2}\diagup \\ \text{CH} \end{array}$$

(XIX)

$$\begin{array}{c} \text{HC===CCH}_2\text{CHNH}_2\text{CH}_2\text{OPO}_3\text{H}_2 \\ | \qquad | \\ \text{HN} \qquad \text{N} \\ \diagdown \quad \diagup \\ \text{CH} \end{array}$$

(XVIII)

Enzymes which catalyse the first two reactions have been isolated from *Neurospora*, that which catalyzes the transformation of imidazole acetol phosphate (XVII) to L-histidinol phosphate (XVIII) being known as imidazole acetol phosphate transaminase and that which brings about the conversion of imidazole glycerol phosphate (XVI) to imidazole acetol phosphate being called imidazole glycerol phosphate dehydrase. The former enzyme in common with most transaminases requires pyridoxal phosphate as coenzyme (Ames and Horecker, 1956). The latter enzyme has been obtained free from the former and is activated strongly by cysteine and by manganous ions and inhibited by ethylenediamine tetraacetic acid (Ames, 1956). Both enzymes fail to act on the dephosphorylated compounds corresponding to XVI–XVIII, which are also accumulated by the histidineless mutants examined. On the other hand, Adams (1954) found that histidinol, but not the phosphate, is oxidized to histidine by an enzyme system found in various organisms including yeast, *Arthrobacter,* and *E. coli.* He showed further that the enzyme preparation from yeast would also oxidize histidinal, the aldehyde corresponding to histidinol (Adams, 1955), but was unable to separate the enzymes respectively responsible for the oxidation of the alcohol and of the aldehyde. He has expressed the view that only one enzyme is responsible for the oxidation of both substrates and that histidinal, being unstable, is held on the enzyme surface for further oxidation after the initial oxidation of histidinol. Since Ames (1957) has now shown by means of histidineless mutants of *Neurospora* that L-histidinol phosphate is converted into L-histidinol by a phosphatase in the normal biosynthetic sequence of reactions, it may be envisaged that the course of histidine formation outlined for this organism also applies to yeast. Histidinol itself has also been shown to function as a precursor of histidine in *E. coli* by Westley and Ceithaml (1956a) who found further that L-imidazole lactic acid is effective in this respect although it does not play any part in the normal biosynthetic processes. These latter workers also emphasize that the five-carbon chain of histidine is formed prior to the imidazole ring. Levy and Coon (1954) have pointed out that the results of their labeling experiments described above do not appear to support the hypothesis that the five-carbon chain originates in pentose. They state that condensation of triose-phosphate-3-C^{14}, produced by glycolysis of glucose-1-C^{14}, with a two-carbon unit derived from C_2 and C_3 of triose phosphate-3-C^{14} would be expected to yield a pentose molecule labeled either at C_1 and C_5 or at C_2 and C_5 by the mechanism demonstrated in yeast by Gilvarg (1952). The partial randomization of the isotope in these two- and three-carbon intermediates via the Krebs cycle is, as already discussed, incompatible with the fact that acetic acid fails to contribute to the histidine carbon chain. Westley and Ceithaml (1956b) have found that in an *E. coli* mutant, however, the carbon chain of histidinol is probably formed by the condensation of a 3-carbon unit with a 2-carbon unit formed by the normal glycolytic pathway. These authors showed that the pattern of labeling of the carbon atoms in histidinol isolated from *E. coli* was the same whether this organism was grown on glucose-1-C^{14} or glucose-6-C^{14}, whereas if the histidinol were formed directly from pentose formed by the monophosphase shunt mechanism (see Chapter VIII), the labeling patterns would be quite dissimilar. They comment, however, that their results are not in agreement with the data of Levy and Coon for yeast where the position must be regarded as open.

Little is known regarding the source of the nitrogen atoms in the imidazole ring of histidine in microorganisms although recent investigations by Neidle and Waelsch (1956) have shown that N_1 of the imidazole ring (that yielding the amino group of glutamic acid on degradation) is derived from the amide group of glutamine in *E. coli*. This observation raised the possibility that the amide group of glutamine participates directly in histidine synthesis by primary formation of an amino sugar or amino aldehyde or more probably indirectly by group transfer from an intermediate such as guanine.

The latter possibility was realized when Neidle and Waelsch (1957) showed that N_1 and C_2 of guanine contribute to N_3 and C_2 of histidine in *E. coli* and that aspartic acid and glutamic acid donate nitrogen to N_3. These findings are consistent with the fact that the N-atom of aspartic acid labels both N_1 of guanine and N_3 of histidine, and that C_2 of guanine yields C_2 of histidine in *Lactobacillus casei*. It was also demonstrated that the amide group of glutamic contributes to N_1 and N_3 of histidine without prior incorporation into N_3 of a purine, the group transfer possibly proceeding via xanthine or a derivative such as ureidoimidazole carboxylic acid.

(6) *The Serine Family*. Reference to Table IV shows that the addition of radioactive serine to growing yeast results in the labeling of the serine, glycine, and cysteine (see also the aspartic acid family (2) for methionine synthesis) of the protein of *T. utilis* at equal levels of specific activity (Abelson and Vogel, 1955). The use of radioactive glycine as substrate gave rise to labeling of serine and cysteine at only 15% of the initial specific activity, a finding in agreement with the earlier observations of Ehrensvärd *et al.* (1947). It was concluded that serine is a major precursor of glycine and cysteine in yeast, which thus resembles *Neurospora* and *E. coli* in this respect (Abelson, 1954). The metabolism of

serine differs in the yeast from that in E. coli, however, since in the former, when grown on a glucose-salt medium, glycine can yield serine and cysteine, while in the latter, exogenous threonine contributes to serine and serine contributes to the members of the pyruvic acid family (see Abelson et al., 1953).

In more detailed investigations, in which the labeling of the individual carbon atoms of glycine and serine derived from yeast (Saccharomyces cerevisiae) protein was determined, Wang et al. (1955) found that the isotopic pattern in these amino acids was similar, each having the same extent of labeling in C_1 and C_2. These authors concluded that the origin of this series of amino acids does not lay directly in the conversion of pyruvic acid into serine, as postulated for rats (Anker, 1948), since the labeling patterns were dissimilar to that of alanine (see above). Further indication that the pathway of serine formation in yeast diverges from that earlier established in animals is given by the results of administering acetic acid-2-C^{14} to baker's yeast (Gilvarg and Bloch, 1951). Under these circumstances serine is found to be heavily labeled in C_3, and to have somewhat different and much smaller labeling in C_1 and C_2; but, if pyruvic acid equilibrated with oxaloacetic acid, direct conversion to serine would yield equal labeling in C_2 and C_3. On the other hand, however, Wang et al. (1955) contend that if glycine precedes serine in the biosynthetic sequence, the heavy labeling in C_3 is to be expected since the labeled methyl group of acetic acid would appear in this carbon atom. The origin of the glycine skeleton itself is to be sought in more complex metabolites and, indeed, Meltzer and Sprinson (1950) earlier proposed that α,β-cleavage of threonine would yield glycine. This hypothesis is not compatible with the results of Wang et al., however, since the isotope distribution in glycine did not match that of the corresponding moiety of threonine and, furthermore, Ehrensvärd et al. (1951a) showed that the proposed cleavage of threonine would yield two molecules of acetic acid-2-C^{14} and that this was contrary to their findings. Wang et al. therefore postulate that glycine is formed from pyruvic acid-2-C^{14} via the Krebs cycle as shown in Fig. 7a (Scheme A). Conversion of α-ketoglutaric acid to the four-carbon dicarboxylic acids followed by α,β-fission would then produce the isotopic pattern experimentally found for glycine. Similar operation of the cycle with acetic acid-1-C^{14} would yield glycine-1-C^{14} (Scheme B) in accordance with the findings of Ehrensvärd. This scheme is also consistent with the observation by Shemin (1949) that C_1 of glycine may arise from C_2 of glutamic acid. A further metabolic pathway involving direct interconversion of the four-carbon acids formed from pyruvic acid-2-C^{14} would result in the preferential labeling of C_2 of both glycine and serine (Scheme C). The slightly higher isotope level in this carbon atom observed by Wang *et al.* (1955) was considered to reflect a limited contribution of this nature. It is apparent that the relationship between pyruvic acid, glycine, and serine is still somewhat obscure and it is possible that the net balance between glycine and serine may vary according to the conditions. Reactions other than those noted above which may well contribute to the formation of serine are: (a) the reverse of the catabolic deamination of serine to pyruvic acid (see above) although no evidence of this has as yet been obtained; and (b) the transamination of β-hydroxypyruvic acid, which has been established in other organisms (see Sallach, 1956). If the

(a)   Scheme A $CH_3C^{14}OCO_2H$

$$\downarrow CO_2$$

$$C—C—C^{14}—C$$

$$\downarrow \text{Randomization}$$

$$C—C^{14}—C^{14}—C \xrightarrow[\text{Succinic acid}]{\text{via Fumaric acid or}} \quad \text{Scheme C} \quad C^{14}—C + C^{14}—C$$

$$\downarrow \text{Krebs cycle}$$

$$CO_2HC^{14}OC^{14}H_2CH_2CO_2H$$

$$\alpha\text{-Ketoglutaric acid}$$

Scheme B $CH_3C^{14}O_2H \xrightarrow{\text{Krebs cycle}} C^{14}—C—C—C^{14}$

$$\downarrow$$

$$CH_2NH_2C^{14}O_2H \leftarrow C—C^{14}$$

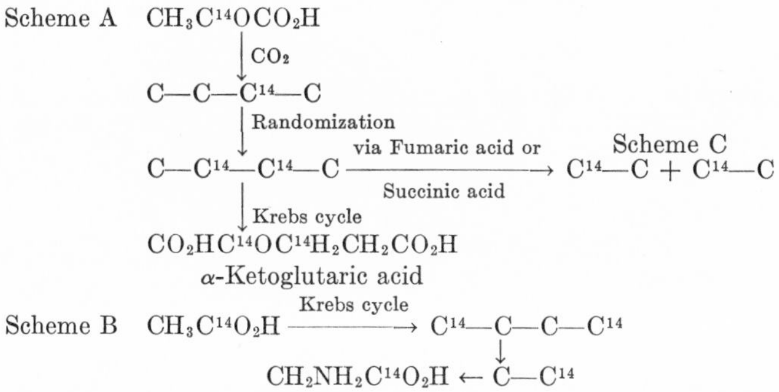

Fig. 7a: Routes for the biosynthesis of glycine in yeast (from Wang *et al.* (1955)).

formation of β-hydroxypyruvic acid from D-glyceric acid can be established, the connection of serine with pyruvic acid would be evident but it is perhaps significant that the reverse of this reaction has been noted (Stafford *et al.*, 1954). The work of Wang *et al.* makes it probable that formylation of glycine can yield serine and the discovery by Olson (1954) that baker's yeast contains an enzyme, isocitric acid lysase, which splits isocitric acid to form succinic acid and glyoxylic acid, affords a means whereby glycine can be formed independently of serine since the glyoxylic acid can undergo transamination to yield the former amino acid. The various routes which might contribute to the formation of glycine and serine have been discussed by Ehrensvärd (1955), who summarizes them in the form of the Fig. 7b. The formation of glycine via the Krebs cycle in the manner shown here would also lead to the labeling patterns of glycine and serine observed by Wang *et al.* (see above) and is presumably, therefore, the major pathway.

The mechanism by which the glycine is converted into serine has not yet been elucidated but, if it resembles that in other organisms, it may

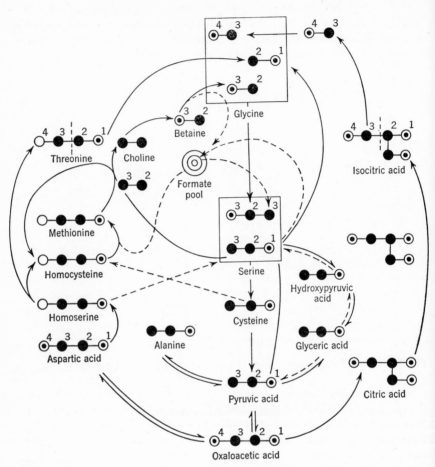

Fig. 7b: Routes for interconverting glycine and serine. Schematic representation of the interrelation between serine-glycine and other amino acids and metabolites. As a guide in judging isotope distribution patterns, the carbon atoms 3 and 2 of pyruvate are represented by filled rings. Carboxyls are denoted with ring and dot. The numeration of pyruvate and oxaloacetate gives the standard for judging the origin of glycine and serine carbon atoms from various sources. As seen the origin of glycine carbon atoms could be separated in at least three different cases. With regard to serine, recycling of the 3-2 fragment via the choline cycle and formate fixation to glycine returns a serine differently labeled as compared with the starting material. Three concentric rings represent the formate pool (from Ehrensvärd, 1955).

well be mediated by folic acid as has been found to be the case for a large number of transfers of single carbon units. Sprinson has suggested that these transfers can take place according to the following scheme (see Glass, 1955; Sakami, 1955; Kisliuk and Sakami, 1956).

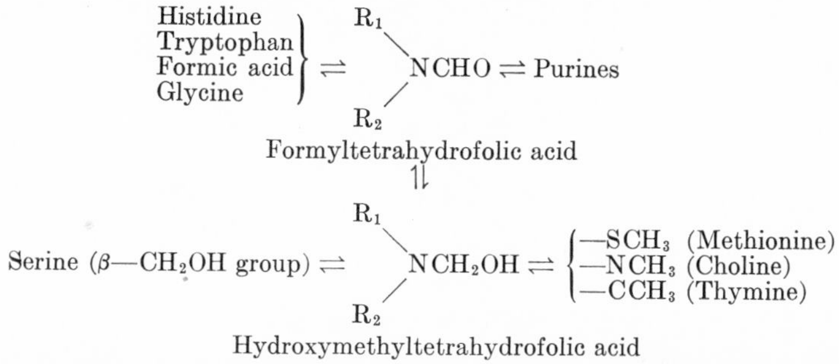

$$
\left.\begin{array}{l}\text{Histidine}\\\text{Tryptophan}\\\text{Formic acid}\\\text{Glycine}\end{array}\right\} \rightleftharpoons \quad \overset{R_1}{\underset{R_2}{\diagdown}} NCHO \rightleftharpoons Purines
$$

Formyltetrahydrofolic acid

$$\updownarrow$$

$$
\text{Serine } (\beta\text{—}CH_2OH \text{ group}) \rightleftharpoons \quad \overset{R_1}{\underset{R_2}{\diagdown}} NCH_2OH \rightleftharpoons \left\{\begin{array}{ll}\text{—}SCH_3 & \text{(Methionine)}\\\text{—}NCH_3 & \text{(Choline)}\\\text{—}CCH_3 & \text{(Thymine)}\end{array}\right.
$$

Hydroxymethyltetrahydrofolic acid

Formyl groups can be transferred from histidine (see above) via formamidinoglutaric acid (Miller and Waslsch, 1956), tryptophan, etc., to tetrahydrofolic acid and in turn to purines, while hydroxymethyl groups can similarly be transferred to folic acid and hence to acceptor compounds, such as homocysteine, by a reductive mechanism or, in the present instance, to an activated glycine molecule to form serine. These observations afford a possible explanation for the observations of Lascelles et al. (1950, 1954) that the amount of serine synthesized is doubled by p-aminobenzoic acid, an integral part of folic acid, in a strain of Saccharomyces cerevisiae requiring this growth factor. The reader is referred to the extensive reviews on the subject of one-carbon transfers and the participation of glycine in the succinate-glycine cycle leading to the elaboration of porphyrins and purines which are given in "Amino Acid Metabolism" (edited by McElroy and Glass, Johns Hopkins Press, Baltimore), since much of the work involved has been effected on organisms other than yeast. It is to be noted in particular that an enzyme system has been isolated from Clostridium cylindrosporum, which catalyzes the conversion of serine into glycine and formic acid. This enzyme system requires DPN, manganous ions, pyridoxal phosphate, and orthophosphate for its activity and, although CF and tetrahydrofolic acid function as cofactors, very much more active natural coenzymes have been isolated (Wright, 1956; Wright and Stadtman, 1956). These natural coenzymes (CoC) are probably pteridine polyglutamates, the monoglutamate being inactive (cf. Blakley, 1957a,b).

Recently, Osborn and Talbert (1957) have isolated an enzyme from beef or pigeon liver acetone powders which catalyzes the above conversion of hydroxymethyltetrahydrofolic acid into N^{10}-formyltetrahydro-folic acid according to the following equation:

Hydroxymethyltetrahydrofolic acid $+$ TPN$^+$ $\rightleftharpoons$ N^{10}-formyltetrahydrofolic acid
$+$ TPNH $+$ H$^+$

The participation of glycine in the metabolism of the one-carbon fragments in yeast is well illustrated by the results of Weinhouse *et al.* (1951), who found that the radioactivity of glycine-α-C^{14} appeared in the carbon atoms of the methyl groups of choline (see Fig. 7b). This carbon atom of glycine also appeared in the fatty acids and was distributed equally among all the carbon atoms of the chain, whereas the fatty acids isolated from yeast grown on glycine labeled in the carboxyl group had negligible radioactivity. Weinhouse *et al.* therefore postulate the following series of changes to occur in yeast:

(a) $C^{14}H_2NH_2CO_2H \rightarrow HC^{14}O_2H$
(b) $C^{14}H_2NH_2CO_2H + HC^{14}O_2H \rightarrow C^{14}H_2OHC^{14}HNH_2CO_2H$
(c) $C^{14}H_2OHC^{14}HNH_2CO_2H \rightarrow C^{14}H_3C^{14}OCO_2H$
(d) $C^{14}H_3C^{14}OCO_2H \rightarrow C^{14}H_3C^{14}O_2H + CO_2$
(e) $C^{14}H_3C^{14}O_2H \rightarrow C^{14}H_3C^{14}H_2 \cdots C^{14}H_2C^{14}O_2H$

Reaction (b) has been demonstrated for *T. utilis* (see Ehrensvärd *et al.* 1947, above) and the subsequent reactions have been established both in yeast and in animals (Chargaff and Sprinson, 1943; Anker, 1948; Weinhouse, *et al.*, 1948) and hence it may be seen that glycine, formerly thought to be rather inert, can participate in the formation of a great diversity of compounds in yeast ranging from fatty acids to purines (see also Fig. 7b and section on purines).

(7) *The Aromatic Amino Acids.* The ways in which these amino acids are synthesized have formed the subject of extensive reviews recently, but the bulk of the work in this general field has been carried out with mutants of *Neurospora crassa* (Davis, 1955a,b,c). It is considered relevant to give a brief resumé of some of this work here, however, as there are preliminary indications that similar biosynthetic pathways are involved in yeast metabolism (Ehrensvärd, 1955).

Certain *Neurospora* mutants accumulate in their culture fluid large amounts of the substrate of genetically blocked reactions while other mutants will grow on later intermediates in the biosynthetic pathway involving the blocked reaction. Hence, by observing cross-feeding between two strains which have a requirement for one amino acid (the end product of the biosynthesis being studied), information on this biosynthesis is obtained since one strain provides quantities of an intermediate previously unavailable while the other strain aids in the recognition of the intermediate by furnishing a method for biological testing. By utilizing a wide variety of such strains of *Neurospora* and other organisms requiring a mixture of tyrosine, phenylalanine, tryptophan, *p*-aminobenzoic acid, and *p*-hydroxybenzoic acid, Davis and his co-workers have established the scheme shown in Fig. 8. This scheme is now widely

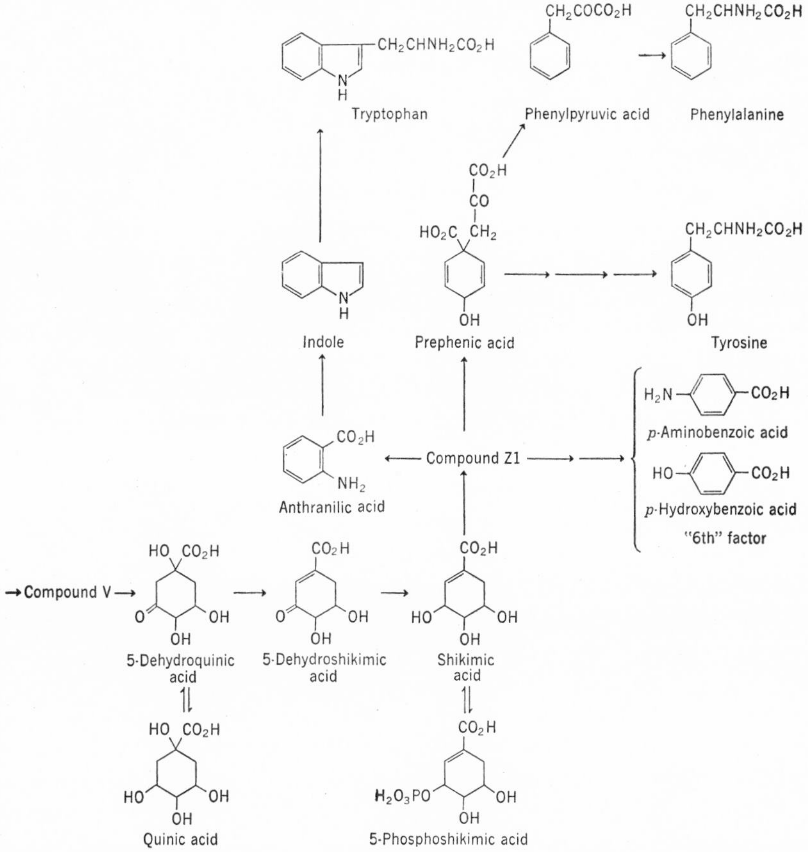

Fig. 8. Scheme for the biosynthesis of the aromatic amino acids (from Davis, 1955c).

thought to apply in its major respects to the synthesis of aromatic compounds from aliphatic compounds in a large number of organisms and in higher plants.

The pathway from 5-dehydroquinic acid through 5-dehydroshikimic acid, shikimic acid, compound Z1, and prephenic acid to phenylalanine and tyrosine has been established as the main route, quinic acid and

5-phosphoshikimic acid being side products. The enzyme leading to the dehydration of dehydroquinic acid to form dehydroshikimic acid has been found in yeast (Mitsuhashi and Davis, 1954). The nature of compound Z1 is not completely certain but Gilvarg (unpublished data) has shown that it is an acid-labile conjugate of shikimic acid with pyruvic acid, the latter being liberated on hydrolysis. Hence it is suggested that the pyruvic acid is attached to the ring by an enol-ether linkage, subsequent rearrangement yielding prephenic acid, which aromatizes extremely readily, indeed spontaneously at pH values greater than 7, losing the elements of water and carbon dioxide to form phenylpyruvic acid (Davis, 1953; Weiss et al., 1954).

The compound V, accumulated by mutants blocked before 5-dehydroquinic acid (Srinivasan et al., 1956a) was shown by Kalan and Leitner (1955) to be an open-chain phosphorylated keto acid. At the same time a study of the incorporation of radioactive glucose into shikimic acid revealed that C_1, C_2, and the carboxyl group of this acid originated in a glycolytic fragment, the remainder of the molecule being derived from a four-carbon compound containing C_3–C_6 of the glucose. Further experiments with cell extracts demonstrated that dehydroshikimic acid can be synthesized from compound V and also in small yield from various hexose phosphates (Kalan et al., 1956). This acid was obtained in large yield from sedoheptulose-1,7-diphosphate (Srinivasan et al., 1956b), carbon atoms 4–7 of the heptose being converted quantitatively and exclusively into C_3–C_6 of the product and the remaining three carbon atoms of the heptose being inverted prior to recombination with the four-carbon fragment and cyclization. A similar mechanism for the biosynthesis of phenylalanine and tyrosine, involving the condensation of four-carbon and three-carbon fragments, has been proposed for yeast on the basis of experiments on the incorporation of glucose-1-C^{14} and labeled acetic acid (Gilvarg and Bloch, 1952; Ehrensvärd, 1955). In the experiments with labeled acetic acid the isotope concentrations in alanine, aspartic acid, and glutamic acid were much greater than those in phenylalanine and tyrosine and, hence, it was apparent that pyruvic acid, oxaloacetic acid and α-ketoglutaric acid, the established sources of the carbon chains of alanine and the dicarboxylic amino acids, are not the direct precursors of the aromatic amino acids. On the other hand, the labeling of the side chains of the latter compounds, formed in yeast grown on glucose-1-C^{14}, conformed in magnitude and distribution with that predicted for triose (Gilvarg, 1952), the β-carbon atom being derived from C_1 and C_6 of glucose. The fact that only a small percentage of the activity in the tyrosine ring resided in carbon 1, 3, and 5 eliminates the possibility that two triose units unite to form this ring and, similarly, the fact that the isotope in carbon 2, 4, and 6 is distributed unsymmetrically excludes the hypothesis that the ring is formed by condensation of three two-carbon units. Gilvarg and Bloch conclude that the ring synthesis involves condensation of a singly labeled triose unit with an unlabeled product of glucose metabolism, presumably tetrose, in line with the findings of Srinavasan *et al.* (1956a).

More recent studies by Srinavasan *et al.* (1956b) have lent support to the above mechanism. Inhibition by fluoride ions of the enzyme catalysing the conversion of triose phosphate to phosphoenolpyruvic acid (XX) completely prevents the synthesis of dehydroshikimic acid from sedoheptulose diphosphate but the synthesis proceeds when phosphoenolpyruvic acid is added together with the fluoride. Furthermore, the addition of D-erythrose-4-phosphate (XXI) and phosphoenolpyruvic acid to an enzyme extract leads to the production of dehydroshikimic acid, thus indicating that sedoheptulose is not an obligatory intermediate in the production of the aromatic compounds. The formation of the ring compounds may therefore be visualized as occurring by the following sequence:

$$
\begin{array}{l}
CO_2H \\
|\ \\
COPO_3H_2 \\
||\ \\
CH_2
\end{array}
\qquad
\begin{array}{l}
CO_2H \\
|\ \\
CO \\
|\ \\
CH_2 \\
|\ \\
CHOH \\
|\ \\
CHOH \\
|\ \\
CHOH \\
|\ \\
CH_2OPO_3H_2
\end{array}
$$

Phosphoenolpyruvic acid (XX)
+
CHO
|
CHOH
|
CHOH
|
CH₂OPO₃H₂
D-Erythrose-4-phosphate (XXI)

→

2-Keto-3-deoxy-7-phospho-D-glucoheptonic acid (XXII)

→

Dehydroquinic acid

The intermediate, 2-keto-3-deoxy-7-phospho-D-glucoheptonic acid (XXII), has been synthesized and shown, at least in *E. coli,* to be readily utilized in producing 5-dehydroshikimic acid (Srinivasan and Sprinson, 1956) and it therefore appears that the complete path of biosynthesis has been outlined in this organism. The picture in yeast, however, is not yet clear. It should be noted that, although the distributions of the labeling in phenylalanine and tyrosine of yeast grown on glucose-1-C^{14} or pyruvic acid-2-C^{14} are almost identical (Gilvarg and Bloch, 1952), wide divergencies between these patterns are observed when the yeast is grown on acetic acid (Thomas *et al.* 1953, 1955). Under the latter conditions the bulk of the radioactivity in the tyrosine ring is found in carbon 2, 4, and 6 while in phenylalanine carbon 1, 3, and 5 of the ring have the higher level of radioactivity. Nevertheless, the labeling patterns of the side chains of the phenylalanine and tyrosine are very similar irrespective of whether acetic acid or pyruvic acid is used as the carbon source and they are in line with the earlier suggestion that these side chains originate in an intact three-carbon unit which is probably pyruvic acid. Thomas *et al.* comment that since acetic acid is not a normal substrate for yeast, caution is required in interpreting the results of its use and that, whereas

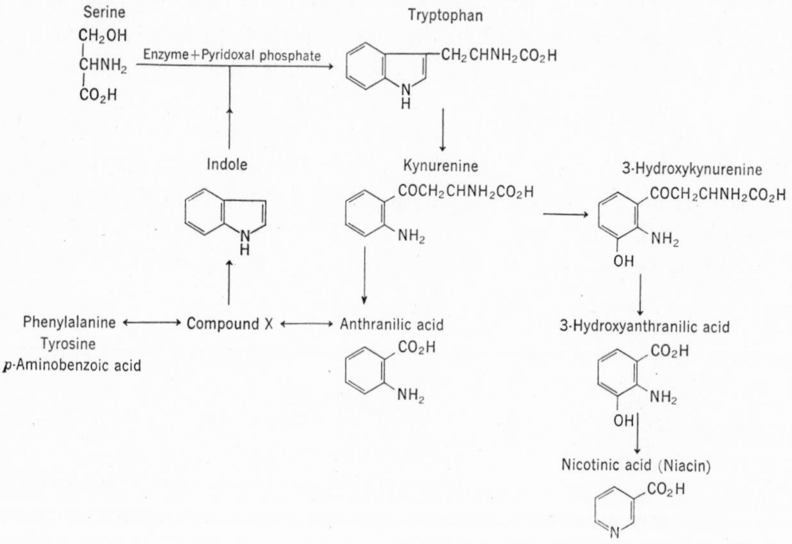

Fig. 9. Synthesis of tryptophan and related compounds in *Neurospora* (see Fig. 8).

under normal conditions phenylalanine and tyrosine are synthesized by similar routes, they may follow divergent paths under the conditions which hold when acetic acid is the sole carbon source.

With regard to the biosynthesis of tryptophan, most evidence for the individual steps involved has been adduced from the study of mutants of *Neurospora*. As a result, Haskins and Mitchell (1949) have been able to demonstrate the series of reactions summarized in Fig. 9. The final step in the formation of tryptophan by this series of reactions consists of the condensation of serine (see above) with indole by means of an enzyme, tryptophan desmolase (or synthetase), which requires pyridoxal phosphate as the coenzyme, while indole originates from anthranilic acid via an unidentified compound (X). The nature of this compound X has been uncertain until recently when Yanofsky (1955a, 1956, 1957) found that, in *E. coli*, anthranilic acid reacts with 5-phosphoribosyl-1-pyrophosphate (PRPP) (derived mainly from the reaction of fructose-6-phosphate with 3-phosphoglyceraldehyde and partly via the shunt mechanism) to yield indole-3-glycerol phosphate:

Anthranilic acid   Indole-3-glycerol phosphate

This compound is split by a separate enzyme to yield indole and triose phosphate and its isolation suggests the possibility that tryptophan may be synthesized in some organisms by a mechanism other than the coupling of serine with indole since the analogous compound, imidazole glycerol phosphate (see section on histidine synthesis) yields histidine directly. The amount of information on the corresponding reactions in yeast is small but Eddy (1955a,b) has shown that various strains of *Saccharomyces cerevisiae* which require tryptophan behave like certain of the mutants of *Neurospora*. For example, one strain grows on tryptophan, indole, or anthranilic acid, another grows only when supplied with indole or tryptophan and accumulates anthranilic acid, and a third grows only on tryptophan and accumulates both indole and anthranilic acid. Thus it appears that the first strain can effect the conversion of anthranilic acid to indole and to tryptophan, the second strain is blocked at the conversion of anthranilic acid to indole and the third strain is blocked between indole and tryptophan. Furthermore, it has been observed that pyridoxine-deficient yeasts accumulate indole (Eddy and Kirsop, 1955) and this fact suggests that yeasts might yield tryptophan via the pyridoxal-dependent enzyme mentioned above. The combined evidence strongly suggests that the sequence, anthranilic acid → indole → tryptophan, occurs in yeasts in the same manner as in *Neurospora*. No indication has been obtained, however, that the further reaction of tryptophan, shown in Fig. 9, occurs in the strains of yeast examined. For example, when the yeasts were supplied with either kynurenine, 3-hydroxyanthranilic acid, or nicotinic acid (niacin) they failed to grow. Neither was it possible to demonstrate the formation of anthranilic acid from kynurenine either in washed cell suspensions or in growing cultures. Certain of the strains produced large quantities of an unidentified indole derivative different from indolyl-3-glycerol mentioned above. This unidentified compound failed to support the growth of the tryptophan-dependent yeasts, however, and may, therefore, lie off the main synthetic pathway or, alternatively fail to be phosphorylated as found by Yanofsky.

The above observations on the nonconversion of tryptophan to nicotinic acid are paralleled by those of Yanofsky (1955b) on bacteria, which are also unable to effect this transformation and, hence, in this respect resemble the yeasts to a greater extent than *Neurospora*. No information is at present available however, on the way in which either yeasts or bacteria synthesize nicotinic acid, although it is possible that this vitamin might be formed via 7-hydroxytryptophan.

Transamination. It may be recalled that the fixation of ammonia by glycolytic products is generally considered to occur via glutamic acid dehydrogenase and perhaps by other similar enzymes (Fig. 4). A further important class of enzymes, originally discovered by Braunstein and Kritzmann (1937) in animal tissues, can also lead to the formation of glutamic acid and other amino acids from the glycolytic intermediates and these enzymes are known as transaminases. They catalyze the transfer of the amino group from a variety of amino acids to the keto acids originating from glycolysis according to the general equation (21):

$$(21) \qquad \begin{matrix} R'' \\ | \\ CO \\ | \\ CO_2H \end{matrix} + H_2NCH \begin{matrix} R \\ | \\ \\ | \\ CO_2H \end{matrix} \rightleftharpoons \begin{matrix} R'' \\ | \\ CHNH_2 \\ | \\ CO_2H \end{matrix} + \begin{matrix} R \\ | \\ CO \\ | \\ CO_2H \end{matrix}$$

Braunstein and Kritzmann originally regarded this reaction as applying generally to a number of amino acids and keto acids but later workers (Cohen, 1939, 1940, 1942) felt that it was restricted to only two reactions, namely those involving glutamic acid and (a) oxaloacetic acid and (b) pyruvic acid. Although these reactions were, and are still of major importance, improved techniques, e.g., the introduction of paper chromatography (cf. Hird and Rowsell, 1950), have facilitated the detection of amino acids and keto acids and have made possible a more detailed investigation of transamination reactions. For example, Roine (1947) found that the amino groups not only of aspartic acid and alanine but also of valine, leucine, and isoleucine were transferred to α-ketoglutaric acid by extracts of the yeast *T. utilis*, and the wider occurrence and specificity of the transamination reaction in various microorganisms and mammalian tissues has been amply demonstrated by various workers (Feldman and Gunsalus, 1950; Cammarata and Cohen, 1950; Rowsell, 1951; Fincham, 1951; Fincham and Boulter, 1956; Bigger-Gehring, 1955). The general aspects of this reaction have been extensively reviewed by Meister (1955a,b) and Bigger-Gehring (1955) has examined more particularly the transaminase activity of the yeast *Saccharomyces fragilis*. It was found that extracts of this yeast would only catalyze those trans-amination reactions in which either glutamic acid or α-ketoglutaric acid was involved. Attempts to demonstrate transaminase activity by the use of oxaloacetic acid or pyruvic acid as acceptors of the amino group from α-aminobutyric acid, leucine, methionine, orni-thine, phenylalanine, tryptophan, tyrosine, or valine were unsuccess-ful. For this reason it appears that the formation of aspartic acid and alanine by transamination in this yeast is dependent on the primary formation of glutamic acid (or possibly glutamine), presumably by means of glutamic acid dehydrogenase. The transaminase activities of yeast ex-tracts, prepared (a) by treatment with acetone and (b) by means of a Hughes press, followed in each case by extensive dialysis to remove TPN and hence glutamic acid dehydrogenase activity, is shown in Table V (taken from Bigger-Gehring, 1955). It is apparent that transaminase activity is high for alanine, aspartic acid, the leucines, norleucine, orni-thine, and the aromatic amino acids when α-ketoglutaric acid functions as the amino acceptor. For the reaction with aspartic acid, maximal activity of the enzyme was observed to occur at pH 7.8, while with leucine it was at pH 8.0. However, neither the formation of glutamic acid from aspartic acid and α-ketoglutaric acid nor the formation of aspartic acid from glutamic acid and oxaloacetic acid was sensitive to pH over the range pH 6–9. The reversibility of the reaction was demonstrated for the transamination of glutamic acid with aspartic acid, alanine, phenyl-alanine, and glutamic acid. Whereas the antibiotics, aureomycin, chloram-phenicol, penicillin, streptomycin, and terramycin failed to inhibit it, semicarbazide caused partial loss of enzymic activity.

The equilibrium in the reaction, *glutamic acid + oxaloacetic acid ⇌ aspartic acid + α-ketoglutaric acid,* favors the formation of aspartic acid in the extracts examined, a result consistent with the findings of Roine (1947) for *T. utilis* and of Cohen (1940) for pig heart. The equilibrium constant,

$$K = \frac{[\text{Aspartic acid}][\alpha\text{-Ketoglutaric acid}]}{[\text{Glutamic acid}][\text{Oxaloacetic acid}]}$$

was found to be 2.2 at pH 7.8 and 37°C. in fair agreement with that found by Cohen for a purified enzyme.

The effect of semicarbazide in inhibiting the reaction is possibly related to its combination with pyridoxal or pyridoxal phosphate. The latter com-pound has been found to be a coenzyme for the transaminases in all the systems so far examined (Meister, 1955a; Longenecker and Snell, 1956) including that in yeast and, in the presence of metals, it can even bring about transamination reactions without the participation of enzymes

(Snell, 1945; Longenecker and Snell, 1956). Both the enzymatic and the nonenzymatic transaminations appear to be due to the combination of one amino acid with the pyridoxal to form a Schiff's base (XXIII) which undergoes isomerization and hydrolysis to yield a keto acid (XXIV) and

TABLE V
TRANSAMINASE ACTIVITY OF DIALYZED EXTRACTS OF *Torulopsis utilis*[a,b]

Amino group donor	Glutamic acid formed (μM/mg. N in extract)			
	Acetone powder extract		Hughes press extract	
	1 hr.	16 hr.	1 hr.	16 hr.
L-Alanine	0	0	5.35	10.29
L-Arginine	0	0	0	0
L-Aspartic acid	5.65	25.14	8.25	15.15
L-Citrulline	0	0	—	—
L-Cysteine	0	0	—	—
L-Cystine	0	0	—	—
Glycine	0	0	—	0
L-Histidine	0	0	—	—
L-Hydroxyproline	0	0	—	—
L-Norleucine	—	—	—	12.02
L-Isoleucine	0.6	2.11	—	12.88
L-Leucine	5.67	16.84	11.39	17.15
L-Lysine	0	0	—	0
L-Methionine	2.79	10.2	4.51	10.6
L-Ornithine	0	0.85	—	12.86
L-Phenylalanine	3.67	11.0	2.24	9.84
L-Proline	0	0	—	—
DL-Serine	0	0	—	0
DL-Threonine	0	0	—	0
L-Tryptophan	1.73	6.39	4.39	9.19
L-Tyrosine	2.03	7.3	2.87	9.44
L-Valine	0.52	3.89	—	11.97

[a] From Bigger-Gehring (1955).
[b] 1 ml. of incubation mixture contained 10 μM of L-amino acid, 10 μM of α-keto-glutaric acid, 0.3 ml. of yeast extract, and 0.1 M phosphate buffer (pH 7.8) containing 20 μg. of pyridoxal phosphate per ml. All solutions were incubated at 37°C. in a nitrogen atmosphere.

pyridoxamine. The pyridoxamine condenses in turn with a second keto acid (XXV) to give a second Schiff's base (XXVI) which isomerizes and is hydrolyzed to form the amino acid (XXVII) and pyridoxal, which can then pass through the cycle again:

$$\underset{\text{Pyridoxal}}{\overset{CO_2H}{\underset{|}{R\,CHNH_2}} + OHCR'''} \rightarrow \underset{(XXIII)}{\overset{CO_2H}{\underset{|}{R\,CHN}}{=}CHR'''} \rightleftharpoons \overset{CO_2H}{\underset{|}{R\,C}}{=}NCH_2R''' \rightarrow \underset{(XXIV)}{RCOCO_2H} + \underset{\text{Pyridoxamine}}{H_2NCH_2R'''}$$

$$\underset{\text{Pyridoxamine}}{\overset{}{R'''CH_2NH_2}} + \underset{(XXV)}{OCR''} \rightarrow \overset{CO_2H}{\underset{|}{R'''CH_2N}}{=}CR''' \rightleftharpoons \underset{(XXVI)}{\overset{CO_2H}{\underset{|}{R'''CH}}{=}NCHR''} \rightarrow \underset{\text{Pyridoxal}}{\overset{}{R'''CHO}} + \underset{(XXVII)}{\overset{CO_2H}{\underset{|}{H_2NCHR''}}}$$

The over-all reaction is thus that shown in equation (21). It is not certain yet whether metal ions are required for enzymatic transamination or whether the appropriate stereochemical configuration can be preserved on the enzyme–pyridoxal complex without the intervention of these ions. Evidence for the above mechanism of transamination has been adduced by Tanenbaum (1956) who showed that pyridoxamine itself transaminated with α-ketoglutaric acid in pig heart extracts and by Meister *et al.* (1954) who found that aspartic–glutamic apotransaminase can be activated by either pyridoxal or pyridoxamine phosphate. Presumably the same general mechanism is operative in all tissues, and it may be assumed that pyridoxamine is active as the phosphate since pyridoxamine kinase has been demonstrated in yeast (Hurwitz, 1952).

The full significance of the transamination reactions in the general nitrogen metabolism of the yeast and other cells remains to be assessed. Meister (1955b) has suggested that many of the deamination reactions of amino acids are in fact due to transamination and among these it is possible that the first stages of the Ehrlich and Stickland reactions, discussed earlier, should be included. For example, comparison of the results in Table V with those obtained by Thorne on the assimilation of amino acids, previously noted, shows that it is the amino acids which undergo transamination least readily which are assimilated most sluggishly, if at all. The wide distribution of the transaminases and their multiplicity in various organisms argue strongly in favor of their major role in amino acid metabolism and, in addition, it will be seen that, coupled with glutamic acid dehydrogenase, their action can lead to the synthesis of a wide variety of amino acids from the keto acids formed by glycolysis and ammonia. Indeed reference to the foregoing discussions of the biosynthesis of the amino acids shows that transamination has been postulated as one step in the elaboration not only of aspartic acid and alanine but also of glycine, histidine, isoleucine, leucine, lysine, ornithine, phenylalanine, tyrosine, valine, and possibly tryptophan. Conversely, the coupling of the glutamic acid dehydrogenase system to the transaminating system can lead to the over-all oxidative deamination of the amino acids since the oxidation of glutamic acid participating in transamination will lead to the production of the α-keto acid corresponding to the other amino acid participant. It is noteworthy that glutamine and asparagine have been observed to undergo transamination in some organisms (Meister, 1955a) but this reaction awaits demonstration in yeasts themselves. However, the important part played by these amides has been demonstrated by Sheffner and Grabow (1953), who found that S. cerevisiae would not grow on a complete mixture of amino acids and ammonia simulating a yeast hydrolyzate, either in the absence of the amides or even in their presence if magnesium ions were at the same time absent. The latter ions play an important part in normal media and this probably accounts for the fact that Nielsen (1941) reported that glutamine is not required for yeast growth. The magnesium ions are presumably required for amide synthesis but the amides themselves are not necessarily involved in amino acid synthesis as shown by examining a mixture of amino acids. It was found that niacin amide could replace glutamine as an amide source, but only in the presence of another utilizable nitrogen compound such as glutamic acid or ammonia. It was concluded, therefore, that the niacin amide must have undergone transamidation, i.e., transfer of the nitrogen of the amide group to that of another compound. Glutamine was in fact identified in extracts of cells grown with a mixture of glutamic acid and asparagine as the only nitrogen source, presumably by this type of amide transfer. Evidence was obtained that the amide groups were necessary for the formation of an unidentified growth factor (purines?) similar to that found to stimulate Lactobacillus casei (Pollack and Lindner, 1943). The fact that only 2–5% of the total nitrogen in the growth medium had to be amide nitrogen to give maximum growth under conditions in which new amide could not be synthesized led Sheffner and Grabow to suggest that the amide nitrogen did not participate directly in the synthesis of peptides or proteins by an exchange mechanism as in that event amide nitrogen would be lost into the medium as occurs with the enzyme glutamotransferase (see Section 4 below).

The failure of Bigger-Gehring (1955) to demonstrate the transamination of lysine and histidine in extracts of S. fragilis is not incompatible with the participation of the transamination reactions in their biosynthesis since the substrates for the latter reactions are, respectively, α-ketoadipic acid (XIV) and imidazole acetol phosphate (XVII). It would be of interest to test these substrates with the yeast extracts in order to obtain direct proof of their role in the biosynthetic reactions. Transaminations involving lysine have certainly been detected in Neurospora and in the rat, the final products being α-ketoadipic acid (XIV) and pipecolinic acid (piperidine-2-carboxylic acid), an amino acid which has been shown to occur widely in nature (Morrison, 1952; Zacharias, Steward and Thompson, 1952; Harris and Pollock, 1952, 1953). The available evidence suggests that transamination is a critical step in the metabolism of yeast as well as of other organisms (Wiame et al., 1953) and its full implications remain to be worked out. It is perhaps relevant to mention here that Wiame et al. (1953) showed that both an amino acid donor and a keto acid acceptor are necessary for the growth of a particular strain of *Bacillus subtilis* and, furthermore, that glutamic acid was an obligatory intermediate for all the nitrogen used by this organism. Thus, α-ketoglutaric acid is necessary to support growth in the presence of aspartic in this organism and it is concluded (a) that the tricarboxylic acid cycle has a synthetic activity without necessarily an energetic role (see Krebs, et al., 1952; Abelson et al., 1953) and (b) that transamination is a necessary step before growth can occur.

3. The Metabolism of Nucleic Acids and Their Constituents

. A. Degradation of Nucleic Acid Derivatives

The nucleic acid of yeast was the subject of many earlier classical researches on nucleic acids generally and on their degradation by various

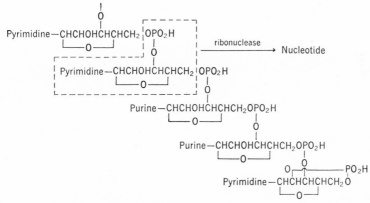

Fig. 10. Action of ribonuclease on yeast ribonucleic acid.

enzymes, in particular ribonuclease (see Chapter VI). This latter enzyme, which has been obtained in crystalline form, hydrolyzes the bond linking C′-5 of one nucleotide residue in nucleic acid with the phosphate group attached to C′3 of an adjacent pyrimidine nucleotide as shown in Fig. 10. The corresponding phosphate links between pyrimidine nucleotides and purine nucleotides or between different purine nucleotides are resistant to the action of ribonuclease, which can therefore be regarded as a specific phosphodiesterase (Markham and Smith, 1952). As a result of its mode of attack on nucleic acid, the major amount of mononucleotides produced consists of the pyrimidine derivatives, uridylic acid (XXVIII, R = uracil) and cytidylic acid (XXVIII, R = cytosine), while the remaining products are polynucleotides derived principally from the purines, adenine and guanine (Schmidt et al., 1947; Carter and Cohn, 1950).

The nucleotides are themselves attacked by nonspecific phosphomonoesterases to yield the nucleosides as follows (where R = pyrimidine or purine):

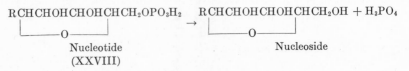

$$\text{RCHCHOHCHOHCHCH}_2\text{OPO}_3\text{H}_2 \quad \text{RCHCHOHCHOHCHCH}_2\text{OH} + \text{H}_3\text{PO}_4$$

| Nucleotide | Nucleoside |
| (XXVIII) | |

For example, dialyzed preparations from an acetone powder of yeast, which are free of phosphate donors, bring about the hydrolysis of adenosine-3-phosphate or adenosine-5-phosphate (XXVIII, R = adenosyl) to yield adenosine and phosphoric acid (Ostern et al., 1938a,b). When yeast is allowed to autolyze, the nucleic acid is converted into adenosine in 60% yield within 20 hours.

Degradation of the nucleosides is brought about by enzymes known as the nucleosidases to give ribose (or deoxyribose from deoxyribosides) together with the appropriate purine or pyrimidine. Such an enzyme is the specific uridine nucleosidase, found in baker's yeast by Carter (1951), which brings about the hydrolysis of uridine to uracil and ribose. This enzyme will not catalyze the degradation of any of the other nucleosides tested and cannot split uridylic acid. It has optimal activity at pH 7.0. A series of similar enzymes capable of hydrolyzing various nucleosides was detected by Heppel and Hilmoe (1951), but, as yet, no evidence has been obtained for the existence in yeast of nucleoside phosphorylases analogous to those found in certain bacteria (Lampen, 1952).

The purines and pyrimidines can undergo further degradation by deamination as shown by Chargaff and Kream (1948) who found a cytosine deaminase, and by Wang et al. (1950) who detected a specific cytidine deaminase in both yeast and E. coli. The former enzyme was detected in S. cerevisiae, together with guanine deaminase, by Di Carlo et al. (1951) but no uricase was found. As a result of studying the action of autolyzing yeast on sodium nucleate, Haehn and Leopold (1935) suggested that deamination of the purine and pyrimidine moieties took place before the splitting of the glycosidic linkage. However, there seems to be no doubt that the nucleosidase and deaminase activities in yeasts may vary considerably since it has now been found that various yeasts attack the nucleosides of brewer's wort in quite different ways (Harris and Parsons, 1956). In general, strains of *Saccharomyces carlsbergensis* formed hypoxanthine unlike the various strains of *Saccharomyces cerevisiae*. Certain other yeasts notably *Kloeckera apiculata, Saccharomyces chevalieri, Schizosaccharomyces pombe,* and *Torula colliculosa* also gave rise to hypoxanthine. Incidentally, whereas brewing yeasts assimilated adenine derivatives in preference to guanine derivatives, the film-forming yeasts, *Kloeckera apiculata, Hansenula anomala,* and in particular *Pichia membranaefaciens,* took up the latter purines more effectively. Our present information on the deaminases is extremely limited, however, since few studies on isolated enzyme systems have been made and those which have been carried out have been concerned with only a limited number of types of yeast. In fact, the enzyme from *T. utilis,* referred to as adenase by Roush (1954), has been partially purified by Armentrout and Goldwasser (1957) and shown to be an adenine transaminase which brings about the transfer of the 6-amino-group of adenine to an α-keto-acid in the presence of pyridoxal phosphate and cupric ions.

A. *Uptake, Interconversion, and Synthesis of Purines and Pyrimidines by Yeasts*

When yeasts are grown in the presence of the purines themselves, direct incorporation of these bases into the nucleic acids occurs. Kerr *et al.* (1951) showed that *T. utilis* incorporated the adenine skeleton into both the adenylic acid and guanylic acid moieties of ribonucleic acid while guanine gave rise to the latter nucleotide portion. This yeast was found to utilize all the naturally occurring purines and pyrimidines except thymine (Di Carlo *et al.,* 1951), but the purine nucleosides were assimilated less readily than the parent bases and the corresponding nucleotides even less readily, whereas the pyrimidine nucleosides and nucleotides, ADP, ATP, ribonucleic acid, and deoxyribonucleic acid did not serve as sources of nitrogen at all (Di Carlo *et al.,* 1951; Kerr *et al.,* 1951). Adenine, guanine, and cytosine supported only limited growth of *S. cerevisiae* but allantoin nitrogen was fully utilized (Di Carlo *et al.,* 1951; Nielsen, 1943) and Di Carlo *et al.* (1953) succeeded in preparing an active allantoinase preparation from brewer's yeast. This yeast requires more biotin in order to grow as well on allantoin, allantoic acid, or urea as it does on normal nitrogen sources. Cook *et al.* (1943), detected an effect of adenosine, guanosine, and yeast adenylic acid on the growth of S. *cerevisiae* but observed that it was probably on the rate of proliferation rather than on the total crop. However, Ostern *et al.* (1938a,b) found that fresh, washed beer yeast is able to synthesize adenosine-5'-phosphate (AMP) from adenosine and inorganic phosphate and that in the presence of glucose or fructose diphosphate this synthesis is extended to the formation of adenosine-5'-polyphosphoric acids. Neither of these reactions takes place if the yeast is freed from nutrients by dialysis. Sable (1950) showed similarly that autolysates of brewer's or baker's yeasts contain enzymes, designated as ribokinase and adenosine phosphokinase, which catalyze the phosphorylation of ribose and adenosine, respectively, in the presence of ATP. The phosphorylation of adenosine was found to occur specifically at the C-5' position of the ribose residue by Ostern *et al.* (1938b) but these authors were unable to demonstrate the phosphorylation of either ribose or guanosine. In their extracts two mechanisms for the formation of AMP were postulated, one dependent upon the decomposition of fructose diphosphate with simultaneous esterification and the other dependent upon the donation of the phosphate group of phosphoglyceric acid (see below).

As a result of experiments involving the growth of yeast (*T. utilis*) on labeled purines, such as adenine-8-C^{14}, guanine-8-C^{14} and 2,6-diaminopurine-2-C^{14}, and the appropriate isotopic competition experiments (see above), Kerr and Chernigoy (1953) came to the following conclusions: (a) in the biosynthesis of RNA, preformed adenine is utilized even more extensively than formic acid (see below); (b) out of each three molecules of adenine incorporated into RNA, two molecules give adenylic acid while one yields guanylic acid; (c) guanine and, to some extent, diaminopurine suppresses the utilization of adenine for the synthesis of guanylic acid; (d) diaminopurine serves readily as a precursor of guanine but not of adenine and it suppresses the utilization of formic acid for guanine synthesis to about the same extent as adenine but less effectively than guanine; and (e) an increased utilization of formic acid for adenylic acid synthesis which occurs in the presence of guanine or diaminopurine probably results from the sparing of formic acid from the synthesis of guanylic acid. In these experiments about 50% of the total purine supplied was utilized for nucleotide synthesis.

The failure of excess of diaminopurine to suppress markedly the use of guanine for the formation of guanylic acid is relevant to the hypothesis of Bendick *et al.* (1950) that it is an intermediate in the transformation of adenine to guanylic acid (in rats). If the diaminopurine were an obligatory intermediate, excess of unlabeled compound should sharply reduce the activity of any guanylic acid synthesized from labeled adenine in comparison with a control. The fact that this is not the case suggested that adenine may be converted into adenosine and hence into the diaminopurine riboside before finally giving rise to guanosine (see below).

The fact that the glycosides of the purines are involved in these conversions parallels the observation that their earlier *de novo* biosynthesis involves the glycosides rather than the free bases. It is generally recognized that yeasts resemble mammals and *E. coli* in being able to synthesize purines and pyrimidines from simple precursors, e.g., carbon dioxide, formic acid, ammonia, and glycine. In the synthesis of guanine, carbon 4 is derived from carbon dioxide, carbon 2 and carbon 8 from formic acid or substances which give rise to formic acid (serine, methionine, etc.), carbon 4, carbon 5, and nitrogen 7 from the carboxyl, methylene, and amino groups of glycine (Abrams *et al.*, 1948; Edmonds *et al.*, 1952; see Sonne *et al.*, 1956) and the remaining nitrogen atoms from ammonia, thus:

$$
\begin{array}{c}
CO_2 \\
\downarrow \\
CH_2-NH_2 \\
NH-C \quad CO_2H \\
HCO_2H \longrightarrow C \quad C-NH \\
NH-C-N \quad C \longleftarrow HCO_2H
\end{array}
$$

The methylene carbon atom of glycine is not used for the synthesis of uracil or cytosine and hence the pyrimidines are synthesized by a route independent of that for the purines. The synthesis of purines and pyrimidines in RNA and DNA has been reviewed by Siminovitch and Graham (1955), who carried out a systematic survey of the precursors of the nucleic acids in one organism, namely *E. coli*, by means of the isotopic competition methods already described for amino acids. In line with the observations made by other workers (see above) these authors conclude that there is no interconversion between the precursors of the purines and pyrimidines. In accord with this conception, orotic acid-6-C^{14} (uracil-4-carboxylic acid) is utilized for the synthesis of uracil in yeast RNA as in mammals but is not incorporated into guanine. Lactic acid-2,3-C^{14} is also used, presumably for the formation of the "non-ureido" carbon atoms via oxaloacetic acid and aminofuramide (or the related ureidosuccinic acid or carbamylaspartic acid) as suggested for *Neurospora* by Mitchell and Houlahan (1947) and for *E. coli* by Weed and Wilson (1954). Of some interest in this connection is the finding of Herrmann and Fairley (1956) that α-aminobutyric acid supports the growth of pyrimidineless mutants of *Neurospora* and that this amino acid is incorporated into the pyrimidines. Mitchell and Houlahan are of the opinion that aminofumaramide or its pentoside, α-N-pentosylaminofumaric acid diamide, is converted into a pyrimidine nucleoside through two intermediates related to orotic acid. One of these intermediates may be an orotic acid riboside which has been isolated from the mycelium of a uridine-requiring mutant of *Neurospora* (Mitchelson *et al.*, 1951). The fact that certain pyrimidine auxotrophs grow better on cytidine or uridine than on the free bases again suggests that the latter are not natural intermediates in nucleoside synthesis. Davis (1955d) has recently suggested that ureidosuccinic acid (carbamyl aspartic acid), formed by donation of a carbamyl group from carbamyl phosphate (see section on arginine biosynthesis) to aspartic acid, gives rise to orotic acid and finally pyrimidines.

A complete sequence for the formation of uridine triphosphate (UTP) and cytidine triphosphate (CTP) in *E. coli* has been postulated by Liebermann (1956a) to consist of the following reactions,

$$
\begin{array}{l}
\text{L-Aspartic acid} \quad \rightleftharpoons \text{L-Ureidosuccinate} \rightleftharpoons \text{L-Dihydro-orotate} \rightleftharpoons \text{Orotate} \\
\qquad + \\
\text{Carbamyl phoshate} \\
\qquad\qquad\qquad \text{UDP} \rightleftharpoons \text{Uridine-5'-phosphate} \leftarrow \text{Orotidine-5'-phosphate} \\
\qquad\qquad\qquad\ \updownarrow \qquad\qquad\quad + \\
\qquad\qquad\qquad \text{UTP} \qquad\qquad \text{CO}_2 \\
\qquad\qquad\qquad\ \downarrow \\
\qquad\qquad\qquad \text{CTP}
\end{array}
$$

and enzymes bringing about several of these transformations have been obtained (cf. also Yates and Pardee, 1956). The enzyme bringing about the final formation of CTP is specific for UTP, and ammonia is the source of the nitrogen atom added during the reaction.

In the experiments on the incorporation of C^{14} into the purines and pyrimidines of yeast the adenine of the nucleotide fraction was labeled far more extensively than the adenine in nucleic acid, a fact indicating a greater turnover rate in this fraction. This is possibly related to the existence in yeast of a pool of free nucleotides similar to the pool of free amino acids (see below).

The intermediates involved in the formation of the purines in yeast have not yet been established with certainty. However, Stetten and Fox (1945) found, in the culture filtrates of bacteria which had been inhibited with sulfonamides, an amine which was identified by Shive *et al.* (1947) as 5-amino-4-imidazolecarboxamide (XXIX). This base accumulates because the sulfonamides inhibit a subsequent step in the biosynthesis of the purines which requires p-aminobenzoic acid as a co-factor. A similar and possibly identical base was also isolated by Chamberlain *et al.* (1952) from the culture filtrates of yeast grown on a medium deficient in biotin and containing excess methionine. An important observation was that this base was able to support the growth of strains of *Schizosaccharomyces octosporus* which require adenine and hence it was concluded that it is a true intermediate in purine synthesis. Similar conclusions were reached by Williams (1951), who showed that authentic 5-amino-4-

(XXIX)

imidazolecarboxamide enables yeast to synthesize adenine and guanine at a rate comparable with that attained with glycine or formic acid, and by Bergmann *et al.* who found that the amine is utilized by purine-requiring mutants of *E. coli*. It has been shown generally that this compound can serve as a purine precursor not only in yeast and *E. coli* but also in lactobacilli, pigeon liver homogenates, and *Ophiostoma* (Bergmann *et al.*, 1952).

An amine closely related to compound XXIX, namely aminoimidazole, has been shown to accumulate in biotin-deficient yeasts (Moat *et al.*, 1956) and a role for biotin has been suggested in the conversion of this amine to the carboxamide. The amine may well be that observed earlier by Chamberlain *et al.* instead of the carboxamide mentioned above. Its accumulation is inhibited by purines and by aspartic acid, the latter fact accounting for the growth stimulatory effect of the amino acid under conditions of biotin deficiency.

A soluble enzyme system, isolated from *Saccharomyces cerevisiae* by Williams and Buchanan (1953), catalyzed the incorporation of the imidazole carboxamide, labeled in the carboxamide group with C^{14}, into inosinic acid (see below). The authors report that this enzyme system is rather unstable but that their studies suggest that it resembles the more stable system from pigeon liver which is described below and which has given substantial information on the steps in purine biosynthesis.

The imidazole derivative (XXIX) requires only one carbon atom to

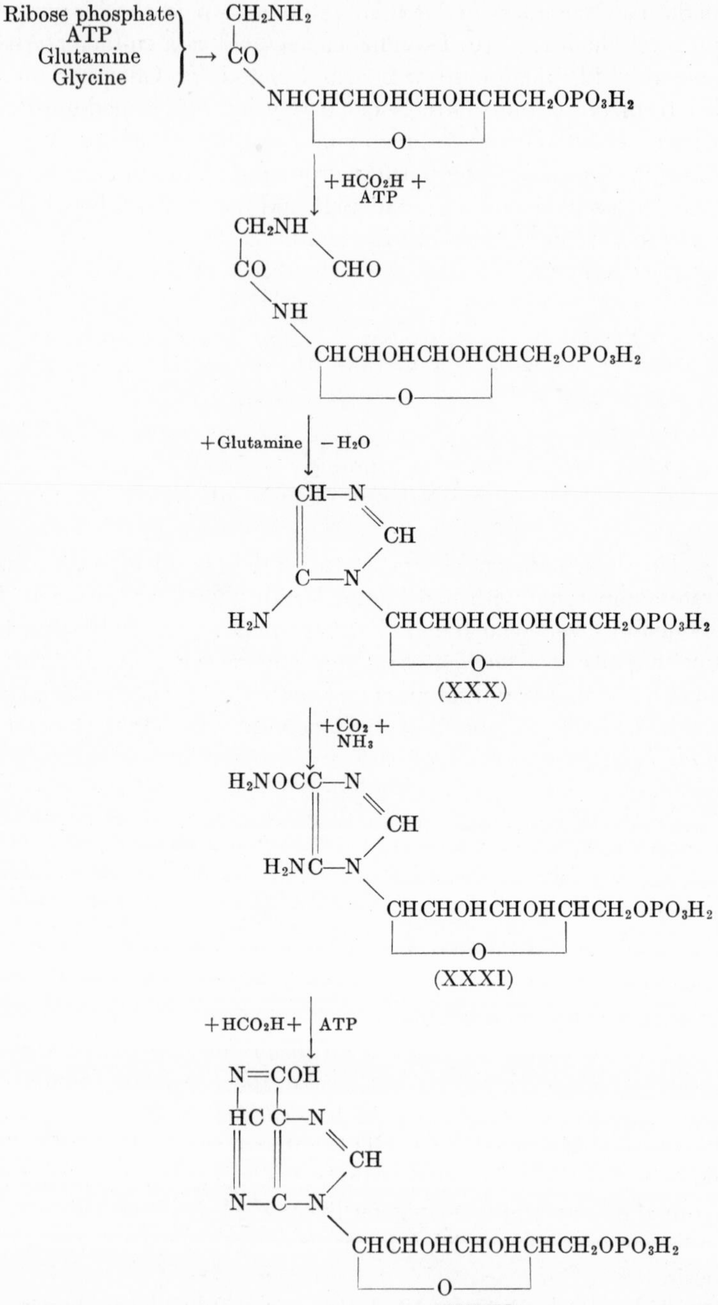

Ribose phosphate ⎫
    ATP   ⎬ →
  Glutamine ⎭
   Glycine

$$CH_2NH_2$$
$$CO$$
$$NHCHCHOHCHOHCHCH_2OPO_3H_2$$
$$\underline{}O\underline{}$$

$+HCO_2H +$
ATP ↓

$$CH_2NH$$
$$CO \qquad CHO$$
$$NH$$
$$CHCHOHCHOHCHCH_2OPO_3H_2$$
$$\underline{}O\underline{}$$

$+\text{Glutamine}$ | $-H_2O$ ↓

$$CH\!-\!N$$
$$\qquad\quad CH$$
$$C\!-\!N$$
$$H_2N \qquad CHCHOHCHOHCHCH_2OPO_3H_2$$
$$\underline{}O\underline{}$$
(XXX)

$+CO_2 +$
NH_3 ↓

$$H_2NOCC\!-\!N$$
$$\qquad\qquad CH$$
$$H_2NC\!-\!N$$
$$\qquad\qquad CHCHOHCHOHCHCH_2OPO_3H_2$$
$$\underline{}O\underline{}$$
(XXXI)

$+HCO_2H+$ | ATP

$$N\!=\!COH$$
$$HC \; C\!-\!N$$
$$\qquad\qquad CH$$
$$N\!-\!C\!-\!N$$
$$\qquad\qquad CHCHOHCHOHCHCH_2OPO_3H_2$$
$$\underline{}O\underline{}$$
(XXXII)

complete the purine ring, i.e., at C_2, and it is of interest that vitamin B_{12} is able to increase the incorporation of the base into the purines (Bergmann *et al.*, 1952). Vitamin B_{12} is known to play a vital role in the transfer of one-carbon fragments in many organisms and it appears that this function is involved in the completion (see above) of the pyrimidine ring, possibly by way of the formylamine. In *E. coli* it was in fact found that the N-formyl compound was utilized to a greater extent than the free base and in this case vitamin B_{12} had no effect.

Recently, important work on the intermediates for purine biosynthesis *de novo* has been carried out with pigeon liver extracts and the preceding sequence of reactions demonstrated (Goldthwaite *et al.*, 1955; Buchanan *et al.*, 1955; Levenberg and Metnick, 1956; Warren and Flaks, 1956, Goldthwaite, 1956; Hartman *et al.*, 1956; Levenberg and Buchanan, 1957). All the intermediates have been isolated and it is assumed that the free base (XXXI) acts sluggishly as a purine precursor in some instances because it must first be converted to the ribose phosphate derivative thus recalling the earlier behavior of 2,6-diaminopurine in its conversion to guanylic acid. It is proposed that carbon dioxide is fixed by the imidazole ribotide (XXX). In this connection it is also relevant to record that an intermediate in the formation of 5-amino-4-imidazole-carboxamide from 5-aminoimidazole ribotide in avian liver has been shown by Lukens and Buchanan (1956) to be 5-amino-4-imidazole-(N-succinylocarboxamide)-ribotide (XXXIII). This compound accumulates when ATP, aspartic acid and bicarbonate are incubated with 5-aminoimidazole ribotide and

(XXXIII)   (XXXIV)

an enzyme concentrate. When this intermediate is incubated with a second enzyme system it yields the carboxamide ribotide and fumaric acid, recalling the fission of arginosuccinic acid described earlier. A related compound, adenylosuccinic acid (XXXIV) (Carter, 1956; Hampton, 1957) has been isolated from yeast autolysates (Carter and Cohen, 1955), and shown to arise from the reaction of fumaric acid with adenosine-5'-phosphate. At the present time the reaction appears to be limited to fumaric acid, adenosine-5'-phosphate, and the corresponding deoxyribosyl derivative of adenine. This compound (XXXIV) is conceivably an intermediate in the incorporation of the 6-amino group into the purine nucleotides. Some support for this view is supplied by the findings of Liebermann (1956b) that a purified enzyme from *E. coli* yields adenylosuccinic acid from inosinic acid, L-aspartic acid, and guanosine triphosphate (GTP). Since there is evidence that inosine (or inosinic acid, XXXII) is the first purine to be synthesized naturally (see Abrams and Bentley, 1955) such a reaction, when coupled to the hydrolytic reaction described for yeast, would provide a mechanism for the formation of adenine. The enzyme isolated was highly specific for aspartic acid and for GTP. Abrams and Bentley (1955) described a similar enzyme system in bone marrow extracts. In this system, one enzyme, known as inosinic acid dehydrogenase, catalyzes the oxidation of inosinic acid (IMP) to

$$CH_2CO_2H$$
$$(22) \qquad XXXII + H_2N\overset{|}{C}HCO_2H + GTP \rightarrow XXXIV$$

xanthosine-5'-phosphate (XMP) by DPN. XMP is then aminated to guanosine-5'-phosphate (GMP) in the presence of L-glutamic acid or L-glutamine, ATP, and magnesium ions. The third reaction in this system is identical with the above-described conversion of IMP to AMP. It seems probable that the intermediate in GMP production from XMP is a guanyloglutamic acid analogous to the adenylosuccinic acid mentioned above. It may be significant that extracts of a guanine-requiring mutant of *Aerobacter aerogenes,* which excretes xanthosine, are unable to aminate XMP, suggesting that the above amination reactions are essential steps in the biosynthesis of the guanine of nucleic acid in this organism (Magasanik *et al.,* 1956).

The link between IMP and the aminoimidazole carboxamide ribotide is the reaction catalyzed by the enzyme, inosinic acid transformylase (Flaks and Buchanan, 1956), which involves the reaction of serine with the carboxamide to form glycine and IMP, an example of the one-carbon transfer reactions described in the section on serine biosynthesis. This reaction has been shown to require anhydroleucovorin as a cofactor together with glutamine, of which the role has not been elucidated as yet (Sloane *et al.,* 1956).

The various nucleotides can also undergo interconversion by exchange reactions in yeasts and other organisms (Berg and Joklik, 1954; Krebs and Hems, 1955), for example, nucleoside triphosphates transfer phosphate groups to nucleoside diphosphates, thus:

(23)   ATP + IDP → ITP + ADP (Nucleoside diphosphokinase)

and to nucleoside monophosphates, thus:

(24)   ITP + AMP → ADP + IDP
(25)   ATP + AMP → 2ADP (Adenylate kinase)

It was observed by Gabriel and Hoffmann-Ostenhof (1956), on the other hand, that the yeast extracts could not effect the transfer of phosphate from ATP to guanosine, cytidine, or uridine but could bring about the transfer to adenosine. The precise role played by such reactions in the over-all metabolism of the cell is still a matter for speculation, although the function of a number of compounds formed in them is beginning to be understood e.g., UTP (uridine triphosphate) is involved in the synthesis of UPDG (uridine diphosphoglucose), which functions as a coenzyme for galactowaldenase (Caputto et al., 1950) and GTP is involved in several reactions involving the conversion of α-ketoglutaric acid to succinic acid in the Krebs cycle (Sanadi et al., 1956; Ayengar et al., 1956) and the above-described amination reactions. It is thought that the nucleoside triphosphates are concerned in the synthesis of nucleic acids (Kalckar, 1951) and, in this connection, it is pertinent to observe that AMP has been shown to be as good a precursor for RNA in pigeon liver as adenine itself and that it is incorporated with the ribose phosphate bond intact (Goldwasser, 1955; Roll et al., 1956a,b) a finding supported for all nucleotides by that of Reichard (1957) working with rats. The latter author also found that the specific activity of pyrimidine deoxyriboside isolated from nucleic acid was identical with that of incorporated labeled pyrimidine riboside and concluded that the deoxyribosides are formed directly from the ribosides. Grunberg-Mango et al. (1956) have recently described an enzyme, polynucleotide phosphorylase, from a number of sources, including yeast, which brings about the condensation of purine and pyrimidine nucleoside diphosphates, thus (where X = purine or pyrimidine, R = ribosyl and P = phosphate):

$$n \text{ X:R.PP} \rightleftharpoons (\text{X.R.P})_n + n\text{P}$$

Ochoa et al. (1957) have shown that the RNA synthesized by this enzyme in systems isolated from Azotobacter vinelandii is identical in all respects with the natural RNA. It is noteworthy that in rat liver, for example, the incorporation of labeled phosphorus into the di- and triphosphates corresponding to all four ribose nucleotides occurs at the same rate and that these nucleotides are in equilibrium with the ATP-ADP system (Brumm et al., 1956). All these compounds are present in yeast (Schmitz, 1954) and this fact coupled with the knowledge of the above phosphate-exchange reactions suggests that the enzyme system described by Grunberg-Manago *et al.* and by Ochoa and his co-workers (1957) is responsible for elaborating ribonucleic acid. It appears likely, on the other hand, that the synthesis of DNA occurs from the appropriate nucleoside triphosphates as Bessman *et al.* (1957) have isolated an enzyme from *E. coli* which brings about the condensation of these compounds derived from adenine (A), guanine (G), thymidine (T) and cytidine (C) according to the following equation:

$$n(\text{TP}^{32}\text{PP} + \text{GP}^{32}\text{PP} + \text{CP}^{32}\text{PP} + \text{AP}^{32}\text{PP}) + \text{DNA} \overset{\text{Mg}^{++}}{\rightleftharpoons} \text{DNA-}(\text{TP}^{32} + \text{GP}^{32} + \text{CP}^{32} + \text{AP}^{32})n + 4n\text{PP}$$

In this system, which has been enriched one thousandfold, DNA is required as a primer and RNA is inactive, a situation quite unlike that in the above reaction with polynucleotide phosphorylase in which preformed RNA is not needed (Olmsted, 1957). TDP cannot replace TTP. The importance of these investigations need hardly be stressed as it is apparent that the nucleic acids are involved in the synthesis of proteins (see below) and that they (or at least the deoxyribonucleic acids) control the hereditary characteristics of all organisms (see Chapter V). In this connection, mention must be made of "transforming factors" which are isolated from certain bacterial cells and which can bring about the induction of a particular hereditable property of the parent cell in another strain of the same organism. The transformed cells then retain the acquired characteristic through all subsequent generations. So far such transformations have not been achieved with yeasts but have been accomplished with several other organisms including pneumococci, *Hemophilus influenzae, E. coli, Shigella paradysenteriae, Bacillus anthracis,* and *Proteus vulgaris* (see Fry, 1955). The factors in each case appear to be deoxypentosenucleic acids (see Avery *et al.,* 1944; Hotchkiss and Marmor, 1954).

A further role of the purines which has recently been clarified (McNutt, 1956) lies in the synthesis of the vitamin, riboflavin. It was found that the pyrimidine ring of adenine is incorporated intact into the isoalloxazine moiety of the riboflavin in the yeast, *Eremothecium ashbyii,* a finding in agreement with earlier observations that biochemical precursors of the purines, e.g., carbon dioxide, formate, and glycine, are also precursors of riboflavin and that the purines increase the yield of riboflavin

4. The Synthesis of Peptides and Proteins

The subject of the synthesis of peptides and proteins generally has been reviewed extensively during recent years and the literature has become so vast that it cannot be treated adequately here. Nevertheless, it is impossible to discuss the synthesis of proteins in yeasts without reference to the work in other fields which bears upon the question and, hence, a brief introduction to the subject is given in the following pages, particular comment being reserved for the results obtained with yeast. To obtain a wider background the reader is referred to the articles by Borsook (1953), Bricas and Fromageot (1953), Putnam (1953), Gale (1953, 1955), Lipmann (1954), Steward and Thompson (1954), Spiegelman et al. (1955), and Dalgleish (1957). The article by Spiegelman et al. is specially apt for those whose primary interest is in yeast.

In considering the question of protein synthesis, account must be taken of a number of different aspects among which the most important are: (a) the energy requirements for the formation of peptide bonds; (b) the necessity of arranging the amino acid units in specific orders; and (c) the arrangement of the molecule in space so that it assumes the particular configuration characteristic of the finished product. Items (b) and (c) must necessarily involve the action of enzymes and of specific "templates" (see below) and our knowledge of these is at present very limited and forms the object of much of the enormous amount of current work on protein synthesis.

A. *The Formation of Peptide Bonds*

As a model for the formation of the peptide linkages in protein molecules much work has been devoted to studying the synthesis of amino acid amides and small peptides. It would appear that the energy required for these syntheses is derived from ATP or possibly in some cases from coenzyme A (CoA). It has been recognized, for example, that the former compound participates in the formation of glutamine, one of the simplest instances of a peptide, from glutamic acid and ammonia (Elliott, 1948; Speck, 1949). The enzyme responsible for this synthesis, known as glutamine synthetase, has been isolated and shown to be widely distributed in nature (Elliott, 1948, 1953). The identification of an activated form of aspartic acid, namely β-aspartyl phosphate, an intermediate in homoserine formation (see above), suggests that the corresponding glutamic acid derivative may participate in the formation of glutamine via the aforementioned enzyme, but this has not been confirmed as yet. The necessity for ATP has been demonstrated in the formation of other peptides, e.g., glutathione and pantothenic acid (Maas and Novelli, 1953; Maas, 1956). The final stage in the synthesis of the former peptide is the condensation of γ-glutamylcysteine with glycine, which is brought about by the enzyme, glutathione synthetase. From our present point of view it is particularly significant that this enzyme has been concentrated by a factor of 5500 from dried, autolyzed brewer's yeast (Snoke, 1955). The enzyme is dependent not only on ATP but also on magnesium ions, and is stimulated by potassium ions. It is independent of vitamin B_{12}, folic acid, or coenzyme A (Anderson and Stekol, 1953), but the latter coenzyme has been shown to be an alternative source of energy for peptide bond formation as shown in the formation of hippuric acid in liver tissue by the reaction of glycine with benzoyl coenzyme A via a mechanism independent of ATP (Chantrenne, 1951).

The data on the synthesis of pantothenic acid have led Lipmann (1954) to put forward a general hypothesis regarding the mode of formation of peptide bonds, in which he has postulated that the first stage consists of the pyrophosphorylation of the enzyme by means of ATP. The enzyme system was then supposed to react with the carboxyl group of an acid, in this case pantoic acid, with the elimination of the pyrophosphate grouping. The enzyme-acid activated complex reacted in turn with an amino compound, in this instance β-alanine, to yield the peptide. This series of reactions may be summarized as follows (where energy-rich bonds are denoted in the usual manner):

(26) $\text{Enzyme} + \text{ATP} \rightleftharpoons \text{Enzyme} \sim \text{PP} + \text{AMP}$
(27) $\text{Enzyme} \sim \text{PP} + \text{RCO}_2\text{H} \rightleftharpoons \text{Enzyme} \sim \text{COR} + \text{PP}$
(28) $\text{Enzyme} \sim \text{COR} + \text{R}'\text{NH}_2 \rightleftharpoons \text{Enzyme} + \text{RCONHR}'$

An analogous process involves the "adenylization" of the enzyme, such as that which occurs in the formation of coenzyme A (Lipmann, 1954; Jones et al., 1953), thus:

(29) $\text{Enzyme} + \text{ATP} \rightleftharpoons \text{Enzyme} \sim \text{PA} + \text{PP}$
(30) $\text{Enzyme} \sim \text{PA} + \text{HSCoA} \rightleftharpoons \text{Enzyme} \sim \text{SCoA} + \text{AMP}$
(31) $\text{Enzyme} \sim \text{SCoA} + \text{RCO}_2\text{H} \rightleftharpoons \text{Enzyme} + \text{RCOSCoA}$

The thiol ester thus formed might react with an amine or amino acid to form a peptide as well as coenzyme A, such a reaction between benzoyl coenzyme A and glycine giving hippuric acid as mentioned above. The formation of acetyl coenzyme A in yeast has now been shown actually to proceed according to a somewhat different mechanism, whereby the primary reaction occurs between ATP and acetic acid to form adenyl acetic acid and pyrophosphate (Berg, 1956a; Berg and Newton, 1956). Furthermore, the important observation has been made that amino acids undergo activation of their carboxyl groups in this manner. For example methionine in the presence of ATP and of the purified enzyme formed an activated complex which underwent reaction with hydroxylamine to yield pyrophosphate, AMP, and methionine hydroxamic acid (Berg, 1956a,b).

ncidentally, the activation of methionine is effected by a fraction resembling one described by Cantoni (1953) which contains enzymes yielding adenosylmethionine (see above) from ATP and methionine. t appears possible that carboxyl activation is an intermediate step in he formation of this active methionine derivative. Enzyme systems catalyzing an amino acid-dependent exchange between labeled pyrophosphate and ATP have been described not only in yeast (Berg, 1955; Berg and Newton, 1956) but in rat liver (Hoagland, 1955) and various microbial extracts (De Moss and Novelli, 1955; De Moss et al., 1956a). A purified system from E. coli has been shown to

$$
\text{32)} \quad \underset{\text{(XXXV)}}{\text{AdOPOCOCHCH}_2\text{CH}\overset{\text{CH}_3}{\underset{\text{CH}_3}{\diagup}}} \quad \xrightarrow[\text{}]{\text{NH}_2\text{OH}} \quad \underset{\text{(XXXVI)}}{\text{CCHCH}_2\text{CH}\overset{\text{CH}_3}{\underset{\text{CH}_3}{\diagup}}} \quad + \text{ AMP}
$$

activate leucine, and leucyladenosine monophosphate (XXXV, Ad = adenosyl) has been suggested as an intermediate in the reaction (De Moss et al., 1956a,b). This amino-substituted acyladenosine monophosphate has been synthesized and shown to react readily with hydroxylamine to form the corresponding hydroxamic acid (XXXVI) as in the case of the

33)   ATP + Pantoic acid + Enzyme ⇌ Enzyme-pantoyl ∼ AMP + PP
34) Enzyme-pantoyl ∼ AMP + β-Alanine ⇌ Pantothenic acid + AMP + Enzyme

methionine hydroxamic acid mentioned above (Berg, 1957). Berg (1957) has made the important observation that the synthetic adenyl-L-methionine rapidly yields ATP in the presence of pyrophosphate and a partially purified enzyme from yeast or E. coli. A similar series of reactions has also been postulated by Maas (1956) to account for the synthesis of pantothenic acid from β-alanine and pantoic acid by an enzyme system derived from E. coli (equations 33–34), and Hoagland et al. (1956) have put forward the same series of reactions to explain the enzymatic carboxyl activation of amino acids by rat liver microsomes. The latter authors point out that the activated amino acid is firmly bound to the enzyme surface, only being liberated in the presence of hydroxylamine, and they make the further important observation that separate activating enzymes probably exist for the individual amino acids.

It would appear that this mechanism of activation may be of quite general character (see Hoagland et al., 1956, for review) thus giving support to Lipmann's original hypothesis though not the details. It appears to be specific for ATP since ITP, CTP, GTP, and UTP are inactive (De Moss et al., 1956a), although GTP appears to be required in the incorporation of amino acids into protein at a later stage (Hoagland *et al.*, 1956; Keller and Zamecnik, 1956). Whether the activated amino acids have a separate existence away from the enzyme surface or whether the activation energy is stored in some way at this surface cannot be decided at present. Thus, Britten *et al.* (1955) have pointed out that if any one amino acid were converted into an active form receiving energy from a common source (ATP) before adsorption it would be expected that an excess of other amino acids would compete for the energy source and thereby interfere with the adsorption. Using *E. coli* these authors found that such an excess of other amino acids had no effect on the specific adsorption of one amino acid and conclude that "It is reasonable that the energy is used to prepare adsorptive sites and that a part of this energy could remain for the synthesis of peptide bonds." On the other hand, the suggestion of Hoagland *et al.* (1956) that specific enzymes are involved in activation would account for the lack of interference of one amino acid in the adsorption of another in the activated form.

B. *The Synthesis of Adaptive Enzymes*

If it is assumed that mechanisms of the type described above are available for activating amino acid units we are faced with the problem of how specific combination between series of such activated units can occur to form peptides or proteins. It is significant that apart from such peptides as glutathione, pantothenic acid, etc., which have definite physiological roles (glutathione, for instance, is the prosthetic group of glyceraldehyde-3-phosphate dehydrogenase, see Krimsky and Racker, 1952, and participates in enzymic transfer reactions, and pantothenic acid has a role as a vitamin), few simple peptides have been isolated from actively growing cells (Geiger, 1950; Britten *et al.*, 1955; Spiegelman *et al.*, 1955, Gale, 1955). Those peptides which have been isolated are of considerable molecular complexity. For example, in actively growing *T. utilis*, cultured on acetic acid-1-C^{14}, the peptides formed, even after growth for only 10 seconds, were sufficiently complex to contain all the common amino acids (Turba and Esser, 1953). These peptides, some 40 in all, contained a very high proportion of glutamic acid and it is of interest to note that the acidic peptides were formed first, being followed by those of neutral character and then by those of basic nature. Since simple peptides fail to accumulate, the view has grown up that protein synthesis does not proceed by what would seem to be the obvious mechanism, combination of specific peptides. This aspect of protein synthesis is discussed in more detail below.

Despite the fact that a direct role of peptides in protein synthesis has not been demonstrated it appears significant that the transpeptidations involving glutathione, studied by Hanes *et al.* (1952), Fodor *et al.* 1953), and Hird and Springell (1954), are so general. In these reactions the γ-glutamyl residue of glutathione is transferred to an acceptor molecule, either an amino acid or a peptide, to form a γ-glutamyl peptide and this process can continue to build up quite complex peptides. An important feature of the reaction is that only a small change in free energy is involved since no net synthesis of peptide bonds occurs. It appears that the peptides formed by transpeptidation may have certain specific structural features and that they may contribute to the general pool for protein synthesis or alternatively constitute reservoirs of certain amino acids. It also appears possible that such peptides may constitute an important proportion of the acidic compounds which accumulate in the early stages of protein synthesis such as those observed by Turba and Esser. For a general review of the influence of peptides on growth and protein synthesis the reader is referred to the article by Ehrensvärd (1955).

The separation and characterization of the complex peptides, such as those described by Turba and Esser, is tedious and the results are difficult to interpret. Many workers have therefore turned to studying the factors involved in the synthesis of proteins with highly characteristic properties, namely enzymes, whose formation can be followed readily in terms of their activities. In this connection the formation of adaptive enzymes whose synthesis can be induced has received much attention since the factors influencing it are susceptible to control. The work of several investigators has shown that the formation of adaptive enzymes involves the synthesis of new protein rather than the activation of nonfunctional precursors (see Spiegelman *et al.*, 1955, for review). Furthermore, these latter authors have drawn attention to the fact that because an enzyme can be a characteristic constituent of one strain of an organism and be inducible in another it is unlikely that the mechanism of protein synthesis in enzyme induction is different from the normal. Hence, it appears that the conclusions regarding protein synthesis derived from experiments on induced enzymes are generally valid.

Broadly speaking, the ability to form enzymes in the absence of an external supply of nitrogen is far more widespread in yeasts than in bacteria and the reason for this has been traced to the existence in yeasts of an "amino acid pool," first observed by Taylor (1947). This pool, absent from organisms such as *E. coli*, can supply the nitrogen required for protein synthesis in the presence of an energy source and is presumably the reason for the temporary increase of the nitrogen content of brewer's yeasts observed during the initial phases of growth on a rich medium such as wort (Nielsen, 1943). A consideration of the properties of this pool is essential for an adequate understanding of the progress of protein synthesis in yeast and is therefore briefly given here. A survey of the amino acid pools of various growing yeasts by Spiegelman et al. (1955) has revealed that they contain all the common amino acids and that they do not vary greatly in quantity or composition from one yeast to another (see Tables VI and VII, taken from Spiegelman et al., 1955).

TABLE VI
LEVEL OF AMINO ACID POOLS IN DIFFERENT YEASTS

Strain	μM of glutamic acid/ 100 mg.	mg. N/100 mg. dry cells	Total mg. pool N/100 mg. dry cells	% pool N as glutamic acid
P strain A (haploid)	23.5	0.225	1.13	19.9
R427 a (haploid)	23.8	0.228	1.342	17.0
R427 A (haploid)	21.1	0.210	0.743	28.6
L1428 A (haploid)	18.2	0.174	1.92	9.05
Saccharomyces cerevisiae (strain K)	13.8	0.132	0.505	26.1
Saccharomyces carlsbergensis (Y-379)	10.2	0.096	0.781	12.3
Saccharomyces carlsbergensis (Y-1005)	10.3	0.097	1.038	9.35
Saccharomyces fragilis (VN)	11.2	0.107	1.13	9.5
Saccharomyces fragilis (Y-1342)	12.3	0.118	1.24	9.5
Saccharomyces chevalieri	13.2	0.126	1.24	10.2
Saccharomyces ludwigii	14.1	0.135	0.921	14.6
Saccharomyces italicus (Y-1434)	16.4	0.157	1.67	9.4

The pool composition can be varied, however, by growing the yeasts in various media; for example, with glucose as the carbon source little difference is observed between cells grown in complete or synthetic medium but several amino acids almost disappear from cells grown on pyruvic acid, lactic acid, or glycerol. Spiegelman suggests that the almost complete absence of serine and glycine in these cases may be explained by the fact that the primarily aerobic mechanism involved in the ultilization of the last-mentioned carbon sources results in an increased demand for porphyrin synthesis and hence for the serine and glycine which contribute to the porphyrins (see above). The level of all the components of the amino acid pool is lowered by starving the yeasts of nitrogen in the presence of glucose and is restored by growing the yeasts in the presence of glucose together with a nitrogen source. The composition of the pool can be varied by replenishing it in the presence of various nitrogen compounds, e.g., casein hydrolysate causes the replenishment of all amino

TABLE VII

COMPOSITION OF AMINO ACID POOLS OF DIFFERENT YEASTS AS DETERMINED BY PAPER CHROMATOGRAPHY

1. Alanine	5. Threonine	10. Threonine
2. Serine	6. Glutamic acid	11. Arginine + Valine
3. Glycine	7. Aspartic acid	12. Tyrosine
4. Leucine	8. Glutamine + Alanine	13. Hydroxyproline
	9. Lysine	

Strain	1	2	3	4	5	6	7	8	9	10	11	12	13
P strain A	3+	2+	2+	3+	+	2+	2+	2+	+	+	2+	+	—
R427 a	2+	2+	+	2+	+	3+	2+	2+	Tr^a	Tr^a	2+	+	+
R427 A	3+	2+	+	3+	+	3+	2+	2+	+	+	2+	—	—
Saccharomyces cerevisiae Sex A	2+	2+	2+	3+	+	2+	2+	3+	+	+	2+	+	—
Saccharomyces cerevisiae Strain K	3+	2+	2+	3+	+	3+	2+	3+	+	+	2+	+	—
Saccharomyces carlsbergensis (Y-379)	3+	2+	2+	2+	2+	3+	2+	3+	+	+	—	—	—
Saccharomyces carlsbergensis (Y-1005)	3+	+	2+	2+	+	3+	+	3+	+	+	+	—	—
Saccharomyces fragilis (VN)	3+	2+	2+	3+	+	3+	+	2+	+	+	—	—	—
Saccharomyces chevalieri	3+	2+	2+	3+	2+	3+	2+	2+	+	+	+	+	—
Saccharomyces ludwigii	3+	2+	Tr^a	2+	+	3+	2+	3+	+	Tr^a	+	—	—
Saccharomyces italicus (Y-1434)	2+	+	+	2+	+	2+	2+	2+	Tr^a	+	—	+	—

^{a} Tr = Trace.

acids but ammonium chloride in limited quantities fails to restore arginine, histidine, lysine, methionine, proline, and threonine. Individual amino acids will also restore the pool but vary in their ability to do so. For example, arginine, leucine, serine, isoleucine, alanine, aspartic acid, methionine, and tryptophan are 20–50% as effective (in decreasing order) as ammonium sulfate while phenylalanine and tyrosine are 15–20%, lysine, cysteine, and hydroxyproline are 9–15% and histidine is 5% as effective as ammonium sulfate. The history of the cell has an effect on the depletion of the pool since, for example, cells grown on glucose and subsequently starved of nitrogen in the presence of ethanol or pyruvic acid *increase* the level of their amino acid pools, whereas cells grown on the latter carbon sources and then starved of nitrogen in their presence *decrease* their pools. Hence, it is apparent that some labile material can break down in yeast to yield free amino acids under certain circumstances. This is well exemplified by the effect of irradiating cells with ultraviolet light during the course of nitrogen starvation in the presence of glucose, when the pool is replenished although to lessening extents as starvation proceeds. It is to be emphasized that the replenished pool in all cases contains all the amino acids and presumably, therefore, the above-mentioned labile material consists of protein. In this respect the yeasts again differ from *E. coli*, which, in addition to containing either no or only a very small amino acid pool, contains no labile protein.

Against this background, Spiegelman *et al.* (1955) and other workers, were able to decide whether the synthesis of the adaptive enzyme, α-glucosidase, took place either at the expense of an inactive precursor or directly from free amino acids. For yeasts, their experiments consisted in reducing the availability of the amino acid pool, (a) by the use of amino acid analogues which function as competitors of specific amino acids, and (b) by depleting the pool and restoring it under conditions which minimally disturbed other cell components. Experiments were also carried out with other organisms, notably *E. coli*, by the use of amino acid-deficient mutants but proved indeterminate with yeasts since the amino acid pools made the results too difficult to interpret.

Halvorson and Spiegelman (1952) found that certain amino acid analogues blocked the synthesis of the enzyme completely and that the relevant amino acid reversed this inhibition. For instance, p-fluoro-phenylalanine caused an inhibition of α-glucosidase formation which was completely reversed by phenylalanine (see also Lee and Williams, 1952; Halvorson *et al.*, 1955). Furthermore, the amino acid analogue prevented the fall in the amount of the amino acid pool on nitrogen starvation in the presence of an energy source such as glucose (Roine, 1947). It was therefore concluded that the prevention of the incorporation of one amino acid into the cellular constituents inhibited the uptake of *all* amino acids. Halvorson and Spiegelman were unable to find small peptides in the yeast under these conditions. They commented that it is very difficult to understand why such compounds involving amino acids, other than the one whose analogue is present, should not be formed unless the synthesis of the enzyme concerned involves the simultaneous use of all the amino acids for the elaboration of an enzyme precursor of considerable complexity, possibly itself of protein nature. As mentioned earlier this conclusion has been reached by other investigators working in diverse fields (see Gale, 1955; Loftfield and Harris, 1956; Ushiba and Magasanik, 1952; Rickenberg et al., 1953). In support of these findings, it was found that the ability of cells suspended in a nitrogen-free medium to synthesize enzyme paralleled the level of the free amino acid pool. The possibility that enzymes are formed by a mechanism independent of amino acids and involving the transformation of a preexistent complex precursor was largely eliminated by these experiments. The further possibility that a precursor could yield the enzyme by the addition of free amino acids was also eliminated by Rotman and Spiegelman (1954) and by Hogness et al. (1955), in this case for E. coli. The former authors isolated à purified β-galactosidase from uniformly C[14]-labeled cells after growth in unlabeled substrates. The newly formed enzyme was unlabeled and hence none of its carbon could have been derived from any cellular components existing prior to the addition of the enzyme inducer. Hogness et al. reached the same conclusion based on experiments on the incorporation of radioactive sulfur into β-galactosidase although Markowitz and Klein (1955) found the opposite result with the α-amylase of Pseudomonas saccharophila, presumably because this organism, like yeast, contains a pool of labile nitrogenous compounds. It is of great interest that Cohn and Torriani (1953) have found a possible precursor, known as Pz, of β-galactosidase in an E. coli mutant, which is immunologically related to the enzyme. This is the only case so far reported in which such an intermediate in enzyme formation has been isolated although other work, e.g., that of Markowitz and Klein (1955) holds promise for the isolation of similar extracellular precursors of the α-amylase of Pseudomonas saccharophila. The formation of the enzyme from Pz is dependent on the addition of the amino acid for which the mutant has a requirement (Monod, et al., 1952).

C. The Template Mechanism for Enzyme Formation

The simultaneous employment of the amino acids for protein synthesis suggests that they must be held, presumably in the activated form discussed above, on the surface of a large molecule or "template" (see Dounce, 1952) in such a way that they can combine with one another in the required specific fashion. Such a template must be at least a very large molecule and the only possibilities in this respect would seem to be proteins, ribonucleic acid (RNA), or deoxyribonucleic acid (DNA). Spiegelman and Kamen (1946, 1947) found that an overflow of radioactive phosphorus occurred during the growth and protein synthesis of yeast subsequent to the incorporation of radioactive phosphorus into the nucleic acids, suggesting that the latter substances might hold activated amino acids (see section on formation of peptide bonds) or participate in their formation prior to combination into protein. In this connection it is relevant to observe that Miettinen (1954) has found a great difference between the ratio of the "ethanol-extractable" and the "trichloroacetic acid-extractable" amino acids in a low-nitrogen yeast and in the same yeast in a state of rapid cell division. The amino acids extracted by trichloroacetic acid increased in proportion to the rate of cell division and it appears probable that they are displaced by the acid from the surface of the template. This is in line with the observations of Britten *et al.* (1955), who found that radioactive amino acids are adsorbed in *E. coli* and are liberated by 5% trichloroacetic acid. The adsorption is specific at certain levels of concentration of the added amino acid in the latter organism and is dependent on an energy supply although it can occur when protein synthesis is blocked. Furthermore, a methionine-requiring mutant rapidly adsorbed labeled proline when growth was prevented by the absence of methionine, but the adsorbed proline was not transferred to protein until methionine was added, thus recalling the earlier findings that a variety of amino acids are required for protein synthesis to occur. Britten *et al.* (1955) also showed that the adsorption process is a necessary step in protein synthesis and does not simply provide a store of amino acids. Moreover, the amino acids appeared to be the only radioactive constituents of the acid-soluble fraction, no peptides having been detected.

Among the possibilities mentioned above, the immediate specific adsorbent for these amino acids, possibly the template, would seem most probably to be ribonucleic acid (see review by Chantrenne, 1953; Gale, 1957). Spiegelman *et al.* (1955) are of the opinion that it is not DNA, as the synthesis of this particular macromolecule is far more sensitive to irradiation with x-rays (Baron *et al.*, 1953) or to treatment with nitrogen mustards (Sher and Mallette, 1954) than is the synthesis of proteins. In addition, both dissociation of RNA formation and cell-growth from DNA synthesis can be achieved by the photoreactivation of either *E. coli* or yeast cells after exposure to ultraviolet light (Kelner, 1953; Halvorson and Jackson, 1956). Further evidence against the participation of DNA has been adduced by Spiegelman *et al.* for a number of thymineless mutants of certain organisms which can continue to synthesize protein and RNA in the absence of thymine, a requisite for DNA synthesis.

Halvorson and Jackson (1956) found that damage to RNA metabolism by irradiation with ultraviolet light, as measured by the incorporation of radioactive phosphorus into the nucleic acid, resulted in profound effects on protein synthesis in yeast. The action spectrum of ultraviolet light was found by Swenson (1950) and Stanier (1951) to coincide with the absorption spectrum of nucleic acid while a parallelism was found between the ultraviolet dosages which inhibited enzyme synthesis and the incorporation of radioactive glycine into protein and the incorporation of this labeled amino acid into RNA (see above) (Halvorson and Jackson, 1956).

Ben-Ishai and Spiegelman (see Spiegelman *et al.*, 1955) found for *E. coli* that the pyrimidine analogue, 5-hydroxyuridine, completely inhibited the formation of adaptive β-galactosidase, a finding which recalls the earlier results with amino acid analogues; similar results were obtained by Pardee (1955), Creaser (1955), and Ottey (1955). Further, the addition of 5-hydroxyuridine suppressed enzyme synthesis even when this had begun and it is concluded that continued RNA synthesis is required for continued enzyme protein synthesis. The synthesis of other proteins continued, however, in the presence of the pyrimidine analogue and Spiegelman has shown that this is due to the fact that the enzyme-forming system is a poor competitor for nucleotides. These results could not be repeated with yeast and this was found to be due to the existence of a nucleotide pool, analogous to the amino acid pool.

The major constituents of this pool are adenylic acid, guanylic acid, and uridine (Ben-Ishai and Spiegelman, 1955). The pyrimidines in the pool of pyrimidineless mutants can be virtually eliminated by incubation of the organisms in media supplemented with amino acids and glucose, although this treatment has no effect on the adenylic acid level and increases the amount of guanylic acid. Under the appropriate conditions it was found that the ability of yeasts to synthesize α-glucosidase paralleled the amount of the nucleotide pool (see Di Carlo *et al.*, 1949) just as it did the amount of the amino acid pool, and in yeast, as in *E. coli* the forcing of rapid protein synthesis could lead to the exhaustion of the nucleotide pool. An interesting feature of these experiments is that cells with partially replenished pools synthesizing enzyme at low rates do not continue to function at these rates until the amount of enzyme formed is comparable with that produced by cells containing greater pools. It has been pointed out (Ben-Ishai and Spiegelman, 1955) that this can be explained if the formation of new enzyme occurs *only* if new nucleic acid can be formed. This conclusion was confirmed by reducing the nucleotide pool in a uracilless mutant of yeast, which had undergone partial induction of enzyme formation, and then incubating the cells with the enzyme inducer with and without a mixture of purines and pyrimidines. In the absence of the latter mixture, no more enzyme was formed whereas it was produced at the normal rate in the presence of the mixture.

Gale and Folkes (1954; 1955) were able to show that the incorporation of uracil into RNA increased during the formation of galactosidase in disrupted *Stapyhlococcus aureus* cells and similar results were obtained by Chantrenne (1956) using yeast. The latter author observed increased utilization of labeled adenine and uridine into RNA during the induced formation by oxygen of cytochrome C^5, cytochrome peroxidase, and catalase in resting yeast. When the purine bases and pyrimidine nucleotides were isolated from the yeast after enzyme induction it was found that in those cases where adenine-8-C^{14} had been added, both purines were labeled while in those cases where uracil-2-C^{14} had been added both pyrimidines were labeled (see section on purines and pyrimidines). The specific activities of the four components increased simultaneously during enzyme formation. Chantrenne also found that the specific activities of the purine bases present in an acid-soluble fraction of these yeasts declined more rapidly during enzyme adaptation than in control experiments. Presumably these materials form part of the nucleotide pool supplying nucleic acid, and the fact that uracil is involved points to the implication of RNA. The incorporation of adenine caused by the enzyme inducer is observed even in the presence of the p-fluorophenylalanine and it is concluded that it does not depend on the actual formation of any new enzyme system. The modification or synthesis of nucleic acid may be a condition for the synthesis of induced enzyme; it is not a consequence of the formation of new enzyme molecules. Chantrenne has shown that the fractionation of the RNA of cells in which enzyme induction has occurred yields nucleotide fractions of very different specific activities and hence it is probable that certain specific nucleic acid fractions are involved in protein synthesis. Reiner *et al.* (1948, 1955) have investigated nucleic acid fractions prepared from *Saccharomyces carlsbergensis*, which had been induced to form β-galactosidase, and from *E. coli*, which had formed glucokinase. These fractions have been shown to possess the property of bringing about the enzyme induction in the absence of the normal inducer, e.g., the (so-called) PN factor from *E. coli* induces the formation of glucokinase in the absence of gluconic acid. This induction can be brought about in smaller degree by nonspecific nucleotide mixtures, including ribonuclease digests of yeast nucleic acid, but these mixtures are much less effective than the PN factor in the absence of inducer. At the present time it is apparent that the factors are exceedingly impure and the recent work of Gale (1956) on a related topic, the glycine incorporated factor (GIF) of *S. aureus*, has suggested that this compound or mixture of compounds, although associated with nucleotide fractions, may not be of nucleotide character at all. The work of Gale and Folkes (1955) has also revealed that DNA plays a definite part in organizing protein synthesis and this is perhaps not surprising in view of the fact that the ultimate control of this process must surely reside in the genes. Allfrey (1954) has also shown that DNA affects protein synthesis in calf thymus nuclei. Gale (1955; 1957) has suggested that DNA organizes RNA synthesis and has advanced the hypothesis that the DNA combines with amino acids and determines their positions relative to each other prior to the formation of specific polypeptide structures. The residues are assumed to be unable to combine with one another while still in contact with DNA but must first be taken over by the corresponding RNA structure and this must be accomplished by combination with pre-existing specific RNA or by synthesis of the RNA from nucleotide residues modeled on the DNA-protein complex; it is supposed that once RNA is available the amino acid residues can combine with each other through peptide bonds in positions determined by the initial DNA template (gene?).

This hypothesis has many points of similarity to that discussed by Arley (1955), which is concerned with the self-duplicating mechanism of DNA. This author draws attention to the suggestion by Gamow that there is a 1:1 correspondence between a double helical polynucleotide chain in DNA and a single peptide chain held in the groove between the helices and synthesized there, so that the order of amino acids is uniquely determined by the order of the purines and pyrimidines. It may be envisaged that the process can be reversed so that the protein (or enzyme) determines the order of the basic units of a freshly formed DNA molecule, which would hence be a replica of the original. Thus the protein "picture" might serve a double purpose, firstly as an enzyme, catalyzing and controlling biochemical reactions in growth, and secondly as a template or mold for the duplication of the DNA of genes and, perhaps, of viruses. It has, in fact, been shown by Burton (1955) that the synthesis of the DNA of the virus, bacteriophage T2, is dependent on the synthesis of protein, just as the latter is dependent on DNA, the only nucleic acid known to be present in this or other bacteriophages.

Gale's hypothesis explains why RNA synthesis will occur only when a full complement of amino acids is present (in S. aureus) and why penicillin, which prevents the exchange of specific amino acid residues, should give rise to the inhibition of both specific protein synthesis and specific RNA synthesis. Furthermore, it might explain why the early stages (lag phase) in enzyme induction are susceptible to ultraviolet irradiation since DNA synthesis is known to be markedly affected (Halvorson and Jackson, 1956). However, when enzyme formation is well under way it is less sensitive to irradiation possibly because RNA has taken control. It is clear that enzyme synthesis and presumably protein synthesis generally is a multi-stage process involving mechanisms for activating, aligning, and combining the amino acids under the influence of RNA, the latter being actively synthesized possibly under the control of DNA located in the cell nucleus and possibly in the genes themselves. The present over-all picture is somewhat confused since much of the evidence for the above conclusions, particularly for yeast, has been obtained by studying intact cells and it is not known whether protein synthesis occurs by the same mechanism in the cell nucleus as in the cytoplasm and whether these two processes only became interrelated during cell division (Ehrensvärd, 1955). It is, of course, necessary to obtain independent evidence by the study of more readily controlled systems such as those used by Gale in the work cited above.

In this connection, recent work on rat liver preparations is of outstanding interest. Centrifugation of these preparations has yielded two fractions (Keller and Zamecnik, 1956; Ziegler and Melchior, 1956), one insoluble consisting of the microsome fraction, containing RNA and being the site of formation of labeled proteins, and the other soluble and catalyzing the carboxyl activation discussed earlier. It has been demonstrated further (Hoagland and Zamecnik, 1957) that the activating enzymes contain RNA (S-RNA) which on incubation with C^{14}-labeled leucine (or valine or glycine) and ATP becomes labeled. The ATP is specific for this reaction and the labeling additive. The C^{14}-leucine-RNA bond is stable to acid and does not exchange with free C^{12}-leucine, and on incubation of the complex with hydroxylamine gives the leucine hydroxamic acid described above. Treatment of the complex with an enzyme preparation and the microsome fraction causes the transfer of C^{14}-leucine to protein and this reaction is specifically dependent upon GTP as foreshadowed in the section on amino acid activation above. Hoagland and Zamecnik (1957) have postulated that the initial activation of amino acids by the formation of an enzyme-bound acyl adenylate is followed by transacylation to S-RNA. This latter reaction is sensitive to ribonuclease, a finding which recalls the observation by Holley (1957) that the alanine-dependent conversion of ATP to AMP in preparations of rat liver is inhibited by ribonuclease.

Similar observations have been made upon microsomal ribonucleoprotein particles from pea seedlings (Webster, 1957) with the exception that guanosine phosphates are not required for the incorporation of the amino acids into protein.

Obviously, clear signposts are emerging from current research and considerable progress is being made in dissociating the steps in protein synthesis and the allied subject of nucleic acid formation.

5. Sulfur Metabolism

Yeast contains a great variety of sulfur compounds of many degrees of complexity and these frequently play essential roles in the general metabolism of the cell. For example, vitamin B_1 (aneurin) is the coenzyme for carboxylase, which brings about the penultimate stage in the series of fermentation reactions producing ethanol, i.e., in the decarboxylation of pyruvic acid to acetaldehyde; again, biotin has a vital function in the carbohydrate metabolism of yeast (see Moat and Lichstein, 1954; Lichstein, 1957). In recent years it has been found that another sulfur compound, coenzyme A (XXXVII; R = adenyl), is responsible for activation of acetic acid and other acids taking part in condensation reactions, such as those of the Krebs cycle (see Fig. 4 and section on lysine) and those involved in the formation of peptide bonds (see section on peptide bond formation). Glutathione (glutamylcysteinylglycine, XXXVIII) is now thought to be a coenzyme for both glyceraldehyde-3-phosphate dehydrogenase, another important enzyme in the fermentation scheme (Krimsky and Racker, 1952), and the enzyme glyoxalase as well as a reservoir of thiol groups. In the latter connection it has been shown that when the sulfur supply to *Rhodotorula gracilis* is limited, all the glutathione is present in the reduced (thiol) form whereas under conditions of adequate sulfur supply, much of it is present in the disulfide form. Under the former conditions, protein synthesis is restricted even in the presence of excess nitrogen and it has been suggested, therefore, that the prime function of sulfur is its contribution to the thiol groups of enzymes able to regulate protein synthesis (Sandegren *et al.*, 1950). It has also been shown that certain thiol compounds, notably cysteine, exert an effect on the morphology of yeasts, maintaining the cells in the discrete form ("yeast phase") as opposed to the pseudomycelial form (see Nickerson and Mankowski, 1953). Both cystine and the oxidized form of glutathione are reduced to the thiol form by specific reductases, the former by means of DPNH (Romano and Nickerson, 1954) and the latter by means of TPNH (Conn and Vennesland, 1951) or DPNH (Racker, 1955). Since the coenzymes are produced while the cell is metabolizing glucose, these enzymes constitute a link between carbohydrate metabolism and the maintenance of thiol groups.

Nickerson and Falcone (1956) have now demonstrated the presence in yeasts of an enzyme, known as protein disulfide reductase, which plays an important part in cell division by reducing the disulfide bonds of the keratin-mannan complex of the cell wall, hence rendering this latter material capable of plastic deformation.

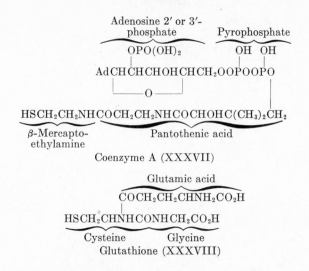

Coenzyme A (XXXVII)

Glutathione (XXXVIII)

The majority of yeasts are able to synthesize all their sulfur compounds when supplied with inorganic sulfate or, better, elemental sulfur (Butlin and Postgate, 1956) as the sole of sulfur and, in order to effect such syntheses, they must first reduce the sulfate. Certain yeasts are unable to bring about the primary reductions; for example Schultz and McManus (1950) found that *Endomycopsis fibuliger, selenospora,* and *javanensis* and certain strains of *Saccharomyces dairensis* and *Zygosaccharomyces rugosus* and *versicolor* would grow only when supplied with methionine, cysteine, or glutathione, whereas the first named of these compounds is utilized by all yeasts (see Ingram, 1955). The precise mechanism whereby the reduction of sulfate is achieved has not been elucidated although it is known that sulfate is converted to thiosulfate and that either of these ions can be reduced to sulfur dioxide and to hydrogen sulfide (Tanner, 1918; Wanderscheck, 1928). The latter product can then be incorporated into organic compounds, e.g., by reaction with acetaldehyde to form thioacetaldehyde, itself reduced to ethyl mercaptan by a mechanism analogous to that producing ethanol from acetaldehyde (Neuberg and Grauer, 1952). The incorporation of hydrogen sulfide into an organic molecule directly by means of a yeast enzyme system has been demonstrated by Schlossmann and Lynen (1957). This enzyme system has been purified from yeast extracts by a combination of procedures including precipitation with protamine sulfate and ammonium sulfate and adsorption on alumina. The purified enzyme catalyzes the reaction of hydrogen sulfide with serine in the presence of pyridoxal phosphate to give cysteine. It is presumably free from the enzymes which reduce sulfate etc. as neither this ion nor the sulfite ion function as substrates. Possibly the sulfate is initially activated before reduction and Wilson and Bandurski (1956) have shown that an enzyme system from yeast activates both sulfate and sufite ions. The enzyme system liberates phosphate from ATP in the presence of magnesium ions and sulfate or sulfite and the "active sulfate" has been shown to be adenosine-3-phosphate-5-phosphoryl sulfate. This compound has been isolated (Bandurski et al., 1956; Robbins and Lipmann, 1956) and shown to be formed in two stages, the first consisting of the formation of adenosine-5'- phosphosulfate (APS), catalyzed by the enzyme adenosine triphosphate sulfurylase, and the second the phosphorylation of APS by the enzyme adenosine phosphosulfate kinase. Both enzymes have been prepared from yeast (Bandurski et al.) and shown to function with selenate as well as sulfate. No formation of sulphur or thiols from the active sulfate has been directly demonstrated and the major function of this compound appears to be in forming sulfuric esters. The interrelationships between certain simple thiols in yeast have been reviewed by Brenner et al. (1955) as follows:

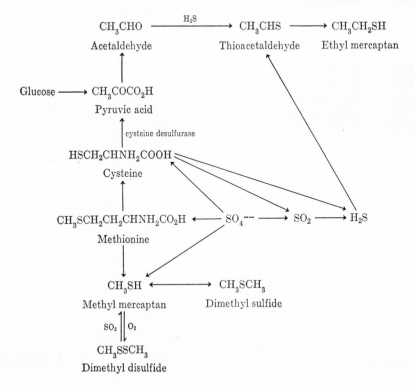

Cysteine is desulfurized by means of the enzyme, cysteine desulfurase (Saz and Brownell, 1954), as mentioned earlier in the section on anaerobic deaminases, but whether or not the reverse reaction plays any significant part in the incorporation of inorganic sulfur compounds into organic molecules has not been established. Methionine is also desulfurized, producing methyl mercaptan (Challenger and Charlton, 1947; Stahl *et al.*, 1949), which can be oxidized to dimethyl disulfide or to dimethyl sulfide, the latter being itself reduced by sulfur dioxide to produce methyl mercaptan (Sullivan, 1929). As mentioned earlier, both methyl mercaptan and ethyl mercaptan are converted by yeast to the corresponding alkylthioadenosine (Schlenk and Tillotson, 1954), presumably via adenosylmethionine and adenosylethionine, and it is also known that fungi can produce methyl mercaptan from sulfate (Birkenshaw *et al.*, 1942). If the mercaptan is produced from sulfate by a direct route these observations lead to a mechanism for the elaboration of organic sulfur compounds from an inorganic source via mercaptans and the corresponding active methionine derivatives or analogues (see section on the aspartic acid family). This might account for the findings of Abelson and Vogel (1955) that serine is a major precursor of cysteine since the cysteine carbon skeleton would be that of serine while the sulfur atom of cysteine would arise from mercaptan via methionine and cystathione or from hydrogen sulfide as described above.

Regarding the actual reduction steps in the production of hydrogen sulfide it is of interest that the film-forming yeast, *Pichia membranefaciens*, brings about the interconversion of the thiol and sulfur (Skerman *et al.*, 1957). When the yeast is aerated and allowed to grow and then treated with hydrogen sulfide, sulfur is rapidly formed. The oxidation system has been shown to reside in the mitochondria and the oxidation reaction is inhibited by the preliminary incubation of the yeast in nitrogen.

The investigation of the part played by methyl mercaptan in yeast cell metabolism has recently afforded evidence of a number of new sulfur compounds (Black *et al.*, 1957). It was found that when yeast was incubated for a brief period with labeled methyl mercaptan ($CH_3S^{35}H$), a number of compounds became labeled, among which, however, cysteine, glutathione, and methionine were not included. Most of the labeled compounds consisted of amino acids hitherto unknown in nature, including S-methylcysteine and a new isomer of β-methyl lanthionine. When the yeast was allowed to grow most of the labeled compounds became bound, but one remained in the free state and Black *et al.* have proposed that this substance, at present being studied, is a coenzyme. S-Methyl cysteine has also been shown to be a natural metabolite in *Neurospora* (Ragland and Liverman, 1956) and to be formed from sulfate. In some strains of *Neurospora* it will serve as the sole source of sulfur, possibly forming methionine via thiomethyladenosine.

The recent work of Singer and Kearney (1953, 1954) has revealed yet another possible path in certain organisms for the incorporation of sulfur, in this case via sulfite. These workers have shown that cysteinesulfinic acid (XXXIX) is a key intermediate in the sulfur metabolism of the organism, *Proteus vulgaris*, undergoing the series of degradations as shown

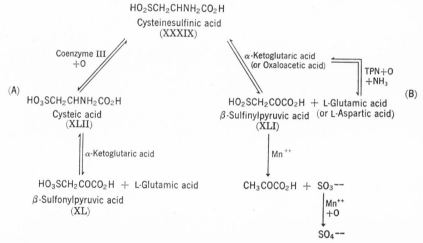

FIG. 11. Degradation of cysteinesulfinic acid.

in Fig. 11. The ultimate products of these degradations are either β-sulfonylpyruvic acid (XL) and glutamic acid (Route A) or pyruvic acid and sulfite or sulfate (Route B). In the organism studied, route B was found to form the major reaction sequence, the primary step consisting in the transamination of cysteinesulfinic acid with α-ketoglutaric acid (or oxaloacetic acid) to form L-glutamic acid (or L-aspartic acid) and β-sulfinylpyruvic acid (XLI). The latter compound loses sulfur dioxide yielding pyruvic acid. In the alternative reaction sequence (Route A), cysteic acid (XLII) is the primary product, then undergoing transamination with α-ketoglutaric acid to yield the β-sulfonylpyruvic acid (XL) and glutamic acid. The conversion of cysteinesulfinic acid into cysteic acid is mediated by an enzyme requiring a new cofactor present in boiled yeast juice, namely coenzyme III, a pyridine nucleotide of which the detailed structure has not yet been elucidated. It remains to be discovered whether intact organisms of the nature of yeast can reverse these oxidative degradations, e.g., by incorporating sulfur dioxide into pyruvic acid to form β-sulfinylpyruvic acid, which could then give cysteine under reductive conditions. However, it appears unlikely that this is a *major* pathway of cysteine biosynthesis in yeast as it might be expected that the labeling pattern of cysteine would match that of pyruvic acid in yeast supplied with radioactive pyruvic acid or acetic acid and it was in fact found by Abelson (see section on aspartic acid family) and by Wang *et al.* (1955) (see section on serine family) that (a) cysteine had the same level of specific activity in *T. utilis* as glycine and serine, and (b) that the labeling patterns of serine and glycine in *Saccharomyces cerevisiae* did not match that of alanine and (by implication) of pyruvic acid. These results suggest again that serine is a major precursor of cysteine (see above) and that the latter is not formed directly from pyruvic acid, but it is apparent that a thorough survey of sulfur metabolism in selected varieties of yeast is needed to define the position more clearly.

References

Abelson, P. H. (1954). *J. Biol. Chem.* **206**, 335.

Abelson, P. H., and Vogel, H. J. (1955). *J. Biol. Chem.* **213**, 355.

Abelson, P. H., Bolton, E. T., and Aldous, E. (1952). *J. Biol. Chem.* **198**, 173.

Abelson, P. H., Bolton, E. T., Britten, R., Cowie, D. B., and Roberts, R. B. (1953). *Proc. Natl. Acad. Sci. U.S.* **39**, 1013, 1020.

Abrams, R., and Bentley, M. (1955). *J. Am. Chem. Soc.* **77**, 4179.

Abrams, R., and Borsook, H. (1952). *J. Biol. Chem.* **198**, 205.

Abrams, R., Hammarsten, E., and Shemin, D. (1948). *J. Biol. Chem.* **173**, 429.

Adams, E. (1954). *J. Biol. Chem.* **209**, 829.

Adams, E. (1955). *J. Biol. Chem.* **217**, 325.

Adelberg, E. A. (1954). *J. Am. Chem. Soc.* **76**, 4241.

Adelberg, E. A. (1955). *In* "Amino Acid Metabolism" (W. D. McElroy and B. Glass, eds.), p. 419. Johns Hopkins Press, Baltimore.

Adelberg, E. A., and Tatum, E. L. (1950). *Arch. Biochem. and Biophys.* **29**, 235.

Adelberg, E. A., Beadle, G. W., and Tatum, E. L. (1951). *J. Biol. Chem.* **190**, 837.

Adler, E., Günther, G., and Everett, J. E. (1938a). *Z. physiol. Chem.* **255**, 27.

Adler, E., Hellström, H., Günther, G., and v. Euler, H. (1938b). *Z. physiol. Chem.* **255**, 14.

Allfrey, V. G. (1954). *Proc. Natl. Acad. Sci. U.S.* **40**, 881.

Ames, B. N. (1955). *In* "Amino Acid Metabolism" (W. D. McElroy and B. Glass, eds.), p. 357. Johns Hopkins Press, Baltimore.

Ames, B. N. (1956). *Federation Proc.* **15**, 210.

Ames, B. N. (1957). *Federation Proc.* **16**, 145.

Ames, B. N., and Horecker, B. L. (1956). *J. Biol. Chem.* **220**, 113.

Ames, B. N., and Mitchell, H. K. (1955). *J. Biol. Chem.* **212**, 687.

Ames, B. N., Mitchell, H. K., and Mitchell, M. B. (1953). *J. Am. Chem. Soc.* **75,** 1015.

Anderson, E. I., and Stekol, J. A. (1953). *J. Biol. Chem.* **202,** 611.

Anker, H. S. (1948). *J. Biol. Chem.* **176,** 1338.

Arley, N. (1955). *Nature* **176,** 465.

Armentrout, S. A., and Goldwasser, E. (1957). *Federation Proc.* **16,** 146.

Avery, O. T., MacLeod, C. M., and McCarty, M. (1944). *J. Exptl. Med.* **79,** 137.

Ayengar, P., Gibson, D. M., Lee Peng, C. H., and Sanadi, D. R. (1956). *J. Biol. Chem.* **218,** 521.

Baddiley, J., and Jamieson, G. A. (1954). *Chemistry & Industry* p. 375.

Baddiley, J., and Jamieson, G. A. (1955). *J. Chem. Soc.* p. 1085.

Bair, W., Rouser, G., and Witter, R. (1952). *Federation Proc.* **11,** 183.

Bandurski, R., Wilson, L. G., and Squires, C. G. (1956). *J. Am. Chem. Soc.* **78,** 6408.

Baron, L. S., Spiegelman, S., and Quastler, H. J. (1953). *J. Gen. Physiol.* **36,** 631.

Barron, E. S. G., Ardao, M. I., and Hearon, M. (1950). *J. Gen. Physiol.* **34,** 211.

Barton-Wright, E. C., and Thorne, R. S. W. (1949). *J. Inst. Brewing* **55,** 383.

Bendich, A., Furst, S. S., and Brown, G. B. (1950). *J. Biol. Chem.* **185,** 423.

Ben-Ishai, R., and Spiegelman, S. (1955); cf. Spiegelman *et al.* (1955).

Berg, P. (1953). *J. Biol. Chem.* **205,** 145.

Berg, P. (1955). *J. Am. Chem. Soc.* **77,** 3163.

Berg, P. (1956a). *J. Biol. Chem.* **222,** 621.

Berg, P. (1956b). *J. Biol. Chem.* **222,** 1025.

Berg, P. (1957). *Federation Proc.* **16,** 152.

Berg, P., and Joklik, W. K. (1954). *J. Biol. Chem.* **210,** 657.

Berg, P., and Newton, G. (1956). *Federation Proc.* **15,** 219.

Bergmann, E. D., Volcani, B. E., and Ben-Ishai, R. (1952). *J. Biol. Chem.* **194,** 521, 531.

Bessman, M. J., Lehman, I. R., Simms, E. S., and Kornberg, A. (1957). *Federation Proc.* **16,** 153.

Bigger-Gehring, L. (1955). *J. Gen. Microbiol.* **13,** 45.

Birkinshaw, J. H., Findlay, W. P. K., and Webb, R. A. (1942). *Biochem. J.* **36,** 526.

Black, S., and Wright, N. G. (1954). *Federation Proc.* **13,** 184.

Black, S., and Wright, N. G. (1955). *In* "Amino Acid Metabolism" (W. D. McElroy and B. Glass, eds.), p. 591. Johns Hopkins Press, Baltimore.

Black, S., Downey, P. F., and Wolff, E. C. (1957). *Federation Proc.* **16,** 155.

Blakley, R. L. (1957a). *Biochem. J.* **65,** 331.

Blakley, R. L. (1957b). *Biochem. J.* **65,** 342.

Bonner, D. M., Tatum, E. L., and Beadle, G. W. (1943). *Arch. Biochem. and Biophys.* **3,** 71.

Borsook, H. (1953). *Advances in Protein Chem.* **8,** 127.

Braunstein, A. E., and Kritzmann, M. G. (1937). *Enzymologia* **2,** 129.

Brenner, M. W., Owades, J. L., and Fazio, T. (1955). *Am. Soc. Brewing Chemists Proc.* p. 125.

Bricas, E., and Fromageot, C. (1953). *Advances in Protein Chem.* **8,** 1.

Britten, R. J., Roberts, R. B., and French, E. F. (1955). *Proc. Natl. Acad. Sci. U.S.* **41,** 863.

Broquist, H. P. (1952). *Federation Proc.* **11,** 191.

Broquist, H. P., and Snell, E. E. (1949). *J. Biol. Chem.* **180,** 59.

Broquist, H. P., and Stiffey, A. V. (1956). *Federation Proc.* **15**, 224.

Brumm, A. F., Potter, V. R., and Siekevitz, P. (1956). *J. Biol. Chem.* **220**, 713.

Buchanan, J. M., Levenberg, B., Flaks, J. G., and Gladner, J. A. (1955). *In* "Amino Acid Metabolism" (W. D. McElroy and B. Glass, eds.), p. 743. Johns Hopkins Press, Baltimore.

Burton, K. (1955). *Biochem. J.* **61**, 473.

Butlin, K. R., and Postgate, J. R. (1956). "Colloque sur la biochimie du soufre," May. Editions du Centre National de la Recherche Scientifique.

Cammarata, P. S., and Cohen, P. P. (1950). *J. Biol. Chem.* **187**, 439.

Cantoni, G. L. (1953). *J. Biol. Chem.* **204**, 403.

Cantoni, G. L. (1955). *In* "Amino Acid Metabolism" (W. D. McElroy and B. Glass, eds.), p. 601. Johns Hopkins Press, Baltimore.

Caputto, R., Leloir, L. F., Cardini, C. E., and Paladini, A. C. (1950). *J. Biol. Chem.* **184**, 333.

Carter, C. E. (1951). *J. Am. Chem. Soc.* **73**, 1508.

Carter, C. E. (1956). *J. Biol. Chem.* **223**, 139.

Carter, C. E., and Cohen, L. H. (1955). *J. Am. Chem. Soc.* **77**, 499.

Carter, C. E., and Cohn, W. E. (1950). *J. Am. Chem. Soc.* **72**, 2604.

Chamberlain, N., Cutts, N. S., and Rainbow, C. (1952). *J. Gen. Microbiol.* **7**, 54.

Challenger, F., and Charlton, P. T. (1947). *J. Chem. Soc.* p. 424.

Chantrenne, H. (1951). *J. Biol. Chem.* **189**, 227.

Chantrenne, H. (1953). *In* "Nature of Virus Multiplication" (P. Fildes and W. E. Van Heyningen, eds.,), pp. 1–15. Cambridge Univ. Press, New York and London.

Chantrenne, H. (1956). *Nature* **177**, 579.

Chargaff, E., and Kream, J. (1948). *J. Biol. Chem.* **175**, 993.

Chargaff, E., and Sprinson, D. B. (1943). *J. Biol. Chem.* **151**, 273.

Christman, J. F., and Williams, V. R. (1952). *J. Bacteriol.* **63**, 107.

Cohen, P. P. (1939). *Biochem. J.* **33**, 1478.

Cohen, P. P. (1940). *J. Biol. Chem.* **136**, 585.

Cohen, P. P. (1942). *Symposium on Respiratory Enzymes* (*Wisconsin*).

Cohen, G. N., and Hirsch, M. (1954). *J. Bacteriol.* **67**, 182.

Cohn, M., and Torriani, A. M., (1953). *Biochim. et Biophys. Acta.* **10**, 280.

Conn, E. E., and Vennesland, B. (1951). *Nature* **167**, 975.

Cook, R. P., and Woolf, B. (1928). *Biochem. J.* **22**, 474.

Cook, E. S., Cronin, A. G., Kreke, C. W., and Walsh, T. M. (1943). *Nature* **152**, 474.

Creaser, E. H. (1955). *Nature* **175**, 899; **176**, 556.

Dalgleish, C. E. (1957). *Science* **125**, 271.

Damlé, W. R., and Thorne, R. S. W. (1949). *J. Inst. Brewing* **55**, 13.

Davis, B. D. (1953). *Science* **118**, 251.

Davis, B. D. (1955a). *Advances in Enzymol.* **16**, 247.

Davis, B. D. (1955b). *In* "Amino Acid Metabolism" (W. D. McElroy and B. Glass, eds.), p. 779. Johns Hopkins Press, Baltimore.

Davis, B. D. (1955c). *Federation Proc.* **14**, 691.

Davis, B. D. (1955d). *Advances in Enzymol.* **16**, 267.

De la Haba, G., and Cantoni, G. L. (1957). *Federation Proc.* **16**, 170.

Delluva, A. M. (1953). *Arch. Biochem. and Biophys.* **45**, 443.

De Moss, J. A., and Novelli, G. D. (1955). *Biochim. et Biophys. Acta* **18**, 592.

De Moss, J. A., Genuth, S. M., and Novelli, G. D. (1956a). *Federation Proc.* **15**, 241.

De Moss, J. A., Genuth, S. M., and Novelli, G. D. (1956b). *Proc. Natl. Acad. Sci. U.S.* **42**, 325.

Dernby, K. G. (1917). *Biochem. Z.* **81**, 107.

Dewan, J. G. (1938). *Biochem. J.* **32**, 1378.

Di Carlo, F. J., Schultz, A. S., and Fisher, R. A. (1949). *Arch. Biochem. and Biophys.* **20**, 90.

Di Carlo, F. J., Schultz, A. S., and McManus, D. K. (1951). *J. Biol. Chem.* **189**, 151.

Di Carlo, F. J., Schultz, A. S., and Lint, A. M. (1953). *Arch. Biochem. and Biophys.* **44**, 468.

Dounce, A. L. (1952). *Enzymologia* **15**, 251.

Eddy, A. A. (1955a). Private communication.

Eddy, A. A. (1955b). *J. Gen. Microbiol.* **13**, xiii.

Eddy, A. A., and Kirsop, B. (1955). *J. Inst. Brewing* **61**, 382.

Edlbacher, S. (1943). *Ergeb. Enzymforsch.* **9**, 131.

Edlbacher, S., and Baur, H. (1938). *Z. physiol. Chem.* **254**, 275.

Edmonds, M., Delluva, A. M., and Wilson, D. W. (1952). *J. Biol. Chem.* **197**, 251.

Ehrensvärd, G. (1955). *Ann. Rev. Biochem.* **24**, 275.

Ehrensvärd, G., Reio, L., and Saluste, E. (1949). *Acta Chem. Scand.* **3**, 645.

Ehrensvärd, G., Reio, L., Saluste, E., and Stjernholm, R. (1951a). *J. Biol. Chem.* **189**, 93.

Ehrensvärd, G., Cutinelli, C., Reio, L., Saluste, E., and Stjernholm, R. (1951b). *Acta Chem. Scand.* **5**, 353.

Ehrensvärd, G., Sperber, E., Saluste, E., Reio, L., and Stjernholm, R. (1947). *J. Biol. Chem.* **169**, 759.

Ehrlich, F. (1907). *Ber. deut. chem. Ges.* **40**, 1027.

Ehrlich, F. (1909). *Biochem. Z.* **18**, 391.

Ehrlich, F. (1911). *Ber. deut. chem. Ges.* **44**, 139.

Ehrlich, F. (1912). *Ber. deut. chem. Ges.* **45**, 883.

Elliott, W. H. (1948). *Nature* **161**, 128.

Elliott, W. H. (1953). *J. Biol. Chem.* **201**, 661.

Erkama, J., and Virtanen, A. I. (1951). *In* "The Enzymes" (J. B. Sumner and K. Myrbäck, eds.), Vol. 1, Part 2, p. 1244. Academic Press, New York.

Euler, H. von, Adler, E., Günther, G., and Das, N. B. (1938). *Z. physiol. Chem.* **254**, 61.

Feldman, L. I., and Gunsalus, I. C. (1950). *J. Biol. Chem.* **187**, 821.

Fincham, J. R. S. (1951). *Nature* **168**, 957.

Fincham, J. R. S. (1953). *Biochem. J.* **53**, 313.

Fincham, J. R. S. (1955). *Biochem. J. Proc.* **61**, xxiii.

Fincham, J. R. S., and Boulter, A. B. (1956). *Biochem. J.* **62**, 72.

Flaks, J. G., and Buchanan, J. M. (1956). *J. Am. Chem. Soc.* **78**, 4497.

Fodor, P. J., Miller, A., Neidle, A., and Waelsch, H. (1953). *J. Biol. Chem.* **205**, 991.

Foulkes, E. C. (1951). *Biochem. J.* **48**, 378.

Fournier, J. P., and Bouthillier, L. P. (1952). *J. Am. Chem. Soc.* **74**, 5210.

Fromageot, C. (1951). *In* "The Enzymes" (J. B. Sumner and K. Myrbäck, eds.), Vol. 1, Part 2, p. 1237. Academic Press, New York.

Fry, B. A. (1955). "The Nitrogen Metabolism of Micro-organisms," p. 134. Wiley, New York.

Gabriel, O., and Hofmann-Ostenhof, O. (1956). *Monatsh. Chem.* **87**, 242.

Gale, E. F. (1940). *Bacteriol. Revs.* **4**, 135.

Gale, E. F. (1947). *J. Gen. Microbiol.* **1**, 53.

Gale, E. F. (1953). *Advances in Protein Chem.* **8**, 285.

Gale, E. F. (1955). In "Amino Acid Metabolism" (W. D. McElroy and B. Glass, eds.), p. 171. Johns Hopkins Press, Baltimore.

Gale, E. F. (1956). *Biochem. J.* **62**, 40P.

Gale, E. F. (1957). *Proc. Roy. Soc.* **B146**, 166.

Gale, E. F., and Folkes, J. (1954). *Nature* **173**, 1223.

Gale, E. F., and Folkes, J. (1955). *Biochem. J.* **59**, 661, 675.

Gale, E. F., and Freeland, J. C. (1947). *Biochem. J.* **40**, 135.

Gale, E. F., and Stephenson, M. (1938). *Biochem. J.* **32**, 392.

Geiger, E. (1950). *Science* **111**, 594.

Gilvarg, C. Unpublished.

Gilvarg, C. (1952). *J. Biol. Chem.* **199**, 57.

Gilvarg, C., and Bloch, K. (1951). *J. Biol. Chem.* **193**, 339.

Gilvarg, C., and Bloch, K. (1952). *J. Biol. Chem.* **199**, 689.

Giri, K. V. (1953). *Current Sci. (India)* **22**, 143.

Glass, B. (1955). In "Amino Acid Metabolism" (W. D. McElroy and B. Glass, eds.), p. 951. Johns Hopkins Press, Baltimore.

Goldthwaite, D. A. (1956). *J. Biol. Chem.* **222**, 1051.

Goldthwaite, D. A., Peabody, R. A., and Greenberg, G. R. (1955). In "Amino Acid Metabolism" (W. D. McElroy and B. Glass, eds.), p. 765. Johns Hopkins Press, Baltimore.

Goldwasser, E. (1955). *J. Am. Chem. Soc.* **77**, 6083.

Grassmann, W. (1927). *Z. physiol. Chem.* **167**, 202.

Grassmann, W., and Dyckerhoff, H. (1928). *Z. physiol. Chem.* **179**, 41.

Grassmann, W., Embden, L., and Schneller, H. (1934). *Biochem. Z.* **271**, 216.

Grisolia, S. (1951). In "Phosphorus Metabolism" (W. D. McElroy and B. Glass, eds.). Johns Hopkins Press, Baltimore.

Grisolia, S. (1955). In "Amino Acid Metabolism" (W. D. McElroy and B. Glass, eds.), p. 258. Johns Hopkins Press, Baltimore.

Grisolia, S., Wallach, D. P., and Grady, H. J. (1955). *Biochim. et Biophys. Acta* **17**, 150, 277.

Grunberg-Manago, M., Ortiz, P. J., and Ochoa, S. (1956). *Biochim. et Biophys. Acta* **20**, 269.

Haehn, H., and Leopold, H. (1935). *Fermentforschung* **14**, 539.

Haehn, H., and Leopold, H. (1937). *Biochem. Z.* **292**, 380.

Halvorson, H. O., and Jackson, L. (1956). *J. Gen. Microbiol.* **14**, 26.

Halvorson, H. O., and Spiegelman, S. (1952). *J. Bacteriol.* **64**, 207.

Halvorson, H. O., Spiegelman, S., and Hinman, R. (1955). *Arch. Biochem. and Biophys.* **55**, 512.

Hampton, A. (1957). *J. Am. Chem. Soc.* **79**, 503.

Hanes, C. S., Hird, F. J. R., and Isherwood, F. A. (1952). *Biochem. J.* **51**, 25.

Harris, G., and Parsons, R. (1956). Unpublished.

Harris, G., and Pollock, J. R. A. (1952). *Chemistry & Industry* p. 931.

Harris, G., and Pollock, J. R. A. (1953). *J. Inst. Brewing* **59**, 28.

Hartelius, V. (1939). *Compt. rend. trav. lab. Carlsberg, Sér. physiol.* **22** (19), 303.

Hartman, S. C., Levenberg, B., and Buchanan, J. M. (1956). *J. Biol. Chem.* **221**, 1057.

Haskins, F. A., and Mitchell, H. K. (1949). *Proc. Natl. Acad. Sci. U.S.* **35**, 500.

Heppel, L. A., and Hilmoe, R. J. (1951). *Abstr. Am. Chem. Soc. 121st Meeting, Milwaukee,* p. 18C.

Herrmann, R. L., and Fairley, J. L. (1956). *Federation Proc.* 15, 274.

Hird, F. J. R., and Rowsell, E. V. (1950). *Nature* 166, 517.

Hird, F. J. R., and Springell, P. H. (1954). *Biochem. J.* 56, 417.

Hoagland, M. B. (1955). *Biochim. et Biophys. Acta* 16, 288.

Hoagland, M. B., and Zamecnik, P. C. (1957). *Federation Proc.* 16, 197.

Hoagland, M. B., Keller, E. B., and Zamecnik, P. C. (1956). *J. Biol. Chem.* 218, 345.

Hogness, D. S., Cohn, M., and Monod, J. (1955). *Biochim. et Biophys. Acta* 16, 99.

Holley, R. W. (1957). *J. Am. Chem. Soc.* 79, 658.

Horowitz, N. H. (1947). *J. Biol. Chem.* 171, 255.

Hotchkiss, R. D., and Marmur, J. (1954). *Proc. Natl. Acad. Sci. U.S.* 40, 55.

Hurwitz, J. (1952). *Biochim. et Biophys. Acta* 9, 496.

Ingram, M. (1955). "An Introduction to the Biology of Yeasts," p. 118. Pitman, London.

Johnson, M. J. (1941). *J. Biol. Chem.* 137, 575.

Jones, M. E., Lipmann, F., Hilz, H., and Lynen, F. (1953). *J. Am. Chem. Soc.* 75, 3285.

Jones, M. E., Spector, L., and Lipmann, F. (1955). *J. Am. Chem. Soc.* 77, 819.

Joslyn, M. A. (1955). *Wallerstein Lab. Communs.* 18, 107.

Kalan, E. B., and Leitner, (1955); cf. Davis, B. D. (1955c).

Kalan, E. B., Davis, B. D., Srinivasan, P. R., and Sprinson, D. B. (1956). *J. Biol. Chem.* 223, 907.

Kalckar, H. M. (1951). *Pubbl. staz. zool. Napoli* 23, suppl. 87.

Keller, E. B., and Zamecnik, P. C. (1956). *J. Biol. Chem.* 221, 45.

Kelner, A. (1953). *J. Bacteriol.* 65, 252.

Kerr, S. E., and Chernigoy, F. (1953). *J. Biol. Chem.* 200, 887.

Kerr, S. E., Seraidarian, K., and Brown, G. B. (1951). *J. Biol. Chem.* 188, 207.

Kisliuk, R. L., and Sakami, W. (1956). *Federation Proc.* 15, 289.

Korzenovsky, M. (1955). *In* "Amino Acid Metabolism" (W. D. McElroy and B. Glass, eds.), p. 309. Johns Hopkins Press, Baltimore.

Kossowicz, A. (1912). *Z. Gärungsphysiol.* 1, 253.

Kossowicz, A. (1914). *Biochem. Z.* 64, 82.

Krebs, H. A., Gurin, S., and Eggleston, L. V. (1952). *Biochem. J.* 51, 614.

Krebs, H. A., and Hems, R. (1955). *Biochem. J.* 61, 435.

Krebs, H. A., and Henseleit, K. (1932). *Z. physiol. Chem.* 210, 33.

Krimsky, I., and Racker, E. (1952). *J. Biol. Chem.* 198, 721.

Krishnaswamy, P. R., and Giri, K. V. (1956). *Biochem. J.* 62, 301.

Lampen, J. O. (1952). *Bacteriol. Rev.* 16, 211.

Lascelles, J., Cross, M. J., and Woods, D. D. (1954). *J. Gen. Microbiol.* 10, 267.

Lascelles, J., and Woods, D. D. (1950). *Nature* 166, 649.

Lee, N. D., and Williams, R. H. (1952). *Biochim. et Biophys. Acta* 9, 698.

Lenney, J. F. (1956). *J. Biol. Chem.* 221, 919.

Levenberg, B., and Metnick, I. (1956). *Federation Proc.* 15, 118.

Levenberg, B., and Buchanan, J. M. (1957). *J. Biol. Chem.* 224, 1005, 1019.

Levy, L., and Coon, M. J. (1951). *J. Biol. Chem.* 192, 807.

Levy, L., and Coon, M. J. (1954). *J. Biol. Chem.* 208, 691.

Lichstein, H. C. (1949). *J. Biol. Chem.* 177, 125.

Lichstein, H. C. (1957). *Federation Proc.* 16, 211.

Liebermann, I. (1956a). *J. Biol. Chem.* **222,** 765.

Liebermann, I. (1956b). *J. Am. Chem. Soc.* **78,** 251; *J. Biol. Chem.* **223,** 327.

Lifson, N., Lorber, V., Sakami, W., and Wood, H. G. (1948). *J. Biol. Chem.* **176,** 1263.

Lindner, P., and Naumann, K. W. (1913). *Wochschr. Brau.* **30,** 589.

Linnane, A. W., and Still, J. L. (1955). *Arch. Biochem. and Biophys.* **59,** 383.

Lipmann, F. (1911). *J. Biol. Chem.* **73,** 263.

Lipmann, F. (1954). *In* "Symposium on the Mechanism of Enzyme Action" (W. D. McElroy and H. B. Glass, eds.). Johns Hopkins Press, Baltimore.

Loftfield, R. B., and Harris, A. (1956). *J. Biol. Chem.* **219,** 151.

Longenecker, J. B., and Snell, E. E. (1956). *Proc. Natl. Acad. Sci. U.S.* **42,** 221.

Lukens, L. N., and Buchanan, J. M. (1956). *Federation Proc.* **15,** 305.

Lynen, F., and Neciullah, N. (1939). *Ann. Chem. Justus Liebigs* **541,** 203.

Maas, W. K. (1956). *Federation Proc.* **15,** 305.

Maas, W. K., and Novelli, G. D. (1953). *Arch. Biochem. and Biophys.* **43,** 236.

Magasanik, B., and Bowser, H. R. (1955). *J. Biol. Chem.* **213,** 571.

Magasanik, B., Moyed, H. S., and Karibian, D. (1956). *J. Am. Chem. Soc.* **78,** 1510.

Markham, R., and Smith, J. D. (1952). *Biochem. J.* **52,** 552, 558, 565.

Markowitz, A., and Klein, H. P. (1955). *J. Bacteriol.* **70,** 649.

Marshall, R. O., Hall, L. M., and Cohen, P. P. (1955). *Biochim. et Biophys. Acta* **17,** 279.

Maschmann, E. (1943). *Naturwiss.* **31,** 136.

Massart, L., and Horens, J. (1953). *Enzymologia* **15,** 359.

McElroy, W. D., and Glass, B., eds. (1956). "A Symposium on Inorganic Nitrogen Metabolism." Johns Hopkins Press, Baltimore.

McManus, I. R. (1954). *J. Biol. Chem.* **208,** 639.

McNutt, W. S. (1956). *J. Biol. Chem.* **219,** 365.

McQuillen, K., and Roberts, R. B. (1954). *J. Biol. Chem.* **207,** 81.

McRorie, R. A., Carlson, G. L., and Satterfield, G. H. (1956). *Federation Proc.* **15,** 210.

Meister, A. (1955a). *In* "Amino Acid Metabolism" (W. D. McElroy and B. Glass, eds.), p. 3. Johns Hopkins Press, Baltimore.

Meister, A. (1955b). *Federation Proc.* **14,** 683.

Meister, A., Sober, H. A., and Peterson, E. A. (1954). *J. Biol. Chem.* **206,** 89.

Meltzer, H. L., and Sprinson, D. B. (1950). *Federation Proc.* **9,** 204.

Miettinen, J. K. (1954). *Ann. Acad. Sci. Fennicae Ser. A. II,* 58.

Miller, H. K., and Waelsch, H. (1952). *Nature* **169,** 30.

Miller, A., and Waelsch, H. (1956). *Arch. Biochem.* **63,** 263.

Mitchell, H. K., and Houlahan, M. B. (1947). *Federation Proc.* **6,** 506.

Mitchell, H. K., and Houlahan, M. B. (1948). *J. Biol. Chem.* **174,** 883.

Mitchelson, A. M., Drell, W., and Mitchell, H. K. (1951). *Proc. Natl. Acad. Sci. U.S.* **37,** 396.

Mitsuhashi, S., and Davis, B. D. (1954). *Biochim. et Biophys. Acta* **15,** 54.

Moat, A. G., and Lichstein, H. C. (1954). *Arch. Biochem. and Biophys.* **48,** 300.

Moat, A. G., Wilkins, C. N., and Friedman, H. (1956). *J. Biol. Chem.* **223,** 985; *Federation Proc.* **15,** 605..

Monod, J., Pappenheimer, A. M., and Cohen-Bazire, G. (1952). *Biochim. et Biophys. Acta* **9,** 648.

Morrison, R. I. (1952). *Biochem. J. Proc.* **50,** xiv.

Myers, J. W., and Adelberg, E. A. (1954). *Proc. Natl. Acad. Sci. U.S.* **40**, 493.

Neidle, A., and Waelsch, H. (1956). *J. Am. Chem. Soc.* **78**, 1767.

Neidle, A., and Waelsch, H. (1957). *Federation Proc.* **16**, 225.

Neubauer, O., and Fromherz, K. (1911). *Z. physiol. Chem.* **70**, 326.

Neuberg, C., and Grauer, A. (1952). *Z. physiol. Chem.* **289**, 253.

Neuberg, C., and Hildesheimer, A. (1911). *Biochem. Z.* **31**, 170.

Newmeyer, D., and Ratner, S. (1955). *In* "Amino Acid Metabolism" (W. D. McElroy and B. Glass, eds.), p. 231. Johns Hopkins Press, Baltimore.

Nickerson, W. J. (1944). *Mycologia* **36**, 224.

Nickerson, W. J., and Falcone, G. (1956). *Science* **124**, 722.

Nickerson, W. J., and Mankowski, Z. T. (1953). *Am. J. Botany* **40**, 584.

Nielsen, N. (1936). *Compt. rend. trav. lab. Carlsberg, Sér. physiol.* **21**, 395.

Nielsen, N. (1938). *Compt. rend. trav. lab. Carlsberg, Sér. physiol.* **22**, 384.

Nielsen, N. (1941). *Biochem. Z.* **307**, 187.

Nielsen, N. (1943). *Ergeb. Biol.* **19**, 375.

Nielsen, N., and Hartelius, V. (1938). *Biochem. Z.* **295**, 211.

Nisman, B., and Mager, J. (1952). *Nature* **169**, 243.

Nisman, B., Cohen, G. N., Wiesendanger, S. B., and Hirsch, M. (1954). *Compt. rend.* **238**, 1342.

Nossal, P. M. (1954a). *Biochem. J.* **57**, 62.

Nossal, P. M. (1954b). *Biochim. et Biophys. Acta* **14**, 154.

Novelli, G. D., and Lipmann, F. (1950). *J. Biol. Chem.* **182**, 213.

Ochoa, S., Mii, S., Schneider, M. C., Smellie, R. M. S., Warner, R. C., and Ortiz, P. J. (1957). *Federation Proc.* **16**, 228.

Olmsted, P. S. (1957). *Federation Proc.* **16**, 229.

Olson, J. A., and Anfinsen, C. B. (1952). *J. Biol. Chem.* **197**, 67.

Olson, J. A. (1954). *Nature* **174**, 695.

Osborn, M. J., and Talbert, P. T. (1957). *Federation Proc.* **16**, 230.

Ostern, P., Terszakowec, J., and Hubl, S. (1938a). *Z. physiol. Chem.* **255**, 104.

Ostern, P., Baranowski, T., and Terszakowec, J. (1938b). *Z. physiol. Chem.* **251**, 258.

Ottey, L. (1955). *J. Pharmacol. Exptl. Therap.* **115**, 339.

Pardee, A. B. (1955). *J. Bacteriol.* **69**, 233.

Pollack, M. A., and Lindner, M. (1943). *J. Biol. Chem.* **147**, 183.

Putnam, F. W. (1953). *Advances in Protein Chem.* **8**, 175.

Racker, E. (1955). *J. Biol. Chem.* **217**, 855.

Ragland, J. B., and Liverman, J. L. (1956). *Arch. Biochem. and Biophys.* **65**, 574.

Ratner, S. (1955). *In* "Amino Acid Metabolism" (W. D. McElroy and B. Glass, eds.), p. 231. Johns Hopkins Press, Baltimore.

Reichard, P. (1957). *Acta Chem. Scand.* **11**, 11.

Reid, J. C., and Landefeld, M. O. (1951). *Arch. Biochem. and Biophys.* **34**, 219.

Reiner, J. M., and Goodman, F. (1955). *Arch. Biochem. and Biophys.* **57**, 475.

Reiner, J. M., and Spiegelman, S. (1948). *Federation Proc.* **7**, 98.

Reiss, O., and Bloch, K. (1955). *J. Biol. Chem.* **216**, 703.

Rickenberg, H. V., Yanofsky, C., and Bonner, D. M. (1953). *J. Bacteriol.* **66**, 683.

Robbins, P. W., and Lipmann, F. (1956). *J. Am. Chem. Soc.* **78**, 2652.

Roberts, E., Ayengar, P., and Posner, I. (1953). *J. Biol. Chem.* **203**, 195.

Roche, J., and Lacombe, G. (1952). *Biochim. et Biophys. Acta* **9**, 687.

Roine, P. (1947). Ph.D. Thesis, Helsinki.

Roll, P. M., Weinfeld, H., and Carroll, E. (1956a). *J. Biol. Chem.* **220**, 455.

Roll, P. M., Weinfeld, H., Carroll, E., and Brown, G. B. (1956b). *J. Biol. Chem.* **220**, 439.

Romano, A. H., and Nickerson, W. J. (1954). *J. Biol. Chem.* **208**, 409.

Rotman, B., and Spiegelman, S. (1954). *J. Bacteriol.* **68**, 419.

Roush, A. H. (1954). *Arch. Biochem. and Biophys.* **50**, 510.

Rowsell, E. V. (1951). *Nature* **168**, 104.

Sable, H. Z. (1950). *Proc. Soc. Exptl. Biol. Med.* **75**, 215.

Sakami, W. (1955). In "Amino Acid Metabolism" (W. D. McElroy and B. Glass, eds.), p. 658. Johns Hopkins Press, Baltimore.

Sakamura, T., and Maeda, K. (1950). *J. Fac. Sci. Hokkaido Univ. Ser. V.* **7** (2), 77.

Sallach, H. J. (1956). *J. Biol. Chem.* **223**, 1101.

Sanadi, D. R., Gibson, D. M., Ayengar, P., and Jacob, M. (1956). *J. Biol. Chem.* **218**, 505.

Sandegren, E., Ekström, D., and Nielsen, N. (1950). *Acta Chem. Scand.* **4**, 1311.

Saz, A. K., and Brownell, L. W. (1954). *Arch. Biochem. and Biophys.* **52**, 291.

Schales, O. (1951). In "The Enzymes" (J. B. Sumner and K. Myrbäck, eds.), Vol. 2, Part 1, p. 216. Academic Press, New York.

Schlenk, F. (1951). In "The Enzymes" (J. B. Sumner and K. Myrbäck, eds.), Vol. 2, Part 1, p. 306. Academic Press, New York.

Schlenk, F., and Tillotson, J. A. (1954). *Federation Proc.* **13**, 290.

Schlossmann, K., and Lynen, F. (1957). *Angew. Chem.* **69**, 179.

Schmidt, G., Cubiles, R., and Thannhauser, S. J. (1947). *Cold Spring Harbour Symposia Quant. Biol.* **12**, 161.

Schmidt, G., Seraidarian, K., Greenbaum, L. M., and Thannhauser, S. J. (1954). *Federation Proc.* **13**, 291.

Schmitz, H. (1954). *Biochem. Z.* **325**, 555.

Schultz, A. S., and McManus, D. K. (1950). *Arch. Biochem. and Biophys.* **25**, 401.

Schultz, A. S., and Pomper, S. (1948). *Arch. Biochem. and Biophys.* **19**, 184.

Shapiro, S. K. (1956). *J. Bacteriol.* **72**, 730.

Sheffner, A. L., and Grabow, J. (1953). *J. Bacteriol.* **66**, 192.

Shemin, D. (1949). *Cold Spring Harbour Symposia Quant. Biol.* **14**, 161.

Sher, H. I., and Mallette, M. F. (1954). *Arch. Biochem. and Biophys.* **53**, 354, 370.

Shive, W., Ackermann, W. W., Gordon, M., Getzendaner, M. E., and Eakin, R. E. (1947). *J. Am. Chem. Soc.* **69**, 725.

Siminovitch, L., and Graham, A. F. (1955). *Can. J. Microbiol.* **1**, 721.

Singer, T. P., and Kearney, E. B. (1953). *Biochim. et Biophys. Acta* **11**, 270, 276, 290.

Singer, T. P., and Kearney, E. B. (1954). In "Amino Acid Metabolism" (W. D. McElroy and B. Glass, eds.), p. 558. Johns Hopkins Press, Baltimore.

Singer, T. P., and Pensky, J. (1954). *Biochim. et Biophys. Acta* **9**, 316.

Skerman, V. B. D., Dementjev, G., and Skyring, G. W. (1957). *Nature* **179**, 742.

Sloane, N. H., Barg, W. F., Boggiano, E., Coulomb, B., and Hutchings, B. L. (1956). *J. Am. Chem. Soc.* **78**, 4497.

Smith, E. L. (1951). In "The Enzymes" (J. B. Sumner and K. Myrbäck, eds.), Vol. 1, Part 2, p. 793. Academic Press, New York.

Smith, M. E., and Greenberg, D. M. (1956). *Nature* **177**, 1130.

Snell, E. E. (1945). *J. Am. Chem. Soc.* **67**, 194.

Snoke, J. E. (1955). *J. Biol. Chem.* **213**, 813.

Sonne, J. C., Lin, I., and Buchanan, J. M. (1956). *J. Biol. Chem.* **220**, 369.

Soucy, R., and Bouthillier, L. P. (1951). *Rev. can. biol.* **10**, 290.

Speck, J. F. (1949). *J. Biol. Chem.* **179**, 1387.

Spiegelman, S., Halvorson, H. O., and Ben-Ishai, R. (1955). In "Amino Acid Metabolism" (W. D. McElroy and B. Glass, eds.), p. 124. Johns Hopkins Press, Baltimore.

Spiegelman, S., and Kamen, M. D. (1946). *Science* **104**, 581.

Spiegelman, S., and Kamen, M. D. (1947). *Cold Spring Harbour Symposia Quant. Biol.* **12**, 211.

Sprinson, D. B. (1951). *Abstr. Am. Chem. Soc. Boston.*

Sprinson, D. B., and Rittenberg, D. (1952). *J. Biol. Chem.* **198**, 655.

Srb, A. M., and Horowitz, N. H. (1944). *J. Biol. Chem.* **154**, 129.

Srinivasan, P. R., Shigeura, H. T., Sprecher, M., Sprinson, D. B., and Davis, B. D. (1956a). *J. Biol. Chem.* **220**, 477.

Srinivasan, P. R., Sprinson, D. B., Kalan, E. B., and Davis, B. D. (1956b). *J. Biol. Chem.* **223**, 907, 913.

Srinivasan, P. R., and Sprinson, D. B. (1956). *Federation Proc.* **15**, 360.

Stafford, H. A., Magaldi, A., and Vennesland, B. (1954). *J. Biol. Chem.* **207**, 62.

Stahl, W. H., McQue, B., Mandels, G. R., and Siu, R. G. H. (1949). *Arch. Biochem. and Biophys.* **20**, 422.

Stanier, R. Y. (1951). *Ann. Rev. Microbiol.* **5**, 35.

Stekol, J. A. (1955). In "Amino Acid Metabolism" (W. D. McElroy and B. Glass, eds.), p. 509. Johns Hopkins Press, Baltimore.

Stelling-Dekker, N. M. (1931). "Die Sporogenen Hefen," Amsterdam.

Stetten, M. R. (1951). *J. Biol. Chem.* **189**, 499.

Stetten, M. R., and Fox, C. L. (1945). *J. Biol. Chem.* **161**, 333.

Steward, F. C., and Thompson, J. F. (1954). In "The Proteins" (H. Neurath and K. Bailey, eds.), Vol. 2, Part A, p. 513. Academic Press, New York.

Stickland, L. H. (1934). *Biochem. J.* **28**, 1746.

Stickland, L. H. (1935). *Biochem. J.* **29**, 288, 889.

Stokes, J. L., Larsen, A., and Gunness, M. (1947). *J. Bacteriol.* **54**, 219.

Strassman, M., and Weinhouse, S. (1952). *J. Am. Chem. Soc.* **74**, 1726.

Strassman, M., and Weinhouse, S. (1953). *J. Am. Chem. Soc.* **75**, 1680.

Strassman, M., and Weinhouse, S. (1955). In "Amino Acid Metabolism" (W. D. McElroy and B. Glass, eds.), p. 452. Johns Hopkins Press, Baltimore.

Strassman, M., Thomas, A. J., and Weinhouse, S. (1953). *J. Am. Chem. Soc.* **75**, 5135.

Strassman, M., Thomas, A. J., and Weinhouse, S. (1955). *J. Am. Chem. Soc.* **77**, 1261.

Strassman, M., Thomas, A. J., and Weinhouse, S. (1956a). *Federation Proc.* **15**, 365.

Strassman, M., Thomas, A. J., Locke, L. A., and Weinhouse, S. (1956b). *J. Am. Chem. Soc.* **78**, 228.

Strassman, M., Locke, L. A., Thomas, A. J., and Weinhouse, S. (1956). *J. Am. Chem. Soc.* **78**, 1599.

Sullivan, M. X. (1929). *Public Health Reps. (U.S.)* **44**, 1421.

Sumiki, Y. (1928). *Bull. Japan Soc. Ferment.* **23**, 33; *Chem. Abstr.* (1929), **23**, 2531.

Swenson, P. A. (1950). *Proc. Natl. Acad. Sci. U.S.* **36**, 699.

Tabor, H., and Hayaishi, O. (1952). *J. Biol. Chem.* **194**, 171.

Tabor, H., Mehler, A. H., Hayaishi, O., and White, J. (1952). *J. Biol. Chem.* **196**, 121.

Tanenbaum, S. W. (1956). *J. Biol. Chem.* **218**, 733.

Tanner, F. W. (1918). *J. Am. Chem. Soc.* **40**, 663.

Tatum, E. L., and Perkins, D. B. (1950). *Ann. Rev. Microbiol.* **4**, 129.

Taylor, E. S. (1947). *J. Gen. Microbiol.* **1**, 86.

Teas, H. J., Horowitz, N. H., and Fling, M. (1948). *J. Biol. Chem.* **172**, 651.

Teas, H. J. (1948). *Oak Ridge Natl. Rept. No. 164.*

Thomas, R. C., Christensen, B. E., Cheldelin, V. H., and Wang, C. H. (1953). *J. Am. Chem. Soc.* **75**, 5554.

Thomas, R. C., Christensen, B. E., Cheldelin, V. H., and Wang, C. H. (1955). *J. Am. Chem. Soc.* **77**, 5448.

Thorne, R. S. W. (1937). *J. Inst. Brewing* **43**, 288.

Thorne, R. S. W. (1941). *J. Inst. Brewing* **47**, 270.

Thorne, R. S. W. (1944). *J. Inst. Brewing* **50**, 222, 186.

Thorne, R. S. W. (1945). *J. Inst. Brewing* **51**, 114.

Thorne, R. S. W. (1946a). *J. Inst. Brewing* **52**, 5, 15.

Thorne, R. S. W. (1946b). *Wallerstein Lab. Commun.* **9**, 97.

Thorne, R. S. W. (1949). *J. Inst. Brewing* **55**, 201.

Thorne, R. S. W. (1950). *Wallerstein Lab. Commun.* **13**, 319.

Toporek, M., Miller, L. L., and Bale, W. F. (1952). *J. Biol. Chem.* **198**, 839.

Turba, F., and Esser, H. (1953). *Angew. Chem.* **65**, 256.

Umbarger, H. E. (1956). *Science* **123**, 848.

Umbarger, H. E., and Adelberg, E. A. (1951). *J. Biol. Chem.* **192**, 883.

Ushiba, D., and Magasanik, B. (1952). *Proc. Soc. Exptl. Biol. Med.* **80**, 626.

Vavra, J. J., and Johnson, M. J. (1956). *J. Biol. Chem.* **220**, 33.

Vescia, A. (1956). *Biochim. et Biophys. Acta* **19**, 174.

Virtanen, A. L., and Tarnanen, J. (1932). *Biochem. Z.* **250**, 193; (1935). *Suomen Kemistilehti,* **B5**, 30.

Virtanen, A. I., Csáky, T. Z., and Rautanen, N. (1949). *Biochim. et Biophys. Acta* **3**, 208.

Vogel, H. J. (1953). *Proc. Natl. Acad. Sci. U.S.* **39**, 578.

Vogel, H. J. (1955). *In* "Amino Acid Metabolism" (W. D. McElroy and B. Glass, eds.), p. 335. Johns Hopkins Press, Baltimore.

Vogel, H. J., and Bonner, D. M. (1954). *Proc. Natl. Acad. Sci. U.S.* **40**, 688.

Vogel, H. J., Abelson, P. H., and Bolton, E. T. (1953). *Biochim. et Biophys. Acta* **11**, 583.

Vogel, H. J., Davis, B. D., and Mingioli, E. S. (1951). *J. Am. Chem. Soc.* **73**, 1898.

Waelsch, H., and Miller, A. (1955). *In* "Amino Acid Metabolism" (W. D. McElroy and B. Glass, eds.), p. 407. Johns Hopkins Press, Baltimore.

Wanderscheck, H. (1928). *Wochschr. Brau.* **45**, 441.

Wang, C. H., Christensen, B. E., and Cheldelin, V. H. (1955). *J. Biol. Chem.* **213**, 365.

Wang, C. H., Thomas, R. C., Cheldelin, V. H., and Christensen, B. E. (1952). *J. Biol. Chem.* **197**, 663.

Wang, T. P., Sable, H. Z., and Lampen, J. O. (1950). *J. Biol. Chem.* **184**, 17.

Warren, L., and Flaks, J. G. (1956). *Federation Proc.* **15**, 379.

Watanabe, Y., and Shimura, K. (1954). *J. Agr. Chem. Soc. Japan* **28**, 678.

Webster, G. C. (1957). *Federation Proc.* **16**, 267.

Weed, L. L., and Wilson, D. W. (1954). *J. Biol. Chem.* **207**, 439.

Weinhouse, S., and Millington, R. H. (1947). *J. Am. Chem. Soc.* **69**, 3089.

Weinhouse, S., Millington, R. H., and Lewis, K. F. (1948). *J. Am. Chem. Soc.* **70,** 3680.

Weinhouse, S., Millington, R. H., and Strassman, M. (1951). *J. Am. Chem. Soc.* **73,** 1421.

Weiss, U., Gilvarg, C., Mingioli, E. S., and Davis, B. D. (1954). *Science* **119,** 774.

Westley, J., and Ceithaml, J. (1956a). *Arch. Biochem. and Biophys.* **60,** 215.

Westley, J., and Ceithaml, J. (1956b). *J. Biol. Chem.* **219,** 139.

White, A. G. C., and Werkman, C. H. (1947). *Arch. Biochem. and Biophys.* **13,** 27.

Wiame, J. M., Storck, R., and Bourgeois, S. (1953). *Biochim. et Biophys. Acta* **10,** 627.

Williams, W. J. (1951). *Federation Proc.* **10,** 270.

Williams, W. J., and Buchanan, J. M. (1953). *J. Biol. Chem.* **202,** 253.

Willstätter, R., and Grassmann, W. (1926). *Z. physiol. Chem.* **153,** 250.

Wilson, L. G., and Bandurski, R. S. (1956). *Plant physiol.* **31,** viii; *Arch. Biochem. and Biophys.* **62,** 503.

Windsor, E. (1951). *J. Biol. Chem.* **192,** 595.

Winzler, R. J., Burk, D., and du Vigneaud, V. (1944). *Arch. Biochem. and Biophys.* **5,** 25.

Wolf, G. (1953). *J. Biol. Chem.* **200,** 637.

Wood, W. A., and Gunsalus, I. C. (1949). *J. Biol. Chem.* **181,** 171.

Woolf, B. (1929). *Biochem. J.* **23,** 472.

Work, E. (1955). *In* "Amino Acid Metabolism" (W. D. McElroy and B. Glass, eds.), p. 462. Johns Hopkins Press, Baltimore.

Work, E., and Dewey, D. L. (1953). *Abstr. 6th Intern. Congr. Microbiol. Rome,* p. 33.

Wright, B. E. (1956). *J. Biol. Chem.* **219,** 873.

Wright, B. E., and Stadtman, T. C. (1956). *J. Biol. Chem.* **219,** 863.

Wright, L. D., Cresson, E. L., and Skeggs, H. R. (1950). *Proc. Soc. Exptl. Biol. Med.* **74,** 334.

Wright, L. D., Cresson, E. L., Skeggs, H. R., Reck, R. L., Wolf, D. E., Wolf, T. R., Valiant, J., and Folkers, K. (1951). *Science* **114,** 635.

Yanofsky, C. (1952). *J. Biol. Chem.* **198,** 348.

Yanofsky, C. (1955a). *J. Biol. Chem.* **217,** 345.

Yanofsky, C. (1955b). *In* "Amino Acid Metabolism" (W. D. McElroy and B. Glass, eds.), p. 930. Johns Hopkins Press, Baltimore.

Yanofsky, C. (1956). *Biochim. et Biophys. Acta* **20,** 438; *J. Biol. Chem.* **223,** 171.

Yanofsky, C. (1957). *J. Biol. Chem.* **224,** 783.

Yanofsky, C., and Reissig, J. L. (1953). *J. Biol. Chem.* **202,** 567.

Yates, R. A., and Pardee, A. B. (1956). *J. Biol. Chem.* **221,** 743, 757.

Zacharias, R. M., Thompson, J. F., and Steward, F. C. (1952). *J. Am. Chem. Soc.* **74,** 2949.

Ziegler, D. M., and Melchior, J. B. (1956). *J. Biol. Chem.* **222,** 731.

Zikes, H. (1909). *Sitzber. Akad. Wiss. Wien., Math. naturw. Kl. Abt.* 118.

CHAPTER X

The Technology of Yeast

Magnus Pyke

1. Baker's Yeast

A. *Historical*

Baker's yeast is, as such, a comparatively new development. During much of the nineteenth century, brewer's yeast, or barm from the brewery, was used as a leavening agent in bread making. According to Frey (1930), although compressed yeast intended for baking began to appear in England, Holland, and Germany as early as 1800, the use by bakers of yeast obtained as a by-product of brewing and distilling was only gradually supplanted. The first yeast used for bread making was derived from the manufacture of top fermentation beer. Later, this was superseded by the yeast which accumulated on the surface of the spirit mash or at the bottom of the fermenting vessels in distilleries. Finally, a method was worked out for growing and pressing distillery yeast specially for baking. It was found that this product was so much more satisfactory than the use in bakeries of beer yeast, which was often acrid from bacterial infection before it reached the baker and in a semi-liquid state, that the employment of specially prepared pressed baker's yeast became general.

It is stated by Jorgensen (1948) that the so-called "Dutch method" of making baker's yeast, used in about the middle of the nineteenth century, gave a yield of pressed yeast equivalent to from 4 to 6% of the weight of raw material employed. About 25% of spirit was obtained at the same time. From about 1860 onwards the "Vienna process" (Wienerverfahren) came into use. This method, in which yeast and spirit were still produced together from a grain mash, gave a yield of about 14% pressed yeast and 30% of spirit. Then came the publication of Pasteur's observations that the amount of yeast produced from a fixed quantity of sugar was very much greater under aerobic conditions than it was in the absence of aeration. This, the "Pasteur reaction," was applied to yeast manufacture in about 1900, some forty years after its discovery. The use of increasing volumes of air to maintain strongly aerobic conditions, together with increasingly dilute solutions, gradually enabled yields of 50 to 60% of yeast to be attained, accompanied by only 20% of spirit.

The final stage in the development of the methods of yeast manufacture used at the present time took place during World War I. Up till then, grain had been the main source of carbohydrate and the sole source of nitrogen for the propagation of yeast. Shortage of grain led to an intensive search for an alternative raw material. The problem was solved almost simultaneously by Sak (1919) in Denmark and by Hayduck (1919) in Germany. The introduction of the new method, "Zulaufverfahren," in about 1920 caused a complete revolution in the technique of yeast production. The process introduced molasses as a source of carbohydrate and ammonium salts as a source of nitrogen. By starting the propagation in a dilute solution and gradually adding molasses wort to keep pace with the growth of yeast, a yield of about 100% of pressed yeast in relation to the quantity of molasses used was obtained and the formation of alcohol was entirely suppressed.

B. Modern Methods of Propagation

(1) *Culture Medium.* Baker's yeast is almost always a strain of *Saccharomyces cerevisiae* and is most easily grown on a medium comprising simple hexoses, including glucose and fructose and disaccharides, usually sucrose or maltose. *Saccharomyces lactis,* which, unlike S. *cerevisiae,* can ferment lactose, has been grown commercially on whey as a baker's yeast (Stanier, 1946; Hanson *et al.,* 1949) but is not widely used. The commonest raw material employed as a substrate for the propagation of baker's yeast today is beet molasses. This may be used alone or with an admixture of refiners' cane molasses.

Beet Molasses. Beet molasses consists of the residue remaining after the bulk of the sugar has been crystallized in the manufacture of beet sugar. It is a black, syrupy mixture usually containing 50% of sucrose, together with about 9% of amino acids, and a variable amount of inorganic ash. It may be contaminated with sulfur dioxide, which is commonly used in the sugar refining process. "Refiners' beet" molasses is occasionally met with. It is the residual mother liquor remaining after crude beet sugar has been recrystallized. It contains lower concentrations of amino acids, mineral substances, and components of the vitamin B complex than normal beet molasses and is not usually employed in yeast manufacture. Apart from sulfur doxide, another trace substance claimed to interfere with the growth of yeast is butyric acid. Dierssen *et al.* (1956) and Andersen (1956) have reported that this and other volatile carboxylic acids in molasses may exert an inhibitory effect during yeast propagation.

Prior to the introduction of chromatographic methods of analysis, the sugar content of beet molasses was expressed as "total invert sugar" and was commonly calculated "as glucose." de Whalley *et al.* showed in 1951 that other sugars might be present in beet molasses besides sucrose. For example, they reported from 1.1% to 2.4% of raffinose. A striking feature of the composition of beet molasses is its comparatively large content of amino acids. Mariani and Torracci (1951) identified alanine as being present in greatest concentrations with glutamic acid, leucine, and γ-amino-butyric acid in next highest amounts while aspartic acid, serine, glycine, valine, and tyrosine were also detected. The total nitrogen content of beet molasses is about 1.5%, of which 0.6% in a normal sample is amino nitrogen.

As might be expected of a material of the nature of molasses, a variety of trace minerals are to be found in it. In actual practice however, Olson and Johnson (1949) found that maximum growth of baker's yeast could be achieved on a medium containing only phosphate, potassium, and magnesium as major mineral nutrients and zinc, iron, and copper as minor ones. Beet molasses normally contains 100 μg./g. of magnesium, 30 μg./g. of zinc, 150 μg./g. of iron, and 20 μg./g. of copper. Refiners' cane molasses contains substantially more magnesium, averaging about 2500 μg./g. Blackstrap molasses contains up to 5000 μg./g. of magnesium. The zinc content of refiners' cane molasses is about 5 μg./g. and that of blackstrap 10 μg/g.

Cane Molasses. Of the several types of cane molasses, two are most commonly employed in the manufacture of baker's yeast, when cane molasses is used at all. "Refiners' cane" molasses is the residue remaining after refined white sugar has been recrystallized from crude, unrefined, brown sugar. "Blackstrap" is the mother liquor remaining from which the crude sugar has initially been recovered. Cane molasses, like beet, is usually marketed containing 50% of "total invert sugar." That this is not solely sucrose has, as in the case of beet molasses, been well established. D-Glucose and D-fructose have both been isolated (Binkley and Wolfrom, 1950; Lew *et al.*, 1946) while D-mannose was identified in cane molasses over 50 years ago (Lobry de Bruyn and van Ekenstein, 1897). De Whalley (1952) found the trisaccharide, kestose, present and considered it to be produced in cane products by the action of microorganisms. The composition of molasses may vary quite widely, depending on the source of the beet or cane used, the cultural conditions under which it has been grown, and the exact process followed in the individual sugar refinery. This variation may be very important to the manufacturer of baker's yeast because he depends on his molasses, not only for the supply of fermentable sugar as the energy source for yeast growth, but also for vitamins and often for zinc and magnesium as well.

Vitamins in Molasses. The difference in vitamin content between beet and cane molasses is of importance to the manufacturer of baker's yeast in that cane molasses contains approximately 1.5 μg./g. of biotin, or about twenty times as much as beet molasses. There is a good deal of variation between individual samples. White (1954) quotes 1.0 to 1.8 μg./g. for refiners' cane and 2.7 to 3.2 μg./g. for blackstrap. "High-test," a grade of cane molasses containing substantially more sugar, contains correspondingly less biotin, namely 0.3 to 0.4 μg./g. Beet molasses is quoted as containing from 0.04 to 0.13 μg./g. of biotin. Rogers and Mickelson (1948) report lower values of 1.2 μg./g. for blackstrap.

So far as other vitamins of possible significance in yeast growth are concerned, the more commonly used beet molasses is richer in nicotinic acid, with about 35 μg./g.; in inositol, with about 5000 μg./g.; and in pantothenic acid with about 50 μg./g. The corresponding figures for refinery cane molasses would be 15, 2000, and 20 μg./g., respectively. Blackstrap molasses contains approximately twice the concentration of each vitamin as refinery cane molasses. The thiamine content of molasses may in some circumstances be a limiting factor in yeast propagation and as one of the more labile of the vitamins it is subject to partial destruction by heat during the manufacture of the molasses. The amount present in beet and in cane molasses is, therefore, variable. A representative figure for both types would be approximately 0.8 μg./g. (Binkley and Wolfrom, 1953).

Molasses contains other vitamins of the B complex in addition to those mentioned but these are seldom required as specific nutrients by the strains usually employed as baker's yeast. Rogers and Mickelson (1948) and Binkley and Wolfrom (1953) have reported figures for riboflavin and folic acid in addition to those of the more significant vitamins.

Mechanical Clarification of Molasses. In recent years the development of improved centrifuges has enabled yeast manufacturers to free their molasses from sediment by mechanical means. The molasses is usually diluted with water so that the "strong wort" contains about 40% of sugar. This molasses solution is heated to 90°C. to 95°C. for about an hour to sterilize it. The hot solution is then passed through a battery of centrifugal clarifiers arranged in parallel. These machines retain the sludge in a rapidly revolving bowl. The clarified wort may either be passed through a cooler for storage in a reservoir before use or may be allowed to pass still hot to the measuring device by which it is fed to the yeast.

Chemical Clarification of Molasses. Molasses can be freed to a remarkably high degree from the coloring matter and impurities that it contains by a number of treatments that are dealt with in detail in the technical literature (Van Damme, 1932; Walter, 1940; White, 1954). The most widely used of what might be called the traditional methods current from the mid-nineteen twenties onwards was based on the entrainment of impurities with a precipitate of tricalcium phosphate and calcium sulfate. In this process, the molasses diluted to a specific gravity of 20° Balling (approximately equivalent to a 20% sugar solution) is acidified with sulfuric acid, heated to 65°C. with steam, and calcium superphosphate added. The mixture is boiled, allowed to stand for an hour and then neutralized with CaO. After a further 8 hours' standing the sediment of calcium salts and organic matter sinks to the bottom and the clarified solution is decanted for use.

An alternative method involves the use of aluminum hydrate. The molasses is diluted with an equal volume of water and 1.5 parts by weight of aluminum sulfate added to each 100 parts of molasses. The whole is heated with steam, boiled for an hour, and cooled by the addition of water. Lime is then added and the solution boiled again for 2 hours. When the mixture cools, part of the impurities rise as scum to the surface and part are carried down with the precipitate.

A number of other methods of purifying molasses solutions have been proposed from time to time. For example, flocculation at pH 3.2 combined with adsorption on activated charcoal has been used as has also decolorization with charcoal in conjunction with treatment with lime or baryta (Van der Snikt, 1934). Precipitation of the molasses with colloidal ferric hydrate (Kharin and Dement'ev, 1938); precipitation of added protein with tannin and simultaneous adsorption on calcium carbonate (Bennett and Peake, 1933); and treatment with sodium silicate followed by filtration of the hot solution (Hoffmann *et al.*, 1932) have all been recommended.

Grain. Much of the baker's yeast manufactured today is produced from molasses, beet molasses being the commonest variety, but mixtures of beet molasses with varying proportions of cane molasses are also used. The use of grain as the source of fermentable carbohydrate is, however, occasionally seen. When a culture medium for yeast propagation is prepared from grain, the starch must first be broken down to maltose and other simple, assimilable sugars which can be utilized by the yeast. The material to be treated, which is normally barley, maize, wheat, or indeed any other cereal, or tapioca, is first cooked at an acid pH in order to gelatinize the starch. It is then cooled to an appropriate temperature between 45°C. and 55°C. and mixed with a suspension of ground barley malt to enable the malt enzymes to break down the starch to maltose and other soluble sugars. The process used is basically the same as that followed in brewing. For the manufacture of yeast, however, most authorities (see Van Damme, 1932; Walter, 1940) have recommended that subsequent to the treatment with malt the mash should be "soured" by the action of lactic acid bacteria, a culture of which is added in the final stages of the process and allowed to act for a period of 12 to 15 hours at a temperature of 59°C. The precise effect of this treatment is obscure. It is claimed on the one hand to bring about a hydrolysis of the proteins present in the grain extract and thus render them more readily available for yeast growth. Earlier authorities quoted by Van Damme (1932) were convinced that the "lactic souring" of grain wort had an important effect on the quality of the yeast produced.

Grain wort for yeast manufacture is customarily sterilized by being heated to 75°C. for 15 minutes and is then filtered before use.

(2) *Temperature and pH.* In the technology of yeast production (provided that the fermentative activity of the ultimate product when used in the bakery can be maintained) the yield of yeast obtained in proportion

to the amount of raw materials used is clearly a matter of considerable importance. The academic study of temperature and pH in yeast propagation is usually concentrated on the effect of these factors on growth *rate*. Somewhat different considerations apply in studying their effect on *yield*.

The temperature most favorable to the growth of baker's yeast varies somewhat from one strain to another. Jorgensen (1948) considered that the optimum temperature was usually between 25°C. and 35°C. The relation between the rate of growth and temperature was first pointed out by Muller in 1895. He and other workers (Barber, 1908; Claypole, 1909; Monod, 1942) showed that the rate increased as the temperature rose until it reached a maximum at about 37°C., after which damage to the cells began to occur. When we turn to yield, however, as distinct from speed of growth, it has been shown by several investigators (Smith, 1920; Monod, 1942; White, 1954) that the total growth of any microorganism when measured in relation to the amount of substrate fed to it is greatest, within certain limits, the lower the temperature. Under practical conditions of yeast manufacture, the best results are reported as being obtained (Walter, 1940) by beginning the propagation at 26°C. and gradually allowing the temperature to rise after 6 hours. Considerable care is taken by manufacturers to ensure, by the use of cooling coils and jackets, that the specified temperature range is not exceeded. Van Damme (1932) also emphasizes the importance of not allowing the temperature to exceed 26°C. in the early stages of propagation.

The temperature used in practice is, in fact, a compromise. Propagation at a low temperature gives an increased yield of yeast. At the same time, however, the rate of growth becomes slower so that the absolute amount of yeast produced is reduced. More important than this, however, is the fact that yeast grown at a lower temperature is less stable when stored and transported as a pressed cake. It has also been pointed out by White (1954) that the content of dry matter of a yeast cake of standard consistency becomes progressively less as the temperature at which it is propagated is reduced, that is to say, the temperature affects the relationship between the intra- and extra-cellular water content.

(3) *Rate of Growth in Relation to Yield*. The modern technique of baker's yeast production is based on applying the principle of the Pasteur reaction at the limit value of its aeration phase. Pasteur defined fermentation as life without air. Its biochemistry involves the breakdown of carbohydrate only to the stage of ethanol. In the anaerobic phase, growth of yeast is minimal. Under aerobic conditions, however, growth occurs and the efficiency of utilization of carbohydrate increases as respiration and

the breakdown of the carbohydrate to carbon dioxide and water becomes more complete. The degree to which the efficiency with which sugar is used for yeast growth improves as the initial concentration of sugar in a solution is reduced in aerated media has been demonstrated by White and Munns (1951). Under the conditions they employed, these workers obtained a yield of 77 parts of pressed yeast per 100 parts of invert sugar when the sugar concentration was 5%. When the sugar concentration was reduced to 0.2%, the yield increased to 165 parts of yeast, and when it was decreased still further to 0.0004%, or 4 parts per million, the yield rose to 210 parts of yeast per 100 parts of sugar.

The modern "Zulaufverfahren" method of yeast manufacture is based on the principle that the sugary feed is added to the strongly aerated yeast suspension at such a rate that it is immediately utilized. Since, therefore, there is never any appreciable amount of free sugar present, there is no opportunity for the formation of alcohol, which might be lost in the air stream and which would consequently cause wastage of sugar and loss of yield. In order to achieve this result, the molasses is fed at a rate calculated to be the same as the rate at which the yeast is growing. The object is to support continuous growth of the ever-increasing amount of yeast present without at the same time allowing surplus sugar to accumulate.

In order to arrange this exponentially increasing feed proportional at any given time to the amount of yeast in the propagation vessel at that time, it is obviously necessary to know the rate of growth of the yeast that the feed rate is designed to follow. A great deal of thought has been applied to this problem and a variety of mathematical expressions of yeast growth have been worked out (Effront, 1927; Stich, 1930; Brahmer, 1947; White, 1948; Benesch, 1949). Monod (1942) has pointed out that during the exponential phase the rate of growth of a population of micro-organisms is proportional to the density of the culture and can be represented by a mathematical expression similar to that elaborated as long ago as 1798 by Malthus for the increase of a human population.

The expression of yeast growth most frequently used in practice (see Chapter VI) is that of Slator (1921):

$$0.434K = \frac{1}{t} \log_{10} \frac{P + p}{P}$$

where K = the growth rate constant, or growth modulus, P = the initial amount of yeast, and p = the growth occurring during time t (in hours).

A convenient concept which can be derived simply from this formula is the "mean generation time," that is to say, the average time for each cell to turn into two cells and for the whole amount of yeast to double itself. Thus:

$$0.434K = \frac{1}{t'} \log_{10} 2$$

or   the mean generation time, $t' = \dfrac{0.3010}{0.434K}$

In practice, the rate of growth is controlled in such a way to obtain maximum yield, by adjusting the temperature, the degree of aeration, and the shape and size of the vessel in which the propagation takes place so that approximately five-fold the initial seed yeast is obtained within a working period of 10 to 13 hours (Walter, 1940; White, 1954). The molasses feed is added exponentially in proportion to the growth of the yeast. Exponential feed is arranged either by running the wort into the propagation vessel through a meter and gradually increasing the rate of addition, or by feeding measured volumes of molasses at progressively shorter intervals. Instruments are today available for carrying out both of these operations automatically. In order to achieve a gradually increasing rate of feed, a time cycle controller may be employed. This may be in the form of an eccentric cam, so shaped as to raise a control lever at an increasing rate as the cam turns. The impulse can be conveniently transmitted to the molasses feed valve by compressed air. A series of cams can be kept in order to deal with any desired changes in feed rate that it is wished at any time to introduce.

An automatic device for arranging exponential feed by discharging the contents of a measuring reservoir into the propagating vessel at shorter and shorter intervals is widely used in yeast factories. The commonest design takes the form of a metal tape wound from one spool to another at a constant speed. The tape is punched with holes which are spaced at decreasing distances one from another. A mercury tumbler switch drops each time a hole appears in the tape. The switch actuates a solenoid that opens a valve and discharges the reservoir into the yeast propagation vessel. With this arrangement, tapes can be specially cut in order to allow for any predetermined exponential rate of feed to be maintained.

White (1954) gives the details of a typical commercial propagation in which 730 kg. pressed weight of seed yeast together with 150 kg. of $Na_2HPO_4 \cdot 12H_2O$, 22 kg. of $(NH_4)_2SO_4$, and 4.5 kg. of $MgSO_4 \cdot 7H_2O$, all dissolved in a total volume of 54,000 l., are aerated for 11 hours at a rate increasing from 1180 to 6000 cu. ft. per minute. The temperature is allowed to rise from 28°C. to 29.5°C. during the propagation. A volume of

5400 l. of wort containing 3600 kg. of beet molasses is added exponentially in 150 batches of 36 l. each, together with 5400 l. of solution containing 140 kg. of a concentrated solution of ammonium hydroxide (containing 25% of NH_3), and 150 kg. of ammonium sulfate also fed exponentially in 150 batches. The latter solution, plus a small addition of sulfuric acid, maintains the pH between 3.8 and 4.5 during the process. The growth modulus of the yeast was 0.072, from which it can be deduced from the formula given earlier that the mean generation time, that is to say, the time required for the yeast to double itself, was $0.3010/0.072 = 4.18$ hours. From the 730 kg. of seed yeast used in this propagation, a final weight of 4400 kg. was reported to have been obtained. Thus 3670 kg. of new yeast was produced from the 3600 kg. of molasses used as feed. This is described as a yield of 102%.

Although the attainment of a high yield of yeast is an important consideration for the yeast manufacturer, it is not the sole factor. For example, there is a general view, although it is not fully substantiated by quantitative observation, that an improved yeast is produced if part of the feed, often amounting to 10% of the total wort, is added at the beginning of the propagation period. The practice of adding this "start wort," which is widespread in yeast technology, is a marked deviation from the strictly exponential feed demanded by theory in order to obtain maximum yield.

(4) *Aeration.* Since the "Pasteur reaction" was described in the nineteenth century, a great deal of thought has been given to the problem of yeast growth under aerobic conditions. Our knowledge of the mechanism of aerobic glycolysis has recently been dramatically increased (Dickens, 1955). Nevertheless, in spite of improved understanding of the mechanisms of the tricarboxylic acid cycle and of the hexose monophosphate cycle, precise knowledge of the quantitative relation between aeration efficiency and yeast growth is not yet available.

The obscurity of the problem is shown by the claims by a number of authors (Welminsky and Butschowitz, 1929; Jansen, 1942; Wilkie and Prochaska, 1943; de Becze and Liebman, 1944) that satisfactory yields of yeast can be obtained without aeration so long as the yeast is agitated mechanically or by a stream of an inert gas such as nitrogen or carbon dioxide. It has, however, been the general finding that, as biochemical theory demands, high yeast yields can only be obtained by efficient aeration.

The difficulty and expense of aerating yeast propagations adequately rests on the fact that whereas the oxygen requirement of the rapidly growing yeast is high, the solubility of oxygen in the aqueous medium is low. Only 0.9 mg. of oxygen can be dissolved in 100 ml. of water at 20°C. and the solubility decreases as the temperature rises. In addition, almost all methods of aeration are exceedingly inefficient. That is to say, most of the oxygen injected into the solution escapes unused as bubbles and is lost. In practice, it is not possible to calculate from biochemical principles the amount of air required. The volume needed to ensure a maximum yield of yeast depends on the depth of the liquid through which the air must pass, the process employed, the type of aeration equipment employed, and the concentration of yeast present (de Becze and Liebman 1944). The quantity of air required can be computed only on a basis of the specified conditions of the individual propagation technique used. Air requirement cannot, for example, be expressed as cubic meters per liter of wort, or per gram of yeast present. The proportional amount needed to obtain the same yield in a 5-l. jar in the laboratory may be fifty times as large as in a 20,000 gallon factory vessel.

It has been pointed out by de Becze and Liebman (1944) that from 10 to 20% of the total costs of producing yeast may be accounted for by the cost of the energy needed to compress air. It is not surprising, therefore, that many modifications have been made to the design of simple aeration pipes in an attempt to reduce this cost by improving aeration efficiency. Among the designs proposed have been devices for moving parts of the pipes without disconnecting them (Maschinenbau A. G., Golzern-Grimma, 1914, 1932, 1934); for various patterns of pipes branching from one another (Strauch and Schmidt, 1932); and for pipes including steam sterilizing devices (Strauch and Schmidt, 1934).

The use of porous materials to produce finely divided bubbles was first suggested in 1921 (Peter, 1921). Later in 1933, Stich patented a series of devices for employing porous candles and diaphragms for improving the efficiency of aeration. A modified scheme was for converting the wort into foam (Stich, 1934). The use of porous aerators was widely adopted in European factories. It was found, however, that, although satisfactory yields of yeast could be obtained with smaller volumes of air, the increased pressure required counterbalanced any consequent saving in cost and the liability of the porous aerators to break or become choked compared unfavorably with the robust simplicity of perforated aerating pipes. Efforts have been made to overcome these difficulties. Safety valves have been fitted to porous candles (Gooda, 1934) and porous plates of sintered glass (Berman, 1935) and copper (Schattaneck, 1934), tubes of silicon carbon (Pavcek et al., 1937), and other materials (Stark et al., 1941) have been used.

The suggestion has been made that smaller bubbles could be produced and a consequent improvement in aeration efficiency obtained by lowering the surface tension of the aerated worts. Trials have been reported of the use of small additions of organic acids for this purpose (Braasch and Braasch, 1934).

Other methods than the forcing of air through porous materials have been used to obtain a reduction in the size of bubbles and hence an economy in the use of air. Vogelbusch (1935a), used a pipe with a slit in it closely wound with wire. The air was blown through the narrow interstices between the wire strands. An alternative device sucked the air into the hollow space in a chamber formed from a number of rings of sheet metal one upon the other (Vogelbusch, 1934). The same worker also blew air through perforations in a tube which had previously been compressed so that the holes in it were converted into narrow slits (Vogelbusch, 1933). The use of wire to split up the air into small bubbles was also proposed by Rank and Hahn (1931). Scholler and Seidel (1940) aerated wort by drawing it from the bottom of the propagating vessel into vertical pipes containing aerators in the form of a stack of toothed rings. The air passing between the rings was broken into small bubbles and carried the wort up the pipes and back into the top of the propagating vessel.

Many mechanical aerating devices have also been suggested. For instance, Lockey (1933) blew air through longitudinal slits in one tube revolving inside another tube also containing slits. Most mechanical aerators, however, in order to sheer the air into finely divided bubbles make use of the difference in speed between the air and the liquid into which it is introduced. Vogelbusch (1935b) used a high-speed metal propeller through which the air was distributed. In order to maintain the maximum difference in speed between the liquid and the air, the rotation of the wort was prevented by means of baffles. A similar arrangement employing an aeration "wheel" was used by the Waldhof Company in Germany for the manufacture of fodder yeast (F.I.A.T., 1945). The converse of this arrangement, in which the liquid is rotated at high speed across an air orifice which is kept stationary, has also been patented (de Becze, 1934).

Other methods of aerating wort which have been suggested have included spraying it through the air (Schultz, 1898; Sigmend, 1893); passing it down packed columns through which the air is passed up (N.V. Internationale Sinker en Alkohol Compagnie, 1937); and drawing off a portion of the liquid, emulsifying it with air in a centrifuge and then returning it to the propagation vessel (Jonas, 1934).

In 1952, Chain and his colleagues published a study of the factors influencing aeration efficiency (see also Chain *et al.*, 1954). It was pointed out that far from the use of baffles improving the aeration efficiency, as suggested by Vogelbusch, the best utilization of the air was obtained by creating a vortex in the wort by rapid stirring without the use either of baffles or injected air.

In spite of all the studies which have been made the commonest method used in practice in aerating yeast propagations is the employment of a simple arrangement consisting of a series of perforated pipes at the bottom of the vessel.

Frothing. The aeration of yeast propagations gives rise to a serious practical problem in the control of frothing. Frothing does not occur continuously throughout the course of a propagation but only at intervals and at one time it was the practice to add lard whenever frothing occurred. Other materials of various types, such as animal and vegetable oils, petroleum oils, and synthetic substances have also been employed (Larsen, 1946; Johnson, 1948; Lee, 1950). Rancid fats have been claimed to suppress foam more effectively than fresh fats (Schulmann, 1939). It has also been reported that a freshly made mixture of olive oil and sulfuric acid is particularly effective in suppressing foaming in yeast propagations (Berti, 1935).

In modern practice, anti-foaming agents are usually added automatically by an electromagnetically controlled valve (Ries, 1937; Stefaniak *et al.*, 1946). Chain and his colleagues (1954) describe a simple automatic arrangement actuated by a sparking plug.

Mechanical devices to control foaming are sometimes used (Garibaldi and Feeney, 1949). These are usually in the form of a revolving beater or paddle. Several arrangements have also been patented for breaking up foam by the use of centrifugal force (Denhard, 1949; Sharples, 1949). Ghosh and Pirt (1954), however, from their own studies on foaming, have reached the conclusion that no really successful mechanical device for foam destruction has yet been developed. These workers argue that arrangements such as that used in the Waldhof system and that described by Humfeld and Feustel (1945) with mechanical foam-breaking elements are really modified vortex systems, and it has been shown that in the vortex system the foam is not destroyed but merely reaches a steady state.

The theoretical principles upon which the selection of an anti-foaming agent must be based have been discussed by Robinson and Woods (1946) while the actual problem of the mechanism and mode of action of anti-foaming agents has been attacked in various ways (Ross, 1950; Pattle, 1950). Ghosh and Pirt, however support the conclusion reached by

Matalon (1953) that fundamental knowledge of the principles underlying foam and the action of defoaming agents is still incomplete. It was found by Ghosh and Pirt in trials with commercial anti-foaming agents, silicone, octadecanol, grape seed oil, lard oil, paraffin, and petroleum ether that the effectiveness of a substance in practice was very greatly affected by the carrier with which it was mixed. In a number of trials the use of paraffin and lard oil markedly improved the performance of an anti-foaming agent.

(5) *Stages of Propagation. Culture.* All manufacturers take considerable care to select an appropriate race or strain of yeast. The properties required are: (1) ability to grow readily in high yield on the molasses or other raw material used, (2) cells which separate from the medium when it is centrifuged and which can be easily filtered, and formed into a cake, (3) yeast which when mixed with water by the baker will form a smooth suspension without flocculating or sedimenting and, most important, (4) the ability to promote a rapid fermentation of the dough sugars and to maintain this fermentation with its associated gas production right up to the time when the flour gluten begins to be denatured by the heat of the baker's oven. A further important technical quality is that the yeast strain used should possess good keeping properties so that it may retain its activity throughout the time elapsing between its production in the factory and its ultimate use in the bakery (Dawson, 1951).

Some commercial baker's yeasts are derived from naturally occurring strains selected by trial and error. In certain instances, strains of brewer's yeast may be found, after appropriate treatment to free them from contamination with copper and other inhibitory substances, to be suitable for propagation as a baker's yeast (Fuchs, 1937). Alternatively, new baker's yeast strains may be produced by the mating of existing types (Winge and Lausten, 1937; Lindegren, 1944; Fowell, 1951). Whatever the strain selected, it must be maintained carefully with all due bacteriological precautions to ensure its purity and to avoid the danger that it may pass through a series of involute forms which might modify its character and subsequent behavior in the bakery (Frey *et al.*, 1936). It is common practice for yeast manufacturers to reselect their laboratory culture from time to time from a single cell.

Seed Stages. The production of baker's yeast in commercial practice is a compromise. The culture is produced under strictly aseptic conditions. The large-scale propagation, while carried out with more care than brewery or distillery fermentations, does to a large degree depend for its success on the capacity that most strains of culture yeast possess for looking after themselves. Yeast can be grown successfully under conditions in which it would be impossible, for example, to produce penicillin. This is the case because the rate at which it grows is faster than that of many of the organisms which might gain access to the plant, and because yeast is an acidophilic organism that thrives at pH values between 4 and 5.

It is primarily because infection *may* gain access to the plant in spite of the precautions taken against it that it is customary practice in many factories for the first propagation stages to be carried out without exponential feed and full aeration. The culture from the laboratory may, indeed, be added with full aseptic precautions to a small volume of sterilized wort in which growth and a substantial measure of fermentation as well will occur. This first stage may then be transferred to a second larger volume of sterilized wort, and then to a third, before full aeration and the exponential addition of wort to the yeast as required for the attainment of maximum yield are adopted.

The conduct of the preliminary seed stages in commercial yeast production has been described in detail by White (1954). He refers to the successive culture vessels arranged one above the other, each filled with the appropriate amounts of wort, sterilized *in situ*. When the process is complete in the first vessel, the yeast suspension can be transferred by gravity into the second vessel and so on, without the possibility of contamination arising from the use of pumps or the passage of the inoculum through long pipe lines.

White (1954) has given this detailed description of a characteristic example of commercial practice. In the first stage, F_1, the culture from the laboratory, is transferred into 45 l. of molasses wort containing added ammonium salts and phosphate and allowed to ferment for 12 hours at 30°C. with gentle intermittent aeration. At the end of this stage the yeast has increased from, say, 250 g. to 1 kg. The fermented wort and yeast are then transferred to a second vessel containing 180 l. of molasses and a second F_2 fermentation continued in a manner exactly like that for the F_1. At the end of this stage the yeast, now weighing about 3.5 kg., is transferred into 900 l. of fresh molasses and another stage, F_3, carried out with intermittent aeration. For the F_4 stage, the 18 kg. of yeast resulting from the F_3 stage, is aerated at 100 c.f.m. with 3400 l. of molasses for 12 hours at 30°C. Finally, the 86 kg. of yeast from F_4 is put into 13,500 l. of molasses wort and aerated for 12 hours at 1000 c.f.m. This produces 450 kg. of yeast which is usually, at this stage, centrifuged off as a cream for use as seed in a fully aerated propagation to which the molasses and ammonium salts are added exponentially in the manner described earlier.

Large-Scale Propagation. The large-scale propagation of baker's yeast is most commonly carried out in a manner similar to that for which characteristic details have already been given. After all the molasses, wort, and ammonium salts have been added exponentially, usually within a period of 11 hours, it is customary to continue aeration of the yeast suspension for a further hour to "ripen" or "mature" the newly formed cells before they are separated from the wash. Little growth occurs during this period, but it is believed that the treatment has a favorable effect on the stability of the yeast when it is ultimately recovered. Yeast is commonly grown in commercial practice in a vessel of 45,000 to 225,000 l. capacity made of copper, mild steel, or stainless steel and fitted with cooling coils or a water jacket. If the vessel is made of copper, it has to be painted with an inert paint since copper contamination will inhibit the growth of the yeast. Both closed and open vessels are used.

Although almost all the baker's yeast produced industrially is manufactured by the process described, modifications have from time to time been devised. De Becze (1940), for example, proposed a number of minor changes, the most significant of which was the addition of the nutrient solution at a rate proportional to the rate at which the yeast was growing during the first half of the propagation but at a rate slower than the yeast growth during the second half. Meyer and Chaffe (1938), on the other hand, carried out the first 4 or 5 hours of propagation at 30°C., then dropped the temperature to 24°C. for about 6 hours and concluded with 2 hours at 30°C.

Several processes have been patented for the production of baker's yeast by continuous propagation. The literature has been reviewed by de Becze and Rosenblatt (1943). The first patent, taken out in 1915 (Verein der Spiritus fabrikenten in Deutschland, 1915), involved the use of a single vessel. Nutrient solution was fed in continuously at the top and the yeast suspension drawn off at the bottom and centrifuged. A modification, to minimize the amount of alcohol formed, was published later (Hayduck, 1923). In 1930, a process was evolved (International Yeast Co., 1930) in which wort was fed continuously into a vessel to which fresh seed was added every 6 to 8 hours. The yeast suspension was drawn off from the first vessel and was passed into a second vessel where the yeast was enabled to utilize the remaining traces of nutrients from the medium. In an alternative procedure (Sak, 1928), the yeast suspension is continuously withdrawn and passed into a centrifuge. Periodically, the yeast is returned to the propagation vessel in order to increase the concentration.

A different system of continuous propagation (Daranyi, 1932) involves the growth of yeast at the comparatively high concentration of 200 to 230 g./l. in the principal propagating vessel. About one-sixth of the total volume is drawn into a seed vessel every 2 hours. Two hours later this is transferred into a third vessel. The first vessel is refilled every 2 hours with a solution of 16–20% molasses.

Manufacturing baker's yeast by a continuous process presents two major problems. The first is to maintain an adequate degree of sterility, and the second is to obtain a yeast of satisfactory biochemical stability. These problems have up to the present prevented the use of continuous techniques on any extensive scale.

A method of yeast manufacture claimed to give high yield combined with stability and superior bakery performance has been described by Deloffre in a series of patents (Deloffre, 1942; 1943; 1945). This depends on the principle that, in a two-stage process, the first seed stage is a fermentation during which the yeast is allowed to produce alcohol. This stage is followed by a second during which the yeast suspension containing the alcohol is strongly aerated, the alcohol is assimilated and, at the same time, additional molasses is added as an exponential feed.

(6) *Recovery of the Yeast.* In the normal type of batch propagation most widely used, the yeast is commonly recovered in two stages after the growth period is brought to an end. The wash is first passed through a battery of centrifuges; the 10-fold concentrated yeast cream coming from the centrifuges is then mixed with water to remove traces of molasses medium adhering to the cells and again centrifuged (Walter, 1940; White, 1954). The washed suspension is then filtered, usually in a filter press. Yeast may also be recovered by means of a revolving vacuum filter (White, 1954; Olsen, 1950).

Pressed yeast is commonly packed as 1 pound blocks wrapped in paper. The extrusion of the blocks and their wrapping is done by an automatic machine. In order to be of an appropriate consistency for extrusion by the machine, the yeast must contain the correct moisture content. The relation between moisture content and consistency is affected to some degree by the yeast culture employed and the conditions of propagation, notably the temperature. When a filter press is used to recover the yeast, rather than a rotary filter, the pressed cake is often remixed with a small amount of water, to bring it to the correct consistency. Small amounts of oil or emulsifiers may be added at this stage in order to facilitate extrusion by the packing machine (White, 1954).

C. *Microbiological Control*

Because of the very fact that the production of yeast on the industrial scale is not fully aseptic in the true sense, stringent precautions to minimize infection must be taken if satisfactory yeast is to be obtained. Three dangers must be guarded against. Provided that proper care is taken, bacterial infection should be kept under control since during the propagation stages. At the acid pH used, it can be expected that the rate of growth of the yeast will exceed that of invading bacteria. The second danger is from mold. Although the presence of small numbers of mold organisms does not, as a general rule, affect the activity of the yeast as a leavening agent, the appearance of mold colonies on the surface of yeast blocks is considered unesthetic. The most serious infection for the yeast manufacturer is wild yeast. Accidentally introduced wild yeast will often grow more vigorously than the culture yeast and, if unchecked, may largely replace the culture yeast by the end of the successive propagation stages. Since wild yeast is almost always an indifferent performer in dough, the effect on the bakery performance of the factory product may be disastrous.

Sterilization of Plant. In most instances, the propagating vessels and other plant and pipelines in yeast factories are sterilized before the start of a propagation by means of steam. The importance of steam locks and steam seals on all pipes leading to and from vessels has been pointed out by Lee (1950). Pipelines should contain as few pumps and valves and other obstructions as possible. Yeast production plant is usually constructed so that it can be cleaned by mechanical means or by high pressure hoses to ensure that subsequent steaming shall effectively sterilize it. As an added precaution during this preliminary cleaning, a variety of detergents and antiseptics may be used. Alkalis, hypochlorite, phenol, and formaldehyde have all been employed. Basically, however, dependence is usually placed on steam.

Air Disinfection. Complete sterilization of the large quantities of air required in the manufacture of yeast would be a matter of considerable difficulty and substantial expense. In general practice, therefore, the air for use in the large-scale commercial stages of propagation is merely filtered, usually by passage through a bed packed with Lessing rings coated with glycerol or oil (Walter, 1940). Numerous other coatings have from time to time been recommended, for example, mixtures of polyhydric alcohols such as triethylene glycol or propylene glycol (Hedberg, 1948), mixtures of trialkyl phosphates and triaryl phosphates (Spiselman, 1948), or solutions of zinc chloride or lithium chloride mixed with wetting agents (Smith, 1944).

Other methods of purifying the air for yeast propagation are filtration through cotton wool, activated carbon, slag wool or glass wool. It is common practice for a supplementary cotton wool filter to be attached to the air line leading to the seed propagations, where infection would be particularly harmful, in order to filter a second time the process air which has already passed through the main plant filter. As an alternative to filtration for the main air supply, scrubbing with caustic alkalis, acids, or disinfectant solutions has been suggested (Lee, 1950). Terjesen and Cherry (1947) have compared a number of these methods and have concluded that filtration through a 3-inch layer of slag wool is the most effective and, provided an efficient installation was available, was claimed to produce sterile air.

Sterilization of air by heat requires a temperature of approximately 300°C. if it is to be effective within a reasonably short time. It is usually considered to be too expensive for large-scale operations (Lee, 1950). Stark and Pohler (1950) described an installation in which the heat of compression, giving a temperature in the region of 200°C., was used as a purifying agent. Sterilization by means of ultraviolet irradiation has also been tried (Mellors, 1950), but it has been found expensive and ineffective for large air volumes. Munden (1950) reported promising results using electronic precipitation.

Water. In the early seed stages of commercial yeast propagation, the molasses wort, suitably diluted with water, is sterilized by heat as in laboratory bacteriological practice. In the later stages, when the scale of operations has increased and the seed yeast is suspended in a dilute aqueous medium, called the "start dip," prior to the exponential addition of the sterilized nutrient wort, it is usually found safe to use tap water adequately chlorinated.

D. *Toxic Metals and Other Contaminants*

Inorganic contaminants may be undesirable in the manufacture of baker's yeast in two respects. Firstly, their presence may inhibit both growth and the subsequent fermentative activity of the yeast in dough and, secondly, they may be inadmissible as constituents of a human foodstuff. Probably the only substance likely to fall into the second category is arsenic. Arsenic has been shown by White (1954) not to be particularly toxic to yeast itself. It can, in consequence, be absorbed by the yeast cell during growth. It therefore behoves the yeast manufacturer to take precautions to ensure that the phosphate salts he employs and the sulfuric acid used to adjust pH values and, indeed, all the other ingredients are free from arsenic.

It has been shown by a number of investigators (Elvehjem and Hart, 1931; van Laer, 1934; Koch, 1935; Guillemet, 1936) that yeast fermentation is inhibited by comparatively small traces of copper. White (1954) has reported that three metals, cadmium, copper, and, oddly enough, silver, are particularly toxic to yeast growth. He found that osmium, mercury, and palladium also fell into the toxic-to-yeast group. Among a second group of eleven elements not particularly inhibitory to yeast growth were lithium, fluorine, chromium, and, as already mentioned, arsenic.

The fact that, with the exception of cadmium, copper was more harmful to yeast than any other of the 50 elements examined by White and yet that copper vessels are quite commonly encountered in breweries and yeast factories is, on the face of it, somewhat remarkable. An explanation is that, as was observed by White, the degree of toxicity is less when the yeast is growing in a molasses medium or in a wort derived from grain than when it is propagated in a solution of pure sugars and added nutrients. Arising from this phenomenon, the precise reason for which is not entirely clear, it must be noted that during the early stages of commercial yeast propagation when, as has been described, the yeast is allowed to grow and ferment in a relatively concentrated molasses medium, it may absorb considerable concentrations of copper, up to 1000 p.p.m., calculated on a dry matter basis. This it can do without harm, apparently due to the protective action of the wort. In the later propagation stages, however, when it is in a medium almost completely free from sugar, with molasses added continuously only as required by the growing yeast, the high copper content acquired in previous stages may inhibit normal growth. The modern trend is towards an increasing use of stainless steel to avoid this danger. Where copper vessels are used, the metal, particularly of those in which the exponential growth stages are to occur, must be adequately protected by paint or other means.

E. *Assessment of Yeast Quality*

Behavior in Dough. Yeast performs a three-fold function in bread making; firstly, the action of the gas produced by the fermentation of the dough sugars stretches the gluten fibers of the flour protein so that, by a combination of thixotropy and work-hardening, they reach a state described by the baker as "ripeness" (Cunningham, 1953). Unless this state is attained, the appropriate bread structure will not be obtained. The second action of the yeast is also derived from the gas it produces; it is the "raising" of the dough to give the appropriate expanded honeycomb of gas bubbles within the framework of gluten fibers which is the characteristic of good bread. The third contribution of yeast is to provide an important part of the attractive bread flavor.

The customary method of making bread in the large plant bakeries in which much of it is produced under modern conditions is broadly as follows. The yeast, salt, and water are mixed with the flour in bulk and the resulting dough allowed to ferment for from 2 to 4 hours. During this period, the dough may or may not be "knocked back" to remix the yeast and thus increase its stretching action on the gluten. At the end of the bulk fermentation, the dough is divided into pieces each of which is to become an individual loaf. The pieces of dough are molded and are then allowed themselves to ferment for sufficiently long to bring them to the appropriate size and consistency for baking. This is called the "proof time" and its duration, usually 40 to 50 minutes, is important to the baker when, as is commonly the case, the fermenting dough pieces are being carried by a continuously moving conveyer towards the oven. The final stage of fermentation occurs in the oven itself during the period elapsing while the temperature of the dough is rising but before it reaches a level high enough to kill the yeast. The increase in the size of the loaf leaving the oven compared with that of the dough entering is called "oven spring" and is an important measure of yeast activity.

It can be seen from this brief description of bread making, that gas production is an essential quality of a baker's yeast. A number of methods for testing yeast, based on the measurement of gas production, have been proposed.

Dough-Raising Test. A simple test that is widely used in practice is described by White (1954) as a "standard baking test." Dough is mixed with yeast and salt in a standard mixer. The dough, at a fixed temperature, after having been mixed for a limited time, is placed in either a rectangular tin or in a cylindrical vessel. This is placed in an incubator in an atmosphere saturated with moisture. The time required for the dough to rise to a fixed height is recorded. The dough is then remixed for a standard time, and is then reincubated until it again rises to the mark. The combined time for the first and second "rise" in minutes is commonly called the yeast "strength." The more vigorous the activity of the yeast, the smaller is the numerical value of the yeast "strength." This simple, empirical test is useful in assessing the uniformity of the yeast produced by a factory. It can also be used to measure keeping quality, by testing the yeast after it has been stored at a predetermined temperature for a specified length of time, usually 21°C. for 7 days. This test, however, although capable of distinguishing between "fast" and "slow" yeasts does not give with any degree of precision an indication of bakery performance.

Chopin Zymotachegraph. This instrument, described by Urie and Hulse (1952), measures automatically and with a high degree of accuracy the rate of gas production by the yeast under test when made into dough with 250 g. of flour. A continuous record is obtained over a period which can, if necessary, be extended up to 6 hours. The difference in behavior of different types of yeast is shown by the varying shapes of the curves they produce. It can readily be seen from the zymotachegraph curves why it is that the simple "strength" test does not supply a complete interpretation of the behavior of a yeast in the bakery. It can also be understood from these curves why certain yeasts will behave more successfully in one bakery technique than another, when, for example, a falling off in gas production may occur at a time undesirable to the baker.

The biochemistry of panary fermentation is still in the process of being worked out. It is, however, clear from the work of Larmour and Bergsteinsson (1936) and the later studies of Koch *et al.* (1954) that a series of reactions occur. First, the free fructose and glucose present in the flour or derived by enzyme action from sucrose and levosin are fermented and only then does the yeast, with greater or less facility, start to deal with maltose (Pyke, 1955). The progression of this series of fermentations is reflected in the shape of the zymotachegraph curve produced by different yeasts.

Swedish Dough Recorder. This instrument (Kent Jones and Amos, 1950) gives, although with very much less detail, a picture of yeast behavior similar to that obtained from the zymotachegraph. In place of a continuous record of gas production, however, a series of "upcomes" of dough to a predetermined volume is obtained. The accuracy of the measurements obtained from this instrument is subject to a number of errors.

Schultz Fermentometer. (Schultz *et al.*, 1942.) The amount of gas produced during the fermentation of dough by yeast is measured by recording the volume of brine displaced. The apparatus gives accurate results but a drawback to its use as a routine test is that it requires the constant attention of a laboratory worker, and the calculation of the results with the necessary corrections of gas volumes is somewhat complicated. Similar methods were described by Bailey (1939) and Eisenberg (1940).

Bennett Fermentometer. (Bennett, 1955.) This is a modification of the Schultz apparatus in which the gas displaces brine at a constant temperature and the volume of brine is measured. This procedure eliminates temperature corrections but allowance for atmospheric pressure variations has still to be made.

Instead of measuring gas volumes, it is possible to measure variations in pressure, and tests based on this principle have, in fact, been introduced (Sansted and Blish, 1934; Malloch, 1939; Doty and Urban, 1940;

Glabe, 1942). Automatic recording was introduced by Mather *et al.* (1943).

A variety of other dough fermentation tests have been used to assess yeast quality. Many of these have been designed to show the quality of the flour rather than the yeast. In the United States, the production of "pup" loaves is a popular method of examining the factors affecting bakery performance (Whinery, 1950; Cathecart, 1953). The effect of high yeasting levels and added sugar on baking tests have been reviewed by Hagberg (1953). The varieties of techniques used in baking practice are reflected in the number of test methods used. The tests most widely used in Germany have been reviewed by Schulz and Doose (1953), the standard techniques employed in Belgium by Maes (1951), and those in Switzerland by Wagner and Bohl (1950). Besides sugar, other materials including milk solids, enzyme preparations, and in some cases ammonium salts may be used in baking formulae. The effect of these supplements on tests of yeast performance has been considered by Bayfield (1950). A review of the different bakery tests used in 40 American laboratories was made by Gust *et al.* (1950).

2. Dried Baker's Yeast

Baker's yeast propagated under the conditions described in the first section of this chapter is in normal commercial practice recovered from the medium in which it has been grown and the mass of cells pressed together into a block. This block of pressed yeast has a moisture content of from 70 to 75%. It is consequently perishable and in warm climates must be transported under refrigerated conditions and used by the baker within a comparatively short time.

It was reported by Morse and Fellers (1949) that in 1945 in the United States 6000 tons of active dried yeast was produced in addition to further quantities manufactured in Great Britain, Australia, and elsewhere. Dried baker's yeast of good quality obviously possesses great advantages in tropical countries, on board ships, and wherever rapid transport from a producing factory is unavailable in that it can be stored for long periods. Dried yeast for baking has been manufactured for some time, indeed one product, "Florylin," was used commercially in Germany during World War I. Yeast propagated in the customary manner cannot be dried successfully. During drying it becomes dark in color, loses a substantial proportion of its activity and, when dried, quickly deteriorates on storage. In 1949, Payen observed that a proportion of the yeast glycogen was converted into trehalose during drying and 2 years later Pollock and Holmstrom (1951) found that, when dried yeast contained an average of 16% trehalose and 40% of total carbohydrate, it was active and possessed good keeping qualities, whereas when its average trehalose content was 11%, with a total carbohydrate of 36%, the dried product was unsatisfactory and unstable. They also observed that the trehalose content of cells in the moist state could be greatly increased by propagating the yeast in a nitrogen-deficient medium.

In the manufacture of dried baker's yeast, a selected strain of yeast must be used and the propagation arranged so as to give a high trehalose concentration. Drying is usually carried out in a current of warm air.

Jorgensen (1945) observed that when dried yeast is suspended in water in preparation for its use in the bakery, significant amounts of glutathione may be extracted and appear in the liquid. This glutathione is damaging to the gluten structure (Cunningham, 1953) and consequently results in the dried yeast proving unsatisfactory as a baking agent. In addition to the gas production tests used for pressed yeast it is usual to assess the quality of dried yeast by means of a test for extractable glutathione as well.

A great deal of work has been done on the storage stability of active dried yeast (Felsher et al., 1955). When packed in evacuated tins, dried yeast, either granular or pelleted, could be stored at room temperature (21°C.) for 2 years without serious loss of activity. It retained its activity almost unchanged during a similar period at low temperatures, for example, 4°C. Under warm-climate conditions, e.g., 32°C., it could be stored satisfactorily for 6 months and still retain its ability for bread baking.

3. Food and Fodder Yeast

It is generally accepted that in the world as a whole there is a shortage of protein. So far as human diets are concerned, there are large populations in Asia and in Africa which subsist on a largely carbohydrate diet of rice or of starchy roots, such as manioch in which the protein component is insufficient. Animal protein foods are of higher quality, both in the nutritional and in the dietetic sense, than most vegetable proteins. In order to produce meat, milk, or eggs intensively, adequate supplies of fodder protein are needed. The production of yeast as a feeding stuff requires a supply of surplus carbohydrate, either as sugar or molasses, or in the form of a cellulose or hemicellulose capable of being degraded into sugars assimilable by yeast. The nitrogeneous element required to convert this carbohydrate into protein is provided by inorganic ammonium salts.

The drive to produce food yeast has come, however, from two directions. The first has been, indeed, to obtain protein, but the second has been the legislation passed in a number of industrial countries requiring that oxidizable substances be removed from liquid industrial wastes before the effluent is allowed to go into the rivers.

The organism most commonly used is not a *Saccharomyces* but a strain of *Torula utilis*. This yeast is remarkably robust, is comparatively undiscriminating in its nutritional demands, and grows rapidly and in good yield. When grown it is usually dried at a temperature sufficient to kill it. Since it is required for use as a foodstuff and is handled in this way, it is of no significance that its fermentative activity in dough is very poor. The first recognition of the possibilities of growing *Torula utilis* as a foodstuff on a commercial scale was made by German workers in Berlin at the Institut für Gärungsgewerbe during World War I (Lindner, 1922). Later it was found that, since the organism was capable of utilizing pentoses, hardwood liquors from the pulp and paper industry could be used as an economical substrate.

A. *Use of Sulfite Liquor*

In the manufacture of food yeast from sulfite liquor (Inskeep *et al.*, 1951), the spent liquor from the manufacture of wood pulp for paper making is first freed from excess sulfite. This may be done either by distillation in a stripping column into which the liquor comes from the top while steam is injected from the bottom, or the liquor may be neutralized with lime. The sugar content under American conditions is commonly about 1.5%, of which 80% is hexose and 20% pentose. Propagation is carried out continuously in a 200,000 l. vessel at a temperature of 37°C. The stripped liquor, together with ammonium phosphate, potassium chloride, and ammonia, is fed into the vessel at the top. Aeration is achieved by means of a central "draft tube" fitted with a Waldhof aeration wheel revolving at 300 r.p.m. (Kiefer, 1947). This creates an emulsion of air and solution. Cooling is achieved by drawing a stream of the fermenting liquor from the bottom of the vessel through a cooler and then returning it. Part of this stream is drawn off at such a rate in proportion to the feed of original liquor that the holding time for yeast in the vessel is 4 hours.

Once the initial seeding of *Torula utilis* is established, the vigor of its growth combined with the conditions of temperature, pH, and aeration are such that little chance of infection arises.

The yeast is recovered as a cream by centrifugation, washed, and finally dried on rollers.

The production of food yeast from sulfite liquor has also been described by Kihara *et al.* (1948), Yamaguchi (1952), and by Wiley (1954).

B. *Use of Molasses*

One of the earliest schemes for the production of food yeast from molasses, sugar juice, or raw sugar was that of the British Colonial Food Yeast, Ltd. in Jamaica (1944). A special thermophilic strain of *Torula utilis* var. *major* capable of being propagated at a temperature of 37.8°C. was used. The sterilized wort was run continuously into a series of 10 comparatively small propagating vessels each with a capacity of about 1200 l. Appropriate amounts of ammonium sulfate, superphosphate, and caustic soda were added and the whole aerated through a simple arrangement of porous ceramic distributors. The fermented wort containing yeast was drawn off continuously throughout the period of propagation, the yeast centrifuged, washed, and dried on single-roll drum driers. The propagation in each vessel was only continued for 24 hours and the equipment then cleaned, sterilized and restarted.

The operation of the plant in Jamaica was described further in the Proceedings of the B.W.I. Sugar Technologists (Sept./Oct. 1947, pp. 38–54), from which it was evident that considerable difficulty was experienced with the breaking and clogging of the fine aerators employed and that the cost of steam and power had been underestimated. Thus the power required was 2.2 K.W.H. per kilogram of dried yeast compared with an estimated 0.48 K.W.H. Steam consumption was also about 2¼ times the amount originally estimated.

A method of producing food yeast from molasses similar to that described for sulfite liquor was used by Basaca (1952) in the Philippines.

C. *General*

Food yeast has been manufactured from a wide variety of raw materials other than sulfite liquor and molasses. Hydrolyzed eucalyptus sawdust has been employed in Spain (Fernandez-Cano and Cid, 1952) while elsewhere potato starch waste (Biyack, 1952; Reiser, 1954), bagasse hydrolysate (Cid *et al.*, 1951), citrus press liquor (Veldhuis, 1952), orange juice (Lobo, 1953), and spent amyl acetate liquor from penicillin recovery operations (Sevcik, 1952) have all been used. Even the mannitol-containing solutions from the hydrolysis of seaweed have been found to be utilizable for the growth of *Candida* (Tomiyasn and Zenitan, 1952).

Although food yeast is produced from sulfite liquor on a large scale in a number of plants using *Torula utilis* as the organism giving the best performance, a number of other yeasts have been employed, a variety of alternate substrates have been found to be suitable, and many types of equipment have been used with both batch and continuous processes. The literature has been most thoroughly reviewed by Dunn (1952) (see Table I).

TABLE I
FOOD YEAST: ORGANISMS, SUBSTRATES, AND USES[a]

Organisms used	Raw materials	Product intended as food for:
Endomyces vernalis	Beer (spent)	Civilians
Hansenula anomala	Citrus waste press juice	Soldiers
Hansenula suaveolens	Fermentation residue	Cats
Saccharomyces cerevisiae	Fruit juices	Cattle
Candida arborea	Grain	Dogs
Candida tropicalis	Gamones roots	Fish
Mycotorula lipolytica	Molasses, beet	Fur-bearing animals
Torulopsis pulcherrima	Molasses, cane	Bees
Torulopsis utilis	Sulfite liquor	Poultry
Torulopsis utilis var. major	Wood sugars	Pigs
Torulopsis utilis var. thermophila	Wood sugar stillage	
Monilia candida		
Oidium lactis		

[a] From Dunn (1952).

As might be expected, the composition of the yeast produced from these diverse sources varies to a considerable extent. Figures derived from Dunn's paper, are shown in Table II.

D. *Fat Production from Yeast*

It has from time to time been suggested that yeast might be used as a source of fat as well as protein although no convincing reports have appeared of this having been successfully achieved on a technical scale. Long periods of fermentation are required and the yield of fat, less than 20% in terms of carbohydrate consumed, would probably render the process uneconomic unless large supplies of cheap, surplus raw material were available.

The maximum synthesis of fat occurs when propagation takes place in the absence of nitrogen. Thus Lundin (1950) grew *Rhodotorula gracilis* rapidly in an initial stage over about 10 hours, using ample sugar, nitrogen, and phosphate during which the mean generation time was 2

TABLE II

The Composition of Food Yeast[a]

Organism	Substrate	Protein	Thiamine	Riboflavin	Nicotinic acid	Pantothenic acid	Pyridoxine	Folic acid	Biotin	p-Aminobenzoic acid
Baker's yeast	Molasses	50	20–40	60–85	200–700	180–330			1–2	
Brewer's yeast	Beer	37	100–250	25–80	300–637	72–86	23–40	19–30	1	15–40
Candida arborea	Molasses	39–49	13–33	46–70	300–500	180		12–26	0.2–3	11–21
Hansenula	Wood sugar	53	8	54	590			2	2	16
Mycotorula	Wood sugar	51	5	59	600			3	2	31
Odium lactis	Molasses	31–42	12–29	40–55	190–250			6–15	1–2	
Torulopsis utilis	Sulfite liquor	50–53	5	43	420	39	33	21	2	
Torulopsis utilis	Molasses	40–61	22–38	51–62	440–600			11–15		

[a] Proteins, per cent; vitamins, micrograms per gram dry matter.

to 3 hours. At the end of this phase, the supply of nitrogen and phosphate is almost completely cut off when the rate of growth is reduced so that the mean generation time becomes 15–18 hours. This phase is continued for about 50 hours at the end of which a dry-matter yield of about 30 g. of yeast per 100 g. of sugar, containing approximately 60% of fat and 13% of protein, is obtained.

Using *Torulopsis lipofera*, Kleinzeller (1944) obtained a dry matter yield of 30–40 g. per 100 g. of sugar, of which 30 to 40% was fat.

The literature on fat production by yeasts has been reviewed by Lindner (1922), Fink *et al.* (1937), Smedley-MacLean (1936), Bernheuer (1943), Damm (1943), Kleinzeller (1948), Hoogerheide (1948), Prescott and Dunn (1949), and Hesse (1949). Dunn (1952) lists the following organisms as having been used: *Candida reukaufii, Endomyces vernalis, Oospora lactis, Oospora walbroth, Rhodotorula glutinis, Rhodotorula gracilis, Saccharomyces cerevisiae,* Starkey's soil yeast, *Torulopsis lipofera.*

E. vernalis and *O. lactis* have only been caused successfully to produce fat when grown by surface culture methods.

Steinberg and Ordal (1954) studied the effect of a number of propagation factors on fat yield. Using *Rhodotorula gracilis* they obtained a maximum yield of 3.1 g. of fat in relation to each 100 g. of nonfat yeast dry matter produced whereas the corresponding yield for *Torula utilis* was 2.2 g. Reports of studies of the production of fat from yeast have appeared in a number of countries: Japan (Ichiro, 1949), Turkey (Nokay, 1951), Yugoslavia (Blinc, 1951), and Czechoslovakia (Bass and Hospodka, 1952) are some of them.

4. Brewer's Yeast

In the traditional method of brewing beer, the types of yeast used are commonly described as either "top" or "bottom" yeast depending on whether they rise to the surface during fermentation and are skimmed off or sink to the bottom and remain as sediment. There is a considerable growth of yeast during the process of brewing and, particularly in the manufacture of beer by a top fermentation process as in Great Britain, it is common practice to recover part of the yeast from one brewing and use it in the next. Reasonable care is taken to avoid infection but the culture is a mixed one and it is not unknown for brewers to find it necessary to change their yeast by obtaining an alternative supply from another brewery.

In most European countries other than Great Britain and in the United States, where bottom fermentation systems are used, a pure yeast culture is usually maintained. The equipment is in most instances similar to that designed by Hansen in Copenhagen in 1883 (Lloyd Hind, 1948) and consists, in essence, of two vessels. In one, hopped wort is sterilized by boiling and the temperature reduced to 7°C. by means of a water jacket. A positive pressure of sterile air is maintained while the wort is cooling. The sterile wort is then run into the previously sterilized propagating vessel, which commonly has a capacity of 150 l. A pure yeast culture from the laboratory is blown in with sterile air, the most rigid aseptic precautions being maintained meanwhile. The yeast is allowed to ferment for ten days during which growth occurs. No effort is made to obtain a high yield or rapid growth by vigorous aeration, as in the production of baker's yeast.

At the end of the fermentation, the bulk of the beer is run off. The residue of 25 or 30 l. is stirred by means of a propeller fitted into the vessel and most of it is run out into a "sterilized bucket" (Lloyd Hind, 1948). This is used to inoculate 1000 l. of beer wort in an open fermenting vessel. After 10 more days, the yeast is again transferred, this time to a brewery vessel of 5700 l. capacity. It is then used for 8 or 9 brewings before being discarded. The residue of the original pure culture is used to obtain 100 to 200 generations more, 100 l. volumes of rigorously sterilized wort being repeatedly added to it.

Variations of this type of apparatus, usually made of stainless steel, are available. Modern equipment is designed to produce a continuous supply of yeast for the brewery. In some instances the cycle of operations is kept going for two years or more before being restarted with a freshly isolated culture.

5. Medicinal and Nutritional Preparations

A. General

The value of yeast in human nutrition and clinical medicine depends partly on its high concentration of vitamins of the B group and partly on the protein it contributes (see Table III) (Van Lanen and Tanner, 1948).

Moist pressed yeast is unsuitable for medicinal or nutritional use because its capacity for fermenting carbohydrate, with the accompanying production of carbon dioxide gas, causes gastrointestinal symptoms and also because it is capable of removing vitamin B_1 from solution (Eijkman et al., 1922), thus bringing about a loss of vitamin to the body (Parsons et al., 1945). Similar considerations apply to riboflavin. The simplest and most effective yeast preparation is dried yeast. This is usually prepared by means of steam-heated rollers.

Dried Yeast. Dried yeast has been recommended for use in the treatment of a diverse series of clinical conditions. Although the combination of nutrients present in yeast is in many instances important of itself it is possible to single out the factor principally involved in a number of the conditions for which yeast has been found beneficial.

TABLE III

VITAMIN CONTENT OF DRIED BREWER'S YEAST AND DRIED BAKER'S YEAST

Vitamin	Dried brewer's yeast (mg./100 g.)	Dried baker's yeast (mg./100 g.)
Vitamin B_1	5.0–36.0	0.9–4.0
Riboflavin (B_2)	3.6–4.2	3.9–7.5
Nicotinic acid	32–100	20–70
Pantothenic acid	10	18.0–33.0
Biotin	0.5–0.18	0.05–0.18
p-Aminobenzoic acid	0.9–10.2	2.2–17.5
Vitamin B_6	2.5–10.0	1.6–6.5
Inositol	270–500	400
Folic acid	1.5–8.0	1.5–8.0

(1) *Vitamin B_1.* The daily amount of vitamin B_1 required is proportional to the number of calories in the diet derived from sources other than fat. A man eating a normal diet providing, say, 3000 calories a day requires not more than 1.5 mg. of vitamin B_1 (U.S. National Research Council, 1948) which would be provided by, say, a 10 g. dose of dried brewer's yeast. A primary deficiency of vitamin B_1 is the cause of beri-beri, certain forms of peripheral polyneuritis, Wernicke's encephalopathy, Korsakoff's syndrome, alcoholic neuritis, and polyneuritis of pregnancy and dried yeast has been found to be effective in the treatment of these diseases (Stepp, 1936; Nutrition Sub-committee, Colonial Medical Research Committee, 1948). The most consistent symptom of moderate vitamin B_1 deficiency, however, is a lack of appetite (anorexia) and a number of reports have appeared of the value of dried yeast in ameliorating this condition (Heinz 1921; Leifer 1935; Lewinsohn 1937).

(2) *Riboflavin and Other Factors of the "Vitamin B_2" Complex.* A series of symptoms affecting the skin, the mouth and tongue, and the eyes are known to arise from a deficiency of riboflavin, often accompanied by a deficiency of the other vitamins, notably nicotinic acid, vitamin B_6, and possibly pantothenic acid and biotin as well, previously known as the "vitamin B_2" complex. The Nutrition Sub-committee of the Colonial Medical Research Committee (1948) listed glossitis, stomatitis, derma-

tosis, and ocular lesions, especially corneal degeneration, as clinical manifestations primarily of riboflavin deficiency and recommended the consumption of dried yeast as a treatment. The daily requirement of riboflavin for an optimum diet for a moderately active man is 1.8 mg. which would be provided by the consumption of about 30 g. of dried yeast.

(3) *Dietary Factors Concerned with Anemia.* Dried yeast has been used successfully by a number of workers in the treatment of different types of anemia. Wills (1931) found it effective in pernicious pregnancy anemias; Davidson (1931) employed it against tropical forms; Sebrell (1934) also obtained good results with yeast. As can be seen from Table III, yeast contains the anti-anemic factor, folic acid, but it does not contain vitamin B_{12}, the specific substance concerned with pernicious anemia. It seems probable that the combination of vitamins together with the contribution of protein in yeast, or, conceivably, a factor not yet elucidated, is responsible for the favorable clinical response obtained from the use of yeast in the treatment of anemias.

B. *Official Preparations of Dried Yeast*

A number of standards have been laid down for dried yeast intended for medical and nutritional use. The British Pharmaceutical Codex

TABLE IV
OFFICIAL SPECIFICATIONS FOR THE VITAMIN CONTENT OF DRIED YEAST

	Vitamin B_1 (mg./g.)	Riboflavin (mg./g.)	Nicotinic acid (mg./g.)
British Pharmaceutical Codex (1954)	Not less than 0.10	Not less than 0.04	Not less than 0.30
U.S. Pharmacopoeia (1947)	Not less than 0.12	Not less than 0.04	Not less than 0.25
Swedish Pharmacopoeia (1948)	Not less than 0.15		.

(1949) requires the drying to be done by "a process which avoids decomposition of the vitamins present." The U.S. Pharmacopeia, 13th edition (1947), stated that dried yeast may be obtained either as a by-product from the brewing of beer or by growing yeast specially for the purpose. It must contain not less than 40% of protein. The vitamin content of dried yeast demanded officially in Britain, the United States, and Sweden is shown in Table IV.

Several official specifications exist for tablets made from dried yeast.

The pharmacopoeia of the United States requires tablets to contain the equivalent of nicotinic acid, riboflavin, vitamin B_1, and protein corresponding to not less than 95% of the labeled amount of dried yeast. The British Pharmaceutical Codex merely specifies that yeast tablets should be made from dried yeast.

The American publication "New and Non-Official Remedies" (1949) contains the formulae for a number of varieties of tablets made from dried brewers yeast enriched with various materials as follows:

(a) *Brewer's yeast tablets (fortified with riboflavin and nicotinic acid):* Tablets of 0.4 and 0.5 g. are described. The individual tablet contains 0.06 to 0.10 mg. vitamin B_1, 0.02 to 0.20 mg. riboflavin, and 0.6 to 1.0 mg. nicotinic acid.

(b) *Other yeast tablets:* Tablets are composed of a mixture of dried brewer's yeast granulated with calcium carbonate, starch, sodium chloride, dried malt syrup, saccharine, vanillin, oil of chocolate, and talc.

Few of the official publications specify the dose of dried yeast to be employed. The British Pharmaceutical Codex recommends 1–8 g., which would hardly appear to be sufficient to provide an effective contribution of vitamins or protein. "New and Non-Official Remedies" refers to doses of 9 or 10 tablets daily equivalent to 4 or 5 g. of dried yeast or fortified dried yeast.

C. Yeast Extract

The use of dried yeast in medicine and dietetics is limited because of its taste. Yeast extracts, on the other hand, although they often possess a strong taste of their own, are usually considered to be palatable. Somogyi (1944) has reviewed the literature bearing on their use.

Yeast extract is prepared in one of three ways. Somogyi quotes Swiss and German authorities as advising that the yeast be hydrolyzed with acid (usually hydrochloric acid) in an autoclave under pressure. By this means the cells are almost entirely disintegrated. The solution is then neutralized, the extract separated from the sediment by centrifugation and concentrated *in vacuo* to the desired consistency. This procedure is reported to cause loss of protein and vitamins but to produce a large quantity of extract.

A second method of preparing yeast extract is by means of heat. Lehmann (1941) describes a procedure in which the yeast is heated to 60–70°C. and allowed to stand for some hours. Alternatively the yeast may be suspended in water and heated to 100–110°C. (Le Clerk, 1940). When brewer's yeast is used, it is first debittered by being stirred with four times its volume of cold 2% sodium carbonate or 1% ammonium carbonate solution and washed with water until it is neutral to litmus. It is then dried on hot cylinders and stored. The extract is prepared by autolyzing a 15% yeast paste at 100–110°C. for 10 minutes. An acid pH is achieved by adding 10 ml. of concentrated hydrochloric acid or acetic acid to each 100 kg. Flavoring is added at this stage. The mixture is quickly cooled to 50–60°C. and the cell walls separated by centrifugation. The residue, after being reextracted with boiling water, is used as cattle food. The extract, to which vegetable flavorings are added, is concentrated *in vacuo*.

The commonest way of making yeast extract, however, is by plasmolysis (Vogel, 1939). This is usually done with salt. Diller (1942) reports the use of salt and the injection of steam into the yeast solution. A patent specification (Soderstrom, 1944) describes the preparation of yeast extract by mixing pressed yeast with 2 to 4% of its weight of salt, heating to 57–67°C. for at least 40 hours, and concentrating the separated extract.

Although yeast extracts prepared from yeast plasmolyzed with salt have enjoyed substantial popularity, the amount of salt in the final concentrated extract is high and the taste consequently very salty. In order to avoid this saltiness a number of alternative plasmolyzing agents have been recommended. Amyl acetate (Wilts United Dairies, 1944) and ethyl acetate (Ambrose, 1930; Zellstoffabrik Waldhof, 1948) are among those which have been found successful.

Yeast extract is known to be a good source of vitamins of the "vitamin B_2 complex." It contains vitamin B_1, but the amount of this substance diminishes on storage. A well-known yeast extract of British manufacture is reported by Davidson and Anderson (1947) to possess the following vitamin content.

Vitamin	mg./100 g.
Vitamin B_1	1.5
Riboflavin	6.1
Nicotinic acid	67.9

Somogyi (1944) analyzed a number of commercial samples of yeast extract made from (a) brewer's yeast, (b) baker's yeast grown on molasses, and (c) mixed extracts and especially those derived from yeast grown on hydrolyzed wood (see Table V).

A number of combinations of yeast extract with other materials have been devised. Oter and Umeda (1935) patented a process in which a yeast suspension was heated to 45°C., plasmolyzed with cane sugar,

TABLE V

THE COMPOSITION OF YEAST EXTRACT[a]

	Moisture (%)	Nitrogen (%)	Fat (%)	Carbo-hydrate (%)	Ash (%)	Salt (%)	pH	Vitamin B$_1$ (μg./g.)
A. *Brewer's yeast extract*								
1. Rather salty; bitter	29.3	4.96	0.70	14.0	25.0	16.6	5.55	39
2. Spicy; rather sharp taste; soluble	24.4	4.96	0.07	8.8	35.6	21.5	5.54	110
3. Acid; spiced; containing malt extract	26.0	4.72	0.12	20.5	23.24	13.2	5.89	200
4. Very salty; acid; spiced; soluble	16.7	5.32	0.14	10.4	39.48	21.6	5.20	30
B. *Baker's yeast extract*								
1. With cabbage hydrolyzates, salty; bitter	31.1	6.10	0.25	9.4	20.2	15.32	5.87	34
2. Spiced, very salty	38.9	5.84	0.14	1.3	23.1	12.92	5.80	63
3. Spiced; salty	33.4	5.46	0.30	18.4	25.3	21.90	5.62	30
4. Spiced; sharp flavor	25.9	5.94	0.61	2.7	33.5	22.33	5.60	80
5. Slightly spicy; very salty	27.4	6.04	0.57	7.7	26.5	19.06	5.58	85
C. *Mixed extracts (especially from yeast from wood hydrolyzate)*								
1. Very salty	35.4	4.07	0.88	15.9	22.2	17.3	4.83	29
2. Spiced; very salty	29.5	4.04	0.55	23.6	21.1	11.0		34
3. Spiced; dark colored	25.1	4.70	0.46	17.3	27.7	12.5	4.40	80
4. Bitter; made by hydrolysis; soluble	18.4	6.21	0.76	15.2	26.9	6.6		68
5. Caramelized; very bitter; soluble	19.8	6.22	0.14	24.5	16.7	3.2	5.75	85

[a] From Somogyi (1944).

filtered, and the filtrate concentrated to a syrup. Lactose was then added and the mixture dried *in vacuo*. A similar process (Vegex, 1936) involved the digestion of dried yeast in sugar syrup with fresh yeast and papain, removal of insoluble material and concentration of the final solution. Weizmann (1938) claimed a process for plasmolyzing yeast by the action of fruits, such as dates, figs, or bananas, rich in sugar. He also used fruit juices such as red currant and pineapple juice as plasmolyzing agents (1941), after which the plasmolyzed mixture was heated and concentrated. Liebers (1931) induced plasmolysis by means of malt extract. After allowing the mixture of yeast and malt extract to stand, it was heated to 50–70°C. It is reported to develop an aroma of fruit.

A different type of preparation has been made by plasmolyzing yeast with a nitrogenous salt solution rich in amino acids. Concentrated broth, obtained by acid or alkaline hydrolysis of meat, casein, gluten, or soya bean can be used for this purpose. The plasmolyzed yeast is heated for several hours at a moderate temperature of, say, 37°C. with stirring and then dried on a heated drum drier (La Société Dizem, 1945). Thus, instead of a sweetmeat, a product resembling meat or cheese is obtained.

A similar result is achieved by a rather different process in another patent by Weizmann (1947). Yeast plasmolyzed with salt is used as a source of proteolytic enzymes. The plasmolyzed yeast is incubated with a material rich in protein, such as soya meal, for example, which has previously been rendered partly soluble by being cooked under pressure. The use of an added proteolytic enzyme has also been proposed in order to break down a food protein and bring about its combination with the yeast protein. In a patent by Kahn (1930), a method is described in which yeast, autolyzed for a period of 3 to 5 days, is added to an approximately equal amount of fish in the presence of the viscera of the fish as a source of enzymes.

The preparation of a food by the addition of fat to plasmolyzed yeast has been described by a number of authors. Simmer (1931) plasmolyzed yeast by heating; fats or oils were then added to the liquefied yeast together with the bacteria commonly used in cheese manufacture. The mixture was allowed to ferment and a product resembling cheese was formed. In an American patent (Standard Brands Inc., 1933), yeast plasmolyzed with salt is mixed with starchy material, partly dried, and then fried in deep fat.

Of all the products described in the preceding paragraphs, simple yeast extract, perhaps flavored with vegetable extracts, is most commonly seen. In some instances the extract may be purified by treatment with an adsorbent, such as charcoal (Miller, 1936), keiselguhr, or fuller's earth

(Van der Sandt, 1934). A somewhat different product, which has also achieved a measure of popularity, is dried autolyzed yeast. This is made by plasmolyzing yeast with salt, allowing autolysis to take place, and drying the product rapidly at a temperature of 82°C. (Standard Brands Inc., 1937). Alternatively the autolyzed yeast may be mixed with starch, subjected to a cooking process under pressure, and finally dried on a roller drier (Soc. Lab. Recherches Appl. Solar, 1942).

D. Yeast Bouillon

Bouillon produced from yeast has enjoyed a fairly extensive popularity. It is prepared by hydrolyzing dried yeast with hydrochloric acid, usually at a temperature of 100°C. and for a period of 8 to 10 hours. Alternatively, the hydrolysis may be carried out under pressure for a shorter period. Vegetables and spice extracts are added and the bouillon filtered. In practice, the production of a well-flavored bouillon which produces a clear or only slightly opalescent solution in hot or cold water demands experience and close attention to the conditions of hydrolysis. Details of the methods of production and of the difficulties which may arise are reported by Benesch (1942).

E. Vitamin-Enriched Yeast

The molecule of vitamin B_1 comprises a thiazole moiety combined with a pyrimidine ring. The vitamin can be produced in the laboratory by synthesizing the two moieties and then linking them together. Whereas the chemical linking is a matter of some difficulty, it was observed by Lanen and his colleagues (1942) that yeast was capable of synthesizing vitamin B_1 in yields of 70–100% if the separate thiazole and pyrimidine fractions of the molecule were present in the culture medium. The production of yeast containing exceedingly high concentrations of vitamin B_1 derived from thiazole and pyrimidine added during the course of propagation has been patented (Anheuser-Busch, 1949; Standard Brands Inc., 1941) and high-vitamin B_1 yeast is manufactured on a substantial scale in a number of countries. It can be employed either as a leavening agent which will enhance the nutritional value of bread or, in dried form, as tablets for pharmaceutical use.

In addition to possessing the power of synthesizing vitamin B_1 from its precursors, yeast is also capable of absorbing vitamin B_1 from the medium surrounding it. This property is made use of in patented processes for preparing enriched yeast (Standard Brands Inc., 1949; Fink, 1944). Yeast rich in vitamin B_1 has also been prepared by adding acetylated vitamin B_1 to the wort in which it is propagated (Hoffman La Roche, 1945). A further elaboration is to add vitamin B_6 to the medium as well as vitamin B_1 (Standard Brands Inc., 1942).

F. Preparations from Ergosterol

(1) *Vitamin D_2.* In 1928, Steenbock patented the irradiation of foods by ultraviolet light to produce anti-rachitic activity. Eight years later, in 1936, he patented the irradiation of yeast for the same purpose and much attention was given to this invention. Irradiated yeast was widely used and numerous variations in its method of production were worked out.

Irradiated yeast containing vitamin D_2 activity has been widely used not only in human nutrition but also in animal feeding. Cows given irradiated yeast in their feed produce milk containing enhanced quantities of vitamin D_2.

The amount of ergosterol in yeast may be increased by special means. For example, Halden (1935) produced additional ergosterol in the cells by subjecting the yeast to the alternate action of alcohol vapor and air, the yeast being allowed to dry during the process. Again, Bennett (1936) found that the concentration could be increased by cultivating the yeast in the presence of an oxidizing agent such as methylene blue and in a medium deficient in nitrogen. The growth of yeast in an aerated medium free from both assimilable nitrogen and fermentable carbohydrate but containing glycerol and inorganic phosphate has also been reported to increase the ergosterol content (Geschwindt. fele Szez-Eleczto-Likor-es-Rum-Gyar Reszvenytarsasag, 1944).

Yeast is the principal source of ergosterol for the synthesis of vitamin D_2 and a number of methods have been devised for the extraction of ergosterol from it. One of the first of these, patented in 1929 (Walz *et al.*, 1929), involved the plasmolysis of the yeast with ethyl acetate, saponification with caustic soda in the presence of excess alcohol, and extraction of the ergosterol with ether. In a modified method, the plasmolyzed yeast stands for several days after which time tyrosine separates and can be removed before the ergosterol is recovered (Winthrop Chemical Co., 1934). Again, the saponification can be done by boiling the yeast fat in an acetone solution and the ergosterol can be precipitated by adding water and cooling to a low temperature (Mead Johnson Co., 1934). Ergosterol can also be precipitated by cooling aqueous alcohol solutions (Standard Brands Inc., 1935).

Benzene has been used in place of ether to separate ergosterol from saponified yeast (Standard Brands Inc., 1936; Hoffmann La Roche, 1936) while Bennett (1939) used a solvent, such as butyl alcohol, partially miscible with water and carried out the saponification in a solution of the organic solvent. A different use of such a solvent has also been reported (F.I.A.T., 1948) in a process in which a solid caustic alkali is added directly to the substance being treated, the mixture heated, and then, when it has fully liquefied, extracted with the solvent.

Recently, Dulaney and Stapley (1954) described a study of 558 yeasts comprising 69 species in 20 genera. The proportion of ergosterol found varied from 0.1% of the cell weight up to a maximum of 7–10% in 8 cultures of S. cerevisiae.

(2) Cortisone. An immense effort has been exerted to find an economic method for the large scale synthesis of cortisone. Cortisone is produced commercially by partial synthesis using bile acids as a starting material (Shoppee, 1953). Nevertheless, ergosterol has been used as a basis for synthesis by Fieser et al. (1951), by Chamberlin and his colleagues (1951), by Heusser and his colleagues (1951, 1952), and by Anderson et al. (1952).

G. Glutathione

The precise function of glutathione in cellular metabolism and its pharmacological significance in medicine are not fully understood. It has, however, been manufactured from yeast in commercial quantities as a therapeutic agent and for research purposes (F.I.A.T., 1948). A number of recent discoveries have underlined the possibility that glutathione may ultimately prove to be of practical value in treatment. Not only has it been found to be interrelated biochemically with vitamin C (Mapson and Goddard, 1951), but it has also been shown to be capable of reversing induced diabetes in rats (Lazarow, 1949) and the diabetes produced in man by ACTH (the adrenocorticotropic hormone) (Conn et al., 1949). Its possible connection with suprarenal metabolism in general has also been discussed (Rinderknecht, 1950).

Considerable interest has been aroused by the use of glutathione in the treatment of "radiation sickness." Shiral (1941) found it to be effective against Roentgen intoxication arising from therapeutic irradiation and Patt et al. (1950) reported that it reduced radiation toxicity.

Black (1947) administered glutathione intravenously to patients with malignant neoplastic disease and considered that they obtained benefit thereby. Glutathione, in common with other sulfhydryl compounds, antagonizes the toxic effect of arsenical compounds (Voegtlin et al., 1923).

The standard method for extracting glutathione from yeast is that of

Pirie (1930). This is inconvenient for large-scale work because it involves the use of a mixture of ether and sulfuric acid for the plasmolysis of the yeast. Schroeder et al. (1939) devised an alternative method which, however, possessed the drawback of employing large amounts of acetone. On an industrial scale plasmolysis of the yeast can be achieved with sodium acetate (F.I.A.T., 1948). Glutathione may be isolated as a copper salt or, alternatively, precipitated by means of cadmium lactate.

H. Nucleic Acid

The ribonucleic acid of yeast is a biologically active substance which is concerned with the synthesis of protein within the cell. Although its value in clinical medicine has never been fully established, its effect on a number of different conditions has been examined.

Nucleic acid plays a part in the water metabolism of the body and it has been reported that its ingestion reduces edema (Ruskin, 1933). Edematous tissues are poor in nucleic acid (Wells, 1925).

Nucleic acid, through its adenylic nucleotide fraction, has an effect on the circulatory system. According to Ruskin and Katz (1936), it causes peripheral vasodilation, an increase in coronary circulation and a simultaneous increase in the concentration of hemoglobin and in the numbers of red cells and of white cells. Reznikoff (1933) reported that adenylic acid was the active factor causing remission of symptoms when nucleotides were administered to patients suffering from agranulocytic angina following barbiturates.

The treatment of (a) agranulocytosis following sulfanilamide, (b) leukopenia, also following sulfanilamide, and (c) a suspected case of pneumonia with a leucocyte count exceeding 8000 per cu. mm. with a commercial preparation of iron nucleotide has also been reported (Reznikoff, 1933).

Guanine, liberated from nucleic acid by the action of the cellular phosphorylating enzymes, has been shown by Colowick and Price (1946) to initiate carbohydrate metabolism in muscle.

The possibility that nucleic acid is specifically concerned with tumor growth has been closely examined. It is interesting to note that injection of nucleotides into tumor-bearing mice has under certain circumstances been found to check the growth of the tumors (Parsons et al., 1947).

Methods for the preparation of nucleic acid on a large scale have been reported in detail (F.I.A.T., 1948). In principle, the procedure involves the treatment of the yeast for a limited time with alkali, preferably in presence of isinglass. The alkali treatment must be followed by immediate neutralization and, after filtration, the nucleic acid is precipitated from the cooled filtrate by means of acid. The crude material is then washed, redissolved, and reprecipitated. Nucleic acid has been produced for clinical and experimental use in the form of the free acid, the copper salt, the iron salt, and the manganese salt.

The preparation of an extract containing yeast nucleic acids is described by Vogel (1939). Methods for increasing the yield of nucleic acids obtainable from yeast have also been reported (Loofbourow, 1941; Loofbourow, 1942). Procedures for separating deoxyribonucleic acid from ribonucleic acid are also available (Veurely, 1946; von Euler, 1947).

Yeast nucleic acid contains the purine bases, adenine and guanine, and the pyrimidines, cytosine and uracil. The preparation of the following individual purines, pyrimidines, nucleotides, and nucleosides from yeast has been reported: adenine (Vischer, 1948), adenosine (Brederick et al., 1941), adenylic acid (Stendal, 1922a), guanine (Vischer, 1948), guanosine (Brederick et al. 1941), guanilic acid (Stendal, 1922a), cytosine (Vischer, 1948), cytidine (Brederick et al., 1941), cytidylic acid (Stendal, 1922b), uracil (Vischer, 1948), uridine (Harris, 1949), uridylic acid (Stendal, 1922b).

Next to the manufacture of nucleic acid from yeast, the preparation of its hydrolysis products has assumed some commercial significance, particularly in Germany. Finally in addition to the purines and pyrimidines and their nucleotides and nucleosides, the sugar, ribose, is a substance which can usefully be produced from yeast nucleic acid.

Ribose is prepared by hydrolyzing nucleic acid, or a nucleoside derived from it, in boiling sulfuric acid. When the solution is cooled, the purines and pyrimidines can be caused to precipitate, after which the solution is concentrated and the ribose finally crystallized from alcohol. (F.I.A.T., 1948.)

For structural details of many of the above individual constituents of yeast, see Chapters V and IX.

6. Technical Uses

A. *As a Chemical Reagent*

(1) *Glycerol.* The production of glycerol by fermentation is an example of the use in chemical technology of reactions brought about by yeast. The principle upon which the manufacture is based, as described in Chapter VII, depends on the immobilization of the acetaldehyde occurring in the Embden-Meyerhof-Parnas scheme of fermentation so that it is prevented from filling its role of hydrogen acceptor. In practice, this

is brought about either by the use of sulfite or by the employment of a high pH.

The Sulfite Process. Connstein and Ludecke (1921, 1924) developed a process in Germany during World War I for the production of glycerol by fermentation. One hundred grams of pressed yeast was used to ferment 1 kg. of sucrose in a solution containing ammonium nitrate, potassium phosphate, and 400 g. of sodium sulfite in 10 l. of water. On a commercial scale the process was carried out in 300,000 l. vessels. The fermentation was continued for 48 to 60 hours at 30°C. when the final filtered solution contained up to 3% of glycerol.

A modification of this process was developed by Fulmer *et al.* (1947) using ammonium sulfite in place of sodium sulfite. This facilitated the recovery of the glycerol from the fermented solution. Careful adjustment of fermentation conditions enabled yields up to 20 g. of glycerol per 100 g. sugar to be obtained.

The Alkaline Process. Underkofler and Hickey (1954) in describing the Eoff process write that it was never used on a full commercial scale. Eoff *et al.* (1919), however, describe pilot plant operations in which 2200 kg. of molasses in a volume of approximately 8000 l. were inoculated with a yeast culture to which sodium carbonate had been previously added. The fermentation was allowed to continue for from 5 to 7 days at 32°C.; during this time 450 kg. of solid sodium carbonate was added in portions after 2, 4, 6, and 17 hours. The fermented solution contained about 3% of glycerol.

Shade and Farber (1947) and Shade (1947) modified this process by bubbling the fermenting solution with air, oxygen, or even nitrogen. The effect of this was to remove the volatile fermentation products, ethanol, acetaldehyde, and carbon dioxide while allowing the yeast to grow and maintain itself in an active state under the unfavorable conditions of the high pH.

Very recently, Spencer (1955) and Spencer and Sallens (1956) have found that certain osmophilic yeasts produce high concentrations of glycerol together with substantial amounts of D-arabitol, not when fermenting under substantially anaerobic conditions, but, surprisingly enough, when growing under strong aeration. It seems possible, therefore, that provided a use can be found for the D-arabitol, this reaction may prove to be a third method for producing glycerol through the agency of yeast.

(2) *Ephedrine.* In 1934, Hildebrandt and Klavehn described an ingenious method by means of which yeast fermentation brings about the conversion of benzaldehyde to 1,1-phenyl-1-hydroxy-2-propanone, a re-

action originally discovered by Neuberg (1921, 1922). This substance is then reductively condensed with monomethylamine to give ephedrine. For the initial reaction, 100 g. of yeast is allowed to ferment for 3 days in a solution of 125 g. of glucose syrup in 2.5 l. of water to which 10 g. of benzaldehyde is gradually added. The mechanism of the reaction by which the biosynthesis is achieved has been studied in some detail by Smith and Hendlin (1953).

(3) *Other Reactions of Technical Interest.* The basic technical use of yeast is to produce alcohol, both for potable and for industrial purposes. However, the carbon dioxide produced during alcoholic fermentation is an important by-product. It is compressed and marketed in both liquid and solid forms as a refrigerant, as a carbonating agent, and for extinguishing fire. A number of other yeast reactions have also been used for technical purposes. Yeast has been employed as a reducing agent (Neuberg, 1927; Kuhn, 1941), as an oxidizing agent (Wieland, 1932), and to induce hydrolysis (Neuberg, 1939).

B. *Invertase*

The technical importance of transforming common sugar, that is sucrose, into "invert sugar" lies in the fact (a) that the latter is hygroscopic and thus helps to keep moist any mixture containing it; (b) invert sugar is more soluble than sucrose and the maximum sugar content of a syrup can consequently be increased from 67% up to 83% without crystallization occurring. This is of two-fold importance. Firstly, a syrup will flow more easily and can be more readily pumped when the sugar is inverted and, secondly, a concentrated sugar solution can be stored . without becoming granular and crystalline. Finally, invert sugar becomes browned at a lower temperature than sucrose so that biscuits and cakes in which it is present can be given an agreeable color without excessive heating in the oven.

An important industrial use of invertase is in the manufacture of chocolates with soft centers. Invertase is incorporated in the fondant formula which is designed to have a sufficiently firm consistency to allow the chocolate coating to be applied. During storage, however, the enzyme converts part of the sugar into the more soluble invert sugar and the center becomes soft or liquid depending on the concentration of invertase employed.

Invertase concentrate is prepared from yeast by plasmolyzing the cells and allowing autolysis to occur. A large number of plasmolyzing agents may be used. Among those most commonly employed are ether, chloroform, toluene, and ethyl acetate (Sumner and Myrbäck, 1950) but benzene, xylene, carbon disulfide, carbon tetrachloride, isosulfocyanates, amyl alcohol, and substances which reduce the surface tension of water have all been used successfully (Neuberg and Lustig, 1942).

The initial invertase content of the yeast used for the preparation of enzyme concentrates can be increased by stimulating its general anabolic activity. This can be achieved by the addition of appropriate amounts of sucrose during the course of a preliminary fermentation (Willstatter et al., 1925; Willstatter and Lowry, 1925).

After the invertase has been released from the yeast cells by plasmolysis and subsequent autolysis it can be purified by adsorption on a number of substances including aluminum hydroxide (Albers and Meyer, 1934), bentonite (Adams and Hudson, 1938) or zinc sulfide (Richtmyer and Hudson, 1938). Alternatively, the enzyme can be precipitated. Strontium hydroxide (Weidenhagen and Nenninger, 1939) or alcohol (von Euler and Josephson, 1923) are among the commoner precipitants used. A number of methods for making purified preparations of yeast invertase are described in detail by Neuberg and Roberts (1946).

In practice, invertase is mostly used in liquid form. A procedure patented in 1934 (Standard Brands, Inc.), involving plasmolysis of the yeast followed by autolysis in the presence of alkali at 30°C., gives a solution of invertase to which preservatives such as ethylene glycol or glycerol may be added. The precipitation of yeast protein by means of acid followed by the addition of glycerol to the filtrate is an alternative process (Gore et al., 1949). In an earlier patent (Wallerstein, 1933), a yeast autolysate was concentrated by evaporation, the invertase precipitated with alcohol and dissolved in a solution of glycerol. The precipitation of the enzyme with dimethyl carbinol, followed by solution in glycerol has also been patented (Wallerstein, 1933). Besides these liquid preparations of invertase, however, a number of dry powders have been described. In one, the invertase solution, concentrated to a syrupy consistency, is dried on glucose or lactose (Wallerstein, 1932); in another, the enzyme is separated in the form of an adsorption complex with calcium phosphate and the precipitate is washed and dried at low temperature. It is claimed that the dry white powder recovered possesses a high enzyme activity and is stable (Neuberg, 1944). Invertase may also be precipitated with water-soluble ethers of the dioxane type and a dry, stable preparation very simply obtained (Neuberg and Roberts, 1946).

C. Miscellaneous Products and Uses

Several patents have been taken out on the production of plastic preparations from yeast. Stein (1926) mixed yeast with the usual fillers, sawdust, or gypsum and also with brewery wastes, such as malt dust or dried spent hops, and dried the mixture until it could be molded by pressing. Mooser-Schliess (1921) made plastics suitable for rolling and molding from mixtures of yeast, glycerol esters, acetyl derivatives of cellulose or sugar, fillers, and hardening agents such as formaldehyde. Blucher (1912, 1915, 1916), in a series of patents, had claimed earlier to make a horn substitute from yeast residues treated with formaldehyde. The use of yeast as an adhesive has been proposed by a number of workers. Beyer in 1909 patented a mixture of yeast and dextrin treated with alkali, which was stated to give a good glue. Later patents covering adhesives prepared from yeast were taken out in 1928 and 1929 (I.G. Farbenind). A Japanese patent of 1948 (Koyama) described an adhesive made by mixing yeast with a small amount of ammonia and coagulating the whole with lactic or acetic acid.

Although satisfactory plastics and adhesives can be prepared from yeast it has not in general been found economical to use it for this purpose owing to its comparatively high cost.

Numerous preparations of yeast have also been reported other than those described above, but in most cases these are of little significance. For example, yeast has been used as a cleaning agent (Vogel, 1939) for removing dirt from the skin and also for cleaning brass, copper, aluminum and other metals. A patent has also been taken out for the use of autolyzed yeast in leather manufacture (McCandlish, 1923) and several reports have been made of its value as a base for making pills (Vogel, 1939; Sabolitschka, 1922).

References

Adams, M., and Hudson, C. S. (1938). J. Am. Chem. Soc. 60, 982.

Albers, H., and Meyer, T. (1934). Z. physiol. Chem. 228, 222.

Ambros, O., and Winthrop Chemical Co. (1930). U.S. Patent 1724706.

Andersen, E. (1956). Intern. Sugar J. 58, 133.

Anderson, R. C., Stevenson, R., and Spring, F. S. (1952). J. Chem. Soc. 1952, 2901.

Anheuser Busch Inc. (1949). U.S. Patent 2359521.

Bailey, C. W. (1939). Cereal Chem. 16, 665.

Barber, J. (1908). Infectious Diseases 5, 379.

Basaca, M. Y. (1952). Philippine J. Sci. 81, 75.

Bass, A., and Hospodka, J. (1952). Chem. Listy 46, 243.

Bayfield, F. (1950). Trans. Am. Assoc. Cereal Chemists 8, 146.

Benesch, R. (1942). Bull. assoc. chim. 59, 624.

Benesch, R. (1949). Rev. fermentations et inds. aliment. 4, 145.

Bennett, R. (1955). Brit. Baking Ind. Research Assoc. Rept. No. 24.

Bennett, W. G., and Peake, A. M. (1933). British Patent 319641.

Bennett, W. G., and International Yeast Co. (1936). British Patent 396206.

Bennett, W. G., and International Yeast Co. (1939). British Patent 504051.

Berman, V. (1935). Czech. Patent 51832.

Bernheuer, K. (1943). *Ergeb. Enzymforsch.* 9, 297.

Berti, P. (1935). *Bull. assoc. chim.* 52, 286.

Beyer, C. (1909). German Patent 224443.

Binkley, W. W., and Wolfrom, M. L. (1950). *J. Am. Chem. Soc.* 72, 4778.

Binkley, W. W., and Wolfrom, M. L. (1953). *Advances in Carbohydrate Chem.* 8, 291.

B.I.O.S. (1946). Final Rept. 691.

Biyack, S. (1952). *Acta Microbiol. Polon.* 1, 65.

Black, M. M. (1947). *Cancer Research* 7, 592.

Blinc, M. (1951). *Acad. Sci. et Art. Sloven.* (*Ljubljana*). *Class III, Ser. A, Dissertationes* No. 3, 41.

Blucher, H. (1912). German Patent 275857; (1915). 285597; (1916). 303133.

Braasch, H., and Braasch, A. (1934). German Patent 605912.

Brahmer, H. (1947). *Svensk Papperstidn.* 50, 53.

Brederick, H., Martin, A., and Richter, F. (1941). *Ber. deut. chem. Ges.* 74B, 69A.

British Colonial Food Yeast Ltd. (1944). "Food Yeast," H.M.S.O.

British Pharmaceutical Codex (1949). P. 228.

Cathcart, W. H. (1953). *Trans. Am. Assoc. Cereal Chemists* 11, 34.

Chain, E. B., Paladino, S., Callow, D. S., Ugolini, F., and Van der Sluis, J. (1952). *World Health Organization Monograph Ser.* 10, 73.

Chain, E. B., Paladino, S., Ugolini, F., Callow, D. S., and Van der Sluis, J. (1954). *Rend. inst. super. sanità* 17, 61.

Chamberlin, E. M., Ruyle, W. V., Erickson, A. E., Chemerda, J. M., Aliminosa, L. M., Erickson, R. L., Sita, G. E., and Tishler, M. (1951). *J. Am. Chem. Soc.* 73, 2396.

Cid, A. R., Fernandez-Cano, L. H., and Marquex, J. G. (1951). *Rev. cienc. apl.* (*Madrid*) 5, 403.

Claypole, J. E. L. (1909). *J. Hyg.* 9, 239.

Colowick, S. P., and Price, W. H. (1946). *Federation Proc.* 5, 130.

Conn, J. W., Louis, Z. H., and Johnston, M. W. (1949). *Science* 109, 279.

Connstein, W., and Lüdecke, K. (1921). U.S. Patent 1368023.

Connstein, W., and Lüdecke, K. (1924). U.S. Patent 1511754.

Cunningham, J. (1953). *Chemistry & Industry* 1953, 163.

Damm, H. (1943). *Chem. Ztg.* 67, (5/6), 47.

Daranyi, S. (1932). British Patent 376038.

Davidson, L. S. P. (1931). *Lancet* i, 26.

Davidson, L. S. P., and Anderson, I. A. (1947). "A Textbook of Dietetics." Hamish Hamilton, London.

Dawson, E. R. (1951). *In* "Dictionary of Applied Chemistry" (Thorpe and Whiteley, eds.). Longmans, Green, New York.

de Becze, G. (1934). Hungarian Patent 110202.

de Becze, G., and Liebman, A. L. (1944). *Ind. Eng. Chem.* 36, 882.

de Becze, G. (1940). U.S. Patent 2199722.

de Becze, G., and Rosenblatt, M. (1943). *Am. Brewer* 76 (2), 11.

Deloffre, M. C. H. (1942). Australian Patent 114926.

Deloffre, M. C. H. (1943). Belgian Patent 449180.

Deloffre, M. C. H. (1945). U.S. Patent 2367931.

Denhard, H. W. (1949). U.S. Patent 2490421.

de Whalley, H. C. S., Albon, N., and Gross, D. (1951). *Analyst* **76**, 287.

de Whalley, H. C. S. (1952). *Intern. Sugar J.* **54**, 127.

Dickens, F. (1955). *Repts. 3rd Congr. Intern. Biochem.* p. 126.

Dierssen, G. A., Holtegaad, K., Jensen, B., and Rosen, K. (1956). *Intern. Sugar J.* **58**, 35.

Diller, H. (1942). *Z. Untersuch. Lebensm.* **83**, 206.

Doty, J. M., and Urban, W. R. (1940). *Cereal Chem.* **17**, 44.

Dulaney, E. L., and Stapley, E. O. (1954). *Appl. Microbiol.* **2**, 371.

Dunn, C. G. (1952). *Wallerstein Labs. Communs.* **15**, 61.

Effront, J. (1927). *Compt. rend.* **184**, 1303.

Eijkman, C., Van Hoogenhuyze, C. J., and Derks, T. J. G. (1922). *J. Biol. Chem.* **50**, 311.

Eisenberg, S. (1940). *Cereal Chem.* **17**, 417.

Elvehjem, C. A., and Hart, E. B. (1931). *J. Biol. Chem.* **91**, 37.

Elvehjem, C. A., and Hart, E. B. (1932). *J. Biol. Chem.* **95**, 363.

Eoff, J. R., Lindner, W. V., and Beyer, G. F. (1919). *Ind. Eng. Chem.* **11**, 842.

Felsher, A. R., Koch, R. B., and Larsen, R. A. (1955). *Cereal Chem.* **32**, 117.

Fernandez-Cano, L. H., and Cid, A. R. (1952). *Rev. cienc. apl.* (*Madrid*) **6**, 37.

F.I.A.T. (1945). Final Rept. No. 499. H.M.S.O., London.

F.I.A.T. (1948). Final Rept. No. 1274. Joint Intelligence Objectives Agency, Washington, D.C.

Fieser, L. F., Herz, J. E., and Huang, W. Y. (1951). *J. Am. Chem. Soc.* **73**, 2397.

Fink, H., Haehn, H., and Hoerburger, W. (1937). *Chem. Ztg.* **61**, 689.

Fink, H. (1944). German Patent 738655.

Fowell, R. R. (1951). *J. Inst. Brewing* **57**, 180.

Frey, C. N. (1930). *Ind. Eng. Chem.* **22**, 1154.

Frey, C. N., Kirby, G. W., and Schultz, A. (1936). *Ind. Eng. Chem.* **28**, 879.

Fuchs, E. (1937). U.S. Patent 2072748.

Fulmer, E. I., Underkofler, L. A., and Hickey, R. J. (1947). U.S. Patent 2416745.

Garibaldi, J. A., and Feeney, R. E. (1949). *Ind. Eng. Chem.* **41**, 432.

Geschwindt. Fele Szez-Eleczto-Likor-es-Rum-Gyar Reszvenytarsasag. (1944). German Patent 72007.

Ghosh, D., and Pirt, S. J. (1954). *Rend. ist. super. sanità* **17**, 147.

Glabe, E. F. (1942). *Cereal Chem.* **19**, 230.

Gore, H. C., Kirby, G. W., and Frey, C. N. (1949). U.S. Patent 2164914.

Gosda, J. (1934). British Patent 412842.

Guillemet, R. (1936). *Compt. rend. soc. biol.* **121**, 465.

Gust, W., Putnam, F. W., and Johnson, J. A. (1950). *Trans. Am. Assoc. Cereal Chemists* **8**, 130.

Hagberg, G. (1953). *Baker's Digest* **27**, 98, 120.

Halden, W. (1935). Austrian Patent 140190.

Hanson, A. M., Rodgers, N. E., and Meade, R. E. (1949). U.S. Patent 2465870.

Harris, R. J. C. (1949). *J. Chem. Soc.* **1949**, 1936.

Hayduck, F. (1919). German Patent 303221.

Hayduck, F. (1923). U.S. Patent 1449108.

Hedberg, C. W. (1948). Canadian Patent 452209.

Heinz, H. (1921). *Therap. Gegenwart* **62**, No. 5.

Hesse, A. (1949). *Advances in Enzymol.* **9**, 653.

Heusser, H., Eichenberger, K., Kurath, P., Dallenbach, H. R., and Jeger, O. (1951). *Helv. Chim. Acta* **34**, 2106.

Heusser, H., Heusler, K., Eichenberger, K., Honegger, C. G., and Jeger, O. (1952). *Helv. Chim. Acta* **35**, 295.

Hildebrandt, G., and Klavehn, W. (1934). U.S. Patent 1956950.

Hoffman, C., Frey, C. N., and Hildebrandt, F. M., and the Fleischmann Co. (1932). U.S. Patent 1687561.

Hoffmann La Roche and National Grain Yeast Corp., U.S. Patent 2328025.

Hoffmann La Roche (1936). German Patent appl. 11118019.

Hoogerheide, J. C. (1948). "Yeasts in Feeding." Garrard Press, London.

Humfeld, H., and Feustel, I. C. (1945). *J. Bacteriol.* **52**, 229.

Ichiro, G. (1949). *Science of Drugs* **3**, 259.

I.G. Farbenind A.G. (1928). British Patent 313101.

I.G. Farbenind A.G. (1928). British Patent 328197.

I.G. Farbenind A.G. (1929). British Patent 328645.

Inskeep, G. S., Wiley, A. J., Holderby, J. M., and Hughes, L. P. (1951). *Ind. Eng. Chem.* **43**, 1702.

International Yeast Co. (1930). German Patent 499506.

Jansen, S. (1942). British Patent 366753.

Johnson, H. G. (1948). U.S. Patent 2443825.

Jonas, V. (1934). Austrian Patent appl. 479/34.

Jorgensen, H. (1945). "Studies on the Nature of the Bromate Effect," Milford, London.

Jorgensen, H. (1948). "Micro-organisms and Fermentation," 15th ed., Griffen, London.

Kahn, R. (1930). British Patent 235834.

Kent Jones, D. W., and Amos, A. M. (1950). "Modern Cereal Chemistry," 4th ed., Northern Publ. Co., Liverpool.

Kharin, S. E., and Dement'eo, A. S. (1938). *Colloid J.* (*U.S.S.R.*) **4**, 711.

Kiefer, F. (1947). U.S. Dept. Commerce P.B. 85158.

Kihara, Y., Sato, T., and Yamaguchi, T. (1948). *J. Agr. Chem. Soc. Japan* **22**, 45.

Kleinzeller, A. (1944). *Biochem. J.* **38**, 480.

Kleinzeller, A. (1948). *Advances in Enzymol.* **8**, 299.

Koch, R. (1935). *Wochschr. Brau.* **52**, 37.

Koch, R. B., Smith, F., and Geddes, W. F. (1954). *Cereal Chem.* **31**, 55.

Koyama, R. (1948). Japanese Patent 176018.

Kuhn, R. (1941). *Ber deut. chem. Ges.* **74B**, 94.

La Société Dizem. (1944). Belgian Patent 446524.

Larmour, R. K., and Bergsteinsson, H. W. (1936). *Cereal Chem.* **13**, 410.

Larsen, R. H. (1946). U.S. Patent 2412276.

Lazarow, A. (1949). *Physiol. Revs.* **29**, 48.

Le Clerk, T. (1940). *J. Inst. Brewing* **46**, 225.

Lee, S. B. (1950). *Ind. Eng. Chem.* **42**, 1652.

Lehmann, E. (1941). *Seifensieder-Ztg.* 178.

Leifer, F. (1935). *Med. Klin.* (*Munich*) **31**, 1428.

Lew, B. W., Wolfrom, M. L., and Goepp, R. M. (1946). *J. Am. Chem. Soc.* **68**, 1449.

Lewinsohn, M. S. (1937). *Z. Vitaminforsch.* **5**, 220.

Liebers, R. (1931). British Patent 242645.

Lindegren, C. C. (1944). Wallerstein Labs. Communs. **7**, 153.

Lindner, P. (1922). *Z. angew. Chem.* **35,** 110.

Lloyd Hind, H. (1948). "Brewing," 3rd ed. Chapman & Hill, London.

Lobo, J. M. V. (1953). *Anales real soc. españ fis y quim* (*Madrid*) **B49,** 245.

Lobry de Bruyn, C. A., and Van Ekenstein, W. A. (1897). *Rec. trav. chim.* **16,** 260, 280.

Lockey, J. (1933). British Patent 387486.

Loofbourow, J. R. (1941). *Nature* **148,** 113.

Loofbourow, J. R. (1942). *Nature* **149,** 328.

Lundin, H. (1950). *J. Inst. Brewing* **56,** 17.

Machinenbau, A. G., Golzern-Grimma (1914). German Patent 246709.

Machinenbau, A. G., Golzern-Grimma (1932). German Patent 1238354.

Machinenbau, A. G., Golzern-Grimma (1934). German Patent 1301453.

Maes, E. (1951). *Getreide Mehl. u. Brot.* **5,** 17.

Malloch, J. G. (1939). *Cereal Chem.* **16,** 178.

Malthus, T. R. (1798). "Essay on the Principle of Population as It Affects the Future Improvement of Society." London.

Mapson, L. W., and Goddard, D. R. (1951). *Nature* **167,** 975.

Mariani, E., and Torracci, G. (1951). *Nature* **168,** 959.

Matalon, R. (1953). *Nature* **172,** 19.

Mather, K., Edgar, J., and Whiteside, A. E. O. (1943). *Cereal Chem.* **20,** 355.

McCandlish, D. (1923). U.S. Patent 1570383.

Mead Johnson Co. (1934). U.S. Patent 1842929.

Mellors, H. (1950). *Chemistry & Industry* **1950,** 806.

Meyer, E. A., and Chaffe, P. W. (1938). British Patent 523019.

Miller, A., and A. Guiness Co. (1936). British Patent 450117.

Monod, J. (1942). "La croissance des cultures bacteriennes." Harmann, Paris.

Mooser-Schliess, W. (1921). U.S. Patent 1367886.

Morse, R. E., and Fellers, C. R. (1949). *Food Technol.* **3,** 234.

Muller, M. (1895). *Z. Hyg. Infektionskrankh.* **20,** 118.

Munden, D. L. (1950). *Chemistry & Industry* **1950,** 806.

N. V. Internationale Sinker en Alkohol Compagnie. (1937). Hungarian Patent appl. 516617.

Neuberg, C. (1921). *Biochem. Z.* **115,** 282.

Neuberg, C. (1922). *Biochem. Z.* **128,** 611.

Neuberg, C. (1927). *Biochem. Z.* **182,** 285.

Neuberg, C. (1939). *Enzymologia* **5,** 389.

Neuberg, C. (1944). U.S. Patent 2361315.

Neuberg, C., and Lustig, H. (1942). *Arch. Biochem.* **1,** 211.

Neuberg, C., and Roberts, T. S. (1946). "Invertase," Sugar Research Foundation, Sci. Rept. No. 4, New York.

New and Nonofficial Remedies (1949). Council on Pharmacy and Chemistry American Medical Association.

Nokay, N. (1951). *Türk. Ljien Tecrübi Biol. Dergisi* **11,** 344.

Nutrition Subcommittee of the Colonial Medical Research Committee (1948). *Brit. Med. J.* **26.**

Olsen, A. J. C. (1950). "Recent advances in the fermentation industries," Roy. Inst. Chem. (London) Spec. Rept.

Olson, B. H., and Johnson, M. J. (1949). *J. Bacteriol.* **57,** 235.

Oter, M., and Umeda, G. (1935). British Patent 376149.

Parsons, H. T., Gulland, J. M., and Barker, H. A. (1947). "Symposium in Nucleic Acid," Soc. Exptl. Biol., Cambridge.

Parsons, H. T., Williamson, A., and Johnson, M. L. (1945). *J. Nutrition* **29**, 273.

Patt, H. M., Smith, D. E., Tyree, E. B., and Straube, R. L. (1950). *Proc. Soc. Exptl. Biol. Med.* **73**, 18.

Pattle, R. E. (1950). *J. Soc. Chem. Ind. (London)* **69**, 368.

Pavcek, P. L., Peterson, W. H., and Elvehjem, C. A. (1937). *Ind. Eng. Chem.* **29**, 536.

Payen, R. (1949). *Can. J. Research* **B27**, 749.

Peter, L. (1921). German Patent 338886.

Pirie, W. (1930). *Biochem. J.* **24**, 51.

Pollock, G. E., and Holmstrom, C. D. (1951). *Cereal Chem.* **28**, 498.

Prescott, S. C., and Dunn, C. G. (1949). "Industrial Microbiology," 2nd ed. McGraw-Hill, New York.

Proc. Brit. West Indies Sugar Technol. (1947). 35–54.

Pyke, M. (1955). *J. Appl. Bacteriol.* **18**, 187.

Rank, W., and Hahn, W. (1931). German Patent appl. N31839.

Reznikoff, P. (1933). *J. Clin. Invest.* **12**, 4553.

Reiser, C. O. (1954). *J. Agr. Food Chem.* **2**, 70.

Richtmyer, N. K., and Hudson, C. S. (1938). *J. Am. Chem. Soc.* **60**, 983.

Ries, J. (1937). German Patent 648672.

Rinderknecht, H. (1950). *Lancet* **258**, 784.

Robinson, J. V., and Woods, W. W. (1946). *U.S. Natl. Advisory Comm. Aeronautics Tech. Note* No. 1025.

Roger, D., and Mickelson, M. N. (1948). *Ind. Eng. Chem.* **40**, 527.

Ross, S. (1950). *Rensselaer Polytech. Inst. Bull. Eng. and Sci. Ser.* No. 63.

Ruskin, S. L. (1933). *Trans. 3rd Intern. Pediat. Congr., Acta Paediat.* **16**.

Ruskin, S. L., and Katz, J. (1936). *Ann. Internal Med.* **9**, 11.

Sabolitschka, T. (1922). *Ber. deut. pharm. Ges.* **32**, 48.

Sak, S. (1919). Danish Patent 28507.

Sak, S. (1928). British Patent 294123.

Sansted, R. M., and Blish, M. J. (1954). *Cereal Chem.* **11**, 368.

Schattaneck, E. (1934). Austrian Patent appl. 1631/34.

Scholler, H., and Seidel, M. (1940). U.S. Patent 2188192.

Schroeder, E. F., Collier, V., and Woodward, G. E. (1939). *Biochem. J.* **33**, 1180.

Schulmann, V. (1939). *Listy Cukrovar.* **57**, 352.

Schultz, M. (1898). German Patent 91501.

Schultz, A., Atkin, L., and Frey, C. N. (1942). *Ind. Eng. Chem.* **14**, 35.

Schultz, A., and Doose, O. (1953). *Brot u Gebäck* **7**, 47.

Sebrell, H. (1934). *Virginia Med. Monthly* **61**, 136.

Sevcik, V. (1952). *Czechoslov. Biol.* **1**, 95.

Shade, A. L. (1947). U.S. Patent 2428766.

Shade, A. L., and Farber, H. (1947). U.S. Patent 2414838.

Sharples, L. P. (1949). U.S. Patent 2489678.

Shiral, M. (1941). *Nagoya Igakkai Zassi* **54**, 183.

Shoppee, C. W. (1953). *Ann. Rev. Biochem.* **22**, 261.

Sigmend, A. V. (1893). German Patent 61328.

Simmer, F. (1931). German Patent appl. 86544/31.

Slator, A. (1921). *J. Chem. Soc.* **119**, 115.

Smedley-Maclean, I. (1936). *Ergeb. Enzymforsch.* **5**, 285.

Smith, G. G. S. (1920). *J. Hyg.* **19**, 133.

Smith, I. N. (1944). U.S. Patent 2353936.
Smith, P. F., and Hendlin, D. (1953). *J. Bacteriol.* **65,** 440.
Société des Laboratoires de Recherches pour Applications Industrielles dite Solar. (1942). British Patent 648244.
Somogyi, J. C. (1944). *Vitaminforsch.* **4,** 1.
Soderstrom, O. (1944). British Patent 596847.
Spencer, J. F. T. (1955). Glycerol production by osmophilic yeasts, Ph.D. thesis, Univ. of Saskatchewan.
Spencer, J. F. T., and Sallans, H. R. (1956). *Can. J. Microbiol.* **2,** 72.
Spiselman, J. W. (1948). Canadian Patent 452208.
Standard Brands Inc. (1933). U.S. Patent 1802645.
Standard Brands Inc. (1937). U.S. Patent 2065332.
Standard Brands Inc. (1949). U.S. Patent 2359521.
Standard Brands Inc. (1942). British Patent 539825.
Standard Brands Inc. (1935). U.S. Patent 1912440.
Standard Brands Inc. (1936). U.S. Patent 1941097.
Standard Brands Inc. (1934). British Patent 418211.
Standard Brands Inc. (1941). British Patent 532013.
Stanier, R. Y. (1946). B.I.O.S. Final Rept. 691, 4.
Stark, W. H, Kolachov, P., and Wilkie, H. F. (1941). *Am. Soc. Brewing Chem. Proc.* **1941,** 49–56.
Stark, W. H., and Pohler, G. M. (1950). *Ind. Eng. Chem.* **42,** 1789.
Steenbock, H. (1928). U.S. Patent 1680818.
Steenbock, H. (1936). U.S. Patent 2057399.
Stefaniak, J. J., Gailey, F. B., Brown, C. S., and Johnson, M. J. (1946). *Ind. Eng. Chem.* **38,** 666.
Stein, F. (1926). German Patent 476031.
Steinberg, M. P., and Ordal, Z. J. (1954). *J. Agr. Food Chem.* **2,** 873.
Stendal, O. (1922a). *Z. physiol. Chem.* **122,** 298.
Stendal, O. (1922b). *Z. physiol. Chem.* **120,** 292.
Stepp, W. (1936). "Die Vitamine and ihre Klinische Anwendung," Stuttgart.
Stich, E. G. (1930). *Chem. Ztg.* **217,** 238.
Stich, E. G. (1933). German Patent 567518; (1934). 594671; 594192; 594193; 594195; (1935). 622962-3.
Stich, E. G. (1934). German Patent 594361.
Strauch and Schmidt. (1932). German Patent 552241.
Strauch and Schmidt. (1934). German Patent 597953.
Sumner, J. B., and Myrbäck, K. (1950). "The Enzymes," Vol. 1, p. 532. Academic Press, New York.
Terjesen, S. G., and Cherry, G. B. (1947). *Trans. Inst. Chem. Engrs. (London)* **25,** 89.
Tominyasn, Y., and Zenitan, B. (1952). *J. Agr. Chem. Soc. Japan* **25,** 406.
Underkofler, L. A., and Hickey, R. J. (1954). "Industrial Fermentations," Vol. 1. Chemical Publ. Co., New York.
Urie, A., and Huls, J. H. (1952). "The Science, Raw Materials and Hygiene of Baking," Macdonald and Evans, London.
Natl. Research Council (U.S.). (1948). *Reprint and Circular Ser.* No. 129.
Van Damme, C. (1932). "L'aerolevure moderne," M. Cock, Brussels.
Van der Sandt, H. (1934). German Patent appl. 95013.
Van der Snikt, L. (1934). *Bull. Assoc. Inst. super. fermentation Gand* **35,** 261, 286.

van Laer, M. H. (1934). *Ann. Brews. Dist.* **32**, 241.

Van Lanen, J. M., Broquist, H. P., Johnson, M. J., Baldwin, I. L., and Peterson, W. H. (1942). *Ind. Eng. Chem.* **34**, 1244.

Van Lanen, J. M., and Tanner, F. W. (1948). *Vitamins and Hormones* **6**, 163.

Vegex Inc. (1936). U.S. Patent 8235827.

Veldhuis, M. K. (1952). *Citrus Ind.* **33**, 11.

Verein der Spiritusfabrikanten in Deutschland. (1915). German Patent 303221.

Veurely, R. (1946). *Bull. soc. chim. biol.* **28**, 60.

Vischer, E. (1948). *J. Biol. Chem.* **176**, 715.

Voegtlin, C., Dyer, H. A., and Leonard, C. S. (1923). *Public Health Repts.* (*U.S.*) **38**, 1882.

Vogel, H. (1939). "Die Technik der Bierhefe-Verwertung," Stuttgart.

Vogelbusch, W. (1933). Austrian Patent 126573.

Vogelbusch, W. (1934). Austrian Patent 136969.

Vogelbusch, W. (1935a). Austrian Patent 128825.

Vogelbusch, W. (1935b). Austrian Patent 142217.

von Euler, H. (1947). *Arkiv Kemi* **24A**, No. 28; **25A**, No. 11.

von Euler, H., and Josephson, K. (1923). *Ber. deut. chem. Ges.* **56**, 446.

Wagner, T. A., and Bohl, Z. (1950). *Trans. Am. Assoc. Cereal Chemists* **8**, 29.

Waldhof, Z. (1948). German Patent 802332.

Walter, F. G. (1940). "The Manufacture of Compressed Yeast," Chapman & Hall, London.

Wallerstein, L. (1932). U.S. Patent 1855591.

Wallerstein, L. (1933). U.S. Patent 1919676.

Walz, E., Griessbach, R., and Ambros, O. (1929). U.S. Patent 1724706.

Weidenhagen, R., and Nenninger, L. (1939). *Z. Wirtschaftsgruppe Zuckesind.* **89**, 149.

Weizmann, C. (1938). British Patent 483587.

Weizmann, C. (1941). British Patent 516343.

Weizmann, C. (1947). British Patent 516343.

Wells, H. G. (1925). "Chemical Pathology," Saunders, Philadelphia.

Welminsky, P., and Butschowitz, E. (1929). *Zentr. Bakteriol. Parasitenk. Abt. II,* p. 178.

Whinery, E. (1950). *Trans. Am. Assoc. Cereal Chemists* **8**, 159.

White, J. (1948). *Am. Brewer* **81**, No. 7, 21.

White, J. (1954). "Yeast Technology," Chapman & Hall, London.

White, J., and Munns, D. J. (1951). *Wallerstein Labs. Communs.* **14**, 199.

Wieland, H. (1932). *Ann.* **499**, 213.

Wiley, A. J. (1954). "Industrial Fermentations," Chemical Publ. Co., New York.

Wilkie, H. F., and Prochaska, J. A. (1943). "Fundamentals of Distillery Practice," Seagram, Louisville.

Wills, L. (1931). *Brit. Med. J.* No. 3676.

Willstätter, R., Lowry, C. D., and Schneider, K. (1925). *Z. physiol. Chem.* **146**, 158.

Willstätter, R., and Lowry, C. D. (1925). *Z. physiol. Chem.* **150**, 287.

Wilts United Dairies Ltd. British Patent 555897.

Winge, Ö., and Lausten, O. (1937). *Compt. rend. trav. lab. Carlsberg, Sér. physiol.* **22**, 99.

Winthrop Chemical Co. (1934). U.S. Patent 1849756.

Yamaguchi, T. (1952). *J. Japan. Tech. Assoc. Pulp Paper Ind.* **6**, 19.

Zellstoffabrik Waldhof. (1948). German Patent 2206, 802332.

CHAPTER XI

Pathogenic Yeasts

G. C. AINSWORTH

1. Introduction

Few yeasts are pathogenic and those which are affect man and higher animals in various ways. Very few cause disease in plants although yeasts are ubiquitous saprophytes of plants and plant products (see Chapter II). Of the 625 pages devoted to plant pathogenic fungi in F. L. Stevens' "The Fungi Which Cause Disease in Plants" (1913) only 4 (0.64%) deal with yeasts while yeasts occupy no less than 298 (38.7%) of the 770 pages of descriptions of fungi pathogenic for man and animals in C. W. Dodge's "Medical Mycology" (1935). This pattern is even more strikingly emphasized by an inspection of handbooks dealing with fungal diseases. The standard texts on plant pathology contain either no reference to yeasts or mention them incidentally, while in the 1954 edition of the "Manual of Clinical Mycology" by N. F. Conant *et al.*, diseases caused by true yeasts occupy 12% of the space given to mycotic infections of man, a proportion which is increased to 43% if the mycoses characterized by a yeastlike *in vivo* phase of the pathogen are taken into account.

A number of yeasts are more or less constantly associated with animals and an analysis by Ainsworth and Austwick (1955) of over twelve hundred isolates of fungi from nine species of farm animals suggested that yeasts are more often associated with the alimentary canal and with respiratory organs than with the reproductive organs, the skin, and feces. Many associations between particular yeasts and animals are incidental, the yeasts having been accidentally acquired from the environment. In other instances the association may be adaptive and it is possible to arrange a number of the well-known yeasts associated with disorders of man and animals in a series on a basis of increasing pathogenicity. More general aspects of yeast ecology and differentiation are discussed in Chapters I and II.

2. Yeasts Pathogenic for Man and Higher Animals

A. *Pityrosporum ovale*

The familiar yeast found associated with skin (particularly that of the scalp) and usually known as *Pityrosporum ovale* appears to have been first described in Italy in 1873 by Rivolta who named the organism *Cryptococcus psoriasis* because it originated from a case of human psoriasis. The following year, Malassez independently discovered the organism in association with alopecia areata (a nonparasitic baldness) and in 1891 the German dermatologist Unna mistook the same yeast, this time associated with pityriasis capitis (dandruff), for a bacterium which, from its shape, he named the "Flaschenbacillus"; a designation which, anglicized as "bottle bacillus," is still current. In 1904 Sabouraud proposed a new genus *Pityrosporum* (based on the species *P. malassezii*) for the "spores of Malassez" and nine years later Castellani and Chalmers transferred to *Pityrosporum* as *P. ovale* the *Saccharomyces ovalis* described by Bizzozero in 1884 from skin; thus, for the time being at least, ending the nomenclatural vicissitudes of this yeastlike fungus.

Morphology. Pityrosporum ovale is a small, asporogenous, nonmycelial, nonfermenting yeast. The cells are ovoid or elongated; 0.8–1.5 × 2–3 μ in skin scales and somewhat larger, 2–3 × 4–5 μ, in culture. They reproduce by terminal buds which when young give cells a bottlelike appearance and which at maturity are separated from the mother cell by fission.

Growth in Culture. Although of such common occurrence, *P. ovale* proved surprisingly difficult to culture and it was not until the second quarter of the present century that its cultivation has been consistently successful. A summary of the early attempts to grow *P. ovale in vitro* was given by Benham (1947), whose own researches contributed so much to a knowledge of the nutritional requirements of this yeast, and they need not be recapitulated here. The clue to the successful culture is that *P. ovale* requires a supply of fatty acids; a requirement which

Benham (1941), by using synthetic media, showed to be absolute. The fatty acid source employed by early workers was lanolin but later it was found that butter, cream, olive oil, and oleic acid are also satisfactory. Malt or beer wort agar (or other common mycological media provided they contain organic, i.e., amino acid, nitrogen and the vitamin thiamin) can be modified so as to allow a satisfactory growth of *P. ovale* by smearing the surface with fat or by pipetting onto the medium an ether extract of butter or lanolin and then allowing the ether to evaporate.

Pathogenic Status. During the nineteenth century it was widely held that *P. ovale* was responsible for the various disorders (and particularly seborrheic dermatitis) with which it is commonly associated. Sabouraud cautiously attributed pityriasis (dandruff) to *P. ovale* but modern opinion is even more sceptical and during the past two decades the view most generally accepted is that of Ota and Huang (1933) who after a careful experimental investigation and a study of the evidence obtained by others concluded that *P. ovale* is merely an inoffensive saprophyte of man. It is generally agreed that *P. ovale* is nonpathogenic for the usual laboratory animals—even when administered in large doses—and no very convincing successes have been claimed for attempts to infect man experimentally. Furthermore, no evidence has ever been adduced that *P. ovale* confers a skin sensitivity on man as do most accepted fungal pathogens.

P. ovale can be isolated from the skin of apparently normal individuals (Martin-Scott, 1952) as can an allied species, recently described by Gordon (1951) as *P. orbiculare*, which differs from *P. ovale* in having globose cells and in its inability to utilize oleic acid as a fatty acid source. *P. ovale* has also been isolated from the dog, for which it appears to be nonpathogenic, and another lipophilic yeast, *P. pachydermatis,* has been obtained from the skin of the rhinoceros and of cattle. These yeasts which have been recorded only in association with animals seem to constitute a group of nutritionally specialized saprophytes but the complexities of the host–parasite relationship in moniliasis (see below) suggest that, while these yeasts may normally be nonpathogenic, it might still be incautious to conclude that they are invariably so. They may on occasion behave as weak pathogens and so become a contributory cause of some of the conditions with which they are associated.

B. *Candida albicans*

Candida albicans is one of the best-known fungal pathogens of man and animals. Since it was first named just over a century ago, it has been redescribed as new at least thirty-six times, classified in a dozen different genera, and Lodder and Kreger-van Rij (1952), in their monograph, list more than ninety synonymous binomials. The literature, which is extensive and confused, has been comprehensively reviewed by Skinner (1947) while the more recent review by Mackinnon and Artagaveytia-Allende (1956) of the incidence and pathology of *Candida* infections in man is valuable.

Morphology in Culture and Nutritional Requirements. C. *albicans* is an asporogenous, pseudomycelial, fermenting yeast. The surface growth on agar media is largely composed of budding cells so that the quite extensive pseudomycelium may be overlooked if there is no examination of the growth within the agar beneath the colony. There, examination with a hand lens shows radiating pseudomycelial strands which on microscopical examination are found to be bearing at intervals whorls of blastospores in chains. On certain media, such as corn meal agar, spherical thick-walled resting spores (chlamydospores), which are often taken to be diagnostic for the species, may be formed. C. *albicans* grows readily on many media. It can utilize ammonium (but not nitrate) nitrogen and most (but not all) strains need to be supplied with the growth factor biotin. Clearly, C. *albicans* has less exacting nutritional requirements than *Pityrosporum ovale*.

Pathogenic Status. C. *albicans* is the cause of classical thrush in infants, one of the first mycotic diseases of man to be recognized. In addition to this infection of the mucous lining of the oral cavity the thrush fungus is able to attack the skin, nails, bronchi, lungs, vagina, and the alimentary tract while budding cells of C. *albicans* are often found in sputum and in feces. The disease complex, in which other species of *Candida* (e.g., C. *tropicalis*, C. *parakrusei*, C. *guilliermondi*) are also involved, is usually designated "moniliasis" (from the generic name *Monilia* which medical men at one time applied to these pathogens), although American authors are now tending to adopt "candidiasis." There are, however, also a number of special terms like "thrush" applied to particular conditions. For example, infection of the corners of the mouth is known as "angular cheilosis" or "perlèche"; that of the nail bed as "paronychia" and there is "monilial onychomycosis" of the nails, "monilial vaginitis," "intertriginous moniliasis" of the interdigital spaces, axillae, and infra-mammary regions, etc. C. *albicans* is also responsible for avian moniliasis (Fig. 1), and it has been recorded from dogs, monkeys, and many other animals.

C. *albicans* is an undoubted pathogen. On the other hand, C. *albicans*, which has a world-wide distribution, is frequently found associated with apparently normal individuals. Many surveys (see Skinner, 1947, for details) have shown C. *albicans* to be frequently present in the human mouth, particularly of individuals having dentures, and the vagina. It is also of common occurrence in the crops of poultry. All isolates of *C. albicans*, whether associated with disease or not, are pathogenic for the rabbit on intravenous injection, but the experimental infection of other animals or of man may be very difficult.

Factors Determining Pathogenicity. As already mentioned, *C. albicans* has a world-wide distribution and is commonly associated with apparently normal individuals. It has been rarely recorded unassociated with

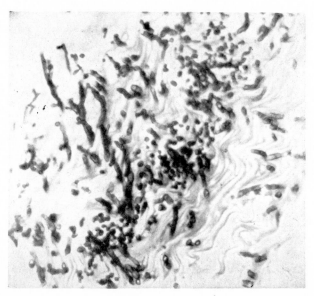

Fig. 1. *Candida albicans* in the crop wall of a fowl showing budding cells and pseudomycelium. × 500. (Stained periodic acid-Schiff.)

man or animals and the evidence points to moniliasis being an endogenous disease spread by contact and by droplet infection. There is, as for *Pityrosporum ovale*, no evidence of a significant external reservoir of infection although *C. albicans* has been recorded from soil in New Zealand by di Menna (1955) and from vegetable sources in Portugal by Van Uden *et al.* (1956). What determines pathogenicity is, however, obscure. Such evidence as there is suggests that there is probably no one general explanation.

C. albicans is of common occurrence in the vagina, especially of pregnant women, but epidemic outbreaks of thrush in infants in maternity wards are rare. It is also frequently present in the crops of poultry but

epidemics of avian moniliasis are rare and sporadic. The simplest expla
nation of epidemic outbreaks of thrush and avian moniliasis is an increase
in virulence of the pathogen. Thrush epidemics may be so severe as
to result in the temporary closing of the affected wards and a twenty-four
hour exposure of healthy chicks to an infected stock may be more than
sufficient for them to contract a fatal infection. The evidence for increased
virulence, is, however, almost entirely circumstantial. Isolates from epi
demics are, like saprophytic isolates, pathogenic for the rabbit but there
is little evidence of any change in the pathogen. Blaxland (1951) ex
perienced difficulty in inducing experimental infection in chickens with
C. albicans isolated from an epidemic outbreak while Rothman (1949)
was able to cause only a mild and easily cured intertriginous infection in
a volunteer with an isolate from a case of severe generalized moniliasis
of the oral mucosa, scalp, face, and finger nails.

It seems clear that the physiology of the host plays a part in determin
ing monilial infections. Women tend to harbor C. albicans as a saprophyte
and to exhibit monilial infections more frequently than do men. It has
been suggested that the increase of saprophytic C. albicans in the vagina
of pregnant women is due to an increase of glycogen in the vaginal
mucosa and the association of monilial infections of the skin with diabetes
is possibly directly correlated with an increase in the glucose content of
the epidermis and horny layer of the skin in diabetics (Rothman, 1949).
For avian moniliasis, vitamin B deficiency is possibly a determining
factor (Blaxland and Fincham, 1950).

Another series of factors is related to the environment. For avian
moniliasis, overcrowding and unhygienic conditions do not seem to be
critical but paronychia is said to be more common among bartenders and
housewives whose work involves prolonged immersion of the hands in
water and for women this condition is probably aggravated or initiated
by manicure injury. The increased humidity of the intertriginous areas
of the body and the tendency to maceration of the skin at such places is
probably the main factor which determines the predilection of moniliasis
for these sites while Raubitschek (1946) has claimed that it is easier to
induce an experimental infection of the fourth interdigital space—the
one most frequently showing natural infection—than of the others, pre
sumably due to higher humidity.

The operation of still other factors is suggested by many records pub
lished during the last decade of the association of monilial infection as
a side effect of antibiotic therapy. The oral use of penicillin has not in
frequently been followed by thrush while in other cases the establishment
of C. albicans infection in the lungs or intestinal tract has had a fatal

termination. The two most generally offered and not mutually exclusive explanations of these infections are that the elimination of bacterial competitors by the antibiotics has allowed *C. albicans* to build up a sufficient inoculum potential to establish itself as a pathogen and that the elimination of the intestinal bacterial flora has resulted in a lowered resistance of the host due to vitamin deficiency.

Observations such as these clearly indicate complicated host–parasite–saprophyte relationships and emphasize the need for caution in assessing the status of *C. albicans* when found associated with any pathological condition. Particular caution is needed when *C. albicans* is found in association with pulmonary disorders, for *C. albicans* is frequently found in tuberculous sputum and it is possibly more frequently a secondary invader rather than a primary pathogen of the respiratory organs.

Therapy. *C. albicans* infection results in a skin sensitivity of the affected individual but, not surprisingly, a number of apparently normal individuals give a positive reaction when skin-tested with an antigen prepared from *C. albicans* so that a positive result is not diagnostic for active moniliasis. The skin test should, however, always be applied and if positive the patient should be desensitized before beginning a course of potassium iodide therapy to which systemic *Candida* infections generally respond. Superficial infections are often readily resolved by the application of dilute aqueous solutions of gentian violet.

C. Cryptococcus neoformans

Like *Pityrosporum ovale* and *Candida albicans*, *Cryptococcus neoformans* was first described from man (by Busse in Germany in 1894) but in the same year it was independently described from fermenting fruit juices by Sanfelice in Italy and named *Saccharomyces neoformans*. Most of the relatively few subsequent records of this yeast have also been from man and animals although it now appears probable that *C. neoformans* is normally a saprophyte on various substrates from which man and animals contract infection. According to Emmons (1955) *C. neoformans* is responsible for approximately 10% of the 300 to 400 fatal cases of mycotic infection in man reported annually in the United States. It is also responsible for mastitis in cattle and is pathogenic for horses, dogs, and other animals, especially mice. (For a detailed survey of all aspects of the disease in man and animals, see Littman and Zimmerman, 1956.)

In the past *Cryptococcus neoformans* has been classified in the genus *Torulopsis* and it has also been designated *Torula histolytica* and *Cryptococcus hominis*. This nomenclatural confusion, though now largely of historical interest only, has resulted in confusion in the disease nomenclature. Current international usage favors "cryptococcosis" for *C. neoformans* infection in man rather than "torulosis," the name under which this mycosis was monographed by Cox and Tolhurst (1946) and reviewed by Lodder and de Minjer (1947).

Morphology and Cultural Characteristics. *C. neoformans* is a nonmycelial, nonfermenting yeast characterized by globose cells 4–6 μ in diameter. Each cell is surrounded by a hyaline gelatinous capsule of polysaccharide material which may equal or exceed in thickness the diameter of the cell. It may be mentioned that capsule development is greatest in old cultures and its presence can be conveniently demonstrated by mounting cells in Indian ink or nigrosin solution. The yeast grows well on malt or beer wort agar to give a moist brownish growth which runs down the slope and collects at the bottom of the tube. Apart from an inability to use nitrate nitrogen and a need for thiamin, the nutritional requirements of *C. neoformans* are not very exacting. It grows both at laboratory temperature and at 37°C.

C. neoformans is generally believed to be asporogenous and the claim made by Todd and Hermann in 1936 to have observed asci and ascospores was discounted by Lodder and Kreger-van Rij (1952). However, Benham (1955) recently published an account of what is apparently ascospore formation in a strain of *C. neoformans* from a dog and on the basis of these observations she tentatively suggested that *C. neoformans* may be identical with the soil-inhabiting yeast *Lipomyces starkeyi*.

The Parasitic Phase. The parasitic phase of *C. neoformans* closely resembles the saprophytic; the main difference being that the capsule is typically rather thicker in animal tissue than in culture. In man *C. neoformans* shows a predilection for the central nervous system and induces a chronic and often fatal meningitis. The large numbers of cells in the spinal fluid may set up marked intracranial pressure, a pressure which, in mice, is sufficient to cause enlargement of the cranium (Lodder and de Minjer, 1947). The brain and particularly the meninges are frequently involved and, in such cases, histological examination shows the presence of large numbers of budding cells which have disorganized the infected tissues (Fig. 2). Less frequently the skin (Cawley *et al.*, 1950) or the lungs may be invaded.

C. neoformans is also pathogenic for domesticated animals and during recent years there have been several authenticated cases in the United States of bovine mastitis caused by *C. neoformans* (Pounden *et al.*, 1952; Emmons, 1952; Simon *et al.*, 1953).

Epidemiology. Human cryptococcis has been recorded from all continents although cases are sporadic and no epidemic outbreak has ever been reported. There is no evidence that the infection is contagious or that it can be acquired from infected animals. Unlike *Pityrosporum ovale* and *Candida albicans*, *Cryptococcus neoformans* is not usually found associated with normal individuals although Benham (1935) has reported the isolation from human skin and feces of avirulent strains of a yeast otherwise similar to *C. neoformans*. Such evidence points to the disease being exogenous and to an external reservoir of infection. As

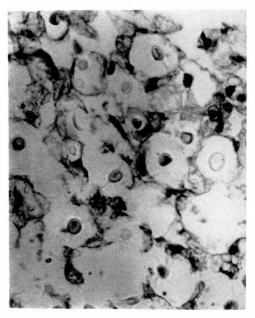

Fig. 2. *Cryptococcus neoformans* in human brain. Note the wide capsule enclosing each yeast cell and the disorganization of the host tissue. (Preparation by J. T. Duncan.) × 500.

already mentioned, *C. neoformans* was first named from an isolate from fruit juice and later there was a record from milk but until recently no reservoir of infection was known. During the past decade the importance of the soil as a reservoir of infection for a number of major mycoses of man and animals such as coccidioidomycosis (*Coccidioides immitis*) and histoplasmosis (*Histoplasma capsulatum*) has become increasingly apparent and this led Emmons to search for *C. neoformans* in soil. Soil was suspended in normal saline solution and, after agitation, the suspension was allowed to stand for 2 to 3 hours after which samples of the supernatant liquid were withdrawn and injected intraperitoneally into mice. Four to 6 weeks after inoculation the mice were killed and cultures made from the spleen and the liver. By this method C. *neoformans* was isolated from 4 of 716 samples of Virginian soil (Emmons, 1951). In a subsequent series of isolations from soil, dust, litter, and animal and bird excreta (by a method which differed only in that penicillin and streptomycin were added to the supernatent liquid before its use as inoculum) Emmons (1954) obtained further isolates of C. *neoformans* including 8 from old weathered pigeon droppings, 1 from debris in a pigeon's nest, and 4 from a granary probably contaminated by pigeons. In a further study (Emmons, 1955) this curious association of C. *neoformans* with pigeon (*Columba livia*) excreta was confirmed by the isolation of C. *neoformans* from 63 of 111 specimens examined, the positive specimens coming from 16 of the 19 premises from which collections were made.

A preliminary examination of 20 young pigeons failed to reveal C. *neoformans* either by direct culture from the spleen, liver, and kidney or by attempted isolation, by mouse inoculation, from material from four levels of the digestive tract. It would thus appear that it is the accumulations of pigeon excreta which provide a favorable substrate for the saprophytic development of this yeast. The significance of this finding is not yet clear but pigeons may very well be involved in the epidemiology of outbreaks of cryptococcal mastitis in cattle.

3. Dimorphic Fungi

A number of the major systemic mycoses of man and animals are characterized by yeastlike cells in the infected tissues. Sporotrichosis (*Sporotrichum schencki*), a common form of which originates from an infected injury to the hand and results in a series of abscesses along the lymphatic vessels of the arm, is characterized by small fusiform budding cells in affected tissues. Although these cells are usually difficult to demonstrate either in tissue or in pus, the pathogen is easily cultured from morbid material. By way of contrast, the budding cells of *Blastomyces dermatitidis* (the causal agent of North American blastomycosis) are very easily seen in tissue (Fig. 3A) and pus. They are larger than the budding cells of S. *schencki* (8–15 μ in diameter as opposed to 3–5 μ for the latter) and they have a thick refractile wall which gives the cells a "double-contoured" appearance. They multiply by the development of single buds, a feature which differentiates them from the tissue phase of *Paracoccidioides brasiliensis,* the cause of South American blastomycosis, a chronic infection of the skin, lungs, and other organs which shows clinical similarities to North American blastomycosis. The globose budding cells of *P. brasiliensis* vary from 10 to 60 μ in diameter. The smaller ones, which may show single buds, resemble those of *B. dermatitidis* while the larger, both in tissue sections and in pus, show multiple budding which is a diagnostic feature. Histoplasmosis (*Histoplasma capsulatum*) which may be chronic and fatal but is usually a benign pulmonary infection, is endemic in parts of North America, Africa, and other regions. It is characterized by groups of small yeastlike cells 1–5 μ in diameter within large mononuclear cells and other cells of the reticulo-endothelial system. An

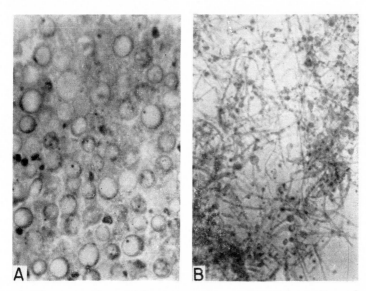

FIG. 3. *Blastomyces dermatitidis.* A, parasitic yeast-like phase in liver of a dog (preparation by F. K. Ramsey); B, mycelial phase in culture. × 500.

allied species, *H. farciminosum* (syn. *Cryptococcus farciminosus*), which causes epizootic lymphangitis (a serious disease of horses and other Equideae in India, Burma, and countries of the Mediterranean basin), also has a yeastlike tissue phase. Finally, mention may be made of the groups of thick-walled, dark brown cells which are a diagnostic histological feature of chromoblastomycosis (caused by species of *Phialophora*), an infection of the skin typical of tropical regions, for although these cells do not multiply by budding but by fission they might be mistaken for a yeast.

With the possible exception of chromoblastomycosis, a knowledge of the tissue phase only of these diverse conditions would suggest that yeastlike pathogens were implicated and in the past a number of the causal agents have in fact been classified in such genera as *Cryptococcus* and *Torulopsis*. Cultural and animal inoculation studies show that, in contrast to *Cryptococcus neoformans* which is yeastlike both *in vivo* and *in vitro*, these fungi are mycelial when growing saprophytically on the usual mycological media under normal laboratory conditions and the various spore forms produced during the saprophytic phase clearly indicate that this series of fungal pathogens are not true yeasts but mycelial Fungi Imperfecti (see *Blastomyces dermatitidis*, Fig. 3B). The phenomenon of a mycelial saprophytic phase and a yeastlike parasitic phase in warm-blooded animals has been termed "dimorphism" by medical mycologists and during recent years there have been a number of physiological studies on dimorphic fungi and particularly on the conditions which determine the mycelial-yeast transformation (for details see the review by Scherr and Weaver, 1953).

It has for long been known that species of *Mucor* and other mycelial fungi when grown under special conditions give rise to yeastlike cells and the conditions for the *in vitro* mycelial-yeast transformation of the important dimorphic fungal pathogens have been elucidated. For *Blastomyces dermatitidis* and *Paracoccidioides brasiliensis*, temperature is the critical factor. Growth is mycelial at 25°C., yeastlike at 37°C., and the transformation in either direction can be effected at will. For *Histoplasma capsulatum* the composition of the medium also plays a part and the yeast form develops at 37°C. only on a cysteine-containing medium, while for *H. farciminosum* there is the additional requirement of an increase of the carbon dioxide tension to 15–30%. The yeast phase of *Sporotrichum schencki* is also most readily attained in an atmosphere containing 5 to 60% or more of carbon dioxide.

4. The Yeast Phase in Relation to Pathogenicity

The frequency of a yeastlike parasitic phase in mycoses of higher animals invites speculation on the relationship of the yeastlike habit to pathogenicity. Most fungi which are mycelial during the parasitic phase and mycelial in culture cause superficial infection as, for example, do the ringworm fungi (dermatophytes) which riddle the outer keratinized layers of the skin. In deep-seated mycoses the pathogen less frequently exhibits hyphae which freely ramify through the tissues; the mycelia are usually localized as "mycetomas," compact, grainlike masses of hyphae, such as those shown by *Actinomyces israeli* and by the various fungi responsible for Madura foot, or they are replaced by a yeastlike phase.

The systemic mycoses caused by dimorphic fungi are all exogenous and for some, such as histoplasmosis, as already mentioned, the external reservoir of infection is the soil. Perhaps the most important factor which has enabled a few of the vast number of saprophytic fungi to establish themselves as internal parasites of warm-blooded animals is the potentiality to develop a yeast phase in the living host. A consideration of the host–parasite relationships suggests that host resistance makes the tissues a relatively unfavorable environment for fungal growth. Most fungal pathogens of man and animals make much more luxuriant growth *in vitro* than in tissue which is in striking contrast to many plant pathogens which complete their life cycle and produce diverse spore forms during the parasitic phase. A number of plant pathogenic fungi have not yet been grown in pure culture while almost without exception fungal pathogens of man and animals have been so cultured.

A few yeasts are pathogenic for plants and a few mycelial plant pathogens have a well-defined yeastlike phase but this phase, as in species of *Taphrina* and various members of the Ustilaginales (Smut fungi), occurs only when the fungi are growing as saprophytes. For well-adapted parasites the saprophytic state may be considered the abnormal, and just as the parasitic phase of dimorphic pathogens of man and animals is the abnormal, so are the budding cells produced by a species of *Mucor* when growing submerged in a solution of high sugar content. It is perhaps legitimate to generalize by saying that a yeastlike phase is a characteristic response of certain mycelial fungi to conditions suboptimal for growth and it is interesting to recall that the endogenous *Candida albicans* which is apparently well adapted for both saprophytic and parasitic growth in higher animals may produce so much pseudomycelium in the invaded tissues (such as the tonsils or the intestinal wall), or even on occasion develop in the spleen or other internal organs of experimental animals as a mycetoma (Mankowski and Diller, 1953), that its essential yeastlike characters may be obscured.

If the parasitic state is the abnormal for dimorphic fungi then as Baker *et al.* (1943) have suggested, the yeastlike form may have been adopted because it is the one which allows the production of the greatest number of reproductive structures with the minimum synthesis of new protoplasm. Further, the pathogenic action of *Cryptococcus neoformans* is possibly largely a mechanical breaking down of the cells of the infected tissue brought about by the encapsulated cells of the pathogen and pressures on other tissues. That is to say, it depends on the number of cells produced. It is possible that damage to tissue may also be largely mechanical in histoplasmosis and North American blastomycosis as in both these conditions tissues may be so heavily infected as to be largely replaced by cells of the pathogen.

Another aspect of the pathogenicity mechanism is the observation by Nickerson and Edwards (1949) that, on a dry weight basis, the endogenous respiration of the yeast form of B. *dermatitidis* is several times that of the mycelial so that the transformation of the mycelial to the yeast phase at the temperature of the animal host would presumably make available to the invading organism a greatly increased energy potential.

5. Yeasts Pathogenic for Lower Animals

A few yeasts or yeast-like fungi of uncertain affinity have been described, associated with insects as either symbionts (see Steinhaus, 1946) or saprophytes, e.g., those associated with bark beetles (Shifrine and Phaff, 1956, see also Chapter II). Fewer still have been recorded as pathogenic for insects (see Steinhaus, 1949) and other invertebrates. One of the most convincing records is that by Keilin (1920) who described larvae of the midge *Dasyhelea obscura* invaded by a yeast which he considered to be distinct from an allied yeast described by Metschnikoff in 1884 as a parasite of *Daphnia magna*. Metschnikoff's generic name *Monospora* being a later homonym, Keilin coined the new name *Monosporella* under which he placed his and Metschnikoff's yeasts as M. *unicuspidata* and M. *bicuspidata*, respectively. These species, which are nonmycelial, are characterized by an ascus which contains a single needle-shaped ascospore. They belong to the family Endomycetaceae as does *Coccidiascus legeri* which was described in 1913 by Chatton as parasitic in the cells of the intestine of *Drosophila funebris* and which has eight needle-shaped spores in each banana-shaped ascus. These three yeasts have not been cultured and are thus imperfectly known. Further details are given by Lodder and Kreger-van Rij (1952), and a few additional records of yeasts claimed to be pathogenic for bees or other insects were compiled by Steinhaus (1949).

6. Plant Pathogenic Yeasts

A consideration of the yeasts pathogenic for plants involves the definition of a "yeast," for one of the best-known plant pathogenic "yeasts" is an organism responsible for the staining of cotton bolls which Ashby and Nowell (1926) designated *Nematospora gossypii* and which is still frequently referred to by this name. While showing ascospore characteristics of the genus *Nematospora*, N. *gossypii* produces true mycelium and does not exhibit budding cells. Lodder and Kreger-van Rij (1952) therefore follow Guilliermond in classifying this species (which has been reviewed by Pridham and Raper, 1950) in the genus *Ashbya* which they exclude from the family Endomycetaceae, and so from consideration as a yeast.

Lodder and Kreger-van Rij treat the genus *Nematospora* as comprising the single species *N. coryli* which has budding cells and eight needle-shaped spores per ascus. This fungus was first described from diseased hazel (*Corylus avellana*) nuts in Italy and it is also now regarded as the causal agent of yeast-spot of Lima beans (*Phaseolus lunatus*) first described by Wingard (1922) from Virginia where he found up to 60% of the crop attacked. Infection, which occurs only in the seed, results in numerous dark sunken areas in the cotyledons from which the pathogen may easily be isolated in pure culture. Other legumes, including soybeans (*Glycine soja*), are similarly affected.

N. *coryli* is widely distributed throughout warmer regions where it is responsible for "stigmatomycosis" of the fruits of tomato, citrus, and other plants and like *Ashbya gossypii* it is also one of the causal agents of the staining of cotton bolls. An interesting feature of this fungus is its close association with insects. Infection is spread by plant bugs and other biting insects and damage by the yeast follows insect injury. The yeast–insect relationship was the subject of a careful study by Frazer (1944) who concluded that *Dysdercus* species transmit *A. gossypii* mechanically. Fungus material contaminates the mouth parts and the deep-seated stylet pouches (in which spore germination was observed). It is eliminated during moulting but recontamination occurs. The insect is unharmed by the fungus and the needle-shaped ascospores are well adapted in shape to reach the stylet pouches from which they are injected into the host when the insect feeds. A similar mechanical association between *N. coryli* and its insect vector was established by Leach and Clulo (1943).

References

General accounts of most of the human mycoses mentioned in this chapter and the essential features of the pathogens will be found in Conant *et al.* (1954).

Ainsworth, G. C., and Austwick, P. K. C. (1955). *Brit. Mycol. Soc. Trans.* **38**, 369.

Ashby, S. F., and Nowell, W. (1926). *Ann. Botany (London)* **40**, 223.

Baker, E. E., Mrak, E. M., and Smith. C. E. (1943). *Farlowia* **1**, 199.

Benham, R. W. (1935). *Am. N.Y. Acad. Sci.* **50**, 1299.

Benham, R. W. (1941). *Proc. Soc. Exptl. Biol. Med.* **46**, 176.

Benham, R. W. (1947). *In* "Biology of Pathogenic Fungi" (W. J. Nickerson, ed.), Chapter 4. Chronica Botanica, Waltham, Mass.

Benham, R. W. (1955). *Proc. Soc. Exptl. Biol. Med.* **89**, 243.

Blaxland, J. D. (1951). *Proc. 9th World's Poultry Congr. Paris, 1951* **3**, 21.

Blaxland, J. D., and Fincham, I. H. (1950). *Brit. Vet. J.* **106**, 221.

Cawley, E. P., Grekin, R. H., and Curtis, A. C. (1950). *J. Invest. Dermatol.* **14**, 327.

Conant, N. F., Smith, D. T., Baker, R. D., Callaway, J. L., and Martin, D. S. (1954). "Manual of Clinical Mycology," 2nd ed. Saunders, Philadelphia.

Cox, L. B., and Tolhurst, J. C. (1946). "Human Torulosis." (Melbourne Univ. Press), Cambridge Univ. Press, New York.

Di Menna, M. E. (1955). *J. Gen. Microbiol.* **12**, 54.

Emmons, C. W. (1951). *J. Bacteriol.* **62**, 685.

Emmons, C. W. (1952). *Mycopathol. et Mycol. Appl.* **6**, 231.

Emmons, C. W. (1954). *Trans. N.Y. Acad. Sci.* [2] **17**, 157.

Emmons, C. W. (1955). *Am. J. Hyg.* **62**, 227.

Frazer, H. L. (1944). *Ann. Appl. Biol.* **31**, 271.

Gordon, M. A. (1951). *Mycologia* **43**, 524; *J. Invest. Dermatol.* **17**, 267.

Keilin, D. (1920). *Parasitology* **12**, 83.

Leach, J. G., and Clulo, G. (1943). *Phytopathology* **33**, 1209.

Littman, M. L., and Zimmerman, L. E. (1956). "Cryptococcosis." Grune & Stratton, New York.

Lodder, J., and Kreger-van Rij, N. J. W. (1952). "The Yeasts." North Holland Publishing Co., Amsterdam.

Lodder, J., and de Minjer, A. (1947). *In* "Biology of Pathogenic Fungi" (W. J. Nickerson, ed.), Chapter 2. Chronica Botanica, Waltham, Mass.

Mackinnon, J. E., and Artagaveytia-Allende, R. C. (1956). *Anales fac. med. Montevideo* **41**, 275.

Mankowski, Z. T., and Diller, I. C. (1953). *Mycopathol. et Mycol. Appl.* **6**, 298.

Martin-Scott, I. (1952). *Brit. J. Dermatol.* **66**, 257.

Nickerson, W. J., and Edwards, G. A. (1949). *J. Gen. Physiol.* **33**, 41.

Ota, M., and Huang, P.-T. (1933). *Ann. parasitol. humaine et comparée* **11**, 49.

Pounden, W. D., Amberson, E. M., and Jaeger, R. F. (1952). *Am. J. Vet. Research* **13**, 121.

Pridham, T. G., and Raper, K. B. (1950). *Mycologia* **42**, 603.

Raubitschek, F. (1946). *Dermatologica* **93**, 295.

Rothman, S. (1949). *Trans. N.Y. Acad. Sci.* [2] **12**, 27.

Scherr, G. H., and Weaver, R. H. (1953). *Bacteriol. Revs.* **17**, 51.

Shifrine, M., and Phaff, H. J. (1956). *Mycologia* **48**, 41.

Simon, J., Nichols, R. E., and Morse, E. V. (1953). *J. Am. Vet. Med. Assoc.* **122**, 31.

Skinner, C. E. (1947). *Bacteriol. Revs.* **11**, 227.

Steinhaus, E. A. (1946). "Principles of Insect Microbiology," Chapter 6. Comstock Publ. Ithaca, New York.

Steinhaus, E. A. (1949). "Principles of Insect Pathology," Chapter 10. McGraw-Hill, New York.

Uden, N. van, de Matos Faia, M., and Assis-Lopes, L. (1956). *J. Gen. Microbiol.* **15**, 151.

Wingard, S. A. (1922). *Phytopathology* **12**, 525.

Yeasts in Food Spoilage

M. Ingram

The object of this chapter is more to indicate how the biological properties of the yeasts determine their participation in food spoilage, rather than to catalogue the different kinds of yeasts concerned therein (see Chapter II). Food spoilage is a competitive process in which, as in other forms of competition, the race tends to go to those strongest at the start and quickest off the mark. When a food is spoiled by yeasts, therefore, it is for particular reasons; and it is an advantage to know in general terms what these are likely to be, before proceeding to a more detailed examination of how they work out in the spoilage of particular foods.

1. General Factors Predisposing towards Spoilage by Yeasts

These may be compared with considerations of the nature of seed, soil, and climate. First there are questions of how many of the microorganisms gain access to the food and of their inherent competitive ability. Second is the nature of the food, as it reacts with the organisms growing on it. Finally come factors like humidity and temperature which are equally important. It must be remembered that such factors may vary sharply within the food, and in the relevant parts of its environment, so that the spoilage pattern may be far from uniform.

A. The Initial Infection

The spoilage flora of a particular food, under particular conditions, is usually rather specific. It follows that spoilage is unlikely to occur unless the food is infected with organisms of the right kind. This may happen in various ways: as a natural occurrence in the fresh material; by chance infection from a generalized source like air; through transmission by some particular carrier, e.g., insects; or by contamination during preparation, through contact with already spoiled food or unclean equipment. Each of these possibilities applies to yeasts.

(1) *Intrinsic Infection.* It is rare for the sole important source of infection to come from within the food itself.

Romwalter and von Király (1939) suggest that the tissues of sound fruit always contain *Saccharomyces,* which ultimately cause fermentation during decay, and similar occurrences will be mentioned later. It is however by no means clear that these yeasts are primarily responsible for the decay. Another conceivable example is the yeasts sometimes found deep in spoiling tissues of joints of meat, which apparently could not readily be introduced from outside, but which might come from the animal's gut—where yeasts occur—especially as Tanner and Ruyle (1932) showed that yeasts fed to rabbits could be recovered from the blood of the living animals. Rather precise identifications of these yeasts are, however, still needed to establish such a connection as fact.

(2) *Generalized Infection from Air, Soil, or Water.* Yeasts, diverse in kind and more or less numerous, are distributed everywhere; hence one might imagine that food spoilage would be likely to arise for example from any chance air-borne infection. This is not true as a general rule; but, in the spoilage of foods by yeasts, there is probably a rather high proportion of cases in which infection does arise through chance contamination from air, as is suggested by the frequency of occurrence of the types of yeast predominant in air. These seem to be: the black yeasts called *Monilia* or *Torula nigra,* which are yeastlike forms of *Cladosporium herbarum* or *Pullularia pullulans;* pink or red yeasts, of the genera *Rhodotorula* and *Sporobolomyces;* and species of *Cryptococcus* (starch formers) as well as of *Debaryomyces* (Table I). It will appear below that the black yeasts, the red yeasts, and *Debaryomyces* species are often prominent in the surface spoilage of foods. Nevertheless there are many infections, e.g., those by osmophilic yeasts, which do not normally originate in this way.

The yeasts in soil are generally few, and mostly have a strongly aerobic character which would hinder their participation in fermentative spoilage. The numbers are larger in the soil of vineyards and fruit orchards, but there is no evidence yet that this is significant in spoiling the produce of these areas. Little is known of yeasts in water and they have seldom been connected with food spoilage; however, Phaff *et al.* (1952) observed that the important yeasts in the flora of shrimps were species (several of

TABLE I

NUMBER OF YEASTS ISOLATED FROM AIR

Species found in 950 cu. ft. of indoor air (Di Menna, 1955)		Other yeasts found in air from various sources, volumes not given (Connell and Skinner, 1953)		
Cryptococcus diffluens	128	Black yeasts		104
Debaryomyces kloeckeri	70	Rhodotorula		49
Torulopsis famata	13	Sporobolomyces		29
Torula nigra form of Cladosporium		Nonpigmented fermenters		26
herbarum	41	Nonpigmented nonfermenters		27
Cryptococcus laurentii	40	including:		
Rhodotorula mucilaginosa	39	Candida zeylanoides	11	
Debaryomyces subglobosus	19	Cryptococcus albidus	5	
Torulopsis candida	7	Cryptococcus diffluens	5	
Rhodotorula glutinis	19	Total		235
Cryptococcus albidus	12			
Miscellaneous to total	431			

them new) of *Rhodotorula, Trichosporon,* and *Candida* similar to those in sea water.

(3) *Infection by Living Carriers.* The association of yeasts with insects like bees and flies is well known and has been discussed at length in Chapter II. The beehive is an unfailing source of yeasts in great variety, which are carried wherever the inhabitants range, and the importance of bees in the infection of honey with osmophilic yeasts was demonstrated by Lochhead and Heron (1929). The present author's observations suggest that bees have a similar importance in infecting oranges, at the flower stage, with the osmophilic yeasts which ferment orange concentrates. The fruit flies which swarm around fruit-processing factories must carry, besides their indigenous flora, infections from refuse within and outside the factory onto the processing equipment for it is practically impossible to exclude such insects from factory operations. Fly infestation in fruit-processing factories is notorious; bees sometimes gorge honey during the fabrication of mixed products and the occasional oc-

currence of wasps in fruit juices shows that they too may carry yeasts into foods. Such agents expose foods, especially fruit products, to a continual and varied infection which, though it may be comparatively small in quantity, serves at once to regenerate contamination even after the most thorough cleaning.

It seems likely that human carriers are important in transferring yeast infection from spoiled to fresh food, as is known with bacteria and molds. It is hard to imagine, for example, how otherwise the surface of dried fruits could become so heavily contaminated as it often is with osmophilic yeasts which, though present, are not numerous all over the fresh fruit. No proof of such connection has, however, yet been published.

(4) *Infection from Already Spoiled Food.* Spoiling food is the most dangerous source of infection, because it is heavily loaded with organisms of the kind which do most damage. Equally important are infections of major components of the food, especially where these are additions, such as salt or sugar, to improve the stability of the food; for example, osmophilic yeasts in sugar may be carried over into confectionery which they are likely to spoil.

Although major outbreaks of spoilage are often far from the place where the food was processed, these considerations are important because there frequently occur, in commercial processing operations, small leakages of material from the flow of production, or small pockets missed in cleaning, and these, if not attended to, are spoiled on the spot. Processors should be constantly vigilant to eliminate these most dangerous sources of infection.

(5) *Contamination from Unclean Equipment.* There can be little doubt that the most serious and immediate source of infection is generally unclean equipment, the methods of cleaning employed in industry being often pitifully inadequate in terms of what they actually achieve. In juice production, for instance, the fruit-squeezing equipment usually carries enormous infections; a few years ago, several *grams* of yeast were commonly to be found on a single reaming head in citrus juice production, the constant supply of fresh nutrient and high degree of aeration clearly favoring their development there. Often, too, the design of the equipment unfortunately assists the contamination; microbiologically, for example, the wooden frames used in squeezing apples for juice could hardly be less desirable. The difficulties of sterilizing things like the joints in taps, or the packing glands on pumps and stirrers, are formidable and the danger of failure not sufficiently appreciated. Manufacturers of food machinery should give serious consideration to such questions in its design.

B. *The Competitive Powers of Yeasts*

Yeasts grow slowly, compared with most bacteria. Whereas the latter have generation times of fractions of an hour under optimal conditions, those of the yeasts are usually of the order of hours reaching—for example with osmophilic yeasts in their natural environment—to days.

There are evidently factors which offset this disparity in appropriate circumstances. One is the greater size of the yeasts and hence greater metabolic activity per cell. Fermentation becomes appreciable in yeast cultures at population levels of the order of 10^3 (English, 1953) to 10^5–10^6 cells/ml., while the corresponding state with bacteria requires populations at least 100 times greater. More important, however, seems the fact that the metabolic products of the yeasts, chiefly acids and alcohol, are inimical to other organisms. Bacterial putrefaction is prevented at acidities greater than about pH 5, such as are commonly brought about by yeasts while some of the acids produced (e.g., lactic and acetic) have specific effects additional to that simply of pH. Alcohol too in moderate concentrations is inhibitory to many vegetative bacteria, and especially to molds (Lüthi, 1954). Further, those organisms which are able to destroy these substances—for instance the molds which oxidize acids and the Acetobacters which oxidize alcohol—require oxygen to do so, and this the yeasts themselves consume. Finally, the yeasts may produce more specific substances which are antibiotic towards competing organisms, such as the unsaturated fatty acids shown by Uroma and Virtanen (1949) to be active particularly against Gram-positive bacteria, and the pulcherrimin-like pigment produced by several lactose-fermenting yeasts (Wickerham and Burton, 1956).

These properties enable yeasts, despite their comparatively slow growth, to overcome competing organisms in circumstances which give scope to their peculiarities.

C. *The Composition and Properties of Food as a Substrate*

The next consideration is what characteristics of foods are likely to allow scope to yeasts rather than to their competitors. These characteristics may be broadly defined in terms of chemical factors of composition, and the physico-chemical factors of pH and redox potential.

(1) *The Chemical Composition of Food.* The importance of carbohydrates to the metabolism of yeasts needs no emphasis while it is also well known that their ability to attack complex nitrogen compounds is comparatively feeble. It is perhaps less generally realized that many yeasts attack fats vigorously and that this may be an important feature

of their role in food spoilage. Besides these major components, foods contain accessory vitamins and minerals which recent work shows to play a decisive part at times. In addition, there may be more or less specific inhibitors.

Carbohydrates. Yeasts attack a wide variety of sugars, and it is from them that alcohol and acids are chiefly produced, especially where access of air is restricted; this corresponds with general experience that it is sugary substrates, above all, which are likely to be spoiled by yeasts. Because different yeasts attack different sugars, there are opportunities for specificity, the most striking being the predominance of lactose-fermenting yeasts in the spoilage of milk and its products, the chief natural source of this sugar.

Frequently, however, much of the carbohydrate is in the form of starch or related substances which must be broken down by pioneering organisms before they become available as sugars. The range of yeasts which can attack these polysaccharides becomes increasingly restricted the higher the degree of polymerization, and it has been doubted whether yeasts can attack the higher polymers at all, though it is well established that some, like *Saccharomyces diastaticus* or *Schizosaccharomyces pombe*, can attack various of the lower oligosaccharides. While this may be true of "ordinary" yeasts, it seems that the more moldlike yeasts, e.g., in the genus *Endomycopsis*, may possess powers in this direction which have hitherto been little regarded. Ability to attack a variety of sugars and polysaccharides is an important property of commercial fermentation yeasts, and hence seems certain to be significant in spoilage by yeasts.

As a rule, competition between the organisms ensures that those which win are those able to exploit the nutritional possibilities of the substratum most fully in the circumstances. Exceptions to this rule are rare with foodstuffs though it is noteworthy that many of the osmophilic yeasts from fruit concentrates, and even from sucrose syrups, may be unable to ferment the sucrose present (Scarr, 1951).

The ability of a few yeasts to hydrolyze pectin has recently been discovered although its significance has still to be established. The yeast in which the property has been most fully worked out, *Saccharomyces fragilis*, is a "lactose" yeast in which the ability to split pectin seems out of place. But, again, the property may be more common among the funguslike yeasts; for instance, it has been reported for *Oidium lactis* and *Endomycopsis chodati*.

Organic Acids. Besides the sugars, many yeasts are able to attack particular acids, oxidatively. This is a property which hitherto seems to have been taken into account insufficiently, especially since organic acids are common in those materials usually attacked by yeasts e.g., fruit products. With this in mind, tests for the ability to attack organic acids are being tried for the sorting of osmophilic yeasts which ferment only glucose (Barnett and Ingram, 1955). When more general use is made of such procedures in routine identification, as Wickerham (1951) recommends, the accumulated information should do much to illuminate the role of yeasts in spoiling foodstuffs. The inability of yeasts to attack individual organic acids has important consequences, for example in the fermentation of apple juices, where large amounts of malic and quinic acids may be unaltered throughout a pure yeast fermentation and remain to promote secondary bacterial fermentations (Phillips et al., 1956). Mrak et al. (1956) suggest that the persistence of aerobic yeasts, Pichia membranaefaciens and Candida mycoderma, beyond the primary fermentation of brined olives is due to their ability to grow on lactic acid produced during the primary fermentation. The ability of salt-tolerant yeasts to oxidize acetic acid may increase the pH of vinegar-pickled herring to a level favoring slime-forming bacteria.

Nitrogen Compounds. Most yeasts have virtually no proteolytic activity. A few species have been observed to attack coagulated whole egg slowly (Endomycopsis albicans, Hansenula saturna, Nadsonia fulvescens, Saccharomyces anamensis, S. festinans, S. pastorianus I, and two commercial strains of S. cerevisiae), and S. pastorianus I attacked native egg white, but this is not known to have any practical significance in the spoilage of egg products. On the other hand, some of the red yeasts degrade casein, which is regarded as important in their ability to spoil milk products (see below).

Their feeble action on nitrogen compounds may be turned to advantage in eliminating yeasts from a mixed flora. Plating on a medium containing for example only peptone and meat extract will give countable bacterial colonies after 24 hours' incubation, where those of yeasts do not appear for several days, a device which the writer used in making bacterial counts in yeast-fermented egg pulp.

A limited quantity of utilizable N is obviously essential to the development of yeasts on a food, but yeasts can grow on such diverse nitrogen sources that it is seldom that the nature of these sources has any notable influence on growth. Nitrogen compounds are, however, much more important to bacteria, especially those which readily use them as energy sources, so that foods with a high N/C ratio are more likely to be spoiled by bacteria than by yeasts.

Fats. As will appear later, many of the yeasts which occur on fat-rich substrates like cheese or meat are lipolytic, so that their activities lead to the development of "free fatty acid rancidity." The nature of the organisms and the processes involved have not been studied in great detail. Nor is the effect of the change on other organisms demonstrated, though it might be expected to hinder putrefactive bacteria.

Vitamins. As a group, the yeasts possess good vitamin-synthesizing powers, and hence are largely independent of an external supply. This applies particularly (a) to the "wild" yeasts, cultivated strains often being more vitamin dependent; and (b) to the vitamins of the B group. It may be one of the reasons why, for example, in fruit products which are comparatively ill-provided with some of the B vitamins, more demanding organisms are at a disadvantage; this applies, for example, to the Lactobacilli which in characters such as microaerophilic habit, tolerance of acidity, and ability to attack sugars and acids, are otherwise well equipped to compete with yeasts in fermentative spoilage. Thus the growth of *Kloeckera apiculata* and *Saccharomyces ellipsoideus*, which required and absorbed this vitamin, removed nicotinamide from grape juice, as judged by a biological assay based on the growth of *Lactobacillus arabinosus* (Lafourcade, 1956).

Minerals. The requirements of yeasts in this respect are quite small, but may nevertheless be critical. Challinor *et al.* (1948) found that fruit juices, after an ion exchange treatment which extracts most of the minerals originally present, supported only poor growth of yeasts. It has since been shown that only the cations need be removed, and suggested that tomato juice might be so treated to yield concentrates which are stable against fermentation (Vas, 1956).

Antimicrobial Constituents. Foods often contain substances which inhibit particular microorganisms (Mossel and Ingram, 1955), and four examples are of special interest in connection with food spoilage yeasts:

(a) The essential oils of spices inhibit a variety of yeasts, perhaps because of their terpene content (Webb and Tanner, 1945). Among the yeasts tested, several show adaptive responses to the inhibition: *Monilia candida (Candida tropicalis)* and *Mycoderma (Oidium or Oospora = Geotrichum) lactis* are the most resistant.

(b) The antimicrobial powers of lipids increase with their degree of oxidation and Zukerman (1951) has shown that the ready autoxidation of unsaturated constituents of citrus oils makes them strongly inhibitory to particular yeasts concerned in the fermentation of citrus juices. On the other hand, to ferment citrus wastes, one needs an organism which resists this inhibition.

(c) Concentrated sugar syrups browned by heating or warm storage contain hydroxymethylfurfural which hinders their fermentation by yeasts (Ingram *et al.*, 1955). Cooking of vegetables produces furfural which has a similar effect. These substances are also produced in dried fruits (Stadtman, 1948) but their influence on the yeast flora there has not been investigated.

(*d*) The foods may contain an added preservative, frequently benzoic acid or sulfur dioxide. The latter is more inhibitory to bacteria than to yeasts in acid media, and more inhibitory to wild aerobic than to fermenting yeasts. Resistance is related to the power of the organisms to reduce sulfite (Scardovi, 1952; Nickerson, 1953) and Schanderl (1954) suggests that the production of elementary sulfur reacts on the accompanying bacterial flora.

TABLE II

GROWTH OF SELECTED YEASTS IN MEDIA OF HIGH ACIDITY AND HIGH SUGAR CONCENTRATION[a]

Species	pH		°Brix of citrus concentrate[b]	
	2.0	1.5	55	65
Candida krusei	+++	+	±	−
Candida guilliermondii	+++	±	− to +++	−
Candida tropicalis var. *lambica*	++	±	++	+
Hanseniaspora melligeri	++	+	±	−
Kloeckera lindneri	+++	±	++	±
Pichia fermentans	+	±	−	−
Rhodotorula mucilaginosa	+++	+	+	−
Saccharomyces cerevisiae	±	−	+++(!)	−
Saccharomyces elongasporus	+	±	++	−
Saccharomyces exiguus	+	+	±	−
Trichosporon fermentans	++	±	+	±
Zygosaccharomyces globiformis	±	−	++	−
Zygosaccharomyces japonicus	±	−	+++	+++
Zygosaccharomyces major	±	−	+++	++
Zygosaccharomyces mellis aceti (*acidi* ?)	+	+	−	−
Zygosaccharomyces priorianus	±	−	++	+

[a] From data of Recca and Mrak (1952).
[b] Orange juice concentrate, suitably diluted.

(2) *pH and Redox Potential.* Acid-intolerant organisms, such as putrefactive bacteria, obviously cannot grow in foods of low pH like fruits and, because yeasts can tolerate rather high degrees of acidity (Table II), this is frequently decisive in giving the latter dominance. A clear example has been provided with bacon, where the normal spoilage bacteria which are suppressed at acidities exceeding pH 5.5 are then replaced by yeasts

(Gibbons and Rose, 1950). The mere mention of foods in which yeasts are predominant spoilage organisms—fruit, sour milk, or pickles—shows how important this factor is in practice.

Though yeasts grow best aerobically, many of them are still able to grow, albeit relatively slowly, under the virtually anaerobic conditions of a fermentation, where the rH may be below 10. It is this which enables them to spoil bottled or canned products from which air is excluded. In assessing their ability to compete with bacteria under such conditions, it would be useful to know in detail how their growth rate is related to oxygen tension or redox potential, but this information is not available.

The redox potentials in foods vary greatly, because they depend on the balance between the natural reducing systems of the food and the access of oxygen to it. In "fresh" (i.e., living) foods, where the reducing enzymes are still active, the potentials are usually low: for instance, rH values below 10 are recorded for both vegetable and animal tissues. Cooking and processing usually raise the rH to 20 or more, through destruction or removal of the vital poising systems (Mossel and Ingram, 1955). For example, the reducing enzymes are largely left behind in the extraction of a fruit juice, and sieving and pasteurization weaken them still more (Lüthi, 1955); hence in the presence of air, the low potentials in the living fruit are replaced by somewhat higher potentials in the juices, which encourages the multiplication of any yeasts which may be present. This is especially so if the juice is aerated, and for this reason a French machine has been designed to extract juice *in vacuo*.

The redox potential is clearly highest at the surface of the food, where air has ready access, for which reason the more aerobic yeasts develop chiefly at the surface, like the well-known mycodermas on wines where the alcohol content discourages molds. Several examples will appear below of surface spoilage by the highly aerobic red yeasts.

The combination of low redox potential and high acidity, which yeasts can tolerate, is inimical to most other organisms. The molds, though even more tolerant of acidity, are mostly more strictly aerobic, and the same is true of highly acid-tolerant bacteria, whereas the bacteria which can grow anaerobically are, in general, not tolerant of acidity. These relations account for the prevalence of yeasts in the fermentation of acid liquids like fruit juices or pickling solutions.

D. *Environmental Factors*

The third important group of influences on the development of yeast infections are the "climatic" factors of temperature and humidity, the former of which profoundly affects the latter.

(1) *Temperature.* Yeasts are usually killed in a few minutes at temperatures in the range 55–65°C. (Lund, 1951) and hence are generally absent from heat-processed foods. In certain circumstances, e.g., in the presence of high concentrations of salt or sugar or of fat, the heat resistance may be raised significantly. It appears, too, that there may be specially heat-resistant strains: one which needs 25 minutes at 75°C. to reduce its numbers by 10^{-5} in a meat homogenate with 5% NaCl has recently been encountered, and *Torula (Candida) monosa,* in milk is reported as being killed only after 10 minutes at 98°C. (Tanner, 1944, p. 136, who gives a brief review of this topic).

Guilliermond and Tanner (1920), following Hansen, quoted maximum and minimum temperatures for many yeasts, which suffice to indicate that most of them grow within the range 0–45°C. The optimum temperatures ranged from 25–40°C., the higher values being more usual for cultivated and the lower for wild yeasts. Various yeasts have been described as thermophilic, but none of the supposedly thermophilic strains which have fallen into the writer's hands have been really unusual in this respect. Confusion may arise because the relations depend strongly on the composition of the medium: for example, sugar-tolerant yeasts with optimum growth near 25°C. on media with a few per cent of sugar grow best near 45°C. on high-sugar media (the same occurs with halophilic bacteria). This may be why osmophilic spoilage, of dried fruits, etc., is usually associated with hot climatic conditions. It seems certain, too, from the development of yeasts on frozen foods, that growth must sometimes be possible substantially below 0°C.; it is even reported at −10°C. (McCormack, 1950). The yeasts which grow on cool substrates may have rather low optimum and maximum temperatures: for instance yeasts like *Trichosporon scottii* isolated from chilled beef had optima below 20°C. and failed to grow above 25°C. (Scott, 1937).

(2) *Humidity.* The influence of water in a food on the microorganisms present is best appreciated in terms of the "aqueous activity," simply measured as the relative humidity of the atmosphere with which the food is in moisture equilibrium and termed "equilibrium relative humidity," or e.r.h. (for discussion see Mossel and Ingram, 1955).

Interpreted on this basis, it becomes clear that the yeasts are adapted, broadly speaking, to drier substrates than bacteria, most of the latter being eliminated in the range 0.95–0.85 in which many yeasts can grow (Fig. 1). A few organisms fall outside these general relations, notably some "osmophilic" yeasts, a few similar fungi which can develop in sugary substrates down to e.r.h. levels near 0.65, and certain strains like those of *Debaryomyces guilliermondii* and *D. membranaefaciens* which have a special ability to tolerate salt solutions in which the aqueous activity is well below 0.85.

This is why yeasts tend to replace bacteria under conditions of partial dryness, the species being osmophilic if the substrate is sugary and the

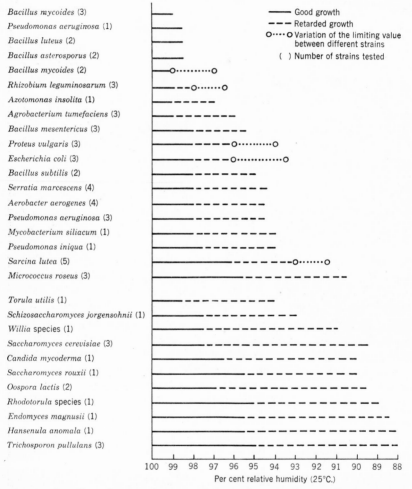

FIG. 1. The effect of aqueous activity of the medium on the growth of some common bacteria and yeasts (from data of Burcik, 1950).

drying substantial, as with dried fruits. Conversely, the admittance of a small proportion of moisture to a dry food gives such organisms an opportunity. It has to be remembered that only part of the food need be affected, e.g., the dried-out surface of a fruit, or the film of moisture on crystalline sugar, in order to provide a suitable micro-habitat. The effect of temperature on relative humidity is very important here, too. If food in a closed container is exposed to large fluctuations in temperature, moisture distils onto the cooler outer layers of the food when the temperature is falling, so that when the temperature rises again they are moister than before.

2. The Spoilage of Particular Foodstuffs by Yeasts

The above discussion has indicated various conditions likely to favor the growth in foods of yeasts rather than other spoilage organisms: these include specific infections, high proportions of sugars and organic acids, deficiency in B vitamins, high acidity and low redox potential, and a fairly low aqueous activity. We have now to see how these factors operate in particular foodstuffs. Clearly the range of foods is so wide that there is not space here to consider them all, so a choice has to be made of more important and representative types.

A. Cereals

Grains or cereal products, in equilibrium with atmospheres of relative humidity 60% or below (e.r.h., 0.60), are too dry to permit the growth of yeasts, although they may contain them in appreciable numbers. A considerable degree of moistening must thus take place before there is any danger of spoilage by yeasts. Such moistening is in fact likely to occur, at least locally, in grain stored in bulk. The accumulation of metabolic heat in the center of the bulk distils moisture into the outer layers, where fluctuations in the external temperature may cause actual condensation and, in this way, the e.r.h. of the outer layers of the mass may rise well above 0.90. At the same time, the respiration of the grain rapidly produces anaerobic conditions with a high tension of carbon dioxide. Under these conditions, there may be rapid multiplication of the yeasts, up to populations of the order of 10^7 per gram.

The yeast flora in this situation in bin-stored rice has been thoroughly investigated by Teunisson (1954). The predominant yeast was *Endomycopsis chodati*, the only one present which was able to hydrolyze starch; it produced so much mycelium as to resemble a true mold. The second predominant species was *Hansenula anomala*, attacking not polysaccharides but a wide range of lower compounds, which suggests that it might be living on breakdown products of the starch hydrolysis. Also isolated were strains of *Oospora lactis* and *Candida tropicalis*, capable of hydrolyzing rice oil; more important in the deeper layers was *Pichia farinosa*, which was moderately proteolytic. Earlier, Del Prado and Christensen (1952) had observed a similar development of *Candida pseudotropicalis* in rice stored in sealed bottles. All these yeasts produced much true or pseudo mycelium, a tendency which Teunisson suggested might be accentuated by the unfavorable conditions of anaerobiosis, high temperature, and minimal nutrition in the rice. However, all were strongly "aerobic," judged by production of pellicles in broth cultures. Teunisson remarked that most of the yeasts found in stored rice have been isolated from lactic acid substrates, which suggests that there might have been a significant amount of lactic acid in the rice as a result of its anaerobic respiration.

Yeasts of the genera *Rhodotorula* and *Sporobolomyces* have lately been shown to abound on cereal crops and to dominate the flora of barley grains (Lund, 1956). It is interesting, therefore, to note that no such red yeasts were recorded by Teunisson, especially in view of the "aerobic" nature of the rice yeasts which led her to suppose that most of their growth must have occurred in the first few days before thoroughly anaerobic conditions were established.

The absence of true fungi in these circumstances also seems to call for explanation. It seems conceivable that yeasts are better able than fungi to tolerate higher ratios of carbon dioxide to oxygen. This view is apparently supported by the observation that true molds do predominate if the containers are unsealed (Semeniuk *et al.*, 1947), but this could be because of greater dryness under those conditions. Bottomley *et al.* (1950), in comparisons of maize stored in atmospheres with different oxygen concentrations, also showed that yeasts tended to replace molds in 0.1% of oxygen—*Candida pseudotropicalis* (with molds) was, again, the dominant species—but here the effects of low humidity (75–85%) and high temperature (35–45°C.) were plainly much more important than those of oxygen tension.

Cooked cereals present a rather different situation, because the water content has often been raised considerably, and because some of the insoluble materials may have been degraded into more readily available forms. In such circumstances, bacteria usually grow within the material and molds on the surface, because of the drier but highly aerobic conditions there, as in the case of bread.

B. *Fresh Fruits*

There are reports that yeasts occur within the tissue of sound fruits; e.g., *Torulopsis albida* in gooseberries and *Rhodotorula glutinis* in cherries (Marcus, 1942). But there is no evidence yet that they do any harm commercially, except that *Nematospora* parasitizes and rots citrus fruits.

There are many more yeasts on the outside of fruits, and fairly thorough surveys of their nature, and sometimes numbers, have now been made for several species (see Chapter II). For instance, Marshall and Walkley (1951) found that, though yeasts were present in the core of sound apples, there were far more (10^2–10^6 per fruit) on the skin, while Clark *et al.* (1954) identified 8 species occurring on wild and cultivated apples in Canada, of which the predominant one was a new

TABLE III

OCCURRENCE OF YEAST GENERA IN GRAPES AND GRAPE PRODUCTS IN CALIFORNIA[a]

Genus	Total number of cultures	Fresh grapes	Musts and new wines	Cloudy bottled wine	Pomace leaves or soil
Saccharomyces	118	43	58	14	3
Zygosaccharomyces	13	7	6	0	0
Hanseniaspora	11	9	2	0	0
Kloeckeraspora	1	1	0	0	0
Pichia	6	2	1	1	2
Debaryomyces	3	3	0	0	0
Hansenula	4	2	1	1	0
Zygopichia	2	0	1	1	0
Torulaspora	1	1	0	0	0
		68	69	17	5
Torulopsis	25	17	4	2	2
Mycoderma	6	2	3	0	1
Kloeckera	16	15	1	0	0
Rhodotorula	6	6	0	0	0
Asporomyces	2	2	0	0	0
Schizoblastosporion	1	0	0	0	1
Candida	26	18	3	2	3
		60	11	4	7

[a] From data of Mrak and McClung (1940).

species, *Candida malicola*. Recca and Mrak (1952) listed 24 species isolated from sound citrus fruits and their products: *Hanseniaspora melligeri* was about the most frequent on the fruits; only 4 species were obtained solely from fresh fruit, *Candida pulcherrima, Hansenula anomala, Trichosporon cutaneum,* and *T. pullulans.* Mrak and McClung (1940) gave the genera, and some indication of the chief species, of 128 isolates from fresh grapes (Table III); about half the species isolated were anascosporogenous yeasts, among which the apiculate species were prominent, generally resembling the situation on the citrus fruits; a relatively few cultures isolated from leaves and soil indicated a distribution roughly similar to that on the grapes, save that apiculate yeasts were not recovered.

In the writer's experience most of the yeasts—especially the osmophilic ones—associated with fruit are to be found on the nectaries at the flowering stage, those on the surface being mainly placed there by chance contacts of visiting insects. For this reason, and also because they may be washed off by rain, the numbers are very variable. Clark *et al.* (1954) speculate that the possession of a capsule, which might fix the organisms onto the fruit and prevent such washing off, accounts for the frequent occurrence of *Cryptococcus* species on apples.

There are generally much larger numbers of yeasts in damaged or rotting fruits, but it is rare that they are primary agents in spoilage, their usual role being that of rather unspecific saprophytes following a more specific fungus which initiates the rot (see Beneke *et al.*, 1954). Though there have been systematic investigations of the yeast flora of a variety of spoiled fruits (reviewed by Mrak and Phaff, 1948), there are still too few such investigations on any one kind of fruit to show what specificity attaches to this flora.

Outside the foregoing generalizations there are occasions where a yeast appears capable of acting as the spoilage pioneer. For example, Lowings (1956) has shown experimentally that *Kloeckera apiculata* can cause a soft rot of picked strawberries; the rotting caused by *Nematospora* was mentioned above. Such functions seem remarkable in yeasts which, so far as is known, lack the powerful enzymes which are the normal weapons of fungi invading plant tissues. No yeast is known to secrete cellulase, and few are able to attack insoluble complex polysaccharides, or pectin (Luh and Phaff, 1951) and Lowings' strain of *K. apiculata* indeed possesses none of these properties.

C. *Fruit Juices*

There is too great a variety of these to consider them all and attention must be restricted to a few important juices, excluding the vast subject of fermentations deliberately encouraged to produce special liquors. The juices most worthy of consideration seem to be orange, apple, and grape.

Citrus Juices. From single strength citrus juices and beverages (mostly orange), Recca and Mrak (1952) got 24 cultures representing 12 species, of which only *Candida krusei, C. parapsilosis, Hanseniaspora melligeri, Pichia fermentans,* and *Oidium lactis* were also isolated from the fresh fruit. The relevance of their isolations to practical conditions has thus still to be decided because, in the spontaneous fermentation of orange juices which still sometimes occurs under European conditions, the causative species are usually either apiculate yeasts or *ellipsoideus* strains of *Saccharomyces cerevisiae*. While these yeasts may come ultimately from the fruit, on which similar species are found, their immediate source is certainly the equipment, especially the juice-extracting machines, where their development is rapid and from which it is impracticable to eliminate them entirely.

From whatever source they may come, large numbers of yeasts find their way into commercial juices. Direct microscopic counts on processed juices during the war regularly revealed dead cells in numbers exceeding 10^6 ml. while published observations showed viable yeast counts on raw juice ranging from 800 to 500,000 ml. (Nolte and von Loesecke, 1940). At these upper levels, fermentation was an immediate hazard but, since then, practice has generally improved, and they are seldom approached now. There is still no quantitative information about the species which make up this yeast flora.

Lemon juice is extracted by procedures similar to those for orange juice and, so far as the scanty data indicate, their microbiological relations are also similar. The flora is composed mostly of yeasts, but the numbers are lower than with orange juices (order of 10^3/ml.) corresponding with the higher acidity (Cole, 1955). Even with orange juices, counts tend to be lower the higher the acidity (Faville and Hill, 1951). There is no worthwhile information about the flora of other citrus juices.

Apple Juices. As with citrus fruits, there is little evidence yet of any close connection between the flora of apples and that of their juices as prepared commercially. If the fruit is in good condition, washing it leads to a reduction of the juice organisms to a few per cent of their original numbers whereas, as might be expected, washing has little effect if the fruit is unsound and heavily infected internally (Marshall and Walkley, 1951).

Nevertheless, it is plain that most of the yeasts on sound apples have little relevance to the subsequent fermentation of the juice; those on the fruit are chiefly nonsporing types with a predominantly aerobic metabolism, while the reverse is broadly true of those found in fermenting juices (Table IV). This hints at important secondary sources of infection which, in the case of apple juice, have not been clearly identified. Juices from poor fruit, which are more likely to contain fermentative species, and in large numbers, may spoil rapidly after extraction.

If apple juice ferments naturally, the normally predominant aerobic yeasts, presumably derived from the fruit, give place to fermenting

Saccharomyces species (Challinor, 1955). Apiculate species thus decline in numbers after a 5 to 10° drop in specific gravity. In the later stages of fermentation, the numbers of yeasts decrease and lactic acid bacteria increase, when conditions are favorable. If the yeast is removed when soluble nitrogen has been reduced to the minimum but before autolysis occurs, subsequent growth of lactic acid bacteria is discouraged, for the latter are otherwise greatly stimulated by the amino acids, purines, and growth factors liberated by the yeasts (Challinor and Rose, 1954).

TABLE IV

NUMBERS OF ISOLATIONS OF YEAST SPECIES FROM APPLES AND FROM APPLE CIDER[a]

Species	Wild apples	Cultivated apples	Apple ciders
Candida malicola	6	21	—
Candida mesenterica	—	—	1
Candida scottii	1	—	—
Cryptococcus albidus	5	1	—
Cryptococcus laurentii	4	—	—
Cryptococcus neoformans	4	1	—
Debaryomyces kloeckeri	—	—	1
Pichia membranaefaciens	—	—	2
Pichia polymorpha	—	—	1
Rhodotorula glutinis var. *rubescens*	—	2	—
Rhodotorula mucilaginosa	—	2	—
Saccharomyces cerevisiae	—	—	1
Saccharomyces oviformis	—	—	2
Saccharomyces steineri	—	—	1
Torulopsis candida	—	—	1
Torulopsis famata	—	3	—

[a] From data of Clark *et al.* (1954).

Centrifuging and enzyme clarification remove many of the micro-organisms from the juice; centrifuging alone, as practised commercially, removes the yeasts but not lactic acid bacteria.

The natural composition of the juice has an important influence on its fermentation. For instance, the rate of fermentation is proportional to the nitrogen content and independent of the phosphorus content; in this connection, it may be mentioned that fermentation is delayed by clarification which removes nitrogenous substances (Challinor, 1955). The high tannin content of some French juices restricts their fermentation and there are indications that thiamin content may be limiting in some British juices (Burroughs, 1952). The importance of mineral constituents has been mentioned earlier.

Grape Juice. Here, on present evidence, it seems more likely that the majority of the important yeasts are derived from the "flor" of the fruit, although there would seem to be just as much opportunity as with other juices for extraneous contamination from equipment, etc. According to Mrak and McClung (1940), rather more than half the strains isolated from grapes were sporing yeasts, mostly *Saccharomyces,* the remainder being chiefly *Torulopsis, Kloeckera,* and *Candida.* In musts and new wines, the 60 nonsporing strains were reduced to 11 but the 68 sporing strains from the fruit were paralleled by 69 from the juices (presumably

TABLE V

PER CENT FREQUENCY OF OCCURRENCE OF YEASTS ISOLATED AS PREDOMINANT IN GRAPE MUSTS FROM VARIOUS LOCALITIES[a]

Region and number of musts examined		*Saccharomyces ellipsoideus*	*Kloeckera apiculata*	*Torulaspora rosei*	*Hanseniaspora guilliermondii*	*Saccharomyces bayanus*	*Saccharomyces oviformis*	*Kloeckera magna*	*Saccharomyces mangini*	*Saccharomyces italicus*	*Candida pulcherrima*	*Saccharomyces uvarum*
Umbria	(92)	80	82	13	—	1	—	17	—	—	6	—
Tuscany	(103)	72	87	20	—	6	2	4	1	1	17	12
Piceno	(40)	77	92	15	—	15	7	12	—	2	7	10
N. Marche	(15)	73	100	13	—	13	7	20	—	—	13	—
Abruzzi	(10)	90	100	—	—	—	—	30	—	—	—	—
Lazio	(22)	91	100	41	—	23	14	14	—	4	4	14
Puglia	(31)	100	64	26	32	26	10	19	6	16	22	6
Calabria	(26)	94	50	15	65	46	4	—	38	42	4	—
W. Sicily, 1948	(12)	100	92	33	55	33	8	—	41	25	—	8
W. Sicily, 1952	(27)	100	48	15	52	41	74	—	70	30	11	15
Trentino	(40)	95	100	17	—	5	10	2	—	2	7	—
Treviso	(19)	100	94	16	—	5	5	—	21	5	—	5
Israel	(10)	100	60	—	100	—	40	—	70	—	—	10

[a] From Castelli (1954).

similar, though few details were given), the chief difference being the considerable diminution in the apiculate *Hanseniaspora* and corresponding increase in *Saccharomyces* (see Table III above). This corresponds broadly with other experience indicating that the apiculate yeasts form the predominant element in freshly pressed grape juice, together with *Saccharomyces* strains of the *ellipsoideus* type, in proportions varying with season and locality (see Cruess, 1943). In a recent important paper, Castelli (1954) has reviewed European work on the flora of grape juices, and collated the observations of his own workers. Their data are summarized in Table V. These too confirm that *Kloeckera apiculata* and

Saccharomyces cerevisiae var. *ellipsoideus* are the two most commonly occurring yeasts in grape juices though certain other species appeared so often that their participation in fermentation seems likely; these latter include *Saccharomyces oviformis, S. mangini, S. bayanus, S. italicus, Torulaspora rosei* and *Candida pulcherrima* (cf. Peynaud, 1957).

The most striking fact to emerge was that the frequency of apiculate yeasts diminishes, while that of *ellipsoideus* strains is augmented with progress to a warmer climate. This is seemingly the first time that any

TABLE VI

FREQUENCY OF DISTRIBUTION OF FERMENTING POWER (ALCOHOL PRODUCED AS VOLUME %) AMONG YEASTS ISOLATED FROM ITALIAN GRAPE MUSTS[a]

Region and number strains examined		Number of strains producing alcohol (%)								
		0–2	2–4	4–6	6–8	8–10	10–12	12–14	14–16	16–18	>18
Veneto	(141)	5	30	12	4	10	35	27	6	0	0
Umbria	(378)	8	16	127	7	54	2	162	2	1	0
Tuscany	(525)	32	39	199	6	9	20	59	160	1	0
Lazio	(132)	4	8	76	2	18	11	64	10	2	0
Piceno	(203)	6	14	63	28	11	12	40	20	3	0
Puglia	(327)	20	24	21	32	19	9	77	105	28	2
Calabria	(439)	1	26	30	60	29	31	114	122	20	2
Sicily	(173)	0	20	23	14	17	9	16	40	27	4

[a] Simplified from Castelli (1954).

such geographical relation has been convincingly demonstrated with yeasts; it entailed the identification of about 4000 isolates over a period of nearly 20 years.[1] Similar relations were discernible with other species. In the hotter climates, a large proportion of the apiculate yeasts formed spores and hence were classified as *Hanseniaspora guilliermondii*, previously noted in American juices but not in European; it was further shown that species of *Hanseniaspora* are more thermophilic and acid tolerant than *Kloeckera*.

The fermenting powers of the yeasts isolated by Castelli's workers were extremely diverse, but also varied systematically with climate, there being a greater proportion of strongly fermenting yeasts, as judged by alcohol production, in the hotter climates (see Table VI). This corre-

[1] Analogous differences in the floras of cucumber brines are mentioned by Etchells *et al.* (1953); and it is beginning to appear that the predominant yeast on apples is *Candida pulcherrima* in Europe but *C. malicola* in Canada,

sponds broadly, of course, with the different distributions of *Kloeckera apiculata* and *Saccharomyces ellipsoideus,* but it was noted that there were wide differences within both of these groups, in alcohol tolerance and in temperature relations. Thus, some of the Kloeckeras tolerated quite high concentrations of alcohol (e.g., *K. magna,* 8–10°). Whatever the region, *K. apiculata* always primed the fermentation of the juice. On the other hand, the apiculate species are gradually eliminated when spontaneous fermentation takes place, by the rising concentration of alcohol to which they are relatively intolerant. Schulle (1953) has further noted that the growth of the *ellipsoideus* strains in such mixtures is accelerated the more the apiculate population declines, which suggests some interchange (e.g., of growth substances) between the two. The variety of wild strains of *Saccharomyces* often gives the ensuing fermentation undesirable characteristics; hence, even when the juice is to be fermented for wine, it is common practice to control the yeasts by means of sulfur dioxide.

D. *Dried Fruits and Juice Concentrates, Sugar and Sugar Products*

Concentrated juices, dried fruits, special products like "malt extract," honey, and sugar, sugar preserves, and sugar confectionery, all possess two over-riding features in common—high proportions of sugar, together with low proportions of water giving aqueous activities of the order of 0.75 or less. It has been plainly shown that it is the over-all aqueous activity and not the nature and amount of the carbohydrates present, which determines the growth of the yeasts under such conditions (Schachinger and Heiss, 1951; English, 1953). This degree of physiological dryness completely prevents the growth of the common microorganisms (see Fig. 1), so that spoilage is effected by the "osmophilic" yeasts (von Schelhorn, 1951; Scarr, 1953; Vas, 1956); but even their growth is relatively slow. Spoilage is much faster if the materials are exposed to humid atmospheres because, being very hygroscopic, the surface layers are rapidly moistened, and though the yeasts are called osmophilic, their most rapid growth occurs with only about 30% (w/v) of sugar (aqueous activity about 0.8). Further, the yeasts themselves, once established, convert sugar into water and so accelerate the process. There is probably a complementary effect of acidity, in raising the aqueous activity below which growth will not occur (see below). This has been demonstrated for *Aspergillus glaucus* (von Schelhorn, 1951); and there are indications that the same is probably true for osmophilic yeasts in the experience that, for example, honey ferments at higher "solids contents" than more acid fruit concentrates.

In many investigations, the majority of the yeasts concerned were identified as strains of *Zygosaccharomyces* (see Mrak and Phaff, 1948), which have since been included in the species *Saccharomyces mellis* and *S. rouxii* by Lodder and Kreger-van Rij (1952). How far the strains from various sources are different is uncertain and clarification of this point has not been assisted by grouping the diversity of strains into two species. Substantial differences in acid metabolism between some of them have already been observed (Barnett and Ingram, 1955). The vitamin requirements of 18 different "species," from a variety of sources, were determined by Lochhead and Landerkin (1942), who recognized three main groups in which pantothenic acid was, respectively, essential, stimulating or unimportant; all required biotin, and inositol stimulated three species. The nutritional pattern corresponded with distinctions in morphology and fermenting powers; hence it was suggested that vitamin requirements could be helpful in classifying such yeasts and although this suggestion has not been pursued, Schultz and Atkin (1947) suggested ways in which it might be done. Landerkin recently confirmed that the above requirements of the strains have not changed significantly since 1942.

There are indications that the flora of sugar is more varied, M. P. Scarr (personal communication) having isolated osmophilic strains of *Schizosaccharomyces* and *Hanseniaspora*, besides *Zygosaccharomyces*. This may be because of the lower acidity, for general experience and the data in Table II suggest that it is the *Zygosaccharomyces* especially which combine ability to grow at high sugar concentrations with a high resistance to acidity. As already noted, spoilage of this sort is especially favored by warm conditions. Some of these strains have been shown to produce large quantities of acid during fermentation, leading to a pH so low as to cause hydrolysis of the sucrose present, which thus becomes available to species which cannot attack sucrose in the intact form (Scarr, 1951). However, Pappagianis and Phaff (1956) suggest that there may be true fermentation even if it be long delayed.

E. *Pickles*

Sweet pickles may undergo gaseous fermentation caused by yeasts, which bloats the incorporated vegetables. With sweet-pickled cucumbers, Bell and Etchells (1952) showed that the yeasts were strains of *Zygosaccharomyces globiformis*, with a combined tolerance of sugar and acetic acid such that fermentation occurs if

$$A < \frac{80 - S}{20}$$

where A and S are the percentages by weight of acetic acid and sucrose.

The yeasts were rather osmophilic, with optimum growth in the region 20–30% sugar. These observations demonstrate the complementary inhibitory action of acidity and low aqueous activity, and confirm that *Zygosaccharomyces* strains are especially resistant to this combination. Preservatives like benzoate, or sorbic acid (Sheneman and Costilow, 1955) permit the use of lower concentrations of acetic acid and sugar.

As the above formula would suggest, yeasts do not attack straight vinegar pickles, in which the concentration of acetic acid is 4% or more.

The same species *Z. globiformis* was discovered in fermentation spoilage of brined cucumbers pickled by a natural lactic fermentation, together with *Brettanomyces versatilis*, *Candida krusei*, *Torulopsis caroliniana* and *T. holmii*, *Hansenula subpelliculosa*, *Torulaspora rosei*, and *Zygosaccharomyces halomembranis* (Etchells *et al.*, 1953). There was more active development of yeast in the stronger (10–15% salt) brines than in the weaker (5%), because the more salt-tolerant yeasts were favored in competition with lactobacilli for the available nutrients. The yeasts which form films on the surface of the brines in which such pickles are made were also examined: the predominating species were *Debaryomyces membranaefaciens* var. *hollandicus* (tolerating 24% NaCl) and *Zygosaccharomyces halomembranis*, with the addition of *Hansenula anomala* and *Pichia alcoholophila* on brines with 10% salt or less. These yeasts are, however, not reported as important agents in spoilage.

Sauerkraut, which is prepared in a similar way, may be spoiled by "pink torulae" (Fred and Peterson, 1922). Again too much salt or too little acid, too high a temperature, or low nitrogen content in the cabbage —indeed anything which interferes with the normal bacterial succession —promoted the growth of the yeasts. Oxygen was essential, agreeing with the markedly aerobic character of the Rhodotorulas.

F. *Meat and Meat Products*

Fresh meat spoils by the development of a microflora on its surface ("slime"), or in its interior. The nature and causes of these two types of spoilage are different: in neither has the yeast element in the microflora been properly investigated.

On the surface of meat, or in mincemeat at temperatures below about 20°C., it is usual to find that bacteria rapidly overgrow the yeasts, unless conditions have been made unfavorable to the former. As we have seen, this happens when the aqueous activity is reduced, by partial drying, or salting; hence yeasts are appreciable in the spoilage flora only on chilled meat which is held at an intermediate (ca. 90%) relative humidity (Scott,

1936), or on lightly salted and partially dried products like sausages (Mrak and Bonar, 1938). Scott (1936) isolated from chilled beef several strains of *Candida* and *Geotrichoides* as characteristic; one of the latter was regarded as a new species *Trichosporon scottii* by Lodder and van Rij (1952). According to Mrak and Phaff (1948), *Debaryomyces* are common on meat products, although the reasons are unknown; the species forming slime on sausage was *D. guilliermondii* var. *nova zeelandicus*. The present author has recently seen an outbreak of spoilage in long-stored chilled beef where red yeasts predominated on those parts of the carcass which had dried out. The predominance of the above yeasts in the meat flora corresponds with their prevalance in air, and no other obvious sources for such contamination have yet been identified in the environment in which meat is normally handled; hence, for the present, it seems reasonable to regard the yeasts spoiling meat as predominantly transmitted from air, like the associated fungi.

Two other factors known to depress the activities on meat of bacteria, which are then replaced by yeasts, are acidity and antibiotics. Gibbons and Rose (1950) showed that yeasts replaced bacteria if the pH of meat was reduced to 5.0, and that no putrefaction took place; and Tarr *et al.* (1952) found that a similar thing happened if tetracycline antibiotics were added to meat. In neither case was any indication given of the nature of the yeasts. Unpublished experiments have shown that the yeasts which appear on chlortetracycline-treated meat resemble *Candida lipolytica* (J. Wight and D. Pearson, personal communication) which emphasizes that the spoilage of meats by yeasts is different from that by bacteria. The latter are mainly proteolytic; while the activities of the yeasts tend towards lipolysis and free fatty acid rancidity.

What part yeasts may play in internal spoilage of meat is still unknown. From within hams, the present writer has occasionally isolated strains of *Rhodotorula* and *Debaryomyces* which again hint at air-borne infection, conceivably indirectly from the meat surface. Recently, however, an outbreak of taint in hams has been investigated in which yeasts were a dominant element in the spoilage flora and it would be interesting to see whether they bear any relation to the yeasts, for example, in the gut of the animal. Another possibility is infection from the curing brines. A survey by Etchells and Costilow confirmed the earlier indications of Mrak and Bonar (1938) that the yeasts forming films on meat-curing brines are, like those on vegetable brines, *Debaryomyces membranaefaciens* var. *hollandicus*. *D. kloeckeri* was isolated from subsurface brine samples. The use of sugar in the cure might be an important influence here.

G. Dairy Products

A recent survey by di Menna (1956) indicates that lactose-fermenting yeasts occur rarely in fresh milk: not significantly more frequently than, for instance, in apple juice. This suggests plainly that the predominance of lactose-attacking yeasts in the spoilage of milk products is due to enrichment by that particular sugar; this is confirmed by the striking exception that "condensed" milk, sweetened with sucrose, is spoiled by sucrose-fermenting species not attacking lactose.

On the surface of milk, the yeastlike form of *Geotrichum candidum* (*Oidium lactis*) frequently produces a wrinkled crust. This organism is lipolytic and proteolytic and, though it produces lactic acid from sugars, the proteolysis prevents the development of an acid reaction. It is universally distributed where milk is handled and in cow dung. Sour milk or cream may develop pink spots on the surface, which are colonies especially of *Rhodotorula glutinis* probably arising through infection from air.

In milk, yeasts are not important spoilage agents. They sometimes occur as a result of infections in the udder and there are indications that such occurrences are increasing because of the treatment of udder infections with antibiotics which yeasts resist. There is no clear evidence that the yeasts are specific. For instance, from one such an occurrence the present writer identified *Candida krusei*, which is widely distributed. *Pichia fermentans* was first isolated from buttermilk, and has been found in cheese, but it also occurs in fruits. Cream in bulk may be fermented by two lactose-fermenting yeasts, *Torula* (*Torulopsis*) *sphaerica* and *Torula* (*Candida*) *cremoris* (Hammer and Cordes, 1920) especially if the cream is sour enough to inhibit lactose-fermenting bacteria like the coliforms and clostridia. In addition, the presence of these yeasts interferes with butter making, and produces a yeasty flavor. A lactose-fermenting *Torula* has also been reported to cause bitter flavor. Sweetened condensed milk is fermented by different yeasts, *Torula* (*Torulopsis*) *globosa* and/or *T. lactis condensi*, which ferment sucrose not lactose, and can grow in highly concentrated sugar solutions (Olson and Hammer, 1935).

On butter, yeasts are much more important. Textbooks state that *Monilia nigra* and *Oidium lactis* produce common discolorations, and attack the fat. In 1911, Jensen isolated various Torulopsidaceae from butter, and showed that they produced high acidity during storage for one month; this author pointed out that such organisms are widely distributed in air. Nissen (1930) regarded red yeasts as particularly harmful in milk and milk products because they both peptonize casein and attack butterfat readily. This was confirmed by Miklik (1953) who demonstrated the ability of a *Rhodotorula* isolated from discolored butter to create near-neutral conditions by proteolysis and, under these conditions, to produce strong rancidity by splitting the fat, a process favored by the presence of lactic streptococci. Miklik too regarded the infection as airborne.

On cheese rinds, *Monilia nigra* and *Oidium lactis* occur, the former producing black spots on the drier cheeses of the Emmenthal type and the latter forming a pellicle on wet cheeses (e.g., Camembert) where it is encouraged by insufficient salinity. From the interior of soft Italian cheeses, Sacchetti (1933) isolated a range of lactose-fermenting species which he believed to be important in softening the cheeses. They included *Zygosaccharomyces casei* and *Z. versicolor*, now regarded as identical with *Saccharomyces lactis* (Lodder and Kreger van Rij, 1952) and related to *S. fragilis* (Wickerham and Burton, 1956). With low-salt cheeses, especially if poor in fat, *S. fragilis* can "blow" the cheese. To avoid this, pasteurization of the starting materials at 65°C. is recommended, because the yeast cannot be inhibited by raising the acidity (Dorner *et al.*, 1950). These authors say, moreover, that red yeasts are common in cheese brines.

Yeasts play a part in the normal ripening of cheeses: the succession on Camembert, for example, being (1) yeasts, (2) *Penicillium camembertii*, (3) *Bacterium linens*. On "brick" cheese, Iya and Frazier (1949) observed that, after 3 days during which bacteria grew, the surface was overgrown by a *Mycoderma* which was in turn succeeded by *B. linens*. The yeast attacked lactate and so brought the pH into the neutral zone; this circumstance, and an apparent liberation of growth factors, encouraged the growth of *B. linens*. Besides these workers, Miklik (1953) observed that the appearance of yeasts is subsequent to that of bacteria, which may be due to gradual drying of the surface on which they are growing. Yeasts are sometimes deliberately added to dairy products. A well-known example is in the fermentation of milk to give kefir by *Saccharomyces fragilis* and *Leuconostoc dextranicum*. This process has been variously explained; for instance, the lactose has been said to be hydrolyzed by the bacteria although this would be curious as *S. fragilis* is a lactose fermenter. *Candida krusei* (*Mycoderma casei*) occurs in rennet where it is believed to have some importance as an auxiliary organism in "starter" cultures in cheese making, through its ability to provide a degree of anaerobiosis and accessory substances suitable for the growth of lactobacilli and streptococci. However, its presence may encourage gum-forming strains which are undesirable (Dorner *et al.*, 1950). Treatment of pasteurized milk for use in cheese making with *Mycotorula* (*Candida*) *lipolytica* is recommended (Peters and Nelson, 1948) to replace the lipase activity of milk, which is desirable for the production of cheese but is destroyed when milk is pasteurized. The addition of cultivated yeasts, in numbers of the order of only thousands per gram, during the preparation of butter has been claimed to delay development of molds and give longer storage life (Bogdanow *et al.*, 1952).

H. *Frozen Foods*

Freezing withdraws water so that the aqueous activity of a food when frozen is lower than that before freezing. This may be why yeasts appear more commonly than bacteria in the spoilage of frozen foods.

For example, yeasts have been reported as the chief spoilage agents on frozen peas (Mulcock, 1955) and on frozen oysters (McCormack, 1950). It is noteworthy that, in these cases, the predominant species were "red" yeasts. Thus, Mulcock identified *Rhodotorula glutinis* and the present author has recovered *Rhodotorula* or *Sporobolomyces* species from a similar occurrence; the yeast spoiling frozen oysters was also reported as "pink."

It would be interesting to know what decides the predominance of the red yeasts under such conditions. There is no reason so far to suppose it due to an unusual tolerance of low aqueous activity (see Fig. 1). It might result from outstanding powers of multiplication at low temperatures, the pink yeast from frozen oysters having been reported as growing at −18°C. Mulcock, however, found that, while the *R. glutinis* from frozen peas grew well at 4°C., it did not at −6°C. or −17°C. Contamination from dust has not been established as the cause either; it is noteworthy in this connection that Mulcock isolated from dust a second strain of *R. glutinis* which, though biochemically identical with that from the peas, lacked the crucial ability to grow at 4°C.

3. Isolation, Identification, and Physiology of Food Spoilage Yeasts

The isolation of the yeasts from a spoiling food is seldom straightforward, because they are frequently accompanied by bacteria and molds. Hence, though yeasts will grow on orthodox bacteriological media especially if they contain a sugar, it is usual to use a selective medium. For this purpose, special media are desirable, the usual yeast media not being sufficiently exclusive.

This problem has been considered at some length by Beech and Carr (1955). They recommend first a pH more acid than 5.0 to eliminate bacteria and then the inclusion in the medium of 100 p.p.m. of diphenyl to inhibit molds. They also list several antibiotics (e.g., chlortetracycline) which are useful in suppressing bacteria. On the other hand, they do not discuss the possibility of using different antibiotics to suppress molds while none of the usual fungicides tested was suitable except diphenyl. Instead of incorporating diphenyl in the medium, the present writer found it effective to evaporate about 0.1 ml. of a saturated alcoholic solution of diphenyl on the lid of the petri dish.

For organisms from foods having high concentrations of salt or sugar, it is often sufficient to isolate them on a medium of similar composition. Thus Kroemer and Krumbholz (1931) recommended the isolation of osmophilic yeasts on media with 50% of sugar while the present writer used this procedure satisfactorily to isolate osmophilic yeasts from citrus concentrates. In this case, 40% glucose (w/v) did not exclude "normal" strains although even at that concentration the osmophilic strains were easily recognizable by their more vigorous growth. Lochhead and Heron (1929) used media with large proportions of honey for the yeasts from honey.

In the identification of the yeasts isolated, the first and chief difficulty is still the decision as to whether spores are produced or not. When this matter is settled, identification is comparatively easy, up to a point, thanks to the invaluable monograph of Lodder and Kreger-van Rij (1952). It may be mentioned, incidentally, that a similar treatise has been prepared by Kudriavzev (1954), but is in the Russian language and not easily accessible. Of course, many new species have been described in the past few years which do not appear in those works. Nevertheless, the investigator of food spoilage is usually concerned with identifying his organisms as precisely as possible, either in order to infer properties reported by other workers, or to trace the origin of the particular spoilage organism. For this purpose, identification as far as the species or even variety is frequently insufficient. There are, for instance, large differences in salt tolerance between different strains in *Debaryomyces guilliermondii* var. *hollandicus,* and of sugar tolerance (and other characters too) in *Saccharomyces mellis.* More precise means of characterization seem desirable: one recalls the typing of Salmonellas by serology or that of Staphylococci by phage reactions and the aid which such procedures give in tracing outbreaks of food poisoning. There is unfortunately nothing equivalent for yeasts.

The only resource is detailed investigation of physiological peculiarities such as conditions for growth. As an instance, a heat-resistant yeast which has been isolated from canned bacon also possesses the uncommon property of growing rapidly on erythritol as sole carbon source and this character is helpful in searching for it in the field. Descriptions of yeasts causing food spoilage frequently contain too little information about useful peculiarities like assimilation reactions and nutrilite requirements, though this situation is rapidly changing, as a result largely of Wickerham's work. From the practical viewpoint, there would be special value in physiological characters which influence the occurrence of the organisms, such as proteolytic or lipolytic powers, even though these are little regarded by the yeast taxonomist despite being used for bacteria. An illustration is Mulcock's use (quoted above) of growth at 4°C. to distinguish between the strain of *Rhodotorula glutinis* from frozen peas and similar strains from air-borne dust; however, far more information about the plasticity of such characters is needed before they can be a reliable guide. All this means of course that further advances in the understanding and control of yeasts, or other microbes, in food spoilage will depend on the extent to which basic research elucidates the biological properties of the organisms themselves.

Acknowledgments

This chapter was prepared as part of the program of the Food Investigation Organisation of the Department of Scientific and Industrial Research of Great Britain. Crown copyright is reserved.

References

Barnett, J. A., and Ingram, M. (1955). *J. Appl. Bacteriol.* **18**, 131.

Beech, F. W., and Carr, J. G. (1955). *J. Gen. Microbiol.* **12**, 85.

Bell, T. A., and Etchells, J. L. (1952). *Food Technol.* **6**, 468.

Beneke, E. S., White, L. S., and Fabian, F. W. (1954). *Appl. Microbiol.* **2**, 253.

Bogdanow, W., Malschewa, E., and Lukownika, L. (1952). *Milchwissenschaft* **7**, 415 (abstr.).

Bottomley, R. A., Christensen, C. M., and Geddes, W. F. (1950). *Cereal Chem.* **27**, 271.

Burcik, E. (1950). *Arch. Mikrobiol.* **15**, 203.

Burroughs, L. F. (1952). *Rept. Long Ashton Research Sta.* 110.

Castelli, T. (1954). *Arch. Mikrobiol.* **20**, 323.

Challinor, S. W. (1955). *J. Appl. Bacteriol.* **18**, 212.

Challinor, S. W., and Rose, A. H. (1954). *Nature* **174**, 887.

Challinor, S. W., Kieser, M. E., and Pollard, A. (1948). *Nature* **161**, 1023.

Clark, D. S., Wallace, R. H., and David, J. J. (1954). *Can. J. Microbiol.* **1**, 145.

Cole, G. M. (1955). *Food Technol.* **9**, 38.

Connell, G. H., and Skinner, C. E. (1953). *J. Bacteriol.* **66**, 627.

Cruess, W. V. (1943). *Advances in Enzymol.* **3**, 349.

Del Prado, F. A., and Christensen, C. M. (1952). *Cereal Chem.* **29**, 456.

Di Menna, M. E. (1955). *Brit. Mycol. Soc. Trans.* **38**, 119.

Di Menna, M. E. (1956). *Antonie van Leeuwenhoek J. Microbiol. Serol.* **22**, 331.

Dorner, W., Demont, P., and Chavannes, D. (1950). "Microbiologie Laitiere," 3rd ed. Librairie Payot, Lausanne.

632 M. INGRAM

English, M. P. (1953). *J. Gen. Microbiol.* 9, 15.
Etchells, J. L., Bell, T. A., and Jones, I. D. (1953). *Farlowia* 4, 265.
Faville, L. W., and Hill, E. C. (1951). *Food Technol.* 5, 423.
Fred, E. B., and Peterson, W. H. (1922). *J. Bacteriol.* 7, 257.
Gibbons, N. E., and Rose, D. (1950). *Can. J. Research* F28, 438.
Guilliermond, A., and Tanner, F. W. (1920). "The Yeasts." Wiley, New York.
Hammer, B. W., and Cordes, W. A. (1920). *Iowa State Coll. Agr. Expt. Sta. Research Bull.* 61, 1.
Ingram, M., Mossel, D. A. A., and de Lange, P. (1955). *Chemistry & Industry* 1955, 63.
Iya, K. J., and Frazier, W. C. (1949). *J. Dairy Sci.* 32, 475.
Kroemer, K., and Krumbholz, G. (1931). *Arch. Mikrobiol.* 2, 352.
Kudriavtzev, V. I. (1954). "The Systematics of Yeasts." Academy of Sciences, Moscow.
Lafourcade, S. (1956). *Inds. aliment. agr.* (*Paris*) 73, 779.
Lochhead, A. G., and Heron, D. A. (1929). *Dominion Can. Dept. Agr. Bull.* [n.s.] 116.
Lochhead, A. G., and Landerkin, G. B. (1942). *J. Bacteriol.* 44, 343.
Lodder, J., and Kreger-van Rij, N. J. W. (1952). "The Yeasts." North Holland Publishing Co., Amsterdam.
Lowings, P. H. (1956). *Appl. Microbiol.* 4, 84.
Luh, B. S., and Phaff, H. J. (1951). *Arch. Biochem. and Biophys.* 33, 212.
Lund, A. (1951). *J. Inst. Brewing* 57, 36.
Lund, A. (1956). *Friesia* V, 3–5, 297.
Lüthi, H. (1954). *Mitt. Gebiete Lebensm. u. Hyg.* 45, 26.
Lüthi, H. (1955). *Flüssiges Obst.* 22, 4.
McCormack, G. (1950). *Com. Fisheries Rev.* 12, (11a), 28.
Marcus, O. (1942). *Arch. Mikrobiol.* 13, 1.
Marshall, C. R., and Walkley, V. T. (1951). *Food Research* 16, 448.
Miklik, E. (1953). *Milchwissenschaft* 8, 23.
Mossel, D. A. A., and Ingram, M. (1955). *J. Appl. Bacteriol.* 18, 232.
Mrak, E. M., and Bonar, L. (1938). *Food Research* 3, 615.
Mrak, E. M., and McClung, L. S. (1940). *J. Bacteriol.* 40, 395.
Mrak, E. M., and Phaff, H. J. (1948). *Ann. Rev. Microbiol.* 2, 1.
Mrak, E. M., Vaughn, R. H., Miller, M. W., and Phaff, H. J. (1956). *Food Technol.* 10, 416.
Mulcock, A. P. (1955) *New Zealand J. Sci. Technol.* 37B, 15.
Nickerson, W. J. (1953). *J. Infectious Diseases* 93, 43.
Nissen, W. (1930). *Milchwirtsch. Forsch.* 10, 30.
Nolte, A. J., and Von Loesecke, H. W. (1940). *Food Research* 5, 73.
Olson, H. C., and Hammer, B. W. (1935). *Iowa State Coll. J. Sci.* 10, 37.
Pappagianis, D., and Phaff, H. J. (1956). *Antonie van Leeuwenhoek J. Microbiol. Serol.* 22, 353.
Peters, I. I., and Nelson, F. E. (1948). *J. Bacteriol.* 55, 581.
Peynaud, E. (1957). *Mitt.* (*Klosterneuberg*) *Ser. A* 7, 1.
Phaff, H. J., Mrak, E. M., and Williams, O. B. (1952). *Mycologia* 44, 431.
Phillips, J. D., Pollard, A., and Whiting, G. C. (1956). *J. Sci. Food Agr.* 7, 31.
Recca, J., and Mrak, E. M. (1952). *Food Technol.* 6, 450.
Romwalter, A., and Király, A. von (1939). *Arch. Mikrobiol.* 10, 87.
Sacchetti, M. (1933). *Arch. Mikrobiol.* 4, 427.

Scardovi, V. (1952). *Ann. microbiol.* **5**, 5.

Scarr, M. P. (1951). *J. Gen. Microbiol.* **5**, 704.

Scarr, M. P. (1953). *Proc. Soc. Appl. Bacteriol.* **16**, 119.

Schachinger, L., and Heiss, R. (1951). *Arch. Mikrobiol.* **16**, 347.

Schanderl, H. (1954). *Naturwissenschaften* **12**, 284.

Schelhorn, M. von (1951). *Advances in Food Research* **3**, 429.

Schulle, H. (1953). *Arch. Mikrobiol.* **18**, 342.

Schultz, A. S., and Atkin, L. (1947). *Arch. Biochem. and Biophys.* **14**, 369.

Scott, W. J. (1936). *J. Council Sci. Ind. Research* **9**, 177.

Scott, W. J. (1937). *J. Council Sci. Ind. Research* **10**, 338.

Semeniuk, G., Nagel, C. M., and Gilman, J. C. (1947). *Iowa State Coll. Agr. Expt. Sta. Research Bull.* **349**, 255.

Sheneman, J. M., and Costilow, R. N. (1955). *Appl. Microbiol.* **3**, 186.

Stadtman, E. R. (1948). *Advances in Food Research* **1**, 357.

Tanner, F. W. (1944). "Microbiology of Foods." 2nd ed. Garrard Press, Champaign, Illinois.

Tanner, F. W., and Ruyle, E. H. (1932). *Proc. Soc. Exptl. Biol. Med.* **29**, 1001.

Tarr, H. L. A., Southcott, B. A., and Bissett, H. M. (1952). *Food Technol.* **6**, 363.

Teunisson, D. J. (1954). *Appl. Microbiol.* **2**, 215.

Uroma, E., and Virtanen, O. E. (1949). *Chem. Abstr.* **43**, 2277.

Vas, K. (1956). *Food Manuf.* **32**, 71.

Webb, A. H., and Tanner, F. W. (1945). *Food Research* **10**, 273.

Wickerham, L. J. (1951). *U.S. Dept. Agr. Tech. Bull.* **1029**.

Wickerham, L. J., and Burton, K. A. (1956). *J. Bacteriol.* **71**, 290.

Zukerman, I. (1951). *Nature* **168**, 517.

CHAPTER XIII

Flocculation of Yeasts

H. E. Jansen

1. Introduction

The formation of clumps of yeast cells from a homogeneous yeast suspension is termed flocculation. Clumping of the cells under the influence of a contaminating microorganism cannot be considered as true flocculation. A yeast which forms clumps of cells in its natural medium is termed a *flocculent* yeast (in German: "Bruchhefe") whereas a yeast which does not is called a *nonflocculent* or a *powdery* yeast (in German: "Staubhefe").

Mainly because of its great importance in practical brewing, investigation of the problem of yeast flocculation has been almost entirely confined to the brewery. Both in bottom and in top fermentation systems the brewer is concerned with the rate of flocculation of the yeast; a highly flocculent or a highly powdery yeast yield, respectively, too low or too high a degree of attenuation. Apart from the difficulties of fermentation, the sedimentation of the yeast in the case of a powdery yeast has also to be taken into account. For instance, when the beer is cooled at the end of a primary fermentation with a bottom yeast, a flocculent type clumps and settles down in the tank whereas a powdery yeast sediments slowly and a large amount remains in suspension in the beer. Top fermentation yeast behaves differently. Formerly the rise of the yeast to the top during fermentation was attributed to flocculation of the yeast only and "flocculation" was even considered to be synonymous with the forming of a yeast head. Opinions, however, have more or less changed and nowadays some authors maintain that head formation is independent of the flocculating power of the yeast. As flocs of top fermentation yeasts are more difficult to observe with the naked eye than those of bottom fermentation yeasts, it is understandable why so much confusion has arisen, a particular top fermentation yeast being sometimes considered as nonflocculent by German brewers and as flocculent by British brewers. It may be said that in the last decade certain controversies with regard to brewery yeast have been eliminated but many questions still require elucidation.

In distilleries and in the manufacture of pressed baker's yeast, flocculation plays a subordinate role and the literature on yeast flocculation in both these branches of the fermentation industries is meager. Formerly, in distilleries working with clear mashes a powdery yeast was preferred but in manufacturing aerated pressed yeast a slightly flocculating yeast was recommended. Nowadays, with centrifuges of high speed and capacity, it seems to be far less important what type of yeast is used in distilleries so long as fermentation itself is not affected. It is only in the bakery that a more powdery type is preferred as it can be more homogeneously incorporated into the dough.

In the present connection, therefore, the problem of yeast flocculation will be mainly considered from the brewing angle.

2. Historical Survey

A. *Relation between Wort Composition and Flocculation*

Although Pasteur (1876) in France described the presence of a flocculating yeast ("levure casséeuse") in an ordinary top fermentation yeast, the first investigations on yeast flocculation were carried out in Germany. Kusserow (1897) mentioned that the addition of peptones to wort causes the yeast to flocculate, whereas asparagine has the opposite effect. Lange

(1899) was of the opinion that this particular phenomenon was caused by mechanical coprecipitation of the yeast with peptones, which are coagulated by alcohol at the end of fermentation, for he found no differences between the peptone- and the asparagine-treated yeast. With regard to the mechanical precipitation of yeast, Delbrück (1901) noticed that yeast cells were carried down with the sludge in the fermentation vessels while Lindner (1901) made an observation which still holds (see below) that sugars influence the flocculation of bottom fermentation yeasts. These early investigations clearly pointed to a relationship between wort composition and the flocculence of the yeast, a conception which was pursued by others as will be shown later. The majority of the observations of these early workers were empirical in nature since the experiments were carried out with different types of yeast propagated under different conditions so that the results are hardly comparable.

B. Symbiotic Theory

Flocculation, also called agglutination, was at others times attributed to the action of several types of bacteria on yeast (symbiotic theory). As this type of flocculation of yeast is caused by other microorganisms, it should not, according to the definition in the Introduction, be regarded as a true yeast flocculation, but nevertheless this particular theory, representative in its time, must be briefly mentioned.

Barendrecht (1901) was the first to describe a bacterium, to which he gave the name of *Leuconostoc agglutinans* (later renamed *Lactococcus agglutinans*), which causes agglutination of industrial yeast grown under aerated conditions. Moreover, this author demonstrated the influence of hydrogen ion concentration on the flocculation of a pure culture yeast in some preliminary tests with acidified suspensions of yeasts. Indeed, the opinion at that time was that flocculation of top fermentation yeasts could be explained by this symbiotic theory alone. Even Beyerinck (1908) was of the opinion that although bottom fermentation yeasts in breweries may flocculate on their own (autoagglutination), this certainly is not the case with top fermentation yeasts. Agglutination of this latter type of yeast could only be caused by symbiosis of the yeast with different types of bacteria. It was assumed that the yeast cell became enveloped by mucilage produced by these bacteria and flocculated in consequence. If under special conditions, the formation of mucilage by these bacteria were suppressed, the agglutination of the yeast was less complete. Although with infected yeasts this mechanism may still hold, it certainly does not explain the flocculation of top fermentation yeasts in ordinary practice.

C. Enzymic Theory

An attractive theory of flocculation was given by Lange (1907) who experimented with pressed yeast. According to his enzymic theory, flocculation is caused by an adsorbed layer of protein on the cell wall, which in the case of a powdery yeast is dissolved by the proteolytic action of certain secreted enzymes ("peptase"). In the case of a flocculent yeast insufficient "peptase" is secreted and the protein layer on the cell wall remains intact. This theory was founded on the determinations of the action of proteolytic enzymes from yeast, so-called "peptase," on thymol gelatin. Measuring the rate of liquefaction of this thymol gelatin by drops of yeast extract, Lange found that an extract from flocculent yeast showed considerably less proteolytic action than one made from a powdery yeast. In the light of modern enzymology, however, this theory cannot be upheld.

D. Influence of Salts on Flocculation

Many authors have investigated the influence of salts on yeast flocculation. For instance, Holderer (1901) and Lange (1901) described the flocculating action of aluminum hydroxide on powdery yeast, and Van Laer (1905) noted the influence of boric acid in combination with different salts on flocculation. As, however, boric acid forms complex compounds with gummy substances of polysaccharide nature (see Will, 1893; Lindner, 1930; Böeseken, 1949), there is ample reason to believe that, if present, it may react similarly with the polysaccharides of the cell wall. The addition of electrolytes as in the experiment of van Laer complicates the conditions and the results become somewhat difficult to interpret. Several articles mentioned the influence of lime and magnesia in the brewing liquor on the flocculation of the yeast. Thus Seyffert (1896) described a pure culture of yeast that lost its flocculence by reason of the softness of the brewing liquor and regained it after addition of lime to the liquor. Hayduck and Schücking (1908) found that by adding a certain amount of calcium carbonate to the wort the flocculence of the yeast could be enhanced although gypsum showed no pronounced action. These latter authors denied the existence of any correlation between flocculence and calcium contents in the dried yeast in contradiction of both Schönfeld (1912) who believed that flocculence corresponds with a lower content of calcium but a higher content of magnesium in the ash of the yeast and of Moufang (1912) in whose opinion "magnesia" yeasts were of a flocculent type while "calcium" yeasts were of a nonflocculent nature. Schönfeld's results lack conviction to some extent as he did not describe his method of rinsing the yeast, which is essential, nor did his figures show any significant difference in ash composition between flocculent and powdery yeasts. As to the influence of salts in the brewing liquor, Schönfeld and Schönfelder (1914) were of the opinion that sulfates give rise to powdery yeasts and carbonates to flocculent yeasts. Later Schönfeld and Krumhaar (1918) stated that calcium salts of strong acids in particular cause powdery yeasts. According to them, flocculence is caused by a layer of insoluble secondary calcium phosphate formed on the cell wall. This can only occur when the initial ratio of lime to phosphate in the wort, about 1:6, undergoes a change to about 2:3. This theory remained without any proof and in fact became unacceptable when it appeared that yeasts grown in worts with higher contents of calcium or phosphate do not show any change in flocculence (as shown by Gilliland, 1951). The authors mentioned were prepared to admit that other factors, such as precipitation of wort proteins on the cell wall, may play a part and that the phenomenon of yeast flocculation cannot be entirely explained in a simple way. Actually, in the case of top fermentation yeasts, Burns (1937) has confirmed the influence of some of the above salts on yeast flocculation.

Schönfeld (1909, 1910) distinguished flocculent and powdery types of yeast by suspending them in water, when the flocculent yeasts settles in flocs, while the powdery yeast formed a milky suspension. Originally this test was intended to distinguish between top and bottom fermentation yeasts, but the author admitted that it was unsuitable for this purpose, as bottom fermentation yeasts yield far more pronounced flocs than top fermentation growths. As to the transformation of a flocculent into a powdery yeast, he mentioned that he could obtain powdery yeasts by propagating certain strains of flocculent yeasts at higher temperatures (25–30°C.) and vice versa. This confirmed the idea of Hayduck (1905) who was of the opinion that nonflocculence of brewery yeasts is enhanced by the action of strong aeration and higher temperatures during fermentation. He also mentioned that for keeping a yeast in the flocculent condition it should be washed for a short time with cold water. A similar idea is found in the manufacturing of pressed yeast.

E. Coated Yeasts

Ranken (1927, 1928) carried out an extensive series of experiments on yeast treated with different substances such as calcium oxalate and phosphate, peptone-tannins, and hop resins, and assumed that these compounds are adsorbed on the cell wall. He examined the influence of the coatings on fermentation both in invert sugar solutions and in hopped wort, on the formation of new cells and on flocculation. In this way, he proved that cells coated with calcium oxalate or hop resins show a more vigorous fermentation and a decrease in flocculence of the yeast. Calcium phosphate and peptone-tannins on the other hand have the opposite effect. At the same time Ranken found that traces of iron reverse the effect of peptone-tannins on yeast flocculation. In the matter of the influence of calcium phosphate on yeast flocculation, Ranken's results agreed with those of Schönfeld and Krumhaar (1918) insofar as this salt promotes yeast flocculation. The coatings seem to have a purely mechanical effect as was proved by coating yeasts with barium sulfate or lamp black and then incubating invert sugar solutions with them. None of these yeasts were flocculent; the cells sedimented but no cohesion between the individual cells could be observed. In order to find out how long the acquired properties of the coated yeasts would last, flocculent and powdery coated yeasts were used repeatedly for successively inoculating invert sugar solutions, hopped wort, and then invert sugar solutions again. The specific effect of the coatings gradually diminished until, after the third crop was harvested, the differences had almost disappeared. These studies showed obviously that changes in flocculence can be induced by the medium alone. Ranken's interpretation of the coating of the yeast cell wall is supported by the fact that there is sufficient evidence of proteins, hop resins or other hop constituents (see later) being adsorbed on the cell wall. However, this is no reason for assuming the adsorption of an insoluble calcium salt as although these salts precipitate as a constituent of "beerstone" on cooler surfaces, etc., it is rather doubtful whether such precipitations will occur on a living cell wall which is continuously excreting salts and nitrogen compounds. On these grounds, Bishop and Whitley (1938) felt that coatings on top fermentation yeast of wort sludge particles were unlikely especially as the particles were visible under the microscope or with the eye and sedimented on the bottom while the yeast rose to the top. Ranken's experiments, however, remain instructive and point to a possible approach to the whole problem.

Gelatin-coated yeasts are discussed in the following section.

F. *Flocculation as a Colloid Chemical Phenomenon*

As has been mentioned before, the influence of wort proteins and of metabolic products on the flocculation of yeasts was described many years ago by various authors. With the development of colloid chemistry, however, efforts were soon made to bring yeast flocculation into the domain of this new branch of chemistry. One of the first papers dealing with yeast flocculation as a colloid chemical phenomenon was by Lüers and Heusz

(1921). They determined the viscosity of yeast suspensions in acetate buffer solutions of different pH values by means of a modified Ostwald viscosimeter and found that maximum viscosity corresponded with maximum flocculation. This method could be applied to measuring flocculence of yeasts. The authors explained the phenomenon by assuming that large flocs of yeast have a high internal resistance, for bulky conglomerates retard the rate of flow more than small ones. Lüers pointed to the mutual action between compounds present on the cell wall and those in the wort and also discussed the electrical charge of this wall. However, his assumption that a maximum of flocculation coincides with the reaching of the isoelectric point (I.E.P.) of the cell proteins could not be proved. His contribution was nevertheless an approach to yeast flocculation from a new angle. Geys (1922) continued the work of Lüers and was the first to measure the charge of the yeast cell by means of microelectrophoresis. The yeast was suspended in buffer solutions of different pH values or, in the case of actual fermentations, in beer itself. As the method of microelectrophoresis was originally not free from serious errors, the results were somewhat doubtful. According to Geys the cells have a positive charge when suspended in water but, during fermentation, becomes neutral and then first acquires a negative and finally again a positive charge, a cycle of charges rather difficult to accept.

Winslow and Fleeson (1926), on the other hand, observed that yeast suspended in water is negatively charged. Although this charge is decreased by the action of hydrogen ions, no reversal of charge could be demonstrated by adding either these ions or trivalent cations. Later it will be seen, however, that in special circumstances the latter ions do cause reversal of charge.

Stockhausen (1927) extensively discussed yeast flocculation which according to him is brought about both by the flocculation of proteins at a pH of 4.7–4.8, which drag the yeast cells with them, and by mutual flocculation of positively charged yeast cells and negatively charged proteins at a pH of 4.4. For the isoelectric point of yeast cells in suspension in water he mentions a figure of 3.8, while at higher pH values the cell wall has a more positive charge. As his conclusions are not based on his own experiments they are of rather doubtful value in the elucidation of the problem of yeast flocculation. In later papers with Silbereisen (Stockhausen and Silbereisen, 1933, 1935) it was assumed that yeast flocculation is mainly caused by the presence of yeast gum. By determining the compound secreted by yeast cells when suspended in distilled water, these authors were able to prove, however, that an increase of these gum substances is not accompanied by an increase of flocculence.

There was, moreover, no evidence that the gum is consumed under conditions of malnutrition of the yeast. Further, only a slight correspondence between flocculence and glycogen content was found. With a view to clearing up the influence of pH on flocculation, Koch (1928) determined the point on the pH scale at which flocculation sets in during fermentation. It appeared that this point is not constant for a given strain of yeast, flocculation beginning at different pH values depending on the initial pH of the wort. Thus contrary to earlier opinions in fermentation practice, the pH does not seem to have a primary affect on the flocculation of the yeast. The results of Koch were confirmed by other authors (see below), although McCandlish and Hagues (1929) brought about an increase of flocculence by lowering the pH of the brewing liquor. Despite these findings, it may be mentioned that the theory of flocculation at the isoelectric point of the yeast cells was not at the time abandoned, De Clerck (1930), for example, being still of this opinion. He argued that flocculation is not so much caused by the end of fermentation, as that the end of fermentation is caused by the flocculation of the yeast. At present, this view is generally accepted. Experiments with pressed yeast, which cannot be compared with results obtained with brewery yeasts but which are nevertheless worth mentioning were carried out by Malkow et al. (1933, 1934). These authors grew yeast in molasses of different pH values and an optimum of flocculation was found at pH 2.85–3.15. However, as in practical fermentations pH values only vary between 5.5 and 4.5, this optimum has little significance. As for the influence of nitrogenous substances, they found that flocculence decreases on propagating the pressed yeast in solutions deprived of a part of the nitrogenous material originally present by precipitation with lead acetate. On the other hand, nitrogen assimilation by the yeast decreased with increasing flocculence so that their results are difficult to interpret and perhaps only establish that metabolic substances from the yeast have a decisive influence on flocculation. For this reason, they added the filtered and sterilized fermentation product of molasses to unfermented molasses with the result that the powdery yeast became flocculent. Moldawskaja (1933) proved by cathaphoretical experiments that yeast cells normally have a negative charge, although, by means of aluminum chloride, reversal of charge could be effected. Cells coated with gelatin could easily be discharged with hydrochloric acid at a pH lower than 3, although eventually a reversal of charge took place and by adding aluminum chloride, the same effect was obtained. Although these phenomena suggested that the treated cells behaved as protein-coated particles, the author admitted that, contrary to the opinion of other workers, the isoelectric point of the gelatin-coated cells is not the same as that of the gelatin itself. In some of his later articles on this subject Silbereisen (1938) thoroughly examined the electrical charge on the yeast cells, both in suspension in water and in dilute solutions of sodium chloride, confirming that yeast ordinarily has a negative charge with an isoelectric point at pH 2.0–1.88. No difference in the influence of electrolytes was observed between the charge of a flocculent bottom fermentation yeast and that on a non-flocculent top fermentation yeast. He further observed that neither sodium salts nor calcium salts cause reversal of charge although this is not true of aluminum chloride. Silbereisen's results were, in fact, similar to those of Moldawskaja using gelatin-coated yeasts. Reversal of charge was also observed although during fermentation in wort the yeast retained its negative charge and reversal was never found. Silbereisen denied a causal relationship between the flocculation at the end of the fermentation and the electrical charge of the yeast cell for, probably by reason of the imperfect methodology of his microelectrophoretical experiments, he was unable to find any change in charge during fermentation. Later authors, however, were successful in demonstrating a decrease in electrical charge during the first days of fermentation. At the same time Hennig and Ay (1938) also confirmed the negative charge of the yeast cell by means of microelectrophoresis and pointed out that living yeast cells with their complex structure of the cell wall cannot invariably be compared with colloid particles. For instance, when the charge of the cell wall is neutralized, the cell excretes substances which oppose this neutralization, as was confirmed by other authors. They were unable to demonstrate, on the other hand, that yeast cells growing in wort lost their negative charge.

G. Flocculation of English Top Fermentation Yeast

Burns (1937), introducing a new method for measuring yeast flocculation, determined the amount of yeast which settles from a yeast suspension in a graduated tube after standing for 10 minutes (for particulars see below). He further showed that the flocculence of the pitching yeast is closely related to the yeast content of the beer at racking, to the attenuation, and to the progress of fermentation in the fermenting vessel. Top fermentation yeast, when rinsed and suspended in distilled water clumps in the presence of most neutral salts. Barium chloride and copper sulfate are exceptions but in these cases the metal ion is toxic. Toxic anions, however, fail to interfere with flocculation. Acids and alkaline solutions, on the other hand, behave in another way. Yeast suspended in dilute mineral acids does not flocculate but becomes totally powdery. After centrifuging, rinsing with distilled water, and again centrifuging, such a yeast suspended in an acetate buffer solution will flocculate again but treatment with sodium hydroxide solutions destroys this ability.

Various yeasts showed no differences in flocculence over the pH range 3.5–5.5 so that it seemed that the pH of itself does not control yeast flocculation in practice. Burns' views on the flocculation of English top fermentation yeasts had, however, a more practical importance and he drew the following picture of the mechanism of yeast flocculation: after pitching the yeast is dispersed by the presence of sugars, which prevent amino acids and mineral constituents from exerting a flocculating action. This inhibitive action naturally ceases to operate after the sugars have been fermented; clumping then takes place and accelerates the rising of the yeast to the top of the vessel. Most of these views have since been confirmed while Burns' method for determining yeast flocculation is in general use.

H. *Influence of Growth-Promoting Substances on Flocculation*

Nielsen (1937) discussed the influence of different factors on the sedimentation velocity of yeasts which is closely related to flocculence and appeared to provide a measure of flocculence. As in the method of Burns, he measured the amount of yeast which sediments in a given time from a suspension of yeast (for particulars see below) and found that yeast grown in nutrient solutions to which different amino acids or peptones had been added shows an increase in sedimentation velocity. Ammonium sulfate, however, shows the opposite effect. Similar results had been obtained by former authors. Nielsen further observed that the lower the temperature during growth, the higher the sedimentation velocity appears to be. By comparing yeasts grown in synthetic nutrient solutions with yeast propagated in the same solutions together with brewery wort, he found that the velocity in the latter case was considerably lower. It was assumed that growth-promoting substances in the wort were responsible for this particular effect, as experiments with other solutions containing similar compounds yielded the same results. In this connection, it may be recalled that at that time knowledge of growth-promoting substances and their effect on the fermentation of yeasts was scanty and interpretations often premature.

To conclude this historical survey it may be said that before 1940 research on yeast flocculation was mainly concerned with bottom fermentation yeasts. Factors influencing yeast flocculation present in the fermenting medium had been investigated and some slight agreement on the influence of electrolytes on flocculation established. Racial differences of flocculation were known, but had not been subjected to genetical research while the complexity of the whole phenomenon of yeast flocculation was generally recognized.

3. Modern Views

A. *Genetical Aspects of Flocculence*

It has been shown that yeast flocculation is associated with the yeast strain and both Gilliland (1951) and Thorne (1951b) have examined the flocculence of top fermentation yeasts from the genetical point of view. They both found that flocculation of the yeast in their particular cases is a hereditary characteristic and thus under genetic control. Gilliland examined the flocculence of four classes of yeast found in Guinness brewery yeast (see below) and classified as follows: class (1) completely dispersed; class (2) flocculating in small clumps; class (3) flocculating in dense masses; class (4) flocculating very early in the fermentation owing to nonseparation of daughter cells. The yeasts of class (2) appeared to be most suitable for the brewery. By plotting the amount of yeast in suspension in the fermenting wort against specific gravities he was able to show that these four classes exhibit different curves with pronounced inflection or so-called flocculation points, where flocculation apparently starts. As these classes appeared to be interconvertible, Gilliland endeavored to establish whether these changes were genetically controlled or due to wort constituents. As normal brewery yeasts form very few spores and so are difficult to use for genetical experiments, he therefore carried out his experiments with two wild yeasts (*Saccharomyces cerevisiae*) having the same flocculating properties as the yeasts from classes (1) and (4). Sporulation of both wild yeasts took place on gypsum slopes and spores were isolated according to Winge and Laustsen (1937). As it was difficult to obtain hybrids by direct copulation of individual spores, the method of Lindegren and Lindegren (1943) was followed by mixing cultures derived from single spores. After the isolation of diploid hybrid yeasts the single cells were grown and put again on gypsum slopes in order to induce sporulation. After isolation from the asci, single spores were cultured and thereupon examined turbidimetrically for their flocculating power. Of a total of 18 asci having 4 spores, each yielded 2 flocculent and 2 dispersed single-spore cultures, so that flocculence of these yeasts appears to be under genetic control and presumably governed by a single gene. From the similarity of these yeasts to the actual brewery yeasts of classes (1) and

(4), it seemed likely that the flocculence of the latter is also under genetic control. This being so, a gain or loss of flocculence of these classes can only be explained by the mutation of a gene. Mutation, however, according to this author very seldom occurs and, indeed, presence of mutagenic agents in brewery practice is regarded as very improbable. Thus an increase in the percentage of yeast of class (4) in a mixture of the four classes is unlikely to be due to mutation but rather to a selection of flocculating types during the procedure of skimming. This view is generally accepted, as most flocculating types will reach the top sooner than the dispersed types. With regard to the changes of yeast class (2) into yeast class (3) or vice versa Gilliland made the reservation that such changes may be due both to genetical and to environmental influences.

Thorne (1951a,b) was also at this time studying genetics with regard to flocculence and had the notable success of being the first to obtain spores from a brewery yeast. Winge (1944) and Laustsen (1947) had tried in vain to make bottom fermentation yeasts sporulate. Thorne, however, working with top fermentation yeasts from various British breweries started from five single-cell cultures, one of which was a flocculent strain, the cells sticking together by surface action and not by the nonseparation of daughter cells. Following the technique of Winge and Laustsen (1938) hybrids were produced between these various strains and also between the flocculent strain and a strain of *Saccharomyces cerevisiae* of American origin (baker's yeast). It was thus found that hybrids made by crossing a flocculent to a nonflocculent strain were of the flocculent type whereas two nonflocculent strains produced a nonflocculent hybrid. The six hybrids obtained from the flocculent and nonflocculent brewing yeasts, however, were infertile which made further genetic segregation impossible. Fortunately, hybrids from the flocculent yeast and the baker's yeast sporulated very well and with these parents, hybrids were obtained which appeared to be under genetic control. From Table I it will be seen that flocculence appears to be dominant over nonflocculence. This last opinion, however, conflicts with that of Pomper and Burkholder (1949). Incidentally, the anomalous hybrids might be attributed to mutation.

Thorne was able to prove that at least three pairs of genes were responsible for flocculence. With regard to *mutation,* Thorne could prove that hybrids could be homozygous for flocculence genes and nevertheless yield some nonflocculent types, which points to mutation in the direction $F \rightarrow f$, towards the recessive form. He found, for example, in a particular case that out of 196 spores, 10 were nonflocculent, the mutation rate $F \rightarrow f$ thus being 5.1%. It appeared that this mutability increases with time, particularly in the case of heterozygotic flocculent cultures, where the preponderance of nonflocculent types may be enormous, monohybrids being reduced to 90%, dihybrids to 75%, and trihybrids even to 10% of the total population. Homozygotes, however, show no such reduction in flocculence, apparently hybridity being of more importance than number of genes. This would seem to show that flocculence genes in top fermentation yeasts are rather unstable. As this is obviously not the case with pure cultured bottom fermentation yeasts, which do not change character in this way, Thorne suggested that the instability of top fermentation yeasts may be due not merely to the mutation of the genes concerned but to a more purely physiological variation in the condition of the yeasts. To this extent the author does not exclude environmental factors, although genetic control has definitely been established. It is interesting that Lund (1951)

TABLE I

NUMBER OF HYBRIDS OF EACH TYPE PRODUCED
FROM DIFFERENT PARENTAL TYPES

F = flocculent   f = nonflocculent

Hybrid types	Parental types		
	F × F	F × f	f × f
F	42	47	0
f	(3)	(3)	12

who observed a permanent change from a flocculating to a nonflocculating character in a bottom fermentation yeast and vice versa, assumed that this change is probably due to mutation and not to segregation, since these types of yeast hardly ever sporulate.

Thorne points out that the astonishingly high apparent rate of mutation in heterozygotes is of importance in the practice of brewing. Out of every 5000 cells one gene can mutate during each generation, with the result that a heterozygous yeast will change from flocculent to the nonflocculent form in the course of a few weeks. It may be wondered, then, how flocculent yeasts can ever survive. Thorne mentions that the relevant genes may be more stable in some genetical environments than in others and that, in addition, selection by reason of the system of skimming may cause flocculent types to collect preferentially in the recovered yeast. It is probably significant that both Gilliland and Thorne realized that although heredity is one aspect of the picture, environmental factors still have to be taken into account.

B. *Flocculence from a Colloid Chemical Point of View*

(1) *The Charge on the Yeast Cell* (*Microelectrophoretical Studies*). Before considering direct measurements of charge, attention may be drawn to the investigations of St. Johnston (1949) who used an indirect method, formerly applied in colloid chemistry. This consisted in adding a gelatin solution to suspensions of pressed yeast at various concentrations and at various pH values when flocculation was evaluated by eye after 30 minutes. It appeared that this particular yeast was flocculated by gelatin between a pH value of 3.8 and 5.0 and according to the author behaved as a colloid with an isoelectric point of 3.9. Although this method was far from accurate it gave a rough impression of the behavior of yeast in media of various pH values. The same action occurred with finings (isinglass), St. Johnston assuming that newly formed negatively charged yeast cells would be coated with positively charged wort proteins and thus assume a positive charge. In the case of cells coated with gelatin or isinglass these latter surface-active compounds will displace the positively charged wort proteins from the yeast cell wall. Though adsorption of proteins on yeast cell surfaces is now generally accepted, his assumption that during the main fermentation the yeast cells acquire a positive charge contradicted earlier findings both of Hennig and Ay (1938) and of Silbereisen (1938) and it has since been definitely refuted by the results of Wiles (1951) and Jansen and Mendlik (1951) who confirmed that during fermentation the yeast never loses its negative charge. Direct measurements of the electrical charges of suspended particles such as yeast cells have to be carried out by means of microelectrophoresis (see Abramson *et al.*, 1942), a method, which has found general application in the determination of electrophoretic mobilities and of the charge densities of protein-coated particles and bacteria. As yeast, however, has comparatively large dimensions and a higher specific gravity than that of buffer solutions, sedimentation in electrophoretic buffer solutions may lead to erroneous estimations of electrical charge. However, by taking such difficulties into account, Rohrer (1947) examined the charges of different baker's and brewing yeasts and was unable to find a reversal of the negative charge. Wiles (1951) applied this same method to top fermentation yeasts and determined the influence of finings on yeast flocculation. He worked with a cylindrical microelectrophoresis cell and measured the mobilities of yeast suspended in 0.01 M acetate buffer solutions. Using a simplified formula of Abramson *et al.* (1942) he was able to calculate the charge densities from the observed mobilities and concluded that most yeasts have a negative charge after

rinsing with buffer solutions, with the exception of two strains of *Kloeckera brevis* T 70 and *Saccharomyces carlsbergensis* T 24 which had no charge. The present author has proved that both yeasts grown in bottom fermentation wort showed negative charges with apparent isoelectric points of 4.0 and 2.3, respectively. Wiles was able to demonstrate that out of ten yeasts grown in wort, eight had a definite negative charge which increased after rinsing the cells with a 0.01 *M* sodium hydroxide solution. Hence he assumed that rinsing removes coated proteins from the cell wall surface and that the negative charge is increased in consequence. By examining the influence of finings (isinglass) he found that powdery yeasts treated with such a preparation became flocculent and showed a positive charge. From the observations that, during the measurements these positive mobilities decreased, the author concluded that the coating of the finings was gradually removed. In addition Wiles demonstrated that by washing coated positively charged cells with acetate buffer solution (0.01 *M*) the positive value of the charge decreased and eventually became negative. His results proved that growing yeast cells are able to adsorb positively charged proteins without losing their negative character. He assumed that this was possible by the formation of remote, positively charged regions of proteins on the yeast cell which would not result in the yeast losing its negative charge. His suggestion seems to be more acceptable as his experiments with finings point in the same direction.

Jansen and Mendlik (1951) measured the mobilities and calculated the charge densities of both flocculating and powdery bottom fermentation yeasts. They confirmed that these charges are negative and that reversal of charge takes place at pH 2.3 in dilute acid solutions. As, however, the yeast cell apparently excretes substances to counteract this high acidity of the medium in which the cell is suspended, they did not attach much importance to this observation nor did they compare it to the isoelectric point of a protein. They examined the change in charge densities of a flocculent and also a powdery bottom fermentation yeast during primary fermentation. This charge density of the former yeast showed a pronounced maximum on the third day of fermentation, decreasing until the fifth day and thereafter remaining fairly constant. The powdery yeast, on the other hand, showed no maximum but decreased from the second until about the fifth day and then remained nearly constant till the end of the fermentation. Clearly the sedimenting of the yeast at the end of the primary fermentation is not caused by a sudden change in the charge density. In this connection it may be said that a certain low level of charge is a requirement for flocculation, but the authors realized that other factors may play a role. This is in accordance with the view of Hartong (1951) who similarly concluded that below a certain level of electrical charge of the cells, the yeast are apt to clump. Trolle (1950) assumed that the charge of the cells played only a secondary role and was of the opinion that flocculation starts as a result of the decrease of carbon dioxide excretion, i.e., of a decrease of fermenting power. According to him the bubbles of carbon dioxide keep the cells afloat and prevent sedimentation.

Jansen and Mendlik (1951) found that a flocculated yeast shows a lower charge level than the same yeast after having been deflocculated. A powdery bottom fermentation yeast shows a higher level than the flocculent yeast and this level can only be slightly reduced by bringing the yeast into a flocculent condition with small amounts of thorium ions. From these observations it was concluded that flocculence and non-flocculence of yeasts are not directly dependent on the discrete charge levels of the yeast cell.

(2) *Action of Bi- and Polyvalent Cations.* By washing flocculent bottom fermentation yeast with ordinary tap water and later with distilled water, Jansen and Mendlik (1951) obtained a deflocculated yeast which could be easily made flocculent again by adding bi- or polyvalent cations in confirmation of the results of other authors. Calcium and magnesium in particular appeared to be essential for flocculation. Reflocculated yeast could be deflocculated again by washing with distilled water, the process being in fact reversible. The presence of calcium ions in nutrient solutions in which the yeast was grown could affect the flocculence, less calcium corresponding with poorer flocculence and a higher charge on the yeast cells and vice versa. Despite similar results using brewery wort (Jansen and Mendlik, 1953), it seems improbable that in brewing practice yeast flocculation is affected by the calcium content of the wort, as this is already four to five times the highest concentrations in the laboratory experiments.

Lindquist (1953) confirmed some of these results by showing that calcium, magnesium, zinc, cadmium, or ferrous ions induce flocculation of bottom fermentation yeast suspended in a powdery condition in distilled water. As to the influence of anions, flocculation was inhibited by oxalate, fluoride, phosphate, and carbonate ions; borate ion, however, accelerated flocculation in media with a pH higher than 8. A similar influence of calcium and magnesium ions was observed by Helm *et al.* (1953). Eddy (1955) examined the influence of different cations on the flocculation of top fermentation yeasts and found that various yeasts differ with respect to their need of calcium ions. Strongly flocculent cultures of top fermentation yeast in wort were washed with distilled water when they were deflocculated. After adding small amounts of calcium chloride the yeasts flocculated again. In the case of one particular yeast in the deflocculated condition, which strongly flocculated in beer, the presence of ethyl alcohol in addition to the calcium ions was essential to obtain reflocculation. Eddy also found that ferric, calcium, and ceric ions cause the immediate flocculation of top fermentation yeasts, while zinc, magnesium, copper, and cobalt ions have a less pronounced effect. Eddy argued that during growth, calcium and perhaps other cations may be necessary for optimal flocculation but, by replacing this ion in a synthetic medium by ferric or ceric ions he found that flocculation during growth is weak compared with the flocculation in a normal medium containing calcium. After suspension of the weakly flocculating yeast in buffer solutions of calcium sulfate they became normally flocculent again. It appears, indeed, that absence of calcium merely decreases the expression of flocculence, but not the property itself. These results fully confirmed those of Jansen and Mendlik (1951).

Investigating the influence of different polyvalent cations on flocculation, Jansen and Mendlik (1951) determined the "ionic spectra" of different yeasts, i.e., the sequence of the logarithms of those concentrations of various polyvalent cations which just cause reversal of charge of the protein (see Kruyt, 1949). As biocolloids can have the character of phosphate, carboxyl, or sulfate colloids and as every type shows a particular sequence of these logarithms, the ionic spectra are specific for the type of the colloid. Three different types of yeast, a flocculent, a powdery bottom fermentation yeast and a powdery top fermentation yeast all showed the typical ionic spectrum of a carboxyl colloid with thorium, cerium, lanthanum, and uranyl ions. These measurements, incidentally, had to be carried out quickly with the yeast suspended at 5–6°C. in order to prevent its excreting compounds which counteract the lowering of the cell wall charge. Hence it seemed that the difference in flocculence of these three types of yeast cannot be attributed to a difference in the biocolloid character of the cell surface. All types of yeast examined became flocculent by adding small amounts of thorium ion to the yeast suspension, but a reversal of charge is not necessary for obtaining flocs. This does not agree with results of Eddy (1955) who found that his top fermentation yeasts failed to flocculate with either thorium or lanthanum ions.

(3) *Action of Substances Adsorbed on the Cell Wall.* Jansen and Mendlik (1953) demonstrated that anionic surface active compounds of organic nature, such as the sodium salts of primary and secondary alkyl

sulfates, are easily adsorbed on the yeast cell surface. Dyar and Ordal (1946), Dyar (1948), and Alexander and McMullen (1949) had earlier described the effect of adsorbing these anionic substances on the charge properties of bacteria. Although it is to be expected that the negative cell wall repels the negatively charged anionic material, the adsorptive forces evidently predominate and the adsorption is demonstrated by an increase in the negative charge of the yeast cell. Thus pure sodium salts of alkyl sulfates with 12–17 carbon atoms were adsorbed on yeast cells causing a decrease of the flocculence, despite an increase in the charge density. That adsorption had taken place could be proved conclusively by titrating the anionic compounds as described by Barr et al. (1948). The adsorption of these compounds followed Traube's rule, according to which adsorption increased in the ascending homologous series. Anionic surface active compounds in beer or in wort, obtained by foaming beer or wort and collecting the foam and residues separately, had a similar effect on flocculation. In the latter case, however, the authors were unable to find a simultaneous increase of charge, as apparently the adsorption of the surface active compounds from beer was less pronounced than the adsorption of the alkyl sulfates, although it is also possible that the adsorbed matter may have been removed by suspending the yeast cells in the buffer solution. Finally, the authors showed that anionic compounds originating from the hops, which could be titrated in an arbitrary way, caused a highly significant decrease of flocculation of the yeast, proving that these compounds, which lower the surface tension of the wort, affect the flocculation (see below). In their first paper the authors mentioned yeasts coated with human fibrinogen and with dialyzed gelatin and in connection with adsorption and flocculation it may be worthwhile to discuss these experiments briefly here. Deflocculated bottom fermentation yeast and powdery bottom and top fermentation yeasts were treated with a 0.3% solution of purified human fibrinogen having an isoelectric point at pH 5.5. The three types of yeast then showed the same behavior with regard to flocculation. All three still showed the same isoelectric point at 5.55. The cells were negatively charged when suspended in acetate buffer solutions at a pH above 5.55 and they could be made to flocculate by adding small amounts of tri- or polyvalent cations, exactly as in the case of uncoated powdery yeasts. At a pH below 5.55, the charge of the cells became positive and this could be reduced and eventually neutralized or reversed by means of polyvalent anions, e.g., by germanin, the sodium salt of a hexavalent sulfonated complex compound derived from urea. On reduction of the charge, but before reversal took place, the positively charged yeasts also became flocculent.

Yeast cells coated with gelatin and suspended in distilled water or in beer lost their coating more easily. These findings showed clearly that the characteristic behavior of the yeast with regard to flocculation can be masked by coatings of different protein molecules, thus proving that in extreme conditions environmental influences can dominate over racial characteristics. It must be borne in mind that in brewing practice it is very doubtful whether the effect of protein coatings will ever predominate over the hereditary tendency to flocculence but the possibility of a limited environmental influence cannot be dismissed entirely.

C. Influence of Different Organic Compounds

(1) *Inhibiting Action of Sugars.* Lindner (1901) was the first to point to the preventive action of sugars on yeast flocculation. Subsequently, other authors did the same, Burns (1937), for instance, showing that flocculation could be impeded by sucrose while Lindquist (1953) found that whereas some sugars showed an inhibiting effect on the flocculation of bottom fermentation yeast, other sugars were indifferent. To the first group belonged glucose, maltose, mannose, and sucrose and to the second group fructose, galactose, lactose, arabinose, and xylose. Inhibition took place with sugar solutions in concentration down to 0.1% at pH values below 7. Gilliland (1951) obtained similar results with maltose and sucrose in that they retarded flocculation of top fermentation yeasts while lactose had no effect. As this latter author found that the amount of available fermentable material left in the beer at the flocculation point varied from 3.5% to 5.5% in beers of different gravities, he concluded that sugars play no dominating role in inducing yeast flocculation. Eddy (1955), however, in an extensive study observed that top fermentation yeasts suspended in fresh worts are dispersed and do not flocculate, even when they do so under test conditions in buffer solutions at pH 3.0. He was able to show that flocculation nevertheless starts at the end of the fermentation and thus seems to be a function of time, the wort sugars apparently behaving as dispersing factors. He further observed that most of the twelve brewery yeasts examined were dispersed by maltose and mannose and that only three strains containing flocs of "branched" cells in which daughter cells remained attached to the mother cells were not dispersed. These clusters were of constant small size and showed only a slight tendency to adhere one to another. In this work, the yeasts were grown in unhopped wort and suspended in phthalate buffer solutions of pH 3.0 to which calcium chloride had been added. The sugar solutions were then added and the degree of dispersion observed after a few minutes. According to their action on one particular flocculating top fer-

mentation yeast, the sugars could in this way be classified into four groups. Curves were obtained for different sugars by measuring the sugar concentrations which were just sufficient to disperse yeast cells of various ages and, in this way, the conclusions of Gilliland (1951) and Helm *et al.* (1953) that flocculence increases with age were confirmed. From this point, Eddy developed a flocculation test which will be described later and with which the effects of various factors on yeast flocculation were investigated. With regard to pH, no general rule was found to hold for top fermentation yeasts. In the matter of the dispersing action of various sugars, the results agreed with those of Burns (1937) and showed dispersing capacity to be in the sequence maltose > sucrose > glucose. Chromatographic analysis revealed that the concentrations of glucose, fructose, and sucrose in the fermenting wort were each less than 0.2% at the time of flocculation and, although that of maltotriose was 1%, this carbohydrate was not a very effective dispersing agent. Less maltose was needed in the wort than in the test to keep the cells dispersed, possibly because there are other dispersing factors in the former medium. With baker's yeast grown in nutrient solutions containing glucose or invert sugar from maize or from mannioc at pH 4.6–4.8 and a temperature of 28–30°C., de Hemptinne (1949) observed agglomeration centered around elongated cells, resulting in the formation of flocs when the sugars had been consumed. When suspended in wort containing a sufficient amount of sugars, these elongated cells reverted to normal cells, the author attributing them to a deficiency of energy required to separate the cells. Deficiency of nitrogen on the other hand yielded many small cells.

(2) *Action of Humic Acids.* Kudo and Kijima (1953) and Kijima (1954) discerned still another factor affecting yeast flocculation in the influence of humic acids, compounds related to melanoidins and present in wort. Small quantities of these compounds would cause flocculation of yeast suspended in buffer solutions. The authors assumed that wort proteins normally protect the yeast against flocculation by metal ions and by humic acids. Bottom fermentation yeast was rinsed many times with distilled water and thus apparently became deflocculated, after which it was treated with solutions of gelatin, calcium chloride, or humic acid. Although humic acid alone caused strong flocculation it appeared that gelatin-coated yeasts failed to flocculate. Calcium chloride (0.7% solution) caused flocculation of untreated yeast at pH 4.2–5.5 but, in these circumstances the flocculation increased considerably in the presence of humic acid and also when the yeast was first coated with gelatin and then treated with this material. These results led to the conclusion that humic acid is the main factor which causes yeast flocculation, a con-

clusion with which Eddy (1956) is at variance. A similar protective action to that of gelatin was found by Kijima (1954) using protein fractions from wort prepared according to St. Johnston (1949). On dialyzing acidified worts freed from precipitated proteins, high molecular substances were deposited. The remaining liquid when brought to pH 3.2, the isoelectric point of melanoidin, showed maximum action on the flocculation of the yeast. Finally these authors found a linear relation to exist between the protein content of wort and the yeast content, as measured by the extinction at 800 mμ, of a fermenting wort. Thus decreasing amounts of proteins appeared to give rise to increased flocculation. As, however, the simultaneous effect of the inhibiting influence of sugars (see above) was not taken into account, the interpretation of these results is rather doubtful.

(3) *Action of the Polysaccharide "Treberine."* Another compound affecting yeast flocculation was isolated by Kudo (1954) from wort from a malt of six-rowed barley. He found that by using this type of malt the flocculation of yeast increased while the attenuation of the resulting beer gradually decreased. This tendency of Japanese six-rowed barley appeared to be independent of hop boiling, pitching rate, temperature, pH of the wort during fermentation, and the contents of total and "formol" nitrogen and reducing sugars in the wort. The flocculation was, on the other hand, affected by wort runnings, mashing temperatures above 60°C. and by adding hot water extracts of the spent grains to the worts. On examining the spent grains, a compound of polysaccharide nature, termed "treberine" (from the German word "Treber" meaning spent grains), was found which could be extracted by means of hot water. It was insoluble in 80% methanol or in 50% ethanol so that, by treating wort with these alcohols, "treberine" could be precipitated directly. Purified "treberine" was devoid of nitrogen and on hydrolysis afforded glucose, xylose, and arabinose. As the action at 60°C. with taka-diastase failed to yield reducing sugars, "treberine" apparently did not contain a dextrine fraction. It was suggested that this polysaccharide might be identical with the barley polysaccharide C_2-B_2 of Preece *et al.* (1950) or with a wort gum of Meredith *et al.* (1951). The substance could, incidentally, also be obtained in very small quantities from a malt from two-rowed barley.

(4) *Influence of Furfural.* Rohrer (1950) drew attention to the effect of furfural which, in concentrations of 0.02%, could inhibit fermentation by yielding hypertrophic yeast and causing flocculation of the opaque cells perhaps by inhibiting their catalase activity, resulting in an increase of hydrogen peroxide. It was suggested that the peroxide may play a

role in forming maleic acid from furfural and by decarboxylation this acid could yield acrylic acid which eventually may polymerize under the action of hydrogen peroxide giving rise to rubberlike substances causing opaqueness in the cell membrane. The opaque flocculated cells did not plasmolyze, but burst at 100°C. Since proteolytic enzymes and acids could disintegrate the yeast flocs, the author assumed that furfural induces secretion of proteinlike substances which cause flocculation and such secretion may have been stimulated by the irritation by the furfural leading to an increase of osmotic pressure in the cell.

D. Surface Tension and Flocculation

According to St. Johnston (1953, St. Johnston et al., 1951) the surface tension of wort during top fermentation normally first increases and then decreases to a value slightly higher than that of the initial wort, flocculation taking place at the maximum point. When, however, the initial surface tension is higher than about 50 dynes/cm., it falls continuously and flocculation starts later by reason of the decrease of pH. It appeared that, if sufficient surface active substances or wort colloids are present in the initial wort, the latter will have a surface tension below 50 dynes/cm. Mutual flocculation may then occur between the yeast and the wort colloids, resulting in an increase in surface tension. When, however, insufficient wort colloids or surface active substances are present in the initial wort, the yeast fails to flocculate normally but remains in suspension until the pH drops to about 3.8, its apparent isoelectric point. Although information on the surface tension of fermenting wort is scanty and St. Johnston's explanation of flocculation is rather speculative it cannot be denied that surface tension may play a role, especially as it draws attention to the presence of surface active compounds in the wort, which may well be adsorbed and affect flocculation. In this light it may be recalled that Jansen and Mendlik (1953) observed that certain hop constituents which cause considerable reduction in surface tension and are consequently highly surface active, influence yeast flocculation (Section 3, B, C above).

E. Methods of Measuring Flocculation

(a) Burns' Method and Its Modification by Helm. In the method of Burns (1937), the volume of yeast which sediments in a given interval is measured. A suspension of washed yeast is placed in a 15-ml. graduated tapering centrifuge tube and a buffer solution of pH 4.6 added. The tube is shaken vigorously, tapped to break any yeast flocs in the froth and, after standing for 10 minutes, the volume of the settled flocculated yeast is read. Burns used the following criteria: if the volume of the settled yeast is more than 1 ml., the yeast is regarded as having strong flocculating power; if the yeast volume is under 0.5 ml., it is likely to show weakness of flocculating power in fermentation. The test has the advantage that it can be carried out with a small quantity of yeast. Burns found that washing the yeast is important as is also the concentration of the yeast suspension and the medium in which the test is carried out. The procedure has been used by various authors and, although somewhat imprecise, it has proved its usefulness in practice.

Lund (1951) confirmed the applicability of this test in the case of bottom fermentation yeasts. He distinguished between strongly flocculent yeasts giving sediments of 1–1.4 ml. and nonflocculent yeasts with sediments of 0.1 ml., the general criterion being that a flocculent yeast yields a sediment of about 0.5 ml. or more while a nonflocculent yeast yields less.

Helm *et al.* (1953) modified Burns' test when used for bottom fermentation yeasts by adding a calcium salt to the acetate buffer solution. The suspension is kept at 20°C. in a water bath for 20 minutes and, after making the suspension homogeneous by shaking once more, the volume of yeast sedimented in 10 minutes is read. The tests should be carried out in triplicate and the reproducibility is satisfactory. Helm examined the influence of different factors on yeast flocculation, finding for instance, for a flocculent and a powdery bottom fermentation yeast a pH optimum of 4.5 and 2.5, respectively, while top fermentation yeasts of both types had an optimum of about 3.0–3.5. Increasing temperatures cause a decrease of sedimentation while increase in the calcium content of the medium causes a slight increase. It was interesting to find that, of 72 different strains of bottom fermentation yeasts, the sedimentation of the 58 flocculent cultures and the 14 nonflocculent ones was fundamentally different. In the case of flocculent yeasts, sedimentation decreased after some minutes whereas nonflocculent strains showed an increase of sedimentation with time. Helm further demonstrated that, during the primary fermentation, flocculation increases from the second until the fourth or fifth day, to remain constant then to the end of the fermentation. There was no difference in flocculence between suspended and sedimented yeasts.

(*b*) *Nielsen's Method.* Nielsen (1933, 1937) described a method by which the sedimentation velocity of a yeast suspension was measured in the following way. Yeast is rinsed three times with pure water and centrifuged after each rinse. A 10-ml. portion of the final suspension in pure water is used to determine the dry solid content (at 105°C.) and the rest is introduced into a 50-ml. burette. After a certain time (2 or 4 hours), 12.5 ml. of the sedimented yeast is collected from the lower part of the burette and the solid content in 10 ml. is determined. The yeast suspension should initially contain 10–100 mg. of dry matter per 10 ml. The sedimentation percentage (SP) is calculated as the percentage of the yeast sedimented during the test from the upper part of the burette into the lower quarter. This percentage is closely dependent upon the sedimentation time and a comparison of results is only valid for a constant time as proposed. The test is not affected by temperature and the reproducibility is fairly satisfactory but the method is rather cumbersome. Nielsen found that the SP value varies for different types of yeast and also for the same yeast grown under different conditions, an increase of temperature during growth, for instance decreasing the SP value. The pH of the test medium only slightly affects the result but that of the medium in which the yeast is grown has a pronounced influence. The highest SP value is found at a pH of about 4.3. This is in agreement with the results of Helm. As already mentioned (see Section 2, H above) Nielsen observed a decrease in SP value when beer wort is added to the synthetic nutrient in which the yeast is grown, a phenomenon which he attributed to growth-promoting substances.

(c) *Jansen and Mendlik's Method.* Jansen and Mendlik (1951) measured the time in which the upper borderline of a yeast suspension in a 250-ml. graduated cylinder drops from the 150 ml. to the 90 ml. mark under standardized conditions. The velocity of this descent proved to be fairly reproducible, the standard deviation of the average being 1.5% for high velocities and 0.6 to 1% for low ones. Although this method cannot be used to assess directly flocculation in practice, the influence of diverse factors on yeast flocculation may be established with its aid. Thus adsorbed coatings of anionic substances induced a markedly reduced sedimentation velocity (see Section 3, B 3 above) by impairing the flocculence. Minimum velocity was observed at pH 4.3. Mono-, bi-, and polyvalent cations reduced sedimentation velocity in the order named. This progressive influence of higher cations is typical in colloid chemistry and is expressed in the rule of Schulze-Hardy (see Kruyt, 1952). Despite these observations, the precise relation between the action of cations and of anionic compounds on the sedimentation velocity remains obscure. Both groups decreased this sedimentation velocity although it was expected that the two groups would show opposite effects. Doubtless, the adsorption of surface active compounds is not in all respects comparable with that of bi- or polyvalent cations of strong electrolytes. The test of Jansen and Mendlik on the one hand and those of Burns and of Nielsen on the other hand showed opposite effects of pH, electrolytes, temperature, and yeast concentration, and possibly no comparison of results of the two kinds of tests is valid. In any event, although rather more sensitive to the action of various factors, the test of Jansen and Mendlik seems to be less suitable in brewing practice and for comparing the flocculence of different brewery yeasts.

(d) *Eddy's Method.* The procedure of Eddy (1955) approaches flocculation from an entirely different point of view. This author measured the amount of maltose which when added by titration to a suspension of a flocculent yeast was just sufficient to render it nonflocculating. The titration was carried out as follows: the yeast was washed three times with a 0.1% solution of calcium chloride and suspended in a phthalate buffer solution of pH 4.0 to which some calcium chloride has been added. From a burette a 20% solution of maltose was added to 2 ml. of the standard yeast suspension contained in a small flask; when flocs could no longer be discerned, the final sugar concentration was calculated. Although the exact degree of aggregation as revealed by microscopic examination does not always correspond with the observation by the naked eye, the test still proves to be satisfactorily reproducible, provided the test conditions are rigorously standardized. Bottom fermentation yeasts showing a similar reaction towards sugars may also be assessed by this test.

4. Flocculation of Yeast in Brewing Practice

A. *General Appearance of Flocculation in Bottom and Top Fermentation*

In both these cases, flocculent yeasts dispersed in the wort after pitching flocculate after a certain period, flocs becoming more and more pronounced. In the case of bottom fermentation yeast, actual sedimentation of the flocs slowly starts in addition. In bottom fermentation, flocs are copiously formed at the end of the fermentation which ceases as a result of this happening. By redispersing the flocculated yeast in the beer, it can easily be seen that the fermentation stops by reason of the yeast flocculating and not the reverse. In both top and bottom fermentation, a lower degree of attenuation is reached with a flocculent yeast than with a powdery one. De Clerck and van Roey (1951) found that, with flocculent yeasts, fermentation starts more rapidly but eventually yields lower attenuations by reason of the decreasing amounts of yeast in suspension. Hartong (1951) examined 44 bottom fermentations and also found that the rate of fermentation is closely related to the amount of yeast in suspension by showing that there is a linear relationship between the negative logarithm of turbidity and the duration of fermentation.

Sedimentation velocity constants calculated from these measurements differed for flocculent and for powdery yeasts, but in succeeding generations these constants approached each other at the time of racking seemingly following an adaption of the yeasts to the fermentation medium. In addition flocculation, if it occurred, began at nearly the final pH value making it probable, as already mentioned that flocculation is to be associated with a certain low level of electrical charge (see Section 3, B1 above).

In bottom fermentation, the flocculation of the yeast must be controlled in order that attenuation shall reach a satisfactory level and that enough yeast is kept in suspension in the beer for a sufficient secondary fermentation in the storage tanks. Accordingly most brewers prefer moderately flocculent types of yeast although powdery types are also used. Gaeng (1954), however, remarks that in primary fermentation, powdery bottom fermentation yeasts are to be preferred. Mixtures of flocculent and powdery types are sometimes employed and in this connection it may be mentioned that Helm *et al.* (1953) demonstrated that the addition of a flocculent yeast to a powdery yeast might yield a mixture which was less powdery than the original. As in top fermentation, the assumption of a powdery texture by an originally flocculent bottom fermentation yeast may be due to mutation. Rohrer (1953) is of the opinion that this change, which is sometimes reversible, might be attributed to the presence of special genes for flocculation (see Thorne, 1951a,b). Some breweries are fortunate in being able to maintain the flocculence of their yeast within certain limits, whereas other breweries, have to change their yeast regularly. In the latter case it is sometimes said that even pure culture apparatus does not provide an adequate remedy.

Flocculation in top fermentation practice has been extensively discussed by many authors. It has already been mentioned that much confusion prevails about the meaning of the word flocculation, this word being sometimes used erroneously in connection with the formation of a yeast head. Gaeng (1954), for instance, even states that in top fermentation "flocculation" is the physical removal of yeast from the fermenting liquid and thus all yeasts, both powdery and flocculent ("casséeuse") would have to "flocculate" during primary fermentation. This interpretation is certainly not the generally accepted meaning of the word. Burns (1948), in order to prevent this confusion, suggested the word "barming" for rising to the top. It is doubtful whether flocculation in top fermentation is an essential condition for barming and indeed Burns (1937) believes that this is not the case as most top fermentation yeasts rise even when powdery. Gilliland (1951) on the other hand is of the opinion that, for one particular yeast at least, he conclusively proved that flocculation is associated with yeast crops in the head. Perhaps although not an essential factor, flocculation may be said to affect the rising to the top. Some authors (Bishop and Whitley, 1938; Burns, 1948; St. Johnston, 1949) have compared the behavior of yeast in rising to the top with froth flotation by envisaging small flocs of yeast being carried to the top by bubbles of carbon dioxide. At the surface of the wort, the gas escapes leaving the yeast. As however this phenomenon only indirectly bears upon flocculation it need not be discussed here in any detail.

In top fermentation breweries, pure culture yeast is only sparsely used. In most breweries, mixtures of different yeasts are employed and as a result changes in flocculation occur more often than in bottom fermentation yeasts. Apart from the possibility of mutation (see Section 3, A above), the use of mixtures tends to complicate matters for other reasons also. Bremner (1942) demonstrated that during a succession of generations of the same yeast, the degree of attenuation decreased as a result of the selective skimming of the yeast, because the more flocculent cells were the first to rise. These are then skimmed and used as pitching yeast for the next brew. On the other hand, the later skimmings caused a higher degree of attenuation. Even in the case of pure single-cell cultures, differences in flocculation may occur, as Curtis (1954) has demonstrated. It must be mentioned that this author is of the opinion that possibly differences in wort composition have great importance and that environmental factors in general play an essential role in top fermentation.

Recently Jeffery (1956) has thrown new light on the flocculence of British brewery yeasts. By measuring the degree of flocculence by means of the method of Burns (see Section 3, E a above) he showed that these yeasts consist of mixtures of flocculent (Burns value, 1.4) and nonflocculent (Burns value, 0.1) strains and that they never seemed to contain strains with an intermediate flocculence. This he could prove by growing yeast on laboratory scale; the yeast collected from the different crops was plated on hopped wort-gelatin and the separately grown yeast colonies were inoculated into hopped wort. Eventually the grown yeast was measured by the Burns method. It appeared that the separate yeast colonies showed either a low (0.1 or less) or high (1.4 or over), but never an intermediate Burns value. In a more extensive experiment with yeasts which had passed through various stages of laboratory fermentation and pitching yeasts direct from breweries, out of 773 colonies tested, 326 had Burns values of 1.4 or over, 435 gave 0.1 or less and only 12 intermediate values; moreover the latter on reculturing gave values conforming to one or other of the two main groups.

In conclusion it may be said that, in bottom fermentation practice, the degree of flocculation of the yeast seems to be more closely associated with environmental conditions than with changes due to mutations. In top fermentation, on the other hand, mutation plays a far more pronounced role although the influence of environmental factors still cannot be ignored. In addition, the general picture with top fermentation yeast seems to be even more complicated because of the heterogenity of the yeast and of the behavior of the yeast in rising to the top.

B. Classification of a Mixed Yeast

It has already been mentioned (see Section 3, A above) that Gilliland (1951) described the particular behavior of four classes of yeast isolated from the mixed Guinness yeast. In brewing practice it is essential to maintain flocculence between certain narrow limits, and in this particular instance this can be done by using a mixture of certain of the four classes for pitching. Gilliland attached great value to this classification which originally had been suggested by Tullo, the four classes behaving as follows: Class (1) yeast is powdery and does not settle before the attenuation limit is almost reached. It gives a poor head crop, the attenuation is excessive and too much yeast is left in the beer. Class (2) yeast flocculates at a gravity of about half the original gravity of the wort and is preferred because fermentation is fast, the head crop well-developed, the beer left relatively clear of yeast, while conditioning is neither too rapid nor too slow. In class (3) yeast, the flocculation is similar to that of class (2) but the yeast falls out very early with the result that attenuation is too low, the crops on skimming are poor, and conditioning is slow. In consequence this yeast is not suitable for brewing. Class (4) yeast flocculates too early, but a normal crop is obtained on skimming; it causes a slow fermentation and is not considered a good brewing yeast.

Gilliland was able to distinguish between these 4 classes by seeding 50 colonies from a hopped wort-gelatin plate culture of the mixed yeast into fifty 10-ml. flasks each holding 5 ml. of sterilized brewery wort and examining the sediments after 3 days' incubation at 25°C. To this end the liquid in the bottle is gently swirled; class (4) yeast was characterized by its sediment of loose clumps or flakes which move with the liquid. If the sediment were heavy, most of the liquid was poured off and the sediment shaken with the last drops. The appearance of the sediment, varying from completely homogeneous with no trace of "graininess" to dense clumps distinguished yeasts of the classes (1), (2), and (3). This classification of selected top fermentation yeasts may constitute a valuable contribution towards the establishment of flocculation standards in brewing practice, although it remains to be seen if it can be generally applied to other top fermentation yeasts. Indeed, as long as knowledge of the nature and variability of the composition of the mixtures of yeast used in brewing practice is lacking, the problem of yeast flocculation in top fermentation can hardly be elucidated in view of the probability of many factors potentially affecting the constituent strains to varying extents.

C. *Influence of Temperature*

High temperature tends to yield less flocculent and low temperature more flocculent yeasts irrespective of their bottom or top nature. Hayduck (1905), Schönfeld (1910), and Nielsen (1937), as have been already mentioned, are among the authors who reported this influence on bottom fermentation yeasts, while Gilliland (1951) found the same for the alternative types. The influence of temperature seems to be reversible, since flocculence returns on lowering the temperature of the later brews. This suggests that temperature does not affect the behavior of the yeast in a purely physico-chemical sense, but rather that there are changes in enzymic or metabolic reactions in the yeast or on the cell wall surface. No knowledge is available, however, about these possible reactions.

D. *Influence of Miscellaneous Factors*

Heron (1926) observed that aeration tends to stimulate yeast flocculation and that yeasts from Yorkshire stone squares, where vigorous rousing is employed, often show clumping. This is in agreement with the opinion of Lange (1904) that aeration of the wort yields a flocculating bottom fermentation yeast. Hayduck (1905) on the other hand found that strong aeration gives rise to powdery yeasts and weak aeration to flocculent ones, while Gaeng (1954) observed a similar effect on aerating top fermentation yeasts. It is clear that opinions vary and that the effect on flocculation of wort aeration may differ from case to case.

Inositol, added to the nutrient medium in which a certain strain of *Saccharomyces cerevisiae* was grown, was shown by Pennington *et al.* (1951) to have an influence in inducing a decreased flocculence. Gilliland (1951) observed a similar effect on adding a complex of bios factors to a fermented wort from which the alcohol had been removed by distillation and to which sugar and peptone had also been added.

Schönfeld (1914, 1924) described increased flocculation apparently brought about by a high protein content of the wort. The use of unmalted grain in the mash on the contrary caused a yeast to become more powdery. These results are at variance, however, with those of St. Johnston (1953) who observed an increase of flocculation following the use of unmalted grain or of barleys with low nitrogen content. Thus even in this very important respect there is no firm agreement.

Certain other factors which more or less affect yeast flocculation may perhaps be discerned, but their discussion here would probably be unprofitable as it is clear that such environmental influences rarely fit into one general pattern. Probably only a new approach along enzymic and metabolic lines will lead to a better understanding of this problem.

5. Conclusion

Although the problem of yeast flocculation has in the past been approached from various sides, it is still impossible to elaborate any one theory which can explain this phenomenon in brewing practice in its entirety. At the present time, general opinion tends towards accepting the complex nature of flocculation but rejecting any comprehensive theories which claim to explain the behavior as a whole. Indeed the subject is still one of largely empirical study, and for this reason the search for new factors present in brewery wort capable of affecting yeast flocculation is being continued. Research in the field of genetics has given more promising results, by demonstrating conclusively that the flocculation of certain top fermentation yeasts is genetically controlled and that flocculence is a dominant factor. Nevertheless, the mechanism of flocculation cannot be explained by genetics alone and, in order to obtain a better understanding of this mechanism, certain factors depending on the surrounding medium, as for example, the electrical charge of the cell wall, and the adsorption and specific action of various substances, have from time to time been taken into account and investigated separately under simplified conditions.

These investigations have often resulted in the elucidation of particular aspects of the picture of yeast flocculation. On the other hand, despite this undeniable progress, application of the experimental results to practical brewing is hampered by the fact that many of the operative factors almost certainly mutually affect each other, so that the final results often deviate from those anticipated from the individual approaches. This obvious complication suggests that new fundamental approaches in the fields of enzymology and cytology may prove of more general and ultimate value.

References

Abramson, H. A., Moyer, L. S., and Gorin, M. H. (1942). "Electrophoresis of Proteins," p. 43. Reinhold Publishing Corp., New York.

Alexander, A. E., and McMullen, A. I. (1949). *Research (London)*, Suppl. *Surface Chemistry* p. 309.

Barendrecht, H. P. (1901). *Centr. Bakteriol. Parasitenk. II* **7**, 623.

Barr, T., Oliver, J., and Stubbings, W. V. (1948). *J. Soc. Chem. Ind.* (*London*) **67**, 45.

Beyerinck, M. W. (1908). *Centr. Bakteriol. Parasitenk. II* **20**, 137.

Bishop, L. R., and Whitley, W. A. (1938). *J. Inst. Brew.* **44**, 73, 125.

Böeseken, J. (1949). *Advances in Carbohydrate Chem.* **4**, 189.

Bremner, T. S. (1942). *J. Inst. Brew.* **48**, 17.

Burns, J. A. (1937). *J. Inst. Brew.* **43**, 31.

Burns, J. A. (1948). *Brew. Digest* **23**, 60.

Curtis, N. S. (1954). *J. Inst. Brew.* **60**, 255.

De Clerck, J. (1930). *Bull. assoc. anciens étud. école supér. brass. univ. Louvain* **30**, 1.

De Clerck, J., and van Roey, G. (1951). *Proc. European Brewery Convention Congr., Brighton* p. 120.

de Hemptinne, Y. (1949). *Fermentatio* p. 58.

Delbrück, M. (1901). *Jahrb. Versuchs-u. Lehranstalt Brauerei, Berlin* **4**, 305.

Dyar, M. T. (1948). *J. Bacteriol.* **56**, 821.

Dyar, M. T., and Ordal, Z. J. (1946). *J. Bacteriol.* **51**, 149.

Eddy, A. A. (1955). *J. Inst. Brew.* **61**, 307.

Eddy, A. A. (1956). *J. Inst. Brew.* **62**, 320.

Gaeng, F. E. (1954). *Petit J. brass.* **62**, 269.

Geys, K. (1922). *Z. ges. Brauw.* **45**, 51, 57.

Gilliland, R. B. (1951). *Proc. European Brewery Convention Congr., Brighton* p. 35.

Hartong, B. D. (1951). *Proc. European Brewery Convention Congr., Brighton* p. 110.

Hayduck, F. (1905). *Wochschr. Brau.* **22**, 661.

Hayduck, F., and Schücking, K. (1908). *Wochschr. Brau.* **25**, 241.

Helm, E., Nøhr, B., and Thorne, R. S. W. (1953). *Wallerstein Labs. Communs.* **16**, 315.

Hennig, K., and Ay, H. (1938). *Biochem. Z.* **299**, 123.

Heron, H. (1926). *J. Inst. Brew.* **32**, 261.

Holderer, H. (1901). *Jahrb. Versuchs-u. Lehranstalt Brauerei, Berlin* **4**, 306.

Jansen, H. E., and Mendlik, F. (1951). *Proc. European Brewery Convention Congr., Brighton* p. 59.

Jansen, H. E., and Mendlik, F. (1953). *Proc. European Brewery Convention Congr., Nice* p. 143.

Jeffery, E. J. (1956). *J. Inst. Brew.* **62**, 309.

Kijima, M. (1954). *J. Inst. Brew.* **60**, 223.

Koch, R. (1928). *Wochschr. Brau.* **45**, 175, 187, 201.

Kruyt, H. R. (1949). "Colloid Science," Vol. II, p. 282. Elsevier Publishing Co., New York.

Kruyt, H. R. (1952). "Colloid Science," Vol. I, p. 81. Elsevier Publishing Co., New York.

Kudo, S. (1954). *Brauerei* **8**, 345.

Kudo, S., and Kijima, M. (1953). *J. Agr. Chem. Soc. Japan.* **27**, 809.

Kusserow, R. (1897). *Brennerei Ztg.* **14**, No. 318.

Lange, H. (1899). *Wochschr. Brau.* **16**, 49.

Lange, H. (1901). *Jahrb. Versuchs-u. Lehranstalt Brauerei, Berlin* **4**, 19.

Lange, H. (1904). *Jahrb. Ver. Spiritusfabrikanten* p. 137.

Lange, H. (1907). *Wochschr. Brau.* **24**, 445.

Laustsen, O. (1947). *Beretning 8 skand. Brygmesterkursus, København* p. 101.

Lindegren, C. C., and Lindegren, G. (1943). *Proc. Natl. Acad. Sci. U.S.* **29**, 306.

Lindner, P. (1901). *Jahrb. Versuchs-u. Lehranstalt Brauerei, Berlin* **4**, 309.

Lindner, P. (1930). "Mikroskopische und Biologische Betriebskontrolle," p. 456, Paul Parey, Berlin.

Lindquist, W. (1953). *J. Inst. Brew.* **59**, 59.

Lüers, H., and Heusz, R. (1921). *Z. ges. Brauw.* **44**, 18.

Lund, A. (1951). *Proc. E.B.C. Congr., Brighton* p. 10.

McCandlish, D., and Hagues, G. (1929). *J. Inst. Brew.* **35**, 61.

Malkov, A. M., Petina, A., and Tzvetkova, N. (1933). *Zentr. Bakteriol. Parasitenk.* **88**, 193.

Malkov, A. M., Petina, A., and Tzvetkova, N. (1934). *Zentr. Bakteriol. Parasitenk.* **90**, 212.

Meredith, W. O. S., Bass, E. J., and Anderson, J. A. (1951). *Cereal Chem.* **28**, 177.

Moldawskaja, E. A. (1933). *Biochem. Z.* **257**, 480.

Moufang, E. (1912). *Wochschr. Brau.* **29**, 721.

Nielsen, N. (1933). *Compt. rend. trav. lab. Carlsberg* **19**, No. 17.

Nielsen, N. (1937). *Compt. rend. trav. lab. Carlsberg, sér. physiol.* **22**, 61.

Pasteur, L. (1876). "Etudes sur la bière," p. 196. Gauthier Villars, Paris.

Pennington, D., Sawyer, C. H., and Schmidt, J. (1951). *J. Bacteriol.* **62**, 677.

Pomper, S., and Burkholder, P. R. (1949). *Proc. Natl. Acad. Sci. U.S.* **35**, 456.

Preece, I. A., Ashworth, A. S., and Hunter, A. D. (1950). *J. Inst. Brew.* **56**, 33.

Ranken, C. (1927). *J. Inst. Brew.* **33**, 76.

Ranken, C. (1928). *J. Inst. Brew.* **34**, 265.

Rohrer, E. (1947). *Mitt. Staatl. Forsch. Inst. Prag.*

Rohrer, E. (1950). *Schweiz. Brau. Rundschau* **61**, 1, 168.

Rohrer, E. (1953). *Schweiz. Brau. Rundschau* **64**, 35.

St. Johnston, J. H. (1949). *Proc. European Brewery Convention Congr., Lucerne* p. 62.

St. Johnston, J. H. (1953). *Wallerstein Labs. Communs.* **16**, 39.

St. Johnston, J. H., Oldfield, A. I., and Taylor, A. E. (1951). *Proc. European Brewing Convention Congr., Brighton* p. 98.

Schönfeld, F. (1909). *Wochschr. Brau.* **26**, 521.

Schönfeld, F. (1910). *Wochschr. Brau.* **27**, 541, 553.

Schönfeld, F. (1912). *Wochschr. Brau.* **29**, 393.

Schönfeld, F. (1914). *Wochschr. Brau.* **31**, 257.

Schönfeld, F. (1924). *J. Inst. Brew.* **30**, 64.

Schönfeld, F., and Krumhaar, H. (1918). *Wochschr. Brau.* **35**, 302.

Schönfeld, F., and Schönfelder, G. (1914). *Wochschr. Brau.* **31**, 245.

Seyffert, H. (1896). *Z. ges. Brauw.* **19**, 318.

Silbereisen, K. (1938). *Wochschr. Brau.* **55**, 153, 161, 171.

Stockhausen, F. (1927). *Wochschr. Brau.* **44**, 121, 133.

Stockhausen, F., and Silbereisen, K. (1933). *Wochschr. Brau.* **50**, 349, 357, 365.

Stockhausen, F., and Silbereisen, K. (1935). *Wochschr. Brau.* **52**, 257.

Thorne, R. S. W. (1951a). *Compt. rend. trav. lab. Carlsberg, sér. physiol.* **25**, 101.

Thorne, R. S. W. (1951b). *Proc. European Brewery Convention Congr., Brighton* p. 21.

Trolle, B. (1950). *J. Inst. Brew.* **56**, 364.

Van Laer, H. (1905) *Bull. soc. chim. belg.* **19**, 31.

Wiles, A. E. (1951). *Proc. European Brewery Convention Congr., Brighton* p. 84.

Will, H. (1893). *Z. ges. Brauw.* **16**, 179.

Winge, Ö. (1944). *Compt. rend. trav. lab. Carlsberg, sér. physiol.* **24**, 79.

Winge, Ö., and Laustsen, O. (1937). *Compt. rend. trav. lab. Carlsberg, sér. physiol.* **22**, 99.

Winge, Ö., and Laustsen, O. (1938). *Compt. rend. trav. lab. Carlsberg, sér. physiol.* **22**, 235.

Winslow, C. E. A., and Fleeson, E. H. (1926). *J. gen. Physiol.* **8**, 195.

Author Index

B

Bach, S. J., 223, *240*
Bacon, J. S. D., 338, *362*
Baddiley, J., 466, *523*
Badian, J., 110, *120*
Bailey, C. W., 556, *579*
Bailey, K., 224, 225, *240*, 328, *362*
Bair, W., 447, 452, *523*
Baird, V., 27, *57*
Baker, E. E., 599, *601*
Baker, R. D., 51, *58*, 587, *601*
Baldwin, I. L., 164, *248*, 299, *318*, 571, *586*
Bale, W. F., 472, *532*
Ballou, C. E., 348, *362*
Baltatu, G. H., 308, *317*
Bamann, E., 223, *249*
Bandurski, R. S., 519, *523*, *533*
Baranowski, T., 325, *367*, 492, 494, *529*
Barber, J., 541, *579*
Bard, R. C., 329, *362*
Barendrecht, H. P., 637, *665*
Barer, R., 211, *240*
Barg, W. F., 500, *530*
Barker, B. T. P., 79, *88*, 94, *120*
Barker, H. A., 337, *364*, 383, *430*, 574, *584*
Barker, S. A., 383, 386, *428*
Barnett, J. A., 28, 29, 30, *57*, 281, 283, *317*, 609, 624, *631*
Baron, L. S., 512, *523*
Barr, T., 652, *665*
Barret, A., 50, *57*
Barron, E. S. G., 453, *523*
Barry, V. C., 192, *240*, 378, *428*
Barthel, C., 88, *88*
Bartholomew, J. W., 112, 113, *120*, 240, *240*, 380, *428*
Barton, A. A., 113, *120*
Barton, D. H. R., 206, *240*
Barton-Wright, E. C., 169, 170, *240*, 283, 284, *317*, 445, *523*
Basaca, M. Y., 560, *579*
Bass, A., 563, *579*
Bass, E. J., 655, *666*
Bass, L. W., 174, *244*
Bauch, R., 142, 143, *153*, 313, *317*
Baumberger, J. P., 408, 418, *430*, *436*
Baur, H., 459, *525*
Bautz, E., 113, *120*
Bayfield, F., 557, *579*
Beadle, G. W., 462, 470, *522*, *523*
Béchamps, 158, *240*

Beck, W. S., 373, *429*
Beech, F. W., 64, 79, *88*, 629, *631*
Beevers, H., 351, *362*, 422, *434*
Beinert, H., 214, *243*
Bell, D. J., 189, 192, *240*, 375, 378, *429*
Bell, T. A., 19, 29, 48, 50, *58*, *60*, 64, 65, 83, *89*, 208, 209, *246*, 622, 624, *625*, *631*, *632*
Bendich, A., 176, *240*, 494, *523*
Beneke, E. S., 618, *631*
Benend, W., 208, *249*
Benesch, R., 542, 571, *579*
Benham, R. W., 45, 46, 49, *57*, *58*, 312, *317*, 588, 589, 594, 595, *601*
Ben-Ishai, R., 168, *247*, 497, 499, 503, 506, 507, 508, 510, 512, 513, *523*, *531*
Bennett, R., 556, *579*
Bennett, W. G., 540, 572, 573, *579*, *580*
Bentley, M., 500, *522*
Bentley, R., 394, *429*
Beraud, P., 424, *429*
Berg, P., 466, 500, 504, 505, *523*
Berger, L., 20, *57*, 328, *362*, 398, *432*
Bergmann, E. D., 497, 499, *523*
Bergsteinsson, H. W., 556, *582*
Berke, H., 422, *434*
Berkhout, C. M., 16, 20, *57*
Berlese, A., 68, *88*
Berman, V., 545, *580*
Bernfeld, P., 383, 388, *429*, *432*
Bernheuer, K., 563, *580*
Bernt, E., 391, *435*
Berry, J. A., 85, *88*
Berti, P., 547, *580*
Bessman, M. J., 502, *523*
Beyer, C., 579, *580*
Beyer, G. F., 576, *581*
Beyerinck, M. W., 53, *57*, 94, *120*, 637, *665*
Bhattacharyya, P. K., 167, *241*
Bidan, P., 50, *57*
Bigger, L. C., 159, 168, 234, *242*
Bigger-Gehring, L., 486, 487, 488, 490, *523*
Binkley, F., 224, *240*
Binkley, W. W., 538, 539, *580*
Bird, O. D., 166, *241*, *246*
Birkinshaw, J. H., 520, *523*
Bishop, L. R., 640, 661, *665*
Bissett, H. M., 626, *633*
Biyack, S., 560, *580*
Black, M. M., 573, *580*
Black, R. A., 47, *58*

Subject Index

A

Acenaphthene, effect on chromosomes, 115

Acetaldehyde,
and glycogen formation, 400
dismutation by aldehyde mutase, 431
in fermentation, 325, 326, 333, 339
in citric acid cycle, 353
in sulfur metabolism, 519
in valine synthesis, 462
oxidation of, 226, 353–354
reduction to alcohol, 333, 334

Acetate,
"active," 356
catabolism of, 354
deutero, 354
effect on sporulation, 309–310
formation of, 353
respiration of, 418

Acetate-1-C^{13}, metabolism of, 394

Acetic acid,
as carbon source, 395
from fermentation, 325
from glycine, 444
in citric acid cycle, 465
in lysine synthesis, 468
oxidation to oxalic acid, 361

Acetic acid-1-C^{14},
formation of peptides from, 506
in amino acid synthesis, 464, 482
in protein synthesis, 454

Acetic acid-1-C^{14}-2-C^{13}, 460

Acetic acid-2-C^{13}, synthesis of glucose from, 473

Acetic acid-2-C^{14}, synthesis of amino acids from, 464, 472, 476

Acetohomolactic acid, 461

Acetolactic acid, synthesis of amino acids from, 462, 471

Acetyl coenzyme A, 356
and tricarboxylic acid cycle, 355
formation of, 504

N-Acetyl-D-glucosamine, 195

N-α-Acetylornithine, 457

Acetylphosphate, in transference of acetyl groups, 226

"Achroocellulose," 377

Acid production, 26
by Brettanomyces, 8
method of testing for, 30

Aconitase activity, 236

Aconitic acid, and amino acid synthesis, 452

Acrylic acid, 656

Actinomyces israeli, 598

Adenase, 493

Adenine, 172, 173, 176, 177, 285, 294
and nutrilites, 286
and thymine, 181
deficiency of, 117
formation, mechanism for, 500
in ribonucleic acid synthesis, 493, 494, 514
preparation from yeast, 575
synthesis, genetic basis for, 145
transformation to guanylic acid, 494
utilization of, 494

Adenine-8-C^{14}, 494, 514

Adenosine, 176
from adenine, 495
from nucleic acid, 492
phosphorylation of, 494, 501
preparation from yeast, 575

Adenosine diphosphate (ADP), 328, 333
and citrulline degradation, 459
and glycogen formation, 400
and oxidation of 3-phosphoglyceralde-hyde, 329
in alcoholic fermentation, 326
reaction with 1,3-diphosphoglyceric acid, 331

Adenosine monophosphate (AMP), 450
and deaminase reactions, 451
in ribonucleic acid synthesis, 501

Adenosine-2'-phosphate, 175

Adenosine-3-phosphate, 492

Adenosine-3'-phosphate, 175

Adenosine-5-phosphate, 356
hydrolysis of, 492

L

extraction of, 377
fermentation of, 338, 389–391
  adaptive, 390–391
  "direct," 390
  formation, effect of pH, 414
  from glycogen, 399
  from labeled ethanol, 396
  from trehalose-6-phosphate, 391
  from uridine diphosphoglucose, 392–393
  hydrolysis of, 390
  rate of, 377
  in yeast, 338, 379, 557–558
  loss of glycogen by, 406
  occurrence of, 374, 376–377
  preparation, 376–377
  properties of, 184–185, 376–377
  structure of, 185
  synthesis of, 416, 419, 420
    and growth rate, 427, 428
    effect of arsenate on, 392
    of fluoride on, 392
    of sodium azide on, 421–422
  utilization, and protein synthesis, 406
Trehalose-6-phosphate,
  effect on fermenting yeast, 392
  formation of, 391–392
  from glucose-6-phosphate, 399
  isolation of, 391, 393
  splitting of, 392
  synthesis, 399
Trialkyl phosphates, use in yeast manufacture, 552
Triaryl phosphates, use in yeast manufacture, 552
Tricalcium phosphate, in molasses clarification, 539
Tricarboxylic acid cycle, 354, 355–356, 396, 491, 544
Trichosporoideae, 8, 19, 44, 55
Trichosporon, 3, 8, 18, 19, 20
  arthrospores, 23, 55
  budding, 23, 55
  fission in, 23
  lipase activity in, 55
  occurrence, 74, 81, 83, 605
T. aculeatum, 56
T. behrendii, 56
T. cutaneum, 3, 55
  from citrus fruit, 617
  production of starch by, 29, 56
  urease activity in, 30
  utilization of aneurin, 293
T. fermentans, 56, 611

T. pullulans, 55
  effect of medium on growth, 614
  from citrus fruits, 617
  urease activity in, 30
T. scottii, 613
Triethylene glycol, use in yeast manufacture, 552
Triglycerides, 199–200, 202
Trigonopsis, 8, 24, 44, 54
T. variabilis, 54
1,3,4-Trihydroxy-2-amino-octadecane, 203
1,5,8-Trimethyl-3-formyl-2,4-divinylporphyrin-6,7-dipropionic acid, 216
2,3,6-Trimethylglucose, 186
2,4,6-Trimethyl-D-glucose, 192
2,3,4-Trimethylmannose, 190
2,4,6-Trimethylmannose, 190
3,4,6-Trimethylmannose, 190
Triose phosphate-3-C¹⁴, and histidine synthesis, 474
Triosephosphate dehydrogenase,
  amino acid content, 228
  isolation of, 225
Tripeptides,
  as nitrogen sources, 283
  hydrolysis of, 440
Triphosphopyridine nucleotide (TPN), 220, 227, 343, 356
  and oxidation of glucose-6-phosphate, 342
  in hexose monophosphate cycle, 349
  in oxidation of acetaldehyde to acetate, 353
  in reduction of aspartyl phosphate, 460
  in sulfur metabolism, 521
Trypan blue, 51
Tryptophan, 453, 479, 487
  and nicotinic acid, 457
  and transamination, 489
  as hydrogen acceptor, 445
  as nitrogen source, 282, 443
  assimilation by Saccharomyces cerevisiae, 284
  effect on amino acid pool, 509
  synthesis of, 139, 481, 484, 485
  synthesis of purines from, 479
L-Tryptophan, as amino group donor, 488
Tryptophan deficiency, 117
Tryptophan desmolase, 484
Tryptophan-indole cycle, 288
Tryptophol, 443
Tungsten, toxicity towards yeasts, 301